Parimal Sanskrit Series No. 4

NĀṬYAŚĀSTRA OF BHARATAMUNI

WITH THE COMMENTARY ABHINAVABHĀRATĪ OF ABHINAVAGUPTA

VOL. I
CHAPTERS 1-7

EDITED BY

R. S. NAGAR
K. L. JOSHI

PARIMAL PUBLICATIONS
DELHI

Published by
PARIMAL PUBLICATIONS
27/28, Shakti Nagar, Delhi-110007 (INDIA)
ph. : +91-11-47015168
e-mail : order@parimalpublication.com
url : http://www.parimalpublication.com

Head Office
PARIMAL PUBLICATIONS
1, Manmohan Complex, Behind Navrangpura Police Station,
Navrangpura, Ahmedabad-380009 (INDIA)
ph. : +91-79-49167674

Edition : Year 2023

ISBN : 978-81-7110-003-3 (Vol. 1)
978-81-7110-002-6 (Set)

Price : ₹ 300.00

Printed at
Vandana Offset Printers
A-9, Sarai Pipal Thala Ext. Delhi-110033 (India)

परिमल संस्कृत ग्रन्थमाला संख्या-४

भरतमुनिप्रणीतं

नाट्यशास्त्रम्

श्रीमदभिनवगुप्ताचार्यविरचितया अभिनवभारती-संस्कृतव्याख्यया समुद्भासितम्

प्रथमो भागः

(अध्यायाः १-७)

सम्पादक

रविशंकर नागर

के० एल० जोशी

परिमल पब्लिकेशन्स

दिल्ली

प्रकाशक :

परिमल पब्लिकेशन्स

२७/२८, शक्ति नगर,

दिल्ली - ११०००७

दूरभाष : ०११-४७०१५१६८

प्रधान कार्यालय :

परिमल पब्लिकेशन्स

१, मनमोहन कॉम्पलेक्स, नवुरंगपरा पलिस स्टेशन के पीछे,

नवरंगपुरा, अहमदाबाद - ३८०००९

दूरभाष : ०७९-४९१६७६७४

ISBN : 978-81-7110-003-3 (Vol. 1)
978-81-7110-002-6 (Set)

संस्करण : वर्ष 2023

मूल्य : ₹ 300.00

मुद्रक

वन्दना ऑफसेट प्रिंटर्स

सराय पीपल थला, दिल्ली-३३

INTRODUCTION

The Nāṭyaśāstra is the oldest available treatise of dramaturgy and kindred arts. Like all other Indian sciences it claims a divine origin and is regarded as a Nāṭya Veda or Gāndharva Veda. It was created by Brahmā on the request of goods as an object of diversion (a Krīḍanīyaka).[1] As the low castes (Śūdras) were not entitled to listen to the four Vedas, Brahmā created Nāṭya as the fifth Veda which was open to all irrespective of their caste and creed.[2] Before creating the fifth Veda, Brahmā entered into Yogic trance and recalled the four Vedas. He drew the Recitative (pāṭhya) from the Ṛgveda, Songs (gīta) from the Sāmaveda, Histrionic Representation (abhinaya) from the Yajurveda and Sentiments (rasa) from the Atharv Veda, which are the four main constituents of the Nāṭya[3] Brahmā thought that the Veda created by him will be fifth Veda as it will be a guide and counsel to people and will conduce them to duty. It will also act as a source of pleasure and diversion of minds already weary of strains and miseries of daily life.[4] When the Nāṭya Veda was ready, the gods expressed their inability to receive and practise it and Brahmā passed it to Bharata and asked him to use it along with the help of his one hundred sons.

---

1. क्रीडनीयकमिच्छामो दृश्यं श्रव्यं च यद् भवेत्। ना. शा. १.११

2. न वेदव्यवहारोयं संश्राव्यः शूद्रजातिषु।
तस्मात् सृजापरं वेदं पञ्चमं सार्ववर्णिकम्।। ना. शा. ३.३२

3. जग्राह पाठ्यमृग्वेदात् म्सामभ्यो गीतमेव च।
यदुर्वेदादभिनयान् रसानाथर्वणादपि।। ना. शा. १. १७

4. दुःखार्तानां श्रमार्तानां शोकार्तानां तपस्विनाम्।
विश्रान्तिजननं काले नाट्यमेतद्भविष्यति।।
धर्म्यं यशस्यमायुष्यं हितं बुद्धिविवर्धनम्।
लोकोपदेशजननं नाट्यमेतद् भविष्यति।। ना. शा. १.११४-११५

This is the story of the divine origin of the Nāṭya Veda as recorded in the first chapter of the Nāṭyaśāstra. Under the garb of this mythical story lies the sanctity and greatness of the Nāṭ ya. Nāṭya is a Veda, for it covers in its wide range all branches of knowledge or lore, art or craft design or activity.[5] It is instructive through the representation of actions and moods and by giving relief and solace to persons afflicted with sufferings and sorrows serves the huminity at large.

The Nāṭyaśāstra treats all possible subjects connected with Nāṭya right from its origin as stated above to its production, presentation, construction of play houses of various types, the costumes, the make up, the musical instruments, the gestures of actors, styles of expression and the aesthetic relish which was the main motive for which it was created.

From the time of its composition, the work has been held in high esteem and all subsequent writers on the theory of literature and dramaturgy owe their allegiance to Nāṭyaśāstra and accord and honorific title "Muni" to Bharata who is believed to be its author.[6]

It is a pity that the Nāṭyaśāstra was not available to modern scholars until it was discovered by Fitz Edward Hall, an American indologist in 1865. H. H. Wilson unable to secure the Nāṭyaśāstra deplored in his Śelect Specimens of the Theatre of Hindus (in 3 Vols) that the work so honoured and frequently quoted in lost for ever. Thus its discovery in 1865 saved it from oblivion.[7] But even Hall could not get it published owing to the corrupt and incomplete condition of the manuscript. However to the study of the Nāṭyaśāstra his valuable contribution was that he added chapters XVII-XX and XXYIV of the manuscript to his edition of the Daśarūpaka of Dhanañjaya, as an appendix. His discovery soon inspired other to trace similar manuscripts elsewhere. Heymann, a German scholar, contributed a valuable

---

5. न तज्ज्ञानं न तच्छिल्पं न सा विद्या न सा कला।
नासौ योगो न तत् कर्म नाट्येऽस्मिन् यत्र दृश्यते॥ ना. शा. १.११६

6. मुनिना भवतीष्वष्टरसाश्रवः प्रयुक्तः।-विक्रमोर्वशीयम् अंक २.१७

7. M.Ghosh, N.S., vol.1, Introduction p.xx., Manisha Granthalay, Calcutta.

article on the contents of the N.Ś. This attracted competent scholars and Paul Regnaud, a noted French scholar Published in 1880 a critical edition of the XVII chapter of the N.Ś Jonny Grosset another Frenchman and pupil of Regnaud published later in 1888 the XXVIII chapter of the N.Ś which treated the general theory of music[8]. The excellent work of foreign scholars gave a clarion call to Indian scholars and Shiva Dutta and Kashi Nath Pandurang Parab published under the Kāvyamālā Series in 1894 the complete text of the N.Ś. It was not a critical edition. A new era in the edition of the N.Ś dawned with the publication of the first volume of chapters I-VII of the N.Ś. along with the learned commentary entitled the Abhinavabhārtī of the Kashmirian author Abhinavagupta from Baroda in 1926. It was edited by the learned scholar Ramakrishna kavi under Gaekwad's Oriental Series on the scrutiny of forty manuscripts obtained from different parts of India. K.S. Rama Swami Shastri in the preface to the Second revised edition of Vol.I which appeared in 1956, gave an account of manuscripts and transcripts which were used in preparing the critical edition of the text of the N.Ś.[9] He classifies them into four categories. अ ब म and त.

The `अ' MS . was obtained from Almora town of Hiamalaya region and it now deposited in the library of Oriental Institute of Baroda as MS No. 14044. It is a very old MS probably copied about 500 years ago and is in a very dilapidated condition, The MS `ब' was obtained from Ujjain in M.P, and is classified as MS No 4629 in the manuscript library of the Oriental Institute of Baroda. This is also a fairly old MS and was copied probably 300 years ago. Though this MS hails from North India, its readings do not agree full with MS `अ' The `म' category is a copy transcribed from a palm leaf MS which is deposited in the Madras Government Oriental Manuscripts Library. The `त' category is also a transcript from the original manuscript of the Palace Library of H.H. Maharaja of Travancore, Trivandrum. It

8. M.Ghosh, N.S., vol.1, Introduction p. xxi-xxii., Manisha Granthalay, Calcutta.
9. Ibid, Vol. I, 2nd. rev. ed., Introduction, p. 8-10.

is collated with another MS from the same Palace Library. This transcript is now deposited under 14042 in the Oriental Institute, Baroda. The second volume of the N.Ś. containing chapters VIII-XVIII along with Abhinavabhāratī appeared in 1936 from Baroda and the third volume consisting of chapters XIX XXVII and the fourth volume containing XXXIII-XXXVII chapters came out from Baroda in 1954 and 1964 respectively. The Baroda edition of the N.Ś. was mainly edited on the basis of the commentary Abhinvabhāratī and is useful as it notes variants in the foot notes. Baldeva Upadhyaya and Batuka Nath Sharma, two scholars of Banaras, edited the N.Ś. consisting of 36 chapters on the basis of two manuscripts preserved in the Saraswatī Bhavan, Banaras and it was published in Kashi Sanskrit Series in the year 1929. M. Ghosh has contributed greatly to the study of the N.Ś. He has critically edited the complete text on scientific lines and meticulously recorded the variants. He has also translated the N.Ś. into English with explanatory notes and a learned introduction.[10] Many editions of the N.Ś. along with translation and exposition into Hindi and other regional languages have appeared now. But none of them gives the complete text. They are partial works on the M.Ś. Raghuvamsha translated chapters I-VII of the N.Ś. in Hindi explanatory notes and an introduction which was published by Motilal Banarasidass in 1964.

Pandit Madhusudana Shastri, a traditional scholar of Varanasi advanced the studies in the N.Ś. further when he wrote his gloss in Hindi on both the text of the N.Ś. and the commentary Abhinavabhāratī with an introduction which was published by Banaras Hindu University in 1971. But the work stillremains incomplete. Acharya Vishveshvara, another learned scholar contributed to the studies of the N.Ś. in editing, translating and explaining the text of both N.Ś. and Abhinavabhāratī with exhaustive introduction, which was

---

10. (a) The Nāṭyaśāstra edited by Manomohan Ghosh, vol. 1 (ch I-XXVII); Manisha Granthalaya, Calcutta 1967; vol.2 (ch. XXVIII-XXXVI), Asiatic Society, Calcutta 1956. (b) The Nāṭyaśāstra translated by Manomohan Ghosh, Asiatic Society, Calcutta, vol. 1 (ch. I-XXVII), 1950 (2nd. ed. Manisha); vol. 2 (ch. XXVIII-XXVI), 1961.

published by the Dept. of Hindi, Delhi University in 1960. But his work is limited to chapters I-II and VI only. Here reconstructed the text and gave variants in foot notes. Babulal Shukla, another Indian scholar translated the text of the N.Ś. in Hindi giving variants and explanatory notes with an appendex containing the exposition of the technical terms which was published in two volumes by Chowkhambha Sanskrit series in 1972 and 1978 respectively. Even Shukla's work does not go beyond chapter XIX of the N.Ś. and work is still to be completed. Another learned work entitled Bharata Nāṭya Mañjarī by G.K.Bhat appeared from Bhandarkar Oriental Research Institute, Pune in 1975. The work presents the choicest selections from Bharats's Nāṭyaśāstra with their English rendering and the variants. The work is very valuable on account of the learned introduction in which all the important subjects discussed in the N.Ś. are critically analysed by the learned author. The two renowned scholars J. L. Mason and M. V.Patvardhan, who contributed an important work on Abhinavagupta, wrote the book entitled 'Aesthetic Rapture' in two volumes, which was published by Deccan College, Pune in 1970. Volume one gives the translation in English of the chapter VI (Rasādhyāya) of the Nāṭyaśāstra and the selected passages from the Abhinavabhāratī and is useful on account of a brilliant introduction. Volume two is valuable due to exhaustive and critical comments on the topic discussed in the first volume P.V.Kane, and S. K. De have also done pioneer work by giving vivid appraisal and critical appreciation of the N.Ś. in their histories of Sanskrit poetics. Besides, scholars like V. Raghvan, G. T. Despande, Mankad, W. Wilson and Rangacarya and others have advanced the studies in the N.Ś. by writing valuable articles on the varied aspects of the Nāṭyaśāstra. Dr. B.M. Chaturvedi, Krishna Dutt Bajpai, Ram Govinda Shukla and many others also presented some chapters of the N.Ś. for the studies in the post-graduate classes which though being text books offered the critical appraisal of the N.Ś. After the exhaustion of the copies of the Baroda edition of the N.Ś. the complete text of the N.Ś. along with Abhinavabhāratī has not yet come out. There are still many aspect of the N.Ś. which have not yet been properly investigated and there is a full scope for further studies because it is a vast ocean of knowledge on dramatic art.

The present Nāṭyaśāstra is known as 'Ṣaṭsāhasrī' which means that it is a treatise consisting of 6000 verses.[11] Abhinavagupta, Dhanika, Śāradāṭanaya and other late writers on dramaturgy refer to Bharata, the author of the N.Ś., as Ṣsṭ sāhasrīkāra' On the basis of the testimony of Śāradātanaya, we also gather that before the composition of the extant Nāṭyaśāstra by Bharata Ādibharata and Vṛdhabharata also composed voluminous works on dramaturgy consisting of 12,000 verses which was also designated as Nāṭyaśāstra.[12] M. Rāmakrishna Kavi in his preface to the first edition of the N.Ś. observes : ' this (the present Nāṭyaśāstra) appears to be an epitome of an earlier work called 'Dvādaśasāhasrī'. He further says, " Both these works seem to have been based upon a still old one called Nāṭyavada, which form. One of the four Vedas extending over 3600 ślokas written by Brahmā himself" Yamlāśṭakatantra also admits that the N.Ś. alias Gāndharva Veda consisted of 36000 verses. No reference to Brahmā is so far available with regard to the composition of the N.Ś. except that recorded in the first chapter of N.Ś. But later writers on drama and commentators refer to Ādibharata or Vṛdhabharata frequently. Rāghava Bhaṭṭa in his commentary Arthadyotanikā on Kālidāsa's Abhijñānaśākuntala refers to Ādhibharata. This has led scholars to believe that the N.Ś. existed in two recessions and by two different authors of which Ādibharata was earlier on whose work Bharata shaped his Nāṭyaśāstra now available to us. But

---

11. (i) षट्त्रिंशकं भरतसूत्रमिदम्– अभिनवभारती पृ० १।

12. (i) नाट्यवेदाद्य भरताः सारमुद्धृत्य सर्वतः।
संग्रहं सप्रयोगार्हं मनुना प्राथितं व्यधुः॥
एकं द्वादशसाहस्रैः श्लोकैरेकं तदर्धतः।
षड्भिः श्लोकसहस्रैर्यो नाट्यवेदस्य संभवः॥ –भावप्रकाशन १०.३४-३५

(ii) 'समाप्यते हि नाट्यज्ञैरङ्कावतार इष्यते'
इति द्वादशसाहसीकारः –बहुरूपमिश्रः १-६२

S.K. De in his article 'The problem of Bharata and Ādibharata[13] has discussed this issue thoroughly and arrived at the conclusion that most of the quoted passages from Ādibhārata are directly traceable in the printed text of Bharata or have parallels in it. The so called Ms. of Ādibhārata described in the catalogue of the Mysore Oriental Library as आदिभारतं श्रीभरताचार्यप्रणीतम् is probably a late work of South Indian origin. He, following P.V.Kane, believes that distinction between Bharata and Ādibharata is made by comparatively late writers. Abhinavagupta, the authoritative commentator of the N.Ś., categorically says that the present Nāṭyaśāstra imbibes three different schools of opinion represented by Brahmā, Sadāśiva and Bharata respectively[14] Kavi, the learned editor, conjectures on this ground that Dvādaśasāhasrī might have been in a form of a dialogue between Pārvatī and Śiva on the matters related to dramaturgy. That there existed three schools of dramaturgy can be inferred from the evidence of the famous lexicographer, Amara Simha, who in his Kośa (II.10.12) mentions the name of Naṭas as (i) Śailālin or Śailūṣa (ii) Kṛśāśvin or Jayājīva (iii) Bharata or Naṭa. These naṭas might have been either founders of closely associated with their respective schools. When Pāṇini says पाराशर्यशिलालिभ्यां भिक्षुनटसूत्रयौः and कर्मन्दकृशाश्वादिनिः he probably refers to the tradition of Śailālin and Kṛśāśva, which might have been prevalent in his days. This shows whether there existed a person named Ādibharata or Vṛdhabharata or not, who is taken to be the author of the Dvādaśasahasrī, it is certain that there were different schools on dramaturgy and as the story goes in the extant Nāṭyaśāstra, Bharata learnt the Nāṭyaveda and received instruction in this regard from Brahmā and Maheśvara whom he pays eloquent tributes in the opening verse of the extant Nāṭyaśāstra. On the evidence of Pāṇini it is certain that there was literature on dramaturgy[15] composed in Sūtra Style. It

---

13. S.K. De, Some problems of Sanskrit poetics, Calcutta, 1959.

14. एतेन सदाशिवब्रह्मभरतमतत्रयविवेचनेन ब्रह्ममतसारताप्रतिपादनाय मतत्रयीसारविवेचनं तद्ग्रन्थरूपेण विहितमिदं शास्त्रम्। — अभिनवभारती पृ० ८ (Present Edition)

15. अष्टाध्यायी ४.३.११०-१११.

is probable that similar works like our Nāṭyaśāstra might have been existing which are lost to us. But they might have been known to Abhinavagupta and early writers. Thus the problem of Ādibharata can not be dismissed easily. Dramatic lore passed from generation to generation until it was systematised and condensed in the present Nāṭyaśāstra which is the only work of that type available today. The Ānuvaṁśya verses quoted by Bharata also support the view that there existed, though in a floating state, vast material on dramaturgy which needed condensation. When even present Nāṭyaśāstra was no available to scholars till Hall discovered it in 1865, how can we definitely say that a work named Nāṭyaśāstra by Ādibharata did not exist before our Nāṭyaśāstra.

There is another problem of the identity of Bharata the supposed author of the present Nāṭyaśāstra. Abhinavagupta holds that the whole work is written by one persons, Bharata and discards the idea of composite authorship.[16] But modern scholars like P.V. Kane, S.K. De, and M., Ghosh have raised doubts about the assertion of Abhinavagupta. The name Bharata like Manu and Vyāsa represents a class which was work to systematise the findings of their predecessors in a concise book and made additions, alterations, adoptations, according to their requirements and the need of the day. Thus there have been many interpolations in the present text and that is evident from the fact that not a single edition of the N.Ś. agrees with regard to number and sequence of chapters and the number of verses in each chapter. M. Ghosh in the introduction of his Asiatic Society edition observes : " Bharata cannot be taken as its author, for in the Nāṭyaśāstra itself him mythical character is very obvious and the majority of Purāṇas are silent about the socalled author of the N.Ś. The word Bharata, which originally meant an actor seems to have given rise to an eponymous author of Bharatasūtra or the Nāṭyaśāstra. There is no doubt that the Nāṭ

16. एकस्य ग्रन्थस्यानेककर्तृवचनसन्दर्भमयत्वे प्रमाणाभावात् स्वपरव्यवहारेण पूर्वपक्षोत्तरपक्षादीनां श्रुतिस्मृतिव्याकरणतर्कादिशास्त्रेष्वेककविरचितेष्वपि दर्शनात्।

—अभिनवभारती भा० पृ०, ८

yaśāstra as it is before us today has passed through the process of gradual interpolation and recasting and has not come down to us in its original form. The colophon at the end of the Kāvyamālā edition that the present N.Ś. is नन्दिभरतसङ्गीतपुस्तकम् पृ. 666 shows the dual authorship of the present text and points that the music portion of the extant N.Ś. might have been the composition of Nandin, which was later added to it for the utility of the work. Tradition accepts Nandin as an authority on music and his work being most appropriate for dramatic art might have been easily amalgamated in the present Nāṭyaśāstra. S.K De, therefore, rightly observes.[17] "The designation, therefore of the latter part of Bharata's text., a part of which deals among other things, with music probably implies that it was compiled or recast at some later period in accordance with the views of Nandikeśvara." Similarly Kohala, Śāṇḍily, Kāśyapa, Sālakarṇi, Viśākhila, Parāśara, Nakhakuṭṭa etc. Who are associated with dramatic art might have had some hand in giving the present shape to the Nāṭyaśāstra. M.R. Kavi also remarks : " Bharata's work has undergone much variations at every point of work that every verse really requires half a printed page to show its various, whether found or not in every one of available manuscripts."

The Structure of the extant Nāṭyaśāstra is that it contains sūtras, prose, fragments, ānuvaṁśya ślokas in Āryā and Anuṣṭ ubh metres and kārikās. Viewing the diverse nature of the text, S.K.De says : " They probably indicate several stages in the growth of particular forms of composition of dramaturgic works each stage betraying its own partiality towards a particular form"[18] He arranges the development of the text in the following order (1) Stage of prose treatise (2) a tentative period of kārikā writing (3) Sūtra Bhāṣya Style and 94) the final period of the composition of compendium which reverts again to the kārikā form. One thing goes against this arrangement as Bharata is known in the tradition as a sūtrakāra Bhavabhūti in his Uttararāmacarita respects him as *Tauryatrikasūtrakāra*. It is

---

17. History of Sanskrit Poetics, Firma KLM, Calcutta, 1979, p. 20.
18. op. cit.; p. 27

therefore possible that the original kernel of the Nāṭyaśāstra might have been in *Sūtra* style. *Ānuvaṁsyaślokas*, as the term signifies, were traditionally handed down from father to son or from teacher to pupil and were possibly added to the Sūtras. Later on Abhinavagupta's assertion that such verses were collected together by former teachers and Bharata took them and inserted them wherever they were found fit[19] further lends support to above conjecture that the original kernel of the N.Ś. might have been in the sūtras form.

This shows that the present N.Ś. was not composed at one time by one person. The use of the word Bharata in the sense of actor even in the extant N.Ś.[20] proves that Bharata is not a name of an individual person but it was a name of a tribe who contributed to the present day text of the N.Ś. P. V. Kane, therefore observes: "It is quite possible that some one who had mastered the traditional lore of histrionic art and was well disposed to Bharatas (actors) put together most of the present N.Ś. and in order to glorify the tribe of Bharatas passed it on as the work a mythical hero."[21]

It appears that the Nāṭyaśāstra was in the same form as it is today even at the time of Kālidāsa and the lexicographer Amarasiṁhà. Kālidāsa's awareness of the contents of the first seven chapters of the present N.Ś. is reflected in his verse in the play Mālavikāgnimitra' which runs as follows:

देवानामिदमामनन्ति मुनयः कान्तं क्रतुं चाक्षुषं
रुद्रेणेदमुमाकृतव्यतिकरे स्वाङ्गे विभक्तं द्विधा।
त्रैगुण्योद्भवमत्र लोकचरितं नानारसं दृश्यते
नाट्यं भिन्नरुचेर्जनस्य बहुधाप्येकं समाराधनम्॥ अ. १/४

The editor of the second revised Baroda edition, K. S.Rama Swami Sastri asserts in the preface that in the first quarter of the above verse Kālidāsa directly echoes the subject matter of the first chapter of present day N.Ś. in which the origin of *Nāṭya* is

---

19. ता एता ह्यार्या एकप्रघट्टकतया पूर्वाचार्यैर्लक्षणत्वेन पठिताः। मुनिना तु सुखसंग्रहाय यथास्थानं निवेशिताः। – अभिनवभारती, भा० १, पृ० ३२३.

20. पृष्ठे कृत्वास्य कुतपं नाट्यं युङ्क्ते यतोमुखं भरतः। ना. शा. १३.६१ (काव्यमाला सं.)

21. *History of Sanskrit poeties.*, Motilal Banarsidass Delhi 1961, p. 28

given that Brahmā created the *Nāṭya* just as a pleasing ritual for the enjoyment of the Devas and for pleasing their minds through eye. The second quarter of the verse touches the substance of the fourth chapter of the N.Ś. in which it is said that the subject of dancing was added to Nāṭya at the instance of Rudra and Umā. The second half of the verse indicates the substance of the sixth and seventh chapters which deal with Rasas and Bhāvas. From the similarity of the text on the Śṛṅgāra in both Amarasiṁha's Kośa and Bharata's present day text[22] it can be assumed that the present text of the N.Ś. was known even Amarasiṁha and this is reflected in his Kośa in the enumeration of the synonyms of Śṛṅgāra Rama Swami Sastri observes rightly when he says " Moreover the whole of Nāṭyavarga of the Amarakośa and the interpretations found in the Kośa for words *Sāttvika, Āṅgika, Anubhāva, Śailālin, Kṛśāśvin, Bharata, Nṛtya Nāṭya, Aṣṭarasa, Tata, Avanadha, Ghana, Suṣira, Tattva,* and *Ogha* clearly indicate that they are closely connected with and traced to the text of Bharata's Nāṭyaśāstra as available to us today." This corrobrates with the view of S.K. De who believes that Bharata's teachings were probably older than Kālidāsa who generally adheres to Bharata's dramaturgic prescriptions.

From the textual evidence it can be gathered that already by the 10th century A.D. the work was available in two recensions. Abhinavabhāratī says that there were two recensions of the N.Ś. Out of these,[23] one dealt with nine *Rasas* including śānta and the other with only eight *Rasas*. Dhanañjaya, the author of the Daśarūpaka probably followed the recension of eight *Rasas*. Kavi in the preface to his edition of the N.Ś. has dealt with this problem in detail. While collating the different manuscripts of the N.Ś., he found that no two of them fully concide in their readings. He, therefore, asserted that there were at least two recensions of the N.Ś. He classified them into A and B categories. To him recension A seemed to be of later origin

---

22. श्रृङ्गार शुचिज्ज्वलः - अमरकोष १७.१७

श्रृङ्गार उज्ज्वलवेषात्मकः। यत् किंचिल्लोके शुचि मेध्यमुज्ज्वलम्। ना. शा. पृ. २९८

23. द्विविधः पाठः दृश्यते - अभिनवभारती on ch. XV.

which was closely fostered by the Sphoṭa school of Kashmir critics to which Abhinavagupta and his predecessors Tota, Utpaladeva and Bhaṭṭendurāja belong. The recension marked B was older than recension A and was followed by the Mīmāṁsā and Nyāya schools of literary critics represented by Śaṅkuka and his predecessors Lollaṭa Udbhaṭa, etc. The MS of the N.Ś. obtained in Telugu and Tamil regions, represent the earlier recension and the copies obtained from Ujjain and Almore and the two copies in the library of the Maharaja of Bikaner represent recension A. He further observes "One may call the earlier recension (B) southern and the later (A) Northern." Kāvyamālā edition of the N.Ś. is based on the recension A (Northern Recension). Some chapters of the N.Ś. published by Hall and other foreign scholars are based on recension B. Apart from the testimony of Abhinavagupta, *dvividhaḥ pāṭhaḥ* as given above, the references as Mūlakārikā, sūtrakāra, Āditor Vṛddhabharata by the writers of dramaturgy pointed out to the existence of two recension of the N.Ś. G.K.Bhat[24] argues that the N.Ś. existed at least in two short and long versions. This is supported by the old name of the work Nāṭ ya Veda or Gāndharva Veda which is used as synonym in the tradition.

M. Ghosh in his introduction to the N.S. Says that it is not easy to settle the claims of older and later recensions as pointed out by Kavi. Shorter recension can be taken as old and may be the representative of the original on the ground that additions and alternations generally take place at a later stage. Thus M. Ghosh also admits two recensions of the N.S.

K.S. Rama Swami Sastri puts his views against the theory of two recensions as advocated by Abhinavagupta. In his preface to the second edition of volume I, he categorically says that the N.Ś has been preserved all over India in one recension only in the same manner as all other Vedas and Śāstras have been preserved. The changes in the text of the N.S. are not due to short and long recensions, but it is plausible that some

24. *Bharata-nāṭya-mañjarī*, Bhandarkar Oriental Research Institute, Pune 1975, p. 2.

commentators might have effected some changes to suit their own methods of interpretation and some scribes might have mixed up portions of other later writers with the text of the N.S. In view of the testimony of Abhinavagupta that there are two recensions of the N.S., statement of Shri Sastri is debatable. When other sciences of knowledge have recensions of the text of their origin, it can be possible that the N.S. as a science of dramaturgy came to us through recensions. The manuscripts of the N.S. even though obtained from one place differ and do not agree with each other. This shows that the difference is not due to the errors of scribes but they were most probably following different recensions.

Keeping in view the fact that the text of the N.S. was amplified modified and constituted at different periods of time and probably by different hands following developments and changes in art, it is not easy to settle the date of the text of the N.S. P.V. Kane[25] thinks that the present chapters VI-VII and VIII-XIV dealing abhinaya, movements and gaits and chapters XVII-XXXV were put together at one time. The prose portions in chapters VI-VII and the Āryā verses taken from older Ācāryas were probably composed about 200 B.C. S.K.De[26] thinks that the portions of the N.S. dealing principally with music might have been compiled about the 4th century A.D. But N.S. certainly older than Bhāmaha when the number of figures had not yet been multiplied as the N.S. mentions four figures only in comparision with Bhāmaha who enumerates much more figures of speech. Thus the N.S. must have attained its present state before 7th century A.D and its lower limit can be fixed around 5th Century A.D. Upper limit of the N.S. can go before the beginning of Christian era on the hypothesis that the Sūtra-Bhāṣ ya style in which N.S. is composed was most prevalent in the last few centuries before Christ. Sūtra-Bhāṣya style of the N.S. may be taken as the earliest composition in comparision with other portions which may be of later origin. Regnaud on the assumption "if the Naṭasūtras which is mentioned by Pāṇini are

25. *History of Sanskrit poeties.*, Motilal Banarsidass Delhi 1961, p. 18
26. *op. cit., p.* 28

taken to be that of Bharata" determines the data of the original form of the N.S. in the fourth century before Christ. Haraprasad Shastri fixes the date of the N.S. round about the 2nd century B.C. M. Ghosh on the basis of his study of linguistic material, and ethnological, mythological, geographical data accords a very high antiquity to the N.S. and pushes it even as far as 500 B.C.

Thus the probable date of N.S. spans the period from the 6th century A.D. as the lowest limit to 500 B.C. as the upper most limit and it can be tentatively fixed round about the beginning of Christian era.

On account of its Kaleoscopic nature the Nāṭyaśāstra was an object of fascination and many scholars were attracted towards it to write commentaries. Śārṅgadeva in his Saṁgītaratanākara mentions the commentators of Bharata as follows—

व्याख्यातारो भरतीये लोल्लटोद्भटशङ्कुकाः।
भट्टाभिनवगुप्तश्च श्रीमत्कीर्तिधरोऽपरः॥

But no commentary on Bharat's Nāṭyaśāstra exists today except that of Abhinavagupta which is named as Nāṭ yavedavivṛti and is popularly known as Abhinavabhāratī. This is the most renowned and erudite commentary available so far. We learn from Abhinavabhāratī and other stray references that there were more commentators of Bharata than those mentioned by Śārṅgadeva, for example, Mātṛguptācārya, Harṣa, Nānyadeva, Bhaṭṭa Yantra, Priyātithi, Rāhula, Bhaṭṭa Gopala, etc. But for went of conclusive proof we are not certain whether all of them were the commentators of Bharata. Bhaṭṭa Tauta is a luminary in Sanskrit poetics. Abhinava frequently quotes his opinion with great respect. We know from that Tauta taught him the Nāṭ yaśāstra. It is plausible that he might have contributed a commentary on the N.S. But his only work which is mentioned by Abhinava and later writers is Kāvyakautuka which is unfortunately lost to us. The work as the designation goes seems to be on poetics rather than on dramaturgy. Any how as he instructed Abhinava in the dramatic art, it is probable that he might have contributed something either directly or indirectly to the N.s. Utpaladeva is quoted in Abhinavabhāratī in the chapters dealing with music. It is presumed that he might have writtensome work on music or commented on the chapters of the N.Ś. dealing with music. Besides the names Śaktigarbha, Taṇḍu and Ṭīkākṛt do occur in the Abhinavabhāratī, but that does not warrant that they were the commentators of Bharata. It is possible that when Bharata's wok gained popularity and proved to be voluminous, later writers might have composed a number of digests which were primarily based on the N.S. These perhaps were taken later on as the commentators of Bharata. On the ground of the reference of Mātṛgupta by Sundara Miśra in his Nāṭyapradīpa on the Nāndī of Bharata अस्या व्याख्याने मातृगुप्ताचार्यैः......इय मुह्ता S. Levi conjectured that Mātṛgupta wrote a Vyākhyāna or commentary on Bharata. That Abhinava in his commentary quotes Udbhaṭa frequently and at one place states that certain views of Udbhaṭa on textual interpretation of the N.S. were not accepted by Lollaṭa, it is presumed that he might have written a commentary on the N.S. S.K. De on the grounds that Abhinava mentions several characteristic views of Lollaṭa on the various topics discussed in the N.S. for instance that Rasas are numerous, Nāṭikā is Ṣaṭpadā against Śaṅkuka's opinion that it is Aṣṭapadā goes to confirm the tradition that Lollaṭa was a regular commentator of Bharata's text.[27] Judging from the way the tradition associates Śaṅkuka with the theory of Rasavāda and seeing him frequently cited in the Abhinavabhāratī, it may be presumed that he must have also contributed to Bharata's N.S. Bhaṭṭa Nāyaka is known as the author of 'Hṛdayadarpaṇa'. The work has been understood as criticism of the theory of Dhvani propounded by Ānandavardhana by later writers like Mahima Bhaṭṭa, etc. If is not certain that the work dealt with dramaturgy. But his views on the theory of Rasa are regularly quoted by abhinavagupta and later writers like Mammaṭa, Hemacandra, etc. If Hṛdayadarpaṇa being mostly the work against Dhvani system and probably composed in the Anuṣṭubh metre with a running commentary in prose, is not accepted a work on dramaturgy, then we have to belive that either Bhaṭṭa Nāyaka

---

27. *op. cit., p.* 36

was not the commentator of Bharata or his work dealing with the N.S. is lost to us. It may be possible that he might have composed an independent treatise on the theory of Rasa. Other names mentioned as the commentators of Bharata such as Harṣa, Kīrtidhara, Nānyadeva, etc. appear to be independent writers on dramaturgy rather than the real commentators of Bharata None of their works has survived. Abhinavagupta's commentary is the only one which has been preserved and fortunately escaped from oblivion. But the commentary is so unintelligible and impenetrable that the first editor of the text Ramakrishna Kavi remarked "Even if Abhinavagupta descended from heaven and saw the MS, he would not easily restore its original reading." Abhinava has his own style. Like an ordinary commentator he does not give the literal meaning of the text but dialates on the subject with all his erudition and scholarship acquired in the field of Śaiva Philosophy, Āgamas and Tantras. Thus Abhinavabhāratī is not N.S. Sometimes Abhinavagupta is not sure about the explanations offered. M. Ghosh says while explaining the Dvibhūmi, Abhninava gives four different views and does not give a special support to this own preference. The word '*Kutupa*' is once explained by him as a group of singers and players of musical instruments and next as four kind musical instruments. Commentaing on the proverbial difficulty of the writing of Abhinava, the learned authors of the Aesthetic Rapture remark "while we have gone through them searching for passages that would be of interest to the reader concerned with Abhinava's theory of beauty, we found most of the possible passages we chose for translation had to be abandoned in despair being too obscure to derive any good sense from them" Not with standing, Abainavabhāratī is the only key to open the vast treasures of the N.S.

Following Nāṭyaśāstra many works were written on dramaturgy, conspicuous among them are the Daśarūpa of Dhanañjaya, Nāṭakalakṣaṇaratnakośa of Sāgara Nandin, Naṭyadarpaṇa of Rāmacandra and Guṇacandra, Nāṭakamīmāṁsā of Ruyyaka (untraced yet), Bhāvaprakāśana of Śāradātanaya. These are the works which directly deal with dramaturgy and along with it treat of psychological states (Bhāvas), Sentiments

(Rasas), histrionic representation, heroes and heroines and the plot construction of plays and their varieties. All these works derive their material from their source Nāṭyaśāstra. Bharata's work being volumeinous as is evident from the contents given below, later works especially the Daśarūpa of Dhanañjaya became more popular for understanding the principles and texts of dramaturgy. Bharata's Nāṭyaśāstra became an ivory tower to be looked and admired from a distance.

Here is a brief survey of the contents of the Nāṭyaśāstra from which the vastness of the scope of the subjects treated of and the encyclopaedic character of the work can be realized: 1. deals with the mythical origin of Nāṭya. 2. characteristics and varieties of the play houses, 3. worship of the deities connected with the stage, 4. description of the class dance and various Aṅgahāras (movements of limbs), Karaṇas (postures), Recakas (gestures), Piṇḍibandhas (group dances), 5. Preliminaries to the performance of the play and remarks on dramatic term like Pūrvaraṅga, Nāndī, Dhruvā, Prastāvanā, etc., 6. Five questions of sages— why *Rasas* are so called, what are Bhāvas, and the eleven elements of the Śāstra such as *Rasa, Bhāva, Abhinaya, Dharmī, Vṛtti, Pravṛtti*, etc., 7. description and classification of *Bhāvas* and their subdivisions, 8. detailed description of the four kinds of acting, 9. The various movement and positions of the hand, chest, sides, abdomen, waist, legs, and feet in Nāṭya, 10. Five kinds of movements of onset, sides, waist and the other parts of the body, 11. description of Cārī, movements earthly and aerial, 12. Number of *Maṇḍalas* and their definitions, 13. Gaits of Various characters under different conditions, 14. Distribution of space in the Nāṭyamaṇḍapa as regards musical instruments and four kinds of Pravṛttis, the two kinds of Nāṭ yaprayoga, *Sukumāra* and *Āviddha*, the definition and illustration of Lokadharmī and Nāṭyadharmī, 15. representation through speech, recitation of Sanskrit and Prakrit, nature of metres, Yati, etc., 16. metres to be employed in drama, their definitions and examples, 17. enumeration of 36 Kāvya-lakṣ aṇas, four Alaṁkāras, the ten blemishes, ten Guṇas, etc., 18. Prakrit recitation in dramas, what characters to speak Sanskrit, Prakrit and other dialects, 19. various modes of addressing high, middling and low characters, Intonation in recitation, inflection of voice speaking, 20. characteristics of ten varieties of Rūpakas and definition of their Aṅgas, 21. structural analysis of play— Sandhis, Avasthās, Artha-prakṛtis, Arthopakṣepakas, etc., 22. the four Vṛttis entitled— Bhāratī, Sātvatī, Kaiśikī, Ārabhaṭi, their origin and definition. 23. description of costumes and make up, 24. Alaṁkāras of young women viz. Bhāva, Helā, Hāva, etc., description of women of various types, eight, kinds of Nāyikās, 25 Courtesans, classifications of heroines 26. determination of success in cases of contest among different troupes of actors, time suitable for holding dramatic performance, 27. Musical instruments, their four kinds, seven svaras, 28. four varṇas, Ārohī, Avarohī etc. and 37 alaṁkāras dependent on them and their definitions. 29. Hollow instruments and flutes, 30. observation of time in songs and playing of instruments, characteristics of some minor plays, 31. Dhrūva songs to be sung during the performance of play. Their definitions and examples, 32. Modes of playing different kinds, of drums and the superintending deities of musical instruments, 33. Three kinds of prakṛtis among men and women in plays, inmates of the royal harem, characteristics of king and his associates, 34. distribution of roles in a play, artificial devices made with clay, wood, qualifications of actors like Sūtradhāra, etc. participating in play, artisans and craftsmen, 35. Mythical account of the descent of the drama on the earth.

Thus the Nāṭyaśāstra deals with all possible subjects linked with drama— Architecture, postures, movements and gestures of actors, songs to be sung, dances to be performed, speeches to be delivered, dresses to be worn, musical instruments to be played and importance and the greatness of the Nāṭyaśāstra.

There are four standard printed editions of the Nāṭyaśāstra 1. Gaekwad's Oriental Series edition, 2. Kashi Sanskrit Series edition, 3. Kāvyamālā edition, and 4. M. Ghosh edition. The present edition is prepared in consultation with the text edited by these learned scholars. The variants of these editions are given in foot notes with the abbreviations G.O.S. (Gaekwad Oriental Series, Baroda edition), K.S.S. (Kashi Sanskrit Series, Banaras edition), N.S. (Nirnya Sagar Press, Bombay edition) M.G.

(Manmohan Ghosh, Calcutta edition), G.O.S. edition of the Nāṭ yaśāstra presents the complete text of the N.S. after the scrutiny of 40 manuscripts and is very useful on account of the inclusion of Abhinavabhāratī commentary which is also carefully edited by the learned scholar Kavi. I have mostly followed this edition with some divergences here and there where the text of other editions seemed to me more appropriate. I sincerely acknowledge the help taken from these editions in preparing mine and owe a deep debt of gratitude to these pioneers in the studies of the N.S. I am grateful to S.K. De, P.V. Kane, G.K. Bhat and other learned scholars from whose work I have taken help in writing the introduction and editing the text. I am further indebted to the respected scholar Shri Satkari Mukhopadhyaya for his suggestions and help in preparing the text and kindly going through the introduction. I have thank to Shri A.L. Sikri of K.M. College, Delhi, who was kind enough to lend me Kāvyamālā and other editions of the N.S. from the college library. Lastly I offer my sincere thanks to an energetic enterpriser Shri K.L. Joshi, proprietor, Parimal Publications, through whose efforts the present work is going to see the light of the day.

It is intended to bring out the complete text of the Nāṭya-śāstra along with the commentary of Abhinavabhāratī with translation in English. The work is stupendous and will take time. At present the first volume of the Nāṭyaśāstra containing chapters I-VII with Abhinavabhāratī commentary is presented to the public. In the last volume of the present series, a critical and exhaustive analysis of the subject matter of the Nāṭyaśāstra will be presented.

विषय सूची

भरतमुनिप्रणीतं

नाट्यशास्त्रम्

प्रथमोऽध्यायः ।

प्रणम्य शिरसा देवौ पितामहमहेश्वरौ ।
नाट्यशास्त्रं प्रवक्ष्यामि ब्रह्मणा यदुदाहृतम्[1] ॥ १ ॥

अभिनवभारती ।

यस्तन्मयान्हृदयसंवदनक्रमेण
द्राक्चित्रशक्तिगणभूमिविभागभागी ।
हर्षोल्लसत्परविकारजुषः करोति
वन्देतमां तमहमिन्दुकलावतंसम् ॥ १ ॥

षड्विंश(षट्त्रिंश)कात्मकजगद्गगनावभास-
संविन्मरीचिचयचुम्बितबिम्बशोभम् ।
षट्त्रिंशकं भरतसूत्रमिदं विवृण्व-
न्वन्दे शिवं श्रुतितदर्थविवेकि धाम ॥ २ ॥

विश्वबीजप्ररोहार्थं मूलाधारतया स्थितम् ।
धर्तृ शक्तिमयं वन्दे धरणीरूपमीश्वरम् ॥ ३ ॥

सद्विप्रतोतवदनोदितनाट्यवेद-
तत्त्वार्थमर्थिजनवाञ्छितसिद्धिहेतोः ।
माहेश्वराभिनवगुप्तपदप्रतिष्ठः
संक्षिप्तवृत्तिविधिना विशदीकरोति ॥ ४ ॥

---

१. यदुदीरितम् ।

उपादेयस्य सम्पाठस्तदन्यस्य प्रतीकनम्

स्फुटव्याख्या विरोधानां परिहारः सुपूर्णता ॥ ५ ॥

लक्ष्यानुसरणं श्लिष्टवक्तव्यांशविवेचनम् ।

सङ्गतिः पौनरुक्त्यानां समाधानसमाकुलम् ॥ ६ ॥

सङ्ग्रहश्चेत्ययं व्याख्याप्रकारोऽत्र समाश्रितः ॥

भरतमुनिरुचितदेवतानमस्कारपूर्वकमभिधेयगुणीभावेन प्रयोजनं मुख्यया वृत्त्या प्रतिजानानो विशेषणद्वारेण गुरुपूर्वक्रममर्थाक्षिप्ततया चाभिधेयप्रयोजनतत्सम्बन्धान्दर्शयति-

प्रणम्येत्यादिना—

'पितामहोऽत्र न पितुः पिता महेश्वरश्च न राजादिरिति देवशब्दः । एतच्च नाशङ्कनीयं प्रसिद्धेः । एको विजिगीषुर्नाट्यप्रवर्तयितेति देवः । भगवांस्त्वानन्दनिर्भरतया क्रीडाशीलः सन्ध्यादौ नृत्यतीति नाट्ये तदुपस्कारिणि च नृत्ते तदुपज्ञं प्रवृत्तिरिति तावेवात्राधिदैवतं गुरू चेति नमस्कार्यौ । लक्ष्मीपतिस्तु यद्यपि वृत्तीनां निर्माता तथापि पितामहादिवदसौ स्वकर्तव्यमात्रनिष्ठस्तथाचरन्नात्र नाट्ये लोकवदुपजीवित इति गुरुत्वाभावान्न नमस्कृतः ।' (इत्ये) तदपि नमस्कारहेतुनिरूपणस्यानुचितत्वादसत् ।

तस्मात्प्रणमनं प्रह्वीभावः कायेन वाचा मनसा च । आद्यः शिरसेति दर्शितः । द्वितीयो देवावित्यनेन । प्रणम्यस्य निरुपपदनामग्रहणानौचित्यात् । तेन प्रथमं देवावित्युक्तम् । अभिनेयप्राधान्याच्चाङ्गिकः शिरसेति । वाचिकश्च देवावित्यादिना[च] वाक्याभिनयो दर्शितः । लोकसिद्धो ह्ययमभिनयो न च नाट्यधर्मिरूपः । चतुर इव भुजादावूर्ध्वादिभिन्न इत्यभिनेयोऽपि प्रदर्शनीय एव । मानसी तु प्रह्वता वाक्कायव्यापारगम्येति नासौ पृथगुक्ता । पितामहमहेश्वराविति क्रमः छेकानुप्रासार्थः । सालङ्कारस्य च वाक्याभिनयतां दर्शयितुम् । सालङ्कारस्य देवतापरितोषहेतुत्वं च दर्शयितुम् । पितामहमहेश्वरावित्यनेन देवयोर्लोकहितैषित्वमुक्तम् ।

नाट्यशास्त्रमिति—

नाट्यस्य नटवृत्तस्य शास्त्रं शासनोपायं ग्रन्थं प्रवक्ष्यामीति ।

नैतदित्यन्ये । 'नाट्यवेदः नाट्यशास्त्रम्' इति हि पर्यायौ । तत्र नाट्यशास्त्रशब्देन चेदिह ग्रन्थः । तद्ग्रन्थस्येदानीं करणम् । न तु प्रवचनम् । तद्धि

व्याख्यानरूपं करणाद्भिन्नं कठेन प्रोक्तमिति यथा । ग्रन्थस्य च नाट्यवेदत्वे उत्पत्त्यादिपञ्चकस्य तद्गतस्यान्यग्रन्थसाधारण्यात् प्रश्नासङ्गतिः । उत्तरग्रन्थस्य चानुपपत्तिः—'दृश्यं श्रव्यं च यद्भवेत्' (१-११) 'जग्राह पाठ्यमृग्वेदात्' (१-१७) इत्यादेर्ग्रन्थं प्रत्यसङ्गतत्वात् । तस्मान्नाट्यं च तच्छास्त्रञ्च । व्युत्पत्तिप्रदत्वात् । प्रवक्ष्यामि व्याख्यास्ये । नाट्याख्यं वेदं लक्षणतो निरूपयिष्य इत्यर्थः ।

एतदप्यमनोहरम् । शब्दात्मताव्यतिरेकेण प्रवचनायोगात् । नाट्यस्य चाशब्दात्मकत्वात् । निरूपणमात्रे च प्रवचने ग्रन्थस्यापि प्रवचनोपपत्तेः । नाट्यस्य च प्रोच्यमानतयैवालाक्षणिकबाह्यस्वरूपनिरासलाभे शास्त्रशब्दानर्थक्य-प्रसङ्गात् । 'य इमं शृणुयात्प्रोक्तं नाट्यवेदम्' इति शास्त्रान्ते यद्वक्ष्यते तस्यासङ्गत्यापत्तेः । शब्दविषयतातिरेकेण शृणुयादित्यस्यावाचकत्वात् ।

तस्मादित्थमेतदिति मद्गुरवः । 'सकलहितकरणप्रवृत्त उत्साहसम्पदोपेतस्त-दभिवृद्धये तत्प्रत्यूहापसिसारयिषया स्वविज्ञानक्रमोपारूढगुरुरूपब्रह्मसर्वाधिपति-परमेश्वरविषयां स्मृत्यौत्सुक्यधृतिमत्यादिलक्षणां व्यभिचारसरणिं बाह्यकरणीय-विषयं च जडतावहित्थप्रभृतिभावगणं पुरस्सरीकृत्य धर्मवीरानुप्रविष्टस्त-दुचिताङ्गिकवाचिकानुभावप्रकटनपूर्वं स्वप्रवृत्तिप्रयोजनमेव निरूपयति । प्रयो-जनस्यैव प्रवर्तकत्वात् । यदाहुः—'यमर्थमधिकृत्य प्रवर्तते तत्प्रयोजनम्' (न्या. सू. १-१-२४) इति ।

तत्र नाट्यं नाम लौकिकपदार्थव्यतिरिक्तं तदनुकारप्रतिबिम्बालेख्यमा-दृश्यारोपाध्यवसायोत्प्रेक्षास्वप्नमायेन्द्रजालादिविलक्षणं तद्ग्राहकस्य सम्यग्ज्ञा-नभ्रान्तिसंशयानवधारणानध्यवसायविज्ञानभिन्नवृत्तान्तास्वादनरूपसंवेदनसंवेद्यं वस्तु रसस्वभावमिति वक्ष्यामः । तस्य शास्त्रं शासनं बाह्यभाण्डप्रायादि-वैलक्षण्येन सम्यक्तत्स्वरूपावगमोपायं प्रकर्षेणापरब्रह्मशिष्योदीरितानुपयोगि-विकासावधानेन वक्ष्यामि । यद्वक्ष्यति—

य इमं शृणुयात्प्रोक्तं नाट्यवेदं स्वयम्भुवा ।
कुर्यात्प्रयोगं यश्चैनं तथाऽधीयीत वा नरः ॥

या गतिर्वेदविदुषां या गतिर्यज्ञवेदिनाम् ।
या गतिर्दानशीलानां तां गतिं प्राप्नुयात्तु सः ॥ इति ॥

(ना. शा. अ. ३६)

एतेन "कामजो दशको गणः" (मनु. ७-४७) इति वर्जनीयत्वेन नाट्य-स्यानुपादेयतेति यत्केचिदाशशङ्किरे तदयुक्तीकृतम् । याज्ञवल्क्यस्मृतिपुराणादौ

समाप्तजप्यं व्रतिनं स्वसुतैः परिवारितम् ।
अनध्याये कदाचित्तु[1] भरतं नाट्यकोविदम् ॥ २ ॥

मुनयः पर्युपास्यैनमात्रेयप्रमुखाः पुरा ।
पप्रच्छुस्ते महात्मानो नियतेन्द्रियबुद्धयः ॥ ३ ॥

चास्य प्रशंसाभूयस्त्वश्रवणात् । न चागमादृते धर्मोऽनुमानगम्य इति न्यायात् ।

एतत्तु वृथैवास्थानभीरून्प्रति शङ्काशमनार्थमभिधीयते नाम । तथा हि— नटानां तावदेतत्स्वधर्माम्नायरूपतयाऽनुष्ठेयमेव । न चास्माकं तच्चेष्टितं विचार्यम् । सोमक्रयोपदेशिनो हि वाक्यस्य न तद्विक्रयिब्राह्मणान्तरगतकृत्या-कृत्यविचारणोद्योगो युक्तः । न चाप्यस्योपदिश्यते 'गायेन्नृत्येत्' इति । किन्तु प्रथमनाट्यावसरक्रमप्रवृत्तविरिञ्चिवचनप्रवर्तकभरतमुनिशासनानुवर्तिशिष्यपर-म्परापरिचयागताद्यतनकालावधिमहानटजनस्वकप्रवृत्तिविशेषोपदेशपरम् । अत एव तद्गतसिद्धसदुपायोपदेशनपरमिदं शास्त्रमिति ।

नटस्य तावन्नानेन किञ्चिदुपदिश्यते तं प्रत्युपकारादृते । कवेरपि स्वहृद-यायतनसततोदितप्रतिभाभिधानपरवाग्देवतानुग्रहोत्थितविचित्रापूर्वार्थनिर्माण शक्तिशालिनः प्रजापतेरिव कामजनितजगतः । परं प्रत्याशङ्का यदि परमत्राव-शिष्यते व्युत्पाद्योपकारः । तस्यापितु नेह 'गायेन्नृत्येद्वादयेत्तन्निरतो वा भवेत्' इत्युपदेशः क्रियते । अपि तु स्वरसत एव तावन्मनोज्ञविषयास्वादप्रवृत्तस्यात एव वेदशास्त्रपुराणादिभीरुहृदयस्य तन्मनोज्ञवस्तुमध्ये तादृगिदं वस्त्वनुप्रवेशितं यद्बलादेव पुमर्थोपायावगतिं करोतीति वक्ष्यामः । उत्पत्त्यादिप्रश्नास्तु ये भविष्यन्ति ते नाट्याख्यवेदविषयाः । न तु नाट्यवेदशास्त्रविषयाः । यतो "नाट्यवेदः कथं ब्रह्मन्" (ना. शा. १-४) इत्यत्र नाट्यमेव वेद इति व्याख्या-स्यामः ।

एतच्च नाट्यशास्त्रं ब्रह्मणोदाहृतं मह्यमुक्तम् । यद्वक्ष्यते—"आज्ञापितो विदित्वाऽहं नाट्यवेदं पितामहात् । पुत्रानध्यापयामास" (ना. शा. १-२५) इति । अत्र तु नाट्यस्य वेदः शास्त्रमिति समासः । अन्यथाऽध्यापनासम्भवात् । तन ब्रह्मप्रोक्तमेव मया यथापरिपाटि निरूप्यत इति यावत् ।

नाट्यं च ब्रह्मणोद्धृत्योद्धृत्य वेदाङ्गान्याहृतमिति तद्विषयं शास्त्रमप्युदा-हृतमित्युक्तम् । यदि हि नाट्यस्य वेदनं सत्तालाभो विचारश्च यत्र तन्नाट्य-

---

1. G.O.S., M.G., N.S. तु K.S.S. तं ।

योऽयं भगवता सम्यग्ग्रथितो वेदसम्मितः ।
नाट्यवेदः कथं ब्रह्मन्नुत्पन्नः कस्य वा कृते ॥ ४ ॥
कत्यङ्गः किंप्रमाणश्च प्रयोगश्चास्य कीदृशः ।
सर्वमेतद्यथातत्त्वं भगवन्वक्तुमर्हसि ॥ ५ ॥

वेदशब्देन नाट्याश्रयरूपं दशरूपकमित्युच्यते—यद्वक्ष्यति "इतिहासो मया दृष्टः" इति, (ना. शा. १-१६) । अत्र पक्षे **ब्रह्मणोदाहृतं** प्रदर्शितोदाहरणं कृतनिदर्शनमित्यर्थः ।

अन्ये तु नटनीयमनुकरणं दशरूपकमेव नाट्यम् । तस्येदं शास्त्रम् । दशरूपकलक्षणमेव हीदम् । एवं दशरूपकं कविना कार्यम् । एवं च नटनीयमिति ग्रन्थतात्पर्यात् । रसादीनां पदार्थानां तत्रैव पर्यवसानात् । तच्च ब्रह्मणोदाहृतं कृतनिदर्शनम् ।

अन्ये तु ब्रह्मणा वेदाख्येन भगवता शब्दराशिनोदाहृतं निरूपितं त्याज्यानुष्ठेयरूपमायदागच्छत् व्युत्पाद्यतया स्वीकुर्वन्नाट्यशास्त्रं प्रवक्ष्यामीति प्रयोजनमनेनैव स्वीकृतमित्याहुः ।

भट्टनायकस्तु 'ब्रह्मणा परमात्मना यदुदाहृतमविद्याविरचितनिस्सारभेदग्रहे यदुदाहरणीकृतं तन्नाट्यं तद्वक्ष्यामि । यथा हि कल्पनामात्रसारं तत एवानवस्थितैकरूपं क्षणेन कल्पनाशतसहस्रसहं स्वप्नादिविलक्षणमपि सुष्ठुतरां हृदयग्रहनिदानमत्यक्तस्वालम्बनब्रह्मकल्पनटोपरचितं रामरावणादिचेष्टितमसत्यं कुतोऽप्यभूताद्भुतवृत्त्या भाति । तथा भासमानमपि च पुमर्थोपायतामेति । तथा तादृगेव विश्वमिदमसत्यनामरूपप्रपञ्चात्मकमथ च श्रवणमननादिवशेन परमपुमर्थप्रापकमिति लोकोत्तरपरमपुरुषार्थसूचनेन शान्तरसोपक्षेपोऽयं भविष्यति ।

'स्वं स्वं निमित्तमादाय शान्तादुत्पद्यते रसः ।' इति । (ना. शा. ६.) तदनेन पारमार्थिकं प्रयोजनमुक्तम् ।' इति व्याख्यानं **सहृदयदर्पणे** पर्यग्रहीत् । यदाह-

'नमस्त्रैलोक्यनिर्माणकवये शम्भवे, यतः ।
प्रतिक्षणं जगन्नाट्यप्रयोगरसिको जनः ॥' इति ॥

एवं नाट्यशास्त्रप्रवचनं प्रयोजनमुक्तम् । तत्प्रयोजनन्तु दर्शितमेव । अभिधेयश्च नाट्यवेदः । व्युत्पाद्यव्युत्पादकभावलक्षणश्च सम्बन्धः । यच्च शास्त्रं यो जिज्ञासते स तावत्तदवसरे तच्छास्त्रप्रणेतरि प्रसिद्धे सिद्धवदेव प्रामाण्यमभिमन्यत इति तद्वचनोक्ताय सम्बन्धाभिधेयप्रयोजनाय तदैव निर्विशङ्कः प्रवर्तते । परस्त्वधिगतसकलशास्त्रार्थो बहुमन्यते न वेति तदिदमन्यत् । प्रथमं तावत्प्रवृत्त-

तेषां तु[1] वचनं श्रुत्वा मुनीनां भरतो मुनिः ।
प्रत्युवाच ततो वाक्यं नाटयवेदकथां प्रति ॥ ६ ॥
भवद्भिः शुचिभिर्भूत्वा तथाऽवहितमानसैः ।
श्रूयतां नाटयवेदस्य सम्भवो ब्रह्मनिर्मितः ॥ ७ ॥

मादिवाक्यं प्रयुक्तमेवेति स्वानुभवप्रसिद्धम् । तेनार्थसंशयतर्ककौतुकजनादिवाक्यं (न) प्रवर्तकमिति किमनेन ।

अथ मुनिरात्मानमेव परत्वेन कल्पयन्ब्रह्मणा यदुदाहृतमित्येतदेव पुराकल्पप्रदर्शनेन निश्चाययति—**समाप्तजप्यमित्यादिना** श्लोकद्वयेन । अनुरागित्वं नाट्यवेदयोग्यता नाट्यस्यादुष्टता विनोदहेतुता सुज्ञानत्वं प्रश्नावसरलाभयोगः प्रसिद्धत्वं चाचार्ययोग्यता शिष्टप्रामाणिकत्वं नियमपूर्वशास्त्रग्रहणं प्रसिद्धाचरणानुमेयोपादेयत्वप्रकटनमनिदम्प्राथम्यप्रवृत्तता शिष्याणामूहापोहपाटवं ग्रहणयोग्यता चेति क्रमेण पदानां तात्पर्यमपुनरुक्तम् । (२-३) ।

किं पप्रच्छुरिति दर्शयति—**योऽयमिति । भगवता** तत्रभवता गुरुणेति भरतमुनिरेवैवमुक्तः । तेन भरतमुनिना यो **ग्रथितः** सुन्दरतमवस्तुसमाहरणयोजनया गुम्फितः कोऽप्ययं **वस्तुविशेषः** स तावत्प्रयोगसमयेऽस्माभिर्दृष्ट इति प्रत्यक्षत्वेन **अयमिति** परामर्शः । अविदितान्तस्सारतया चास्माकं प्रत्यक्षोऽप्यप्रत्यक्षकल्प इति यच्छब्देनानिर्वाच्यविशेषत्वमुक्तम् । अत एव न तच्छब्दसङ्गतिरत्र मृग्यते यथा यत्किञ्चिद्वदतीति । स चायं परीक्षणीयतत्त्वो यतो **वेदैः सम्मितः** तुल्यः ।

तथा हि—धीरोदात्तधीरललितधीरोद्धतधीरप्रशान्तानां पूर्णोपायप्रवृत्तत्वेन नायकानामतादृगुपायाश्रयेण प्रतिनायकानां च चरितं सफलत्वाफलत्वेन साक्षात्क्रियमाणं वीराद्भुताभ्यां वीरशृङ्गारहास्यैः वीररौद्रभयानककरुणैः वीरबीभत्सशान्तैश्च प्रतिनायकगतरसान्तरसान्तरतया सातिशयचमत्कारगोचरीभूतैर्हृदयानुप्रवेशं विदधद्धर्मादिचतुष्कोपायोपादेयधियमधर्मादिभ्यश्च निवृत्तिं निर्विशङ्कं विधत्त इत्यस्माकमधिगतश्रुतितत्त्वानामपि प्रत्यक्षसिद्धमेवैतत् । प्रसिद्धा चास्य नाट्यवेदसंज्ञा विदिता । अत एवोपदेशहेतुत्वाद्वेदः । एवं च जिज्ञास्यतत्त्व एवायम् ।

स **कथमुत्पन्नः** । केन प्रयोजनप्रकारेणोत्पन्नः । तत्प्रयोजनस्य वेदेभ्य एव सिद्धेः । उत्पन्न इति यदि पूर्वमेव वेदवदपदा(वेदपदा)र्थः स्यात्तत्कथं नामायं पर्यनुयुज्येत । श्रुतिचतुष्टयवदेवेत्यर्थः । अथ यस्य वेदेभ्यो नोपदेशः सिद्धः, स कस्तादृगित्याह—**कस्याधिकारिणः** । **कृते** प्रयोजनकरणाय । किं वेदाधिकृत एवात्राधिकारी उत तदन्योऽपीत्यधिकारिविषयोऽयं प्रश्नः । पूर्वस्तु सिद्धसाध्यतया

---

१. K.S.S., M.G., N.S. तद् G.O.S. तु ।

निष्प्रयोजनत्वेनाक्षेपाय प्रश्नः । **कत्यङ्ग इति** । यद्वस्य सुबहून्यङ्गानि तद्दुरवधारतयाऽशक्यनिर्णयः । तथा परिदृश्यमानगीतातोद्याभिनयादिमध्ये कत्यस्याङ्गानि । किञ्च तदङ्गिरूपमुताङ्गसमुदायमात्रं नाट्यमिति तृतीयः प्रश्नः ।

किंप्रमाणश्चेति । ननु प्रत्यक्षप्रमाणसिद्धत्वं तावन्नाट्यस्य । यद्वक्ष्यति— 'दृश्यं श्रव्यं च यत्' (ना. शा. १-११) इति । श्रेयःप्राप्त्युपायज्ञापकत्वमपि मुनीनां स्वसंवेदनसिद्धम् । अन्यथा तु विचार्यत्वमेवास्य न स्यादित्युक्तम् । तत्कोऽयं प्रश्नः । सत्यम् । किन्तु यान्यङ्गानि कानिचित्तानि यदि विज्ञेयानि, केन प्रमाणेन किमङ्गता ज्ञायते । तेन किंप्रमाणाङ्ग इति । तथा केन प्रमाणेनाङ्गाङ्गिभावनियमोऽत्र ज्ञेयः । प्रमाणमत्र निश्चयजनकम् ।

अन्ये तु नाट्यगतानां रूपकादीनां पाठ्याभिनयरसगीतानां च किं प्रमाणं का सङ्ख्येति विभागविषयोऽयं प्रश्न इत्याचक्षते ।

अस्येति नाट्यस्य । कीदृक्प्रयोगः । यदि युगपदङ्गानि प्रयुज्यन्ते तद्भिन्नाक्षग्राह्येषु युगपत्संवेदनाभावात् कथमेकं नाट्यमिति प्रतिपत्तिः । क्रमप्रयोगेऽपि नि(न)तराम् । तस्मात्कथं प्रयोग इति । तथा किं नियतेनैवाङ्गाङ्गिभावेन प्रयोग उतानियतेनेति नाट्याङ्गप्रयोगद्वारेण सामान्याभिनयचित्राभिनयनाटकादिरूपकवैचित्र्यविषयः प्रश्नः पञ्चमः । एवं प्रश्नपञ्चकात् कविप्रयोक्त्रोरुपदेशपरं शास्त्रमिति लक्ष्यते । तेन यदिह 'तस्मात्कर्तुर्द्रष्टुः प्रयोक्तुरुपदेशपरमिदं शास्त्रम्' इति, तत्र द्रष्टुरित्यसत् । न ह्यनेन सामाजिको विनीयते । अयोग्यत्वात् । श्रुतिस्मृतीतिहासादिष्विवात्रापि न च तदुपदेशोऽत्र श्रूयते । द्रष्टा तु यदि प्रेक्षाप्रवर्तक उच्यते तदा तस्यापि न प्रबन्धेनोपदेशः । अपि तु क्वचिदेव 'नर्तकोऽर्थपतिर्वा' इत्यादौ । एवं चोपदेश्यत्वे स्थपतिमालाकारप्रभृति विश्वमपीहोपदेश्यं स्यादित्यलमनेन ।

यथातत्त्वमिति । नात्र क्रमं प्रति भरोऽस्माकम् । नापीयत्तां प्रति । अज्ञा हि वयमत्र प्रष्टारः । अत एवोपेयपरत्वेनैव मुख्यतया प्रश्नो यथा बालक आह— 'दुःखं मे शमय' इति । तज्ज्ञस्तूपायं प्रश्नयति 'कुतोऽन्नं लभ्यत' इति । तेनोपेयमुखेन प्रवृत्तमिदं शास्त्रमुत्तरदानोपनतवस्त्वन्तरोपेयप्रश्नक्रमेण तदुपेयोपायादिप्रबन्धेन स्थितमिति मन्तव्यम् । तेन यादृशा क्रमेण रूपणयोग्यं तथाप्यप्र(थाऽप)श्नितमपि यदि किञ्चिदस्ति तदपि स्वयमेव निरूपयेति । तत्त्वानतिक्रमेण तत्त्वयोग्यं तत्त्वं च निरूपणीयम् । **एतदिति** । लक्षणपरीक्षापर्यन्तमेतत् । (४-५)

यदि त एवं पप्रच्छुः भरतमुनिः किमकार्षीदित्याह—**तेषामिति** । **तुर**वधारणे । श्रुत्वैव न तु विलम्ब्येति । **पौर्व**काल्यमात्रे क्त्वाल्यपोर्विधानात् ।

पूर्वं कृतयुगे विप्रा वृत्ते स्वायम्भुवेऽन्तरे ।
त्रेतायुगेऽथ सम्प्राप्ते[1] मनोर्वैवस्वतस्य तु[2] ॥ ८ ॥

ग्राम्यधर्मप्रवृत्ते[3] तु कामलोभवशं गते ।
ईर्ष्याक्रोधादिसंमूढे लोके सुखितदुःखिते ॥ ९ ॥

तत इति । यतः स तत्त्वविन्मुनिः ते च तदुपदेशयोग्याः तस्माद्धेतोः । कथाग्रहणं यथातत्त्वमित्येतस्यैवार्थं स्फुटीकरोति ।

यत्तु प्रयोगप्रश्ने प्रत्यक्षेण प्रयोगप्रकटनमुत्तरं स्यादित्याशङ्कां परिहर्तुं कथा ग्रहणमिति तत्त्वसत् । वक्तुमर्हसीत्युक्ते तस्याः कोऽवसरः । एवं भरतमुनिः परवदात्मानं प्रकल्प्येयन्तं ग्रन्थमभिहितवान् । अन्ये त्वियन्तं ग्रन्थं कश्चिच्छिष्यो व्यरीरचत् तत्र ब्रह्मणेति भरतमुनिः प्रथमश्लोके निर्दिष्टः । कथं ब्रह्मन्नुत्पन्न इत्येतदेवमेकवाक्यत्वेन निर्वहति । तदनन्तरन्तु भवद्भिः शुचिभिरित्यादिर्भरतमुनिरचितो ग्रन्थः । मध्येऽत्र षट्त्रिंशदध्याय्यां यानि प्रश्नप्रतिवचनयोजनवचनानि तानि तच्छिष्यवचनान्येवेत्याहुः ।

तच्च सत् । एकस्य ग्रन्थस्यानेकवक्तृवचनसन्दर्भमयत्वे प्रमाणाभावात् । स्वपरव्यवहारेण पूर्वपक्षोत्तरपक्षादीनां श्रुतिस्मृतिव्याकरणतर्कादिशास्त्रेष्वेकविरचितेष्वपि दर्शनात् ।

एतेन सदाशिवब्रह्मभरतमतत्रयविवेचनेन ब्रह्ममतसारताप्रतिपादनाय मतत्रयीसारासारविवेचनं तद्ग्रन्थखण्डप्रक्षेपेण विहितमिदं शास्त्रम् । न तु मुनिविरचितमिति यदाहुर्नास्तिकधुर्योपाध्यायास्तत्प्रत्युक्तम् । सर्वानपह्नवनीयाबाधितशब्दलोकप्रसिद्धिविरोधाच्च ।

अत्र केचिदाहुः—प्रश्नपञ्चकमत्रैवाध्याये तावन्निर्णीयते । उद्देशस्थितत्या तद्विभागलक्षणपरीक्षापराणि चाध्यायान्तराणीति । अन्ये त्वाहुः पञ्चभिरध्यायैः पूर्वरङ्गविधानपर्यन्तैः प्रश्नद्वयं निर्णीतम् । सामान्याभिनयचित्राभिनयान्तैः शिष्टैस्तु प्रश्नत्रयमिति ।

वयं तु ब्रूमः—नात्र क्रमः कश्चित् । अपि तु यथावसरं महावाक्यात्मना षट्सहस्रीरूपेण प्रधानतया प्रश्नपञ्चकनिरूपणपरेण शास्त्रेण तत्त्वं निर्णीयते । न तु क्रमः कश्चित् । एतच्च ग्रन्थव्याख्यानप्रसङ्ग एव स्फुटीकरिष्यामः । (९)

---

१. G.O.S, K.S.S., M.G. ऽथ सम्प्राप्ते N.S. सम्प्रवृत्ते
२. K.S.S. N.S. च G.O.S. तु
३. G.O.S, K.S.S., M.G. धर्मप्रवृत्ते N.S. धर्मे प्रवृत्ते

देवदानवगन्धर्वयक्षरक्षोमहोरगैः[1] ।
जम्बूद्वीपे समाक्रान्ते लोकपालप्रतिष्ठिते ॥ १० ॥
महेन्द्रप्रमुखैर्देवैरुक्तः किल पितामहः ।
क्रीडनीयकमिच्छामो दृश्यं श्रव्यं च यद्भवेत् ॥ ११ ॥

तत्र 'कथं कस्य वा' इत्यमुमर्थं निर्णिनीषुराह—**भवद्भिरित्यादि** । घटादीनामुत्पत्तिर्व्यवहारसिद्धैव कुलालादिभिरनुगम्यत इति घटः क्रियत इति युक्तम् । नत्वेवं नाटचस्य । तस्य तूत्पत्तिरेव विरिञ्चोपज्ञतया स्थितेति **सम्भवो ब्रह्मनिर्मित** इत्युक्तम् । केचिदत्रानादित्वं वेदवन्नाटचस्याचक्षाणाः उत्पत्त्यादिशब्दान् स्मरणाभिव्यञ्जनादावुपचरन्ति (७) ।

तत्र सम्भूतेः कारणमुखेनाभिधाने कर्तव्ये कालस्य सर्वत्र पूर्वकारणत्वादुचितकालपरिग्रहेण तद्विधाधिकारिविषयतां दर्शयितुमाह—**पूर्वमि**त्यादिना श्लोकपञ्चकेन । अस्मिन्नवसरे पितामहो देवैरिदमुक्त इति महावाक्यस्य सङ्गतिः—कस्मिन्नवसरे **पूर्वमिति** । नास्मिन्नेव कल्पेऽपि तु पूर्वकल्पेष्वपीत्यर्थः । मन्वन्तराणि चतुर्दश तावत्कल्पो यत्तद्ब्राह्मं दिनम् । तत्र स्वायम्भुवं नाम यत्कल्पस्य प्रथमं मन्वन्तरम् । वैवस्वतमन्वन्तरन्तु सप्तमम्, यत्राद्य वर्तामहे । तत्र सर्वेष्वेव मन्वन्तरेषु त्रेतावसरे ब्रह्मणा नाटचवेदः प्रवर्तितः । कृतयुगे तु नेति तात्पर्यम् । योजना तु स्वायम्भुवे आद्ये मन्वन्तरे यत्कृतयुगं तस्मिन् वृत्ते सति यत्त्रेतायुगं तस्मिन् सम्यक्सन्ध्यतिक्रमेण स्फुटतरं प्रवृत्ते । न केवलं तत्रैव मन्वन्तरे । **तु** शब्दो यावच्छब्दार्थे । यावद्वैवस्वतस्य मनोरन्तरे समये यत्त्रेतायुगं तस्मिन्प्रवृत्तेऽपि । तेनाद्यन्तनिरूपणेन सर्वेषां मध्यममन्वन्तराणां सङ्ग्रहः । तेन सर्वेषु त्रेतायुगेषु नाटचप्रवृत्तिरित्युक्तं भवति ।

अस्मिन्नवसरे किमसावुक्तः । आह—**जम्बूद्वीपे** कर्मभूमिस्थाने यो लोकः सुखितो दुःखितश्च तद्विषयं क्रीडनीयकं क्रीडचते चित्तं विक्षिप्यते विह्रियते येन तदिच्छामः । करणे कृत्यो बाहुलकात् । चित्तं च इतोऽमुतश्च नीयमानं मार्गेऽपि नियोज्यते । यदि वा क्रीडनाय हितं क्रीडनीयकम् । उभयत्राज्ञाताद्यर्थे कः । इदमस्माकं गुडप्रच्छन्नकटुकौषधकल्पं चित्तविक्षेपमात्रफलमिति यन्न ज्ञायते । तच्च क्रीडनीयकं **सुखितदुःखित** एव भवति । न ह्येकान्तसुखिते काले देशे वा क्रीडया किञ्चित् । नाप्येकान्तदुःखिते । तेन कृतयुगे कलिप्रान्ते वा इलावृतादिनिवासिनि जने नारके वा न क्रीडोपपत्तिः । उत्तरपदार्थप्रधानस्तत्पुरुषः दुःखस्य बाहुल्यमाह । कथं ज्ञायते सुखितदुःखितो लोक इति । यत ईर्ष्याक्रोधादिभिः

---

१. G.O.S.. K.S.S., M.G. देवदानवगन्धर्वयक्षरक्षोमहोरगैः N.S. देवदानवगन्धर्वै रक्षोयक्षमहोरगैः ।

न वेदव्यवहारोऽयं संश्राव्यः शूद्रजातिषु।

तस्मात्सृजापरं वेदं पञ्चमं सार्ववर्णिकम्॥ १२॥

संमूढोऽधिवासितहृदयः। आदिग्रहणादनुरागतृष्णादिभिः। तत्र क्रमेण कारणमाह-कामवशगतत्वादीर्ष्यादयो राज्यलोभादिना क्रोधादयः। धिमित्यधिकौ कामलोभौ। यतः सुखितदुःखितत्वस्य कारणं कामादीनां हेतुः **ग्राम्यधर्मप्रवृत्तत्वम्।** ग्राम्योऽश्रुतशास्त्रार्थजनाकीर्णदेशोचितो धर्मः स्वधर्माननुपालनलक्षणः। तद्विषये यतोऽसौ लोकः प्रवृत्तः। (८-९)

नन्वेवं सत्यधर्मबाहुल्यात् सुखमेषां कुत इत्याह—**देवैः** श्रीमद्विजयाविमुक्तादिरुद्रावतारैः तथा राजसतामसहृदयजनकल्प्यमानसपर्याकैर्दानवादिभिराक्रान्ते **जम्बूद्वीपे।** देवादिभिश्चाक्रान्ते स्ववशीक्रियमाणे। नन्वेवं सत्स्वपि विशुद्धव्यामिश्रधर्मसाधनेषु कथं धर्मः। तेषां तत्राप्रवर्तमानत्वात्। सत्यम्। किन्तु **लोकपालैः** लोकपालांशसंविभागसमुत्पादितैः नरपतिभिः। **प्रतिष्ठते** स्वधर्मसाधनं प्रति नियोजिते लोके। **दृश्यं श्रव्यं** चेति। द्रष्टुं श्रोतुं चार्हम्। न धर्मसाधनम्। शक्यं च। न तु दुर्भगपरुषप्रायम्। लोक इत्येकवचनेन सर्वसाधारणतयैव यद्योग्यं तच्च स्पृश्यादिरूपं न भवति। दृश्यश्रव्ययोस्तु बहुतरसाधारण्योपपत्तिः। असाधारणे चेर्ष्याक्रोधादय एव प्रवर्तन्ते।

एतदुक्तं भवति—कृतयुगे सत्त्वप्रधाने स्वधर्ममात्रनिष्ठो लोको न सुखदुःखे प्रति हेयोपादेयधिया प्रयस्यति। त्रेतायान्तु राजसत्वाद्दुःखं जिहासति। सुखं च प्रेप्सति। रजसश्चलत्वात्। तदाऽसौ शास्त्रीयेषु राजनियन्त्रणया प्रवर्त्यते। तत्र च तादृगुपायो निरूप्यो येन स्वयमेषां भवति प्रवृत्तिः। तच्च नाट्यमेवेति।

चकारणेदमाह-तादृशा केनचिदुपायेन सम्बन्धस्तत्कुरुते (स्तु कृतः) येन भिन्नेन्द्रियग्राह्ये अपि दृश्यश्रव्ये एकानुसन्धानविषयत्वं न विजहीत इति सामान्याभिनयकालप्राणत्वं प्रयोगस्य सूचितम्। दृश्यमिति हृद्यं श्रव्यमिति व्युत्पत्तिप्रदमिति प्रीतिव्युत्पत्तिदमित्यर्थ इति। अनेन त्वि(नन्वि)न्द्रादीनां क एतावता स्वार्थः। आह। लोकपालप्रतिष्ठिते जम्बूद्वीपे गता ये लोकाः ते हि स्वधर्मावस्थिता इज्यादिना नाकमाप्याययन्ति। अत एवेच्छाम इति सर्वेषामैकमत्यमाह। अतोऽन्योन्योपकारवृत्त्या च दैवमानुषसर्गौ निरूपितौ **विन्ध्यवासि** प्रभृतिभिः। अन्ये तु स्वप्नयोजनमेव क्रीडा महेन्द्रादीनामित्याहुः। त्रेतायुगे प्रवृत्ते एवम्भूते च लोक इत्यनेनेदमुक्तं भवति—स्वर्गेऽपि हि तदा तदा मानुषगतराजसधर्माभिसम्बन्धचित्रितयागादियोगसरजसीकृतहृदयत्वाद्देवा अपि क्रीडनीयकमभिलेषुरिति। (१०-११)

एवमस्त्विति तानुक्त्वा देवराजं विसृज्य च ।
सस्मार चतुरो वेदान्योगमास्थाय तत्त्ववित् ॥ १३ ॥
(नेमे वेदा यतः श्राव्याः स्त्रीशूद्राद्यासु जातिषु ।
वेदमन्यत्ततः स्रक्ष्ये सर्वश्राव्यं तु पञ्चमम् ॥)

एवं शास्त्राधिकृतोऽपि जनः नाट्येन सुखं विनीयत इति प्रयोजनप्रयोजनमुक्त्वा प्रयोजनान्तरमप्याह—**न वेदव्यवहार** इत्यादिना । कृतयुगे सत्त्वोत्कर्षबलादेव सर्वः स्वधर्ममनुपालयति । अद्यत्वे तु राजसत्वात् शूद्रप्रकाराः करणादिजातीयाः सर्वेऽखर्वगर्वाक्रान्ता वर्णत्रयानुवृत्तिं न विदधते । शास्त्रं भवद्भ्य एवमादिशतीति च ते वचनमात्रेण नाद्रियन्ते । न च ते वेदशास्त्रोपदेशयोग्याः । अत एवमाह—सम्यगिह स्थाने । श्रुत्या भवतामेतदुपदिष्टमिति ना(न) श्राव्याः । **सार्ववर्णिकमिति** । अधिकृतानामनधिकृतानामपि सुकुमाराणां व्युत्पत्तिदायीत्यर्थः । सर्वे वर्णाः प्रयोजनं विनेयत्वेन यस्येत्यनेन पूर्वोक्तस्याधुनोक्तस्य च समस्तस्योपसंहारः ।

अन्ये तु पौनरुक्त्यं परिहर्तुमाहुः—'सर्वेषां वर्णानां सरससुकुमारेण नयेन स्वकर्तव्यनिरूपणं यत्र काव्ये तस्मिन् भवं तदाश्रितम् । येन सर्वो जनः सरससुकुमारानुरज्यदाशयः तदुपभोगनान्तरीयकतयैव कार्याकार्यज्ञानमप्युपयुङ्क्ते क्षीरमध्यावस्थितौषधोपयोगवत् । तेनाधिकृतानामनधिकृतानामपि सुकुमाराणां व्युत्पत्तिदायि नाट्यम् । अश्रुतशास्त्राणामपि संवादादविचलकार्याकार्यविवेकसिद्धिरिति । (१२)

एवमस्त्विति तानिति । **देवराजमिति** । तानुक्त्वा तान्विसृज्य । देवराजं विसृज्येति प्राधान्यादुपादानम् । **योगमिति** । येन सर्ववेदानां युगपदवभासो भवति । **तत्त्वविदिति** समस्तलोकवेदज्ञ इत्यर्थः । (१३)

ततः किं चकारेत्याह श्लोकत्रयेण **धर्म्यमित्यादिना** । एवमिति (११-६) धर्म्यमित्यादियुगलोक्तमर्थं सङ्कल्प्य । चतुर्वेदस्मरणेन हेतुना **तत** इति । चतुर्भ्यो नाट्यवेदं चक्रे । हेतौ शता । **धर्म्यमिति** । धर्मे साधूपदेशाय । एवमर्थेऽपि । अन्ये तु धर्मार्थाभ्यामनपेतं यशः प्रयोजनमस्येति । अत्र व्याख्यानद्वयेऽपरपुरुषार्थासङ्ग्रहः स्यात् । नाट्योत्पत्तिगर्भाधानकल्पे चास्मिन् सङ्कल्पे यत्त्यक्तं तत्त्यक्तमेव । यशसश्च धर्मफलत्वात् पृथगुपादानं किमर्थम् । सोपदेशमित्यादेश्च पौनरुक्त्यम् । तस्मादयमत्रार्थः—धर्मशब्देन चत्वारोऽपि पुरुषार्थाः । तेषु साधु साधकम् । ननु किं साक्षात् । नेत्याह । **सोपदेश्यं** सहोपदिश्यमानैरुपायैर्यद्वर्तते चतुर्वर्गोपायप्रदर्शकमित्यर्थः । ननु वेदादयोऽप्येवम् । नैतत् । सम्यग्ग्रहणं सङ्ग्रहः । यतः परं निर्विशङ्कप्रतीत्यर्थं प्रमाणान्तरं नाभ्यर्थ्यते । तच्च साक्षा-

धर्म्यमर्थ्यं यशस्यं च सोपदेश्यं[1] ससङ्ग्रहम् ।

भविष्यतश्च लोकस्य सर्वकर्मानुदर्शकम् ॥ १४ ॥

सर्वशास्त्रार्थसम्पन्नं सर्वशिल्पप्रवर्तकम्[2] ।

नाट्याख्यं पञ्चमं वेदं[3] सेतिहासं करोम्यहम् ॥ १५ ॥

त्काररूपमेव । यदाहुः—"सर्वा च प्रमा प्रत्यक्षपरा" इति । तेन सहेति **ससङ्ग्रहम्** । एवमपि प्रत्यक्षेण सदाचारयज्ञादिदर्शनात्कोऽस्य भेदः । आह— सर्वेषां कर्मणां क्रियमाणानामनु पश्चादचिरेणैव कालेन दर्शकं पञ्चषादिभिरेव दिवसैः शुभाशुभकर्मतत्फलसम्बन्धसाक्षात्कारो यत्रेत्यर्थः । कस्येत्याह—यो यः कश्चिदस्मात्क्षणादूर्ध्वं भविष्यति लोकस्तस्योपदेश्यस्येत्यर्थः ।

अनुकार्याभिप्रायेणात्र भविष्यत इति व्याख्यातम् । [न] च शब्देन भूत-वर्तमानग्रहणमित्यधरोत्तरीभूतम् । वृत्तराजर्षिवंशकीर्तनादेहि प्रधानतया स्वकण्ठेनाभिधानं युक्तम् । न तु भविष्यत इत्यास्तामेतत् ।

तस्मात् व्युत्पाद्याभिप्रायेणैव **लोकस्येति** व्याख्येयम् ।

एवमपि तत्रैव केन लोकः प्रवर्त्यंत इत्याह—**अर्थ्यम्** । हृद्यतया सर्वजना-नामपि नानाधिकारत्वेनाभिलषणीयमित्यर्थः । ननु प्रथममज्ञातपरमार्थे कथम-भिलषणम् । आह । **यशस्यम्** । सर्वत्र हृद्यतया प्रथितम् ।

न केवलं प्रधानपुरुषार्थोपायदर्शकं यावत्सर्वेषां शास्त्राणां कलाप्रधानानां येऽर्था गीतनृत्तवाद्यादयस्तैः सम्पन्नं युक्तम् । तथा सर्वाणि शिल्पानि चित्रपुस्ता-दीनि प्रवर्तयति स्वोपयोगत्वेनाक्षिपतीत्येवमेकेन यत्नेन समस्तवस्तुसिद्धिर्यतो भवति तन्नाट्यमित्युक्तं भवति । तच्च **सेतिहासम्** । इतिहासोपदेशकरूपं सप्र-भेदम् । इतिरेवमर्थे प्रत्यक्षनिर्देशं द्योतयति । हः इहशब्द आगमः । आसनमासः । एवंप्रकाराः प्रत्यक्षपरिदृश्यमाना आगमिकार्थाः कर्मफलसम्बन्धस्वभावा यत्रासते तेनेतिहासेन सहेतिपाठे मत्वर्थीयोऽकारः । इतिः ज्ञानम् । तस्य हासो हर्षपूर्वको विकासो यत इति केचित् । इतिहासश्च—तल्लक्षणमित्थं किलासनं यत्र रूपक-भेदानां भण्यते । उपदेशशब्देन च दशरूपकं तदुपयोगवदेव (वद्देश) द्विहस्ता-दिलक्षणनाट्यवेदशास्त्रम् । तत्सहितस्यैवं करणीयत्वेनस ङ्कल्पः । अन्यथा बुद्ध्या कलितस्यापि नाट्यस्य कथमन्य ङ्क्रमणम् । तेन च विना कथं प्रयोगः ।

---

१. G.O-S, सोपदेश्यं NS., K.S.S. M.G. सोपदेशम्

२. G.O.S., N.S. प्रवर्तकम् K.S.S., M.G. प्रदर्शकम् ।

३. G.O.S., N S., M.O.G. नाट्याख्यं पञ्चमं वेदं K.S.S. नाट्यसंज्ञमिमं वेदं

एवं सङ्कल्प्य भगवान्[1] सर्ववेदान[2]नुस्मरन् ।
नाट्यवेदं ततश्चक्रे चतुर्वेदाङ्गसम्भवम् ॥ १६ ॥
जग्राह पाठ्यमृग्वेदात्सामभ्यो गीतमेव च ।
यजुर्वेदादभिनयान् रसानाथर्वणादपि ॥ १७ ॥

पञ्चममिति । य एकोऽपि चतुरो वेदानतिशेत इत्यर्थः । **अर्हमिति** यस्य सर्वलोककृत्योद्वहनमेव परं कृत्यम् ।

एवं सङ्कल्प्येति । सङ्कल्पव्यापार एवायं बुद्ध्या वेदाङ्गीकारलक्षणो ब्रह्मणो नाट्यवेदोत्पादनम् । ननु वेदस्मरणेन तत्र कथं हेतुता लब्धा । आह । **चतुर्वेदाङ्गसम्भवमिति** । चत्वारो वेदाः । अङ्गानां पाठ्यादीनां सम्भवो यस्य । सम्भवत्यस्मादिति सम्भवः । अत एव वेदचतुष्टयमपि यत्राङ्गानि प्रत्युपकरणीभूतमिति (स तथोक्तः) (१४-१६) ।

कुत्राङ्गे कस्य वेदस्योपयोग इति दर्शयति—**जग्राह पाठ्यमृग्वेदादिति** । इह पठ व्यक्तायां वाचीत्युक्तं व्यक्तत्वं विवक्षाविशिष्टस्वार्थार्पणक्षमत्वम् । तच्च काक्वध्यायवक्ष्यमाणस्वरालङ्कारादिसामग्रीयोजनेन भवतीति तयोपस्कृतं पाठ्यमुच्यते । तच्च प्राधान्यात्प्रथममुपात्तम् ।

तथा हि वक्ष्यति—

'वाचि यत्नस्तु कर्तव्यो नाट्यस्यैषा तनूः स्मृता ।
अङ्गनैपथ्यसत्त्वानि वाक्यार्थं व्यञ्जयन्ति हि ॥ इति (१४-२)

अत एवाभिनयान्तर्भूतत्वेऽपि पृथगुपात्तम् । तदृग्वेदाद्गृहीतम् । तस्य त्रैस्वर्यप्रधानस्य स्तोत्रशब्द(स्त्र)द्वारेण यागोपकारित्वात् । पाठ्यमपि च त्रैस्वर्योपेतम् । ऐकस्वर्ये काक्वभावाभ्यां च स्वस्वादौ (चैकस्वभावाच्च स्वरादौ) गीतरूपापत्तेरिति हि वक्ष्यामः । (ना. शा. १७.)

पाठ्यगतस्वरप्रसंगात् तदनन्तरं सामभ्यो गीतं जग्राहेत्युक्तम् । उपरञ्जकत्वेन हि पश्चात्तस्याभिधानं न्याय्यमिति केचित् । 'गीतं प्राणाः प्रयोगस्य' इति वक्ष्यमाणत्वात् । तदायत्तत्वाद्रसचर्वणायाः समुचितमस्यात्रैवाभिधानमित्यस्मदुपाध्यायाः । चकारेणैतत्तुल्यकक्ष्यतामाह । एवकारेण गीतमात्रं ततो गृहीतं 'गीतिषु सामाख्या' (जैमिनि. २-१-३६) इति न्यायात् । तदाधारध्रुवापदयोजनमृग्वेदादेवेति दर्शयति । तत एव ध्रुवाध्याये वचनादत्रैव सङ्गृहीतम्(?) ।

---

१. G.O.S., K.S.S. M.G. एवं सङ्कल्प्य भगवान् N.S. सङ्कल्प्य भगवानेवं ।

२. N.S. सर्वान् वेदान् G.O.S. M.G. K.S.S. सर्ववेदान् ।

वेदोपवेदैः सम्बद्धो नाट्यवेदो महात्मना ।
एवं भगवता सृष्टो ब्रह्मणा सर्ववेदिना[1] ॥ १८ ॥
उत्पाद्य नाट्यवेदं तु ब्रह्मोवाच सुरेश्वरम् ।
इतिहासो मया सृष्टः[2] स सुरेषु नियुज्यताम् ॥ १९ ॥
कुशला ये विदग्धाश्च प्रगल्भाश्च जितश्रमाः ।
तेष्वयं नाट्यसंज्ञो हि वेदः संकाम्यतां त्वया ॥ २० ॥
तच्छ्रुत्वा वचनं[3] शक्रो ब्रह्मणा यदुदाहृतम् ।
प्राञ्जलिः प्रणतो भूत्वा प्रत्युवाच पितामहम् ॥ २१ ॥
ग्रहणे धारणे ज्ञाने प्रयोगे चास्य सत्तम ।
अशक्ता भगवन् देवा अयोग्या नाट्यकर्मणि[4] ॥ २२ ॥

घनावनद्धरूपिसामगानक्रियाप्राणभूतकालसाम्यात्मकतालसामान्यस्त्रीकृतमत्रैव प्रविष्टम् (?) । आध्वर्यवकर्मप्रधाने तु यजुर्वेदेऽङ्गकर्मणां प्रदक्षिणगमनादिक्रम एव प्रथमम् । पठिष्यति 'या ऋचः पाणिका' (३२-२) इत्यादि । ततसुषिरात्मकं चाप्यातोद्यं स्वरप्राधान्यात् ।

आथर्वणवेदे तु शान्तिकमारणादिकर्मसु नटस्येव तस्यर्त्विजः प्राड्डुदवैषुणाद्यनुभावानां प्रजाशत्रुप्रभृतिनाऽवधानग्रहणादिना लोहितोष्णीषादेर्नेपथ्यस्य तेषु तेषु च कर्मसु विशिष्टप्रयत्नपुरुसम्पाद्यमनोवष्टम्भात्मनः सत्त्वस्य सम्भवात् ततोऽभिनयानामग्रहणम् । वाचिकस्त्वभिनयः पूर्वमेवोक्तः । प्राधान्यवि(न्यात् वि) भावानां धृतिप्रमोदादिव्यभिचारिणां च परमार्थसतां समाहरणं प्रधानमिति विभावादिसामग्रीरूपरसात्मकचर्वणासम्भव इति ततस्तद्ग्रहणमुक्तमिति न तटस्था एवैते । अत एव रस्यन्ते । तत्रैव च रस्यन्त इति हि वक्ष्यामः ।

तदेवं नाट्यादिरूपकोपक्रमं गीतातोद्यप्राणाभिनयवर्गपरिपुष्यद्रसचर्वणात्मकं परप्रीतिमयमेव नाट्यम् । ततस्तद्व्युत्पत्तिरिति नाट्यमेव वेद इति क्रमेण प्रदर्शितम् । तेनाक्रम्य योजनात्मकनियोगात्मकशासनप्राणशास्त्रवैलक्षण्येन स्वयमुपारूढज्ञानाभिधानविदः प्राणवेदरूपता नाट्यस्यैवेति सिद्धम् ।

---

१. G.O.S., N.S. M.G. सर्ववेदिना K.S.S. ललितात्मकम् ।
२. G.O.S., N.S., M.G. सृष्टः K.S.S. दृष्टः ।
३. G.O.S., M.G. वचनं K.S.S., N.S. भगवान् ।
४. G.O.S., N.S. K.S.S. अयोग्या नाट्यकर्मणि M.G. न योग्या नाट्यकर्मसु ।

य इमे वेदगुह्यज्ञा ऋषयः[1] संशितव्रताः[2] ।
एतेऽस्य ग्रहणे शक्ताः प्रयोगे धारणे तथा ॥ २३ ॥
श्रुत्वा तु शक्रवचनं मामाहाम्बुजसम्भवः ।
त्वं पुत्रशतसंयुक्तः प्रयोक्ताऽस्य भवानघ ॥ २४ ॥
आज्ञापितो विदित्वाऽहं नाट्यवेदं पितामहात् ।
पुत्रानध्यापयामास[3] प्रयोगं चापि[4] तत्त्वतः ॥ २५ ॥

एतदुपसंहरति—**वेदोपवेदै**रित्यादि । वेदा व्याख्याताः वेदार्थानामुपकारकोऽर्थो वेद्यते येन स उपवेदात्मा । तद्यथा ऋग्वेदस्य मन्त्रार्थवादादिव्याख्यानोपनयनप्रजारक्षणप्रदर्शक आयुर्वेदः । यतो **महात्मा** ततः **सर्ववेदी** । सर्ववित्त्वाच्च तथाविधसृष्टिशक्तः । **एव**मित्युपसंहरन् प्रश्नत्रयं कृतोत्तरमिति दर्शयति । प्रयोजनस्याधिकारिणामङ्गानामङ्गाङ्गिभावस्य च निर्णीतत्वात् (१७-१८) ।

एवं पितामहसदृशेन सर्वदा नाट्यवेदशरीररूपकनिर्माणे कविना भाव्यमिति प्रदर्श्य तत्र विभवयुक्तो विधेयनटजनश्च राजा प्रयोजयिता । भरतमुनिसदृशश्च सम्पन्नपरिवारः सर्ववित्प्रयोक्ता । प्रयोजकमहोत्सवप्रायः प्रयोगकालः । क्रीडाप्रस्तावव्याजोपदेशकाः विगतरागद्वेषा मध्यस्थवृत्तयः निर्मलहृदयमुकुरे सति तन्मयीभवनयोग्यतोपेता आहितरसास्वादाः सामाजिका इत्येतत् पुराकल्पमुखेन दर्शयत्यध्यापन(ध्यायान्त)ग्रन्थेन—**उत्पाद्य नाट्यवेदं** **त्वि**त्यादिना । राजैव प्रयोजयितुं शक्त इति **तु** शब्दः । **इतिहासो** दशरूपकम् । **कुशलाः** । ग्रहणधारणयोग्याः । **विदग्धाः** । ऊहापोहसमर्थाः । **प्रगल्भाः** । परिषद्यभीरवः । **जितश्रमाः** । योग्याः समुचितदेहा अखिन्नकायाश्च । **ग्रहण** इति । पूर्वं गुरुमुखाद्ग्रहणम् । तस्याविस्मरणं **धारणम्** । **ज्ञान**मूहापोहविचारः । **प्रयोगः** पर्षदि प्रकटीकरणम् । चकारेण च तदुपयोगिगुणनिका व्यायामाभ्यासादिः । **देवाः** सुखभूयिष्ठत्वात् । स्वाम्यादेशात्कथमपि यदि प्रवर्तेरन् तत्पूर्णपर्यवसानत्वं दुर्लभमेतैरित्यर्थः । (१९-२२)

तर्हि किं क्रियतामित्याह—**य इम** इति । **वेदज्ञा** इति ग्रहणधारणसामर्थ्यम् । **गुह्यज्ञ**त्वेनाध्यात्मोपनिषदर्थवेदनधारणकौशलेन रसाद्युपयोगिसात्त्विकसम्पादितसामर्थ्यम् । यद्वक्ष्यति—"सत्त्वं मनःप्रयत्ननिर्वर्त्यम्" इत्यादि । **तेन**—

---

१. G.O.S. N.S. ऋषयः K.S.S. M.G. मुनयः ।
२. G.O.S. M.G. N.S. संशित K.S.S. संश्रित ।
३. G.O.S. M.G. N.S. पुत्रानध्यापयामास K.S.S. पुत्रानध्यापयं योग्यान् ।
४. G.O.S. N.S. चापि K.S.S. M.G. चास्य ।

शाण्डिल्यं चैव[1] वात्स्यं च कोहलं[2] दत्तिलं तथा ।
जटिला[3]म्बष्टकौ चैव त[4]ण्डुमग्निशिखं तथा ॥ २६ ॥
सैन्धवं सपुलोमानं शाड्वलिं विपुलं तथा ।
कपिञ्जलिं बादिरं[5] च यमधूम्रायणौ तथा ॥ २७ ॥
जम्बुध्वजं काकजङ्घं स्वर्णकं तापसं तथा ।
कैदारिं[6] शालिकर्णं च दीर्घगात्रं च शालिकम् ॥ २८ ॥
कौत्सं ताण्डायनिं चैव पिङ्गलं चित्रकं[7] तथा ।
बन्धुलं भल्लकं चैव मुष्ठिकं[8] सैन्धवायनम् ॥ २९ ॥

न्यस्येत्प्राणं भ्रुवोर्मध्ये स्तम्भो बाष्पश्च चाक्षुषः ।
स्वेदो हृदि गुदे कम्पः पुलको मूर्ध्नि वक्त्रतः ॥
वैवर्ण्यं स्वरितं कण्ठे प्रलयो नासिकान्तरे ॥

इत्यादियोग्यत्वं तेषाम् । अत एवानुषङ्गतो नटस्यापि परमपुरुषार्थलाभो धारणादिबशात् । **ऋषय** इति । दर्शा(र्शना)दृषिरिति । ऊहापोहयोग्याः । **संशितव्रता** इति । अभ्यासे शक्ताः । **तथेति** । ग्रहणादीनामार्थक्रमः प्रदर्शनीय इत्यर्थः । इम इति प्रत्यक्षेणैव दृष्टमेषां तदिति दर्शयति । (२३)

श्रुत्वा त्विति । **मां** त्विति तु शब्देन ऋषिभ्योऽप्यन्येभ्योऽस्य विशेषमाह । ब्रह्मैव मामाहेत्यादरातिशयः । पुत्रशतयोगाद्य (द) न्योन्यप्रवर्तितबहुतरपरिवारयोगः । **अनघे**त्यद्येषणया सोत्साहपरिषदा कृतसम्मानस्य सम्यक्प्रयोगनिष्पत्तिरिति सूचितम् । **आज्ञापित** इत्यनुल्लङ्घनीयवचनताऽस्योक्ता । **पितामहा**वित्यनाचार्योषितत्वाशङ्कां व्युदस्यति । प्रयुज्यत इति प्रयोगो दशरूपकम् । प्रयुज्यते निर्वर्त्यतेऽनेनेति प्रयोगः । नाट्यलक्षणशास्त्रम् । तदहं

---

१. G.O.S. N.S. चैव K.S.S. M.G. चापि ।
२. G.O.S. N.S. M.G. कोहलं दत्तिलं K.S.S. केहावं दन्तितं ।
३. K.S.S. जटुल G.O.S. N.S. M.G. जटिल ।
४. G.O.S. N.S. M.G. तण्डु K.S.S. ताण्डु ।
५. G.O.S. N.S. बादिरं K.S.S. M.G. वार्दारं ।
६. K.S S. केदारं N.S. G.O.S. कैदारिं M.G. केदारिं ।
७. K.S.S. छत्रकं N.S. G.O.S. M.G. चित्रकं ।
८. G.O.S. मुष्ठिकं K.S.S. मुष्टीकं N.S. N.G. मुष्टिकं ।

तैतिलं भार्गवं चैव शुचिं बहुलमेव च ।
अबुधं बुधसेनं च पाण्डुकर्णं सुकेरलम्[1] ॥ ३० ॥
ऋजुकं मण्डकं चैव शम्बरं वञ्जुलं तथा ।
मागधं सरलं चैव कर्तारं चोग्रमेव च ॥ ३१ ॥
तुषारं पार्षदं चैव गौतमं बादरायणम्[2] ।
विशालं शबलं चैव सुना[3]भं मेषमेव च ॥ ३२ ॥
कालियं भ्रमरं चैव तथा पीठमुखं मुनिम् ।
नखकुट्टा[4]श्मकुट्टौ च षट्पदं सोत्तमं तथा ॥ ३३ ॥
पादुकोपानहौ चैव श्रुतिं[5] चाषस्वरं[6] तथा ।
अग्निकुण्डाज्यकुण्डौ च वितण्ड्यं[7] ताण्ड्यमेव च ॥ ३४ ॥
कर्तराक्षं हिरण्याक्षं कुशलं दुस्सहं तथा ।
लाजं भयानकं चैव बीभत्सं सविचक्षणम् ॥ ३५ ॥

पुत्रान्पाठयाञ्चकार । प्रयुक्तिश्च प्रयोगः । तमध्यवसायपर्यन्तमहं पुत्रानध्यापयामास । तथाऽहं चकार यथा प्रयुक्तिं ते पुत्राः सम्यक्प्राप्तवन्त इत्यर्थः । चापिशब्दाभ्यां सूचिते द्वे द्वे आवृत्ती । मुनिसमुचितकर्तव्यान्तरव्यासङ्गोऽपि लिटा सूचितः । तत्त्वत इति नाट्याचार्यस्य सम्यगाप्तत्वं गम्यते । (२४-२५)

पुत्रान्नामभिर्दर्शयति—शाण्डिल्यमित्यादिना । अत्र प्रसिद्धत्वं नटानामादरकारणमिति तावन्मुख्यं नामग्रहणे प्रयोजनम् । आनुषङ्गिकं त्वन्यदपि । तद्यथा विदूषकतापसादिनाम्नां तलाकमीनां । (तथार्कमिणां) निर्वचनलब्धार्थयुक्त्या भूमिकाविशेषोपयोग इति । अन्यस्त्वाह—शतमेवेह पठितम् । कञ्चनना (तच्चा) भिनेयानां स्थाय्युत्पादनरसनवकतद्गतव्यभिचारित्रयस्त्रिंशत्सात्त्विकाष्टकानुरूपाणां पञ्चाशतोऽर्थानां न्याय्यान्याय्यभेदेन नायकप्रतिनायकविषयतया प्राधान्याभिप्रायेणेति । तत्र तु 'कैशिक्यपि प्रयुक्ता स्यात्'

१. G.O.S. N.S. सुकेरलम् M.G. K.S.S. सकेरलम् ।
२. G.O.S. M.G. N.S. बादरायणम् K.S.S. बादरायणिम् ।
३. G.O.S. M.G. N.S. सुनाभं K.S.S. सुनाली ।
४. G.O.S. M.G. N.S. नखकुट्टाश्मकुट्टौ K.S.S. तरुकुट्टात्मकुट्टौ ।
५. G.O.S. M.G. N.S. श्रुतिं K.S.S. श्रुतिकं ।
६. G.O.S. M.G. N.S. चाषस्वरं K.S.S. षट्स्वरं ।
७. G.O.S. N.S. वितण्ड्यं K.S.S. M.G. विताण्ड्यं ।

पुण्ड्राक्षं[1] पुण्ड्रनासं[2] चाप्यसितं[3] सितमेव च ।
विद्युज्जिह्वं महाजिह्वं शालङ्कायनमेव च ॥ ३६ ॥
श्यामायनं[4] माठरं च लोहिताङ्गं तथैव च ।
संवर्तकं पञ्चशिखं त्रिशिखं शिखमेव च ॥ ३७ ॥
शङ्खवर्णमुखं षण्डं शङ्कुकर्णमथापि च ।
शक्रनेमिं गभस्तिं चाप्यंशुमालिं शठं तथा ॥ ३८ ॥

इत्युत्तरग्रन्थावकाशाभाव इत्यलमभिरसहृदयाभिनिवेशव्याख्याभिः ।(२६-३९)

यस्मिन्निति । उत्तमप्रकृतिविचेष्टितादौ । **यथेति** । कश्चित् तदीयहृदयहर्षप्रदर्शनप्रकारेण योग्योऽन्यस्तदीयशोकप्रकटीकरणेनेति । (४०)

अथ सकलप्रयोगप्राणभूतकैशिक्युपयुज्यमानोपकरणान्तरसंहरणायोपक्रमं दर्शयति **भारतीमित्यादि** । **वृत्तिमिति** । धर्मादिपुरुषार्थचतुष्टये साध्ये वागङ्गसत्वचेष्टासामान्यम् । तच्च संक्षिप्तेनावान्तरभेदेन चतुर्धा । यद्यत्किल कर्मारभ्यते तत्र वाङ्मनःकायव्यापारस्तावदस्ति । तत्र कस्यचिल्लालित्यवैचित्र्यक्रमस्यानुप्रवेशः । यत उत्तमप्रकृतीनां सौष्ठवमय एव सर्वो व्यापारः । तदेव तद्वृत्तिचतुष्टयम् । भारती वाग्वृत्तिः । मनोव्यापाररूपा सात्त्विकी सात्वती । सदिति प्रख्यारूपं संवेदनम् । तद्यत्रास्ति तत्सत्वं मनः । तस्येयमिति । 'इर्यति' इत्यरा भटाः सोत्साहा अनलसाः । तेषामियमारभटी कायवृत्तिः । केशाः किञ्चिदप्यर्थक्रियाजातमकुर्वन्तो देहशोभोपयोगिनः । तद्वत्सौन्दर्योपयोगी व्यापारः कैशिकी वृत्तिरिति तावन्मुख्यः क्रमः । अन्यस्य तु यस्तद्व्यपदेशः स तत्प्रधानत्वादनेकरसप्रधानं पानकरीत्या कैशिकीत्यादि मधुरव्यपदेशवत् । एतच्च प्राग्रे वितनिष्यामः ।

एवं यत्किञ्चिल्लालित्यं तत्सर्वं कैशिकीविजृम्भितम् । सा च तैः प्रयोक्तुमशक्येति **तुशब्देनोक्तम्** । तेन दशरूपं सर्वं वैचित्र्यशून्यं तान्प्रति योजितम् । अत एव तादृशे प्रयोगेऽवज्ञां वै शब्देन द्योतयति । **प्रयुक्त** इति । तेषामभ्यासभूमौ योजित इत्यर्थः । (४१)

---

१. G.O.S. M.G. N.S. पुण्ड्राक्षं K.S.S. पुण्डाक्षं ।
२. G.O.S. N.S. M.G. पुण्ड्रनासं K.S.S. पूर्णनासं ।
३. G.O.S. चाप्यसित N.S. M.G. K.S.S. च असितं ।
४. G.O.S. M.G. N.S. श्यामायनं K.S.S. त्यामायनं ।

विद्युतं शातजङ्घं च रौद्रं वीरमथापि च ।
पितामहाज्ञयाऽस्माभिर्लोकस्य च गुणेप्सया ॥ ३९ ॥

प्रयोजितं पुत्रशतं यथाभूमिविभागशः ।
यो यस्मिन्कर्मणि यथा[1] योग्यस्तस्मिन् स योजितः ॥ ४० ॥

भारतीं सात्वतीं चैव वृत्तिमारभटीं तथा ।
समाश्रितः प्रयोगस्तु प्रयुक्तो वै मया[2] द्विजाः ॥ ४१ ॥

परिगृह्य प्रणम्याथ ब्रह्मा विज्ञापितो मया ।
अथाह मां सुरगुरुः कैशिकीमपि योजय ॥ ४२ ॥

क्षममिति । प्रयोगसमर्थं सादरविचित्रं प्रयुङ्क्ते । अत एवाह—**द्रव्यम्** । सुन्दरम् । यतः सौन्दर्यप्राणैव सा । **एवमिति** । बुद्धिकौशलं मदीयं ज्ञातुं तेनाहमेतत्पृष्टः । **चकारेण** प्रत्युत्पन्नप्रतिभानत्वं दर्शयति । अनेन झटिति कविहृदयग्रहणयोग्यत्वं नाटचाचार्यगुण इति सूचयति । (४२-४३)

न चात्यन्तापरिदृष्टे वस्तुनि उपकरणमुन्नेतुं शक्यम् । ब्रह्मणा तूपदेशसमये वचनमात्रेणोक्तमेतन्मध्ये हृदयहारि वैचित्र्यं योजनीमिति । अनेनाभिप्रायेण कैशिकीसाक्षात्करणं वर्णयति **नृत्ताङ्गहा**रेत्यादिना युगलकेन । नर्तनं **नृत्तम्** । गात्राणामङ्गोपाङ्गानां विलासेन क्षेपः । न तु केनचित्कर्तव्यांशेन । लोकोऽप्येवंविधे विषये एवमेवाह—'नृत्यतीव गच्छति' इत्यादि । तत्र येऽङ्गहारा अङ्गानां हरणानीति अत्रुटितरूपतया समुचितस्थानप्राप्तिः । तैः सम्पन्ना । शङ्करस्यैव भगवतः परिपूर्णानन्दनिर्भरीभूतदेहोच्चलदान्तरनिर्वारसुन्दराकारस्य अत एव **नृत्यतः** इतिकर्तव्यान्तरवैकल्यादानन्दनृत्तमात्रस्थितस्य । प्रयोज्यत्वेन **मया दृष्टा** ।

ननु सा नाटचोपयोगिनी **कथम्** । आह । सैव यदि श्लक्ष्णेन श्लिष्यतोचितेन नेपथ्येन सहिता भवति । यद्वक्ष्यति—"शृङ्गार उज्ज्वलवेषात्मक" (ना.शा. ६-५०) इति तन्नाटचोक्तशृङ्गाररसः सम्भवति । नान्यथा । नेपथ्यग्रहणं सुकुमारस्याङ्गिकादेरप्युपलक्षणम् । तेन शृङ्गाराभिव्यक्तिहेतौ सुकुमारे चतुर्विधेऽप्यभिनये योजिते मधुरमन्थरवलनावर्तनाभ्रूक्षेपकटाक्षादिना विना शृङ्गाररसास्वादस्य नामापि न भवति ।

---

१. K.S.S. तथा G.O.S. N.S. M.G. यथा ।

२. K.S.S. मह्य G.O.S. N.S. M.G. मया ।

यच्च तस्या:[1] क्षमं द्रव्यं तद्ब्रूहि द्विजसत्तम ।
एवं तेनास्म्य[2]भिहित: प्रत्युक्तश्च मया प्रभु: ॥ ४३ ॥
दीयतां भगवन्द्रव्यं कैशिक्या: सम्प्रयोजकम् ।
नृत्ता[3]ङ्गहारसम्पन्ना रसभावक्रियात्मिका ॥ ४४ ॥
दृष्टा मया भगवतो नीलकण्ठस्य नृत्यत: ।
कैशिकी श्लक्ष्णनैपथ्या शृङ्गाररससम्भवा ॥ ४५ ॥
अशक्या पुरुषै: सा[4] तु प्रयोक्तुं स्त्रीजनादृते ।
ततोऽसृजन्महातेजा मनसाऽप्सरसो विभु: ॥ ४६ ॥

किमत्रैव सोपयोगेत्याह—**रसभावक्रियात्मिकेति** । रसानां भावो भावना कविनटसामाजिकहृदयव्याप्ति: । तस्या या क्रिया इतिकर्तव्यता सैवात्मा स्वभावो ऽस्या: । एतदुक्तं भवति—रौद्रादिरसाभिव्यक्तावपि कर्तव्यायां योऽभिनय उपादीयते सोऽप्यनुप्रासवलनावर्तनाद्यात्मकसुन्दरवैचित्र्यस्यामिश्रणया दु:श्लिष्टोऽश्लिष्ट एव वा न रसाभिव्यक्तिहेतुर्भवतीति सर्वत्रैव कैशिकी प्राणा: । यद्वक्ष्यति—"अस्य शाखा च नृत्तं च वस्तून्यभिनयस्य" (ना.शा. ८-१५) इति शृङ्गाररसस्य तु नामग्रहणमपि न तया विना शक्यम् । **स्त्रीजनादृत** इति । अयं भाव:—यावन्निजहृदयरसविलसद्विकस्वरनिर्वारचमत्कारपवित्रता न जाता भगवत इव, तावच्छिक्षाशतैरपि वैचित्र्यमनाहार्यम् । मुनीनां च निसर्गविषयविमुखचित्तवृत्तीनां को निर्वृतिचमत्कार: । योऽपि वा ससमाधिज: सोऽपि देहपर्यन्ततां न भजति । प्रत्युत तत: पलायमाना:(न:) । अत: स्त्रीणां तादृगस्ति वैचित्र्यम् । तत्सम्पर्कसम्भवदार्द्रभावास्तु कदाचिच्छक्नुयुरपि ।

ये त्वाहु:—'न भगवत: कैशिकीप्रयोगसामर्थ्यम् । तेन दृष्टोमयेति पाठे उमया सह भगवतो नृत्यतो भगवन्तमप्यनादृत्य भगवत्या प्रयुज्यमाना मया दृष्टा' इति—त उक्तनीत्या पराकृता: । तथा—

विचित्रैरङ्गहारैस्तु देवो लीलासमन्वितै: ।
बबन्ध य: शिखापाशं कैशिकी तत्र निर्मिता ॥ (ना.शा. २०-१३)

१, K.S.S. तस्याक्षमं G.O.S. M.G. N.S. तस्या:क्षमं ।
२, K.S.S. तेनाम्यभिहित: G.O.S. N.S. M.G. तेनास्म्यभिहित: ।
३, K.S.S. M.G. मृद्वङ्गहारसंयुक्ता G.O.S. N.S. नृत्ताङ्गहारसम्पन्ना ।
४, K.S.S. N.S. M.G. साधु G.O.S. सा तु ।

नाट्यालङ्कारचतुराः प्रादान्मह्यं प्रयोगतः ।
मञ्जुकेशीं सुकेशीं च मिश्रकेशीं सुलोचनाम् ॥ ४७ ॥
सौदामिनीं देवदत्तां देवसेनां मनोरमाम् ।
सुदतीं सुन्दरीं चैव विदग्धां विपुलां[1] तथा ॥ ४८ ॥

इति भगवतो विष्णोः कैशिकीनिर्माणमनुचितं स्यादित्यलं बहुना । जनशब्देन रागिताशङ्कां परिहरति । **ततोऽसृजदिति** । **मनसेति** । यथारुचि विनिर्मिता इत्यर्थः । (४४-४६) ।

नाट्यस्य योऽलङ्कारो वैचित्र्यहेतुः कैशिकी । तत्र **चतुराः** । अन्ये तु नाट्यालङ्काराः सामान्याभिनये (अ-२२) वक्ष्यमाणाः स्वभावजा 'लीला विलास' इत्याद्या दश 'शोभा कान्तिः' इत्याद्याश्च सप्त (प्ता) यत्नजा इति । अनेन मुनिकन्यानामत्रायोग्यत्वं तावदुक्तम् । तासां नामग्रहणे पूर्ववत्प्रयोजनं निरूप्यम् । **मे ददाविति** । नाट्याचार्यपरवशत्वमुपकरणसम्भारस्य दर्शयति—**ददाविति** । ताश्च मया यथोचितं शिक्षादानेन प्रतिगृहीता इति सूचयन् कैशिकीमप्यहं योजितवानिति दर्शयति । एवं वृत्तिचतुष्टयसम्पूर्णं नाट्य गुणनिकायामभ्यस्तमिति प्रदर्श्य गीतातोद्याभ्यामुपरञ्जकाभ्यां योगं दर्शयति—**स्वातिरित्यादि** । येन जलधरसमयनिपतत्सलिलधारावैचित्र्याभिहन्यमानपुष्करदलविलसितरचितविचित्रवर्णानुहरणयोजनया यथास्वं वृत्तिनियमेन पुष्करवाद्यनिर्माणं कृतमित्यर्थः । **सह शिष्यैरिति** । त्रिपुष्करस्य वाद्यस्यापूरकपणवमृदङ्गझल्लर्याद्युपयोगेन पक्षातोद्यपरिग्रह उक्तः । भाण्डस्यात्र पूर्वमुपादानं वृत्ति (त्ते)र्येन तस्यैव परिक्रमणादौ सति सोपयोगात् । कैशिकी चात्र मध्ये नियोजितेत्युक्तम् । न (तेन) तत्प्रधानमेतत् । **गानयोग** इति । गानशब्देन ततसुषिरपरिग्रहः । गानशब्देन गान्धर्वस्यात्रानुपयोगमाह । **नियुक्तो** नियोजित इत्यनेन वादकगायकादीनां नाट्याचार्यायत्ततां दर्शयति । नृत्तगीतातोद्याभिनयानां साम्यसिद्ध्यर्थमेकीभावेन सम्मेलनं प्रकृत्य प्रयोगः कार्य इति दर्शयति श्लोकद्वयेन—**एवं नाट्यमित्यादिना** । एवं मेलनिकायां 'नाट्यमिदम्' इत्येकबुद्धिग्राह्यं सम्मिलितं **सम्यक्सम्पन्नमिति बुद्ध्वा** ज्ञात्वा । पुत्रैः स्वातिनारदाभ्यां च सह **ब्रह्माणमुपस्थितः** उपनिमन्त्रणार्थं ब्रह्मणोऽग्रे स्थित इत्यर्थः । (४७-५२)

उपनिमन्त्रणं दर्शयति—**नाट्यस्येति** । **ग्रहणमिति** । **गृहीतं** शिक्षितं तावन्नाट्यमित्यर्थः । ग्रहणं तदवलोकनं तत्प्राप्तं प्रेक्षणयोग्यं जातमित्यर्थः । **एतत्त्विति** । तुशब्द एवकारार्थे । श्रुत्वैव । अत एव **प्रत्युपस्थितः** अयत्नादेवा-

---

१. G.O.S. N.S. विपुलां K.S.S. विक्धिां M.G. विबुधां ।

सुमालां सन्तर्ति चैव सुनन्दां सुमुखीं तथा ।
मागधीमर्जुनीं चैव सरलां केरलां धृ[1]तिम् ॥ ४९ ॥
नन्दां सपु[2]ष्कलां चैव क[3]लमां चैव मे ददौ ।
स्वातिर्भाण्ड[4]नियुक्तस्तु सह शिष्यैः स्वयम्भुवा ॥ ५० ॥
नारदाद्याश्च गन्धर्वा गा[5]नयोगे नियोजिताः ।
एवं ना[6]ट्यमिदं सम्यग्बुध्वा सर्वैः सुतैः सह ॥ ५१ ॥
स्वातिनारदसंयुक्तो वेदवेदाङ्गकारणम् ।
उपस्थितोऽहं ब्रह्मा[7]णं प्रयोगार्थं कृताञ्जलिः ॥ ५२ ॥
नाट्यस्य ग्रहणं प्राप्तं ब्रूहि किं करवाण्यहम् ।
एतत्तु वचनं श्रुत्वा प्रत्युवाच पितामहः ॥ ५३ ॥

भिमुख्येनोपस्थितो दैवसङ्घटित इत्यर्थ । ध्वजस्येन्द्रार्थस्य महनं पूजनं यत्र स ध्वजमहः । ध्वजमहस्य विशेषणद्वारेण सम्भवं दर्शयति **निहतासुरदानव** इत्यादिना ।

तत्र प्रयोगे क्रमं दर्शयति—**पूर्वं कृता मया नान्दीति** । नान्द्याख्यं मुख्यं मङ्गलं सकलपूर्वरङ्गाङ्गोपलक्षणमिति **केचित्** । पूर्वरङ्गाङ्गानां मध्यान्नान्दी केवलापि प्रयोज्येत्येवंपरमेतदित्यन्ये । **अस्मदुपाध्यायास्तु**—यावद्दैत्यैस्तत्र विघ्नाद्याचरणं न कृतं तावत्पूर्वरङ्गस्य विधिपूर्वकस्य कोऽवकाशः । स हि विघ्नरक्षाकरणेन मण्डपभागनिवेशितदेवतापरितोषहेतुः प्राधान्येन । नान्तरीयकतया च दैत्यपरितोषकारणम् । विघ्नास्तु यदा जातास्ततः प्रभृति पूर्वरङ्गः । तथा चतुर्थेऽध्याये वक्ष्यते—(ना. शा. ४-१०) पूर्वरङ्गे कृते मया भगवते शिवभट्टारकाय दर्शित इति—यथा तथा तु यः कुतपविन्यासादि न (दिः स न) पूर्वरङ्गशब्दवाच्यः । तस्मादिह नान्दीमात्रस्य प्रयोगः । किमर्थाऽसावित्याह—**वेदनिर्मिता** । 'तत्राशिषमाशास्ते' इति हि श्रुतिः सर्वकर्मस्वाशीःपूर्वकत्वमाह । यत्ततो नान्दीप्रयोगः । न तु पूर्वरङ्गाङ्गत्वेन । (५३-५६)

१. K.S.S. केरलान्धतीम् G.O.S. M.G. N.S. केरलां धृतिम् ।
२. G.O.S. N.S. M.G. सपुष्कलां K.S.S. सुपुष्पमालाम् ।
३. K.S.S. N.S. M.G. कलभां G.O.S. कलमां ।
४. K.S.S. स्वातिभाण्डो नियुक्तस्तु G.O.S. N.S. M.G. स्वातिर्भाण्ड नियुक्तस्तु ।
५. K.S.S. नाट्य G.O.S. N.S. M.G. गान ।
६. K.S.S. भावनाट्य G.O.S. M.G.N.S. एवं नाट्य ।
७. K.S.S. M.G. N.S. लोकेशं G.O.S. ब्रह्माणं ।

महानयं प्रयोगस्य समयः प्रत्युपस्थितः ।
अयं ध्वजमहः श्रीमान् महेन्द्रस्य प्रवर्तते ॥ ५४ ॥
अत्रेदानीमयं वेदो नाट्यसंज्ञः प्रयुज्यताम् ।
ततस्तस्मिन्ध्वजमहे निहतासुरदानवे ॥ ५५ ॥
प्रहृष्टामरसंकीर्णे महेन्द्रविजयोत्सवे ।
पूर्वं कृता मया नान्दी[1] ह्या[2]शीर्वचनसंयुता ॥ ५६ ॥

अष्टौ यान्यङ्गभूतानि पदानि वाक्यं प्रति महावाक्यं वा । तानि सुप्तिङन्तान्यवान्तरवाक्यानि वेत्युभयथा । अत एव विचित्रेत्युक्तम् । तेन—

जितमुडुपतिना नमः सुरेभ्यो द्विजवृषभा निरुपद्रवा भवन्तु ।
अवतु च पृथिवीं समृद्धसस्यां प्रतिपच्चन्द्रवपुर्नरेन्द्रचन्द्रः ॥ (रत्ना. १-४)

इत्येषाऽपि भारतीयत्वेन प्रसिद्धा कोहलप्रदर्शिता नान्द्युपपन्ना भवति । अत्र तु पक्षे—

नान्दीपदान्तरेष्वेषु ह्येवमस्त्वित्ति नित्यशः ।
वन्देतां सम्यगुक्ताभिर्वाग्भिस्तौ पारिपार्श्विकौ ॥ (ना. शा. ५-११४)

इति श्लोकेऽन्तरशब्दोऽवान्तरवाक्यविच्छेदवाची द्रष्टव्यः ।

विवेचकास्त्वाहुः—अङ्गग्रहणादत्रावान्तरवाक्यान्येव तावदुपात्तानि । तत्र चाष्टद्वादशसङ्ख्या चतुरस्रत्र्यश्रकालानुसारिपूर्वरङ्गद्वयाभिप्रायेण । तत्र

नान्दीं पदैर्द्वादशभिरष्टाभिर्वाप्यलङ्कृताम् ॥ (ना. शा. ५-१०९)

इत्यत्रापिशब्दाच्चतुष्पदत्वं षोडशपदत्वं चतुरश्रगतं लभ्यते । त्र्यश्रगतं च त्रिपदत्वं षट्पदत्वं चेत्येवमल्पमपि तद्भेदेन तिस्रस्तिस्रो नान्द्यः । ततः परमपि भूयस्त्वात् । तेन जितमुडुपतिनेति चतुष्पदेयम् । षोडशपदा तु "जयति भुवनकारणम्" इत्यादि । तदन्त इति । नान्द्यन्ते परिसमाप्तौ । अनुकृतिरिति नाट्यम् । तत्र च बद्धेति गुणनिका योजिता । न तु प्रयोग इत्येतच्चासत् । तत्पूर्वोत्तरव्याघातात् । पूर्वं ह्युक्तम्—एवं नाट्यमिदमित्यादि नान्दी

1. K.S.S. G.O.S पूर्वं कृता मया नान्दी N.S. M.G नान्दी कृता मया पूर्वं ।
2. G.O.S. adds हि K.S.S. N.S. M.G. Omit हि ।

अष्टाङ्गपदसंयुक्ता विचित्रा वेदनिर्मिता[1]।

तदन्तेऽनुकृतिर्बद्धा यथा दैत्याः सुरैर्जिताः ॥ ५७ ॥

सम्फेटविद्रवकृता च्छेद्यभेद्याहवात्मिका ।

ततो ब्रह्मादयो देवाः प्रयोगपरितोषिताः ॥ ५८ ॥

प्रददुर्मत्सुतेभ्यस्तु[2] सर्वोपकरणानि वै[3] ।

प्रीतस्तु प्रथमं शक्रो दत्तवान्स्वं [4]ध्वजं शुभम् ॥ ५९ ॥

कृतेत्यन्तम् । वक्ष्यते च—ब्रह्मादयः प्रयोगपरितोषिता इति । तस्माद्बद्धेति प्रस्ताविता । न तु निष्पादिता । प्रस्तावना तावत्प्रयुक्तेत्यर्थः ।

अन्ये त्वनुकृतिरिति नाट्यानुकाररूपा प्रस्तावनेत्याहुः । 'कृता तदन्तेऽनुकृतिः' इति च पठन्ति । एतदुपजीवनेनैव चिरन्तनाः कवयो "नान्द्यन्ते सूत्रधारः" इति पुस्तके लिखन्ति स्म । किं प्रस्तावितमित्याह—**यथा दैत्या** इति । डिमसमवकारेहामृगादीनामन्यतमः प्रयोगः प्रास्तावीत्यर्थः । यद्यपि भरतपुत्रैर्दशरूपकमभ्यस्तं तथापि न युगपत्सर्वः प्रयोक्तुं पार्यत इत्येवमुक्तम् । यत्केचिदचूचुदन्—समवकारे कः कैशिकीयोजनावसर इति पूर्वग्रन्थोऽसङ्गत इति तन्निरवकाशमेव । समवकारादावपि च सौन्दर्यात्मकं वैचित्र्यं कैशिकीविजृम्भ एवेत्युक्तम् । (५७) ।

रोषग्रथितवाक्यस्तु **सम्फेटः** । शङ्काभयत्रासकृतो **विद्रवः** । छेदमर्हतीति च्छेद्य शस्त्राहवः । भेदमर्हतीति **भेद्यं** मल्लयुद्धात्मकनियुद्धम् । **ततः** इति । प्रभुपरितोषाय प्रभुचरितं कदाचिन्नाट्ये वर्णनीयमिति यथा दैत्याः सुरैर्जिता इत्येतस्माल्लभ्यत इति केचिदाहुः । तदसत् । दशरूपकलक्षणयुक्तिविरोधात् । तत्र हि किञ्चित्प्रसिद्धचरितं किञ्चिदुत्पाद्यचरितमिति वक्ष्यते । न च वर्तमानचरितानुकारो युक्तः । विनेयानां तत्र रागद्वेषमध्यस्थतादिना तन्मयीभावाभावे प्रीतेरभावेन व्युत्पत्तेरप्यभावात् । वर्तमानचरिते च धर्मादिकर्मफलसम्बन्धस्य प्रत्यक्षत्वे प्रयोगवैयर्थ्यम् । प्र(अप्र)त्यक्षत्वे 'भविष्यति प्रमाणाभावात्' इति न्यायेन व्युत्पत्तेः सम्भवान्नायिका (सम्भावना का) । (?) एतच्च दशरूपकाध्याये वितनिष्याम इत्यास्तां तावत् ।

---

१. G.O.S. N.S. वेदनिर्मिता K.S.S. M.G. देवसंमता ।

२. K.S.S. N.S. M.G. हृष्टमनसः G.O.S. मत्सुतेभ्यस्तु ।

३. K.S.S. N.S. M.G. नः G.O.S. वै ।

४. G.O.S स्वं ध्वजं N.S. K.S.S. M.G. स्वध्वजं ।

ब्रह्मा कुटिलकं[1] चैव भृङ्गारं वरुणः शुभम्[2] ।
सूर्यश्छत्रं शिवस्सिद्धिं वायुर्व्यंजनमेव च ॥ ६० ॥
विष्णुः सिंहासनं चैव कुबेरो[3] मकुटं[4] तथा ।
श्राव्यत्वं प्रेक्षणीयस्य ददौ देवी सरस्वती ॥ ६१ ॥
शेषा ये देवगन्धर्वा यक्षराक्षसपन्नगाः ।
तस्मिन्सदस्यभिप्रेतान्[5] नानाजातिगुणाश्रयान् ॥ ६२ ॥
अंशांशैर्भाषितं[6] भावान् रसान् रूपं बलं तथा ।
दत्तवन्तः प्रहृष्टास्ते मत्सुतेभ्यो दिवौकसः[8] ॥ ६३ ॥

देवानां त्वद्य प्रसिद्धवर्णनीयासम्भवात्पूर्वकल्पमन्वन्तरादिगतदेवासुरचरित-कीर्तनम् । अनादित्वात्संसारस्य श्रुतिस्मृत्यनुमतदेवासुरकीर्तनवदिति । तत्र वर्तनो(वर्तमानो)पवर्णनं तज्जातीयानाम् । अथ चरित्रभ्रमविप्रलब्धास्त्वसुराश्चुक्षुभुरिति वक्ष्यामः । न च स्वचरितवर्णनाद्देवानां परितोष इह । यत आह—**प्रयोगपरितोषिता** इति । **ध्वजमिति** । यस्य विघ्नशान्त्यै पूजार्थमुपयोगो भावी । (५८-५९)

कुटिलकमिति । वक्रदण्डको विदूषकोपयोगी । ब्रह्मायुधात्मा दण्डः । अपकामत्वेन भीषणत्वावात्यादपीत्यर्थः (?) । **भृङ्गारः** पारिपार्श्विकोपयोगी । **छत्रमत्र** वितानः । जलदानां सूर्योद्भवत्वात् तत्प्रतिमः । यदाहुः—ऋतवे वर्षान्ते महतो मेघसम्प्रवानिति । भगवदायत्ता दैवी मानुषी च सिद्धिरिति मध्ये तदुपादानं सर्वव्यापकत्वं दैव्याः सिद्धेः प्रतिपादयितुम् । **व्यजनं** घर्मापनुत्तये । सिंहा-

---

१. G.O.S. M.G. N.S. कुटिलकं K.S.S. कमण्डलुं ।

२. N.S· K.S.S. M.G. तथा G.O.S. शुभं ।

३. G.O.S. N.S. कुबेरो M.G. K.S.S. कुवेरो ।

४. K.S.S. N.S. M.G. मुकुटं G,O.S. मकुटं ।

५. K.S.S. G.O.S. अभिप्रेतान् N.S. अतिप्रीतान् M:G. अतिप्रीता ।

६. K.S.S. N.S. भावितान् G.O.S. भाषितं M.G. भाषितान् ।

७. G.O.S. N.S. रूपं वलं तथा K.S.S. रूपबलिं क्रियाम् M.G. रूपं क्रियाबलम् ।

८. N.S. प्रददुर्मत्सुतेभ्यश्च चित्रमाभरणं बहु । G.O.S. M.G. K.S.S. दत्तवन्तः प्रहृष्टास्ते मत्सुतेभ्यो दिवौकसः ।

एवं प्रयोगे प्रारब्धे दैत्यदानवनाशने ।
अभवन्क्षुभिताः सर्वे दैत्या ये तत्र सङ्गताः ॥ ६४ ॥

विरूपाक्षपुरोगांश्च[1] विघ्नान्प्रोत्साह्य[2] तेऽब्रुवन् ।
न क्षमिष्यामहे[3] नाटचमेतदागम्यतामिति ॥ ६५ ॥

ततस्तैरसुरैः सार्धं विघ्ना[4] मायामुपाश्रिताः ।
वाचश्चेष्टां स्मृतिं चैव स्तम्भयन्ति स्म नृत्यताम् ॥ ६६ ॥

तथा विध्वंसनं[6] दृष्ट्वा सूत्रधारस्य[7] देवराट् ।
कस्मात्[8]प्रयोगवैषम्यमित्युक्त्वा ध्यानमाविशत् ॥ ६७ ॥

सनादि राजभूमिकायामुपयोगि । यक्षादयो ये तत्त्वज्ञा नाटचस्य । **भाषितमिति** । तत्तद्भूमिकोपयोगिवाचिके शिक्षा । **भावानिति** । विभावादिषु । तथा हि रक्तमांसादीनि भयजुगुप्साविभावरूपाणि यक्षरक्षसां हर्षोत्साहविभावतां यान्तीति तदुपदेशादेव तज्ज्ञेयम् । **रसानिति** । स्वोचितस्थायिभावसम्बध्यमानतत्तद्रसोपयोगिनोऽनुभावव्यभिचारिवर्गस्य शिक्षा दर्शिता । **रूपमिति** मुखरागस्य । **बलमित्याङ्गिकस्य** । प्रतिभूमिकं परितुष्टेन । अन्ततोऽत्र शिष्टा(क्षा)पि काचिद्देया । सामाजिकेभ्यश्च धनविज्ञानमित्याहरणीयातोद्या (द्याद्या) जिहीर्षता च परिषत्परितोषाय यतितव्यमित्येतदनेन दर्शितम् । (६०-६३)

अथ विघ्नोपशमनाय जर्जरपूजा कार्येति दर्शयितुमितिहासेनोपक्रमते—**एवं प्रयोग** इति । दैत्यानां विनाशनं यत्र प्रयोज्यतया । **आगम्यतामिति** । अवधार्यतां यदि वा सम्भूयास्यताम् । **मायामिति** अदृश्यत्वमित्यर्थः । चेष्टेत्याङ्गिकी ।

---

१. G.O.S. N.S. पुरोगांश्च K.S.S पुरोगास्तु M.G. पुरोगांस्तु ।

२. G.O.S. M.G. प्रोत्साह्य N.S. उत्सा (त्पा)द्य K.S.S. प्रोत्साद्य ।

३ G.O.S. क्षमिष्यामहे N.S इच्छामहे M.G. ईक्षामहे K.S.S. इष्यामहे ।

४. K.S.S. विघ्नमायाम् G.O,S. N.S. M.G. विघ्ना मायाम् ।

५. K.S.S. वचः G.O.S. N.S. M.G. वाचः ।

६. G.O.S. M.G. K.S.S. विध्वंसनं N.S. विध्वंसितं ।

७. G.O.S. N.S. सूत्रधारस्य देवराट् K.S.S. M.G. तत्र तेषां स देवराट् ।

८. G.O.S. M.G. K.S.S. कस्मात् N.S. तस्मात् ।

अथापश्यत्स[1]दो विघ्नैः समन्तात्परिवारितम् ।
सहेतरैः सूत्रधारं नष्टसंज्ञं जडीकृतम् ॥ ६८ ॥
उत्थाय त्वरितं शक्रः गृहीत्वा ध्वजमुत्तमम्[2] ।
सर्वरत्नोज्ज्वलतनुः[3] किञ्चिदु[4]द्वृत्तलोचनः ॥ ६९ ॥
रङ्गपीठगतान्विघ्नानसुरांश्चैव देवराट् ।
जर्जरीकृतदेहांस्तानकरोज्जर्जरेण सः ॥ ७० ॥
निहतेषु[5] च सर्वेषु विघ्नेषु सह दानवैः ।
सम्प्रहृष्य ततो वाक्यमाहुः सर्वे दिवौकसः ॥ ७१ ॥
अहो प्रहरणं दिव्यमिदमासादितं त्वया ।
जर्जरीकृतसर्वाङ्गा येनैते दानवाः कृताः[6] ॥ ७२ ॥
यस्मादनेन ते विघ्नाः सासुरा जर्जरीकृताः ।
तस्माज्जर्जर एवेति[7] नामतोऽयं भविष्यति ॥ ७३ ॥
शेषा[8] ये चैव हिंसार्थमुपयास्यन्ति[9] हिंसकाः[10] ।
दृष्ट्वैव जर्जरं तेऽपि गमिष्यन्त्येवमेव तु ॥ ७४ ॥

यद्यपि स्मृतिस्तम्भनेन सर्वं स्तम्भितं भवति तथापि तत्तदभिनयप्राधान्येन तदेव स्तम्भितमित्युक्तम् । सूत्रधारस्येति । सपरिवारस्येति । प्रस्तावनाप्रयोगमध्य एवायं विघ्न इति यावत् । ध्यानमिति । यत्र माया न प्रभवति । (६४-६७)

---

१. G.O.S. M.G. N.S. सदो K.S.S. तदा ।

२. G.O.S. M.G. गृहीत्वा ध्वजमुत्तमम् । K.S.S. क्रोधात् जग्राह तं ध्वजम् N.S. Reads differently अथोत्थाय द्रुतं क्रोधाद्दिव्यं जग्राह स ध्वजम् ।

३. N.S. G.O.S. M.G. सर्वरत्नोज्ज्वलतनुः K.S.S. सर्वरत्नोज्ज्वलन्तं तु ।

४. N.S. G.O.S. K.S.S. किञ्चिदि् M.G. कोपाद् ।

५. M.G. गतेषु तत्रेषु G.O.S. K.S.S. N.S. निहतेषु च सर्वेषु ।

६. G.O.S N.S. जर्जरीकृतसर्वाङ्गा येनैते दानवाः कृताः K.S.S. M.G. नाट्यविध्वंसिनः सर्वे येन ते जर्जरीकृताः ।

७. M.G. K.S.S. इत्येव G.O.S. N.S. एवेति ।

८. M.G. सेर्षा G.O.S. N.S. K.S.S. शेषा ।

९. G.O.S. M.G. K.S.S. उपयास्यन्ति N.S. उपस्थास्यन्ति ।

१०. G.O.S K.S.S. हिंसकाः M.G. N.S. विघ्नकाः ।

एवमेवास्त्विति ततः शक्रः प्रोवाच तान्सुरान् ।
रक्षाभूतश्च सर्वेषां भविष्यत्येष[१] जर्जरः ॥ ७५ ॥
प्रयोगे प्रस्तुते ह्येवं स्फीते शक्रमहे पुनः ।
त्रासं सञ्जनयन्ति स्म विघ्नाः शेषास्[२]तु नृत्यताम् ॥ ७६ ॥
दृष्ट्वा तेषां व्यवसितं दैत्यानां[३] विप्रकारजम् ।
उपस्थितोऽहं ब्रह्माणं सुतैः सर्वैः समन्वितः ॥ ७७ ॥
निश्चिता भगवन्विघ्ना नाट्यस्यास्य विनाशने ।
अस्य[४] रक्षाविधिं सम्यगाज्ञापय सुरेश्वर ॥ ७८ ॥
ततश्च[५] विश्वकर्माणं ब्रह्मो[६]वाच प्रयत्नतः ।
कुरु लक्षणसम्पन्नं नाट्यवेश्म महा[७]मते ॥ ७९ ॥
ततोऽचिरेण कालेन विश्वकर्मा महच्छुभम् ।
सर्वलक्षणसम्पन्नं कृत्वा नाट्यगृहं तु सः[८] ॥ ८० ॥
प्रोक्तवान्द्रुहिणं गत्वा सभायान्तु कृताञ्जलिः ।
सज्जं नाट्यगृहं देव तदवेक्षितुमर्हसि ॥ ८१ ॥

सद इति यत्र प्रयोगः क्रियते सीदत्यस्मिन्निति । जीर्यत्यतिशयेनेति पचाद्यचि यङ्लुकि रूपम् । अतिशयेन जीर्णीकृतो देहो येषान्ते तथा । जर्जरेणेति यङ्लुगन्ताण्णिचि पुनः पचाद्यचि रूपम् । एवं राज्ञा सिद्धिविघातका दण्ड्या इति दर्शितम् । यदि वा मूलत एव तत्परिरक्षायै मण्डपः कार्यः । ये च

---

१. G.O.S. M.G. N.S.S. एष K.S.S. एव ।
२. K.S.S. मद्वधबुद्धयः G.O.S. N.S. शेषास्तु M.G. सेर्ष्यास्तु ।
३. G.O.S. N.S. दैत्यानां M.G. K.S.S. मदर्थे ।
४. G.O.S. K.S.S. अस्य M.G. N.S. अतो ।
५. G.O.S. च N.S. तु K.S.S. M.G. स ।
६. G.O.S. M.G. K.S.S. ब्रह्मोवाच N.S. आह ब्रह्मा ।
७. K.S.S. चकार सः G.O.S. N.S. M.G. महामते ।
८. G.O.S. N.S. (Same as above) M.G. K.S.S. कृत्वा यथोक्तमेवं तु गृहं पद्मोद्भवाज्ञया ।

ततः सह महेन्द्रेण सुरैः सर्वैश्च सेतरैः[1] ।
आगत[2]स्त्वरितो द्रष्टुं द्रुहिणो नाट्यमण्डपम् ॥ ८२ ॥
दृष्ट्वा नाट्यगृहं ब्रह्मा प्राह सर्वान्सुरांस्ततः ।
अंशभागैर्भवद्भिस्तु रक्ष्योऽयं नाट्यमण्डपः ॥ ८३ ॥
रक्षणे मण्डपस्याथ[3] विनियुक्तस्तु चन्द्रमाः[4] ।
लोकपालास्तथा दिक्षु[5] विदिक्ष्वपि च मारुताः ॥ ८४ ॥
नेपथ्यभूमौ मित्रस्तु निक्षिप्तो वरुणोऽम्बरे[6] ।
वेदिकारक्षणे वह्निर्भाण्डे सर्वदिवौकसः[7] ॥ ८५ ॥
वर्णाश्चत्वार एवाथ[8] स्तम्भेषु विनियोजिताः ।
आदित्याश्चैव रुद्राश्च स्थिताः[9] स्तम्भान्तरेष्वथ[10] ॥ ८६ ॥
धारणीष्वथ[11] भूतानि शालास्वप्सरसस्तथा ।
सर्ववेश्मसु यक्षिण्यो महीपृष्ठे महोदधिः ॥ ८७ ॥

दण्डस्याविषया वातातपवर्षादयश्च तत्कृतो हि सिद्धिविघातो मण्डपे सति न भवति । एतेनैवाभिप्रायेण पुराकल्पमाह—**प्रयोग** इत्यादि । **शेषा** इति । जर्जरीकृतशरीरशेषा अपीत्यर्थः । यद्वक्ष्यति—'निश्चिता भगवन्विघ्ना' इति । तथाऽस्मिन् जर्जरीकरणकाले एते चान्तर्निहिता अभूवन् । **आसमिति** । सर्वथा

---

१. K.S.S. सत्तमैः G.O.S. M.G. N.S. सेतरैः ।

२. G.O.S. आगतः M.G. N.S. अगच्छत् K.S.S. आगच्छत् ।

३. G.O.S. M.G. मण्डपस्याथ K.S.S. मण्डपेऽस्याथ N.S. मण्डपस्यास्य ।

४. G.O.S. N.S. M.G. विनियुक्तस्तु चद्रमाः K.S.S. नियुक्तो रजनीकरः ।

५. G.O.S. M.G. K.S.S.(Same as above)N.S. यथादिग्लोकपालाश्च ।

६. G.O.S. M G. वरुणोऽम्बरे K.S.S. N.S. वरुणेश्वरः ।

७. G.O.S. M,G, N.S. (Same as above) K.S.S. वेदिकां पावकः पातुं भाण्डं सर्वे दिवौकसः ।

८. G.O.S. M.G. K.S.S. अथ N.S. अस्य ।

९. G.O.S. M.G. K.S.S. स्थिताः N.S. न्यस्ताः ।

१०. N.S. च G.O.S. M.G. K.S.S. अथ ।

११. G.O.S. N.S. अथ K.S.S. M.G. स्थिताः ।

द्वारशाला[1] नियुक्तौ तु कृतान्तः काल एव च ।
स्थापितौ द्वारपत्रेषु नागमुख्यौ महाबलौ ॥ ८८ ॥
देहल्यां यमदण्डस्तु शूलं तस्योपरि स्थितम् ।
द्वारपालौ स्थितौ चोभौ नियतिर्मृत्युरेव च ॥ ८९ ॥
पार्श्वे च[2] रङ्गपीठस्य महेन्द्रः स्थितवान्स्वयम् ।
स्थापिता मत्तवारण्यां विद्युद्दैत्यनिषूदनी ॥ ९० ॥
स्तम्भेषु मत्तवारण्याः स्थापिताः परिपालने[3] ।
भूतयक्षपिशाचाश्च गुह्यकाश्च महाबलाः[4] ॥ ९१ ॥
जर्जरे तु[5] विनिक्षिप्तं वज्रं दैत्यनिबर्हणम् ।
तत्पर्वसु[6] विनिक्षिप्ताः सुरेन्द्रा ह्यमितौजसः ॥ ९२ ॥

तु न शक्ता नाशयितुमिति जर्जरप्रभावः । 'गमिष्यन्त्येवमेव' इति य उक्तः सोऽज्ञः (ये वक्तारः तेऽज्ञाः) (?) । ततो विश्वकर्मेति । वास्तुविद्यातत्त्वविदो नाटचमण्डपे स्थपतित्वं सूचयति । द्रुहिण इति ब्रह्मा । इतरे विद्याधर-गन्धर्वाद्याः । अंशैर्यानि भजनान्यधिष्ठानानि तैः । मण्डपस्यांशेषु वः भवतां ये तृतीयचतुर्थादयो भागास्तैः । (६८-८३)

अंशविभागमेवाह—रक्षण इति । अनेन चैतत्तुल्या एव मण्डपभागरक्षा काचिन्नियोज्या इति दर्श्यते । मण्डपस्य सर्वस्याधिष्ठाता हि सौम्यप्रकृतिः सोमः प्रधानो योज्य इति दर्शयति—चन्द्रमा इति । अपि चेति । विदिक्ष्विति । न केवलं पश्चिमोत्तररूपे स्वकोणे यावदन्यास्वपि विदिक्षु । चकाराद्दिक्ष्वपि । ते हि घर्मदोषवारकत्वादत्यन्तोपकारिणः । अनेन गवाक्षकरणं सूच्यत इत्येके । आदित्ये मित्रशब्दः पुल्लिङ्ग इति । तेन यद्वार्तिककारी(रीयं) तदुपलक्षितो

१. G.O.S. M.G. K.S.S. शाला N.S. शाखा ।
२. G.O.S. N.S. च K.S.S. M.G. तु ।
३. G.O.S. K.S.S. M.G. परिपालने N.S. परिरक्षणे ।
४. G.O.S. N.S. (Same as above) M.G. K.S.S. भूता यक्षाः पिशाचाश्च गुह्यकाश्च महाबलाः ।
५. G.O.S. N.S. तु K.S.S. M.G. चैव ।
६. K.S.S. च निक्षिप्ताः G.O.S. N.S. M.G. विनिक्षिप्ताः ।

शिर:पर्वस्थितो[1] ब्रह्मा द्वितीये शङ्करस्तथा ।
तृतीये च स्थि[2]तो विष्णुश्चतुर्थे स्कन्द एव च ॥ ९३ ॥

पञ्चमे च महानागा: शेषवासुकितक्षका: ।
एवं विघ्नविनाशाय स्थापिता जर्जरे सुरा: ॥ ९४ ॥

रङ्गपीठस्य मध्ये तु स्वयं ब्रह्मा प्रतिष्ठित: ।
[3]इष्टच्यर्थं रङ्गमध्ये तु क्रियते पुष्पमोक्षणम् ॥ ९५ ॥

पातालवासिनो ये च यक्षगुह्यकपन्नगा: ।
अधस्ताद्रङ्गपीठस्य रक्षणे ते[4] नियोजिता: ॥ ९६ ॥

नायकं रक्षतीन्द्रस्तु नायिकां च[5] सरस्वती ।
विदूषकमथौङ्का[6]र: शेषास्तु प्रकृतीर्हर: ॥ ९७ ॥

यान्येतानि नियुक्तानि दैवतानीह रक्षणे ।
एतान्येवाधिदैवानि[7] भविष्यन्तीत्युवाच स: ॥ ९८ ॥

एतस्मिन्नन्तरे देवै: सर्वैरुक्त: पितामह: ।
साम्ना तावदिमे विघ्ना: स्थाप्यन्तां वचसा त्वया ॥ ९९ ॥

पूर्वं साम प्रयोक्तव्यं द्वितीयं दानमेव च ।
तयोरुपरि भेदस्ततो दण्ड: प्रयुज्यते ॥ १०० ॥

नर्तकी हि(भि:)लज्जापरिहारहेतो: नपुंसको नेपथ्यगृहे' इति तदपरामृष्टाभिधानम् । मित्र इति तेजस्विता आहार्योपयोगी रत्नादेरुक्ता । वेदिका ।

---

१. N.S. शिर:पार्श्वे ततो G.O.S. K.S.S. शिर:पर्वस्थितो M.G. शिर:पर्वस्थितो ।

२, K.S.S. भगवान् G.O.S. N.S. M.G. च स्थितो ।

३. N.S. M.G. K.S.S. इत्यर्थं G.O.S. इष्टच्यर्थम् ।

४. G.O.S. M.G. N.S. ते नियोजिता:, K.S.S. विनियोजिता: ।

५. G.O.S. च K.S.S. N.S. M.G. तु ।

६. G.O.S. अथौङ्कार: K.S.S. N.S. M.G. अथोङ्कार: ।

७. N.S. एतेषामधिदेवास्तु G.O.S. K.S.S. M.G. एतान्यैवाधिदैवानि ।

देवानां वचनं श्रुत्वा ब्रह्मा विघ्नानुवाच[1] ह ।
कस्माद्भवन्तो नाटचस्य विनाशाय समुत्थिता:[2] ॥ १०१ ॥

ब्रह्मणो वचनं श्रुत्वा विरूपाक्षोऽब्रवीद्वच: ।
दैत्यैर्विघ्नगणै: सार्धं सामपूर्वमिदं तत:[3] ॥ १०२ ॥

योऽयं भगवता सृष्टो नाटचवेद: सुरेच्छया ।
प्रत्यादेशोऽयमस्माकं सुरार्थं भवता कृत: ॥ १०३ ॥

रङ्गवेदिका । तत्र तीक्ष्णोऽधिष्टातेत्यर्थः । **भाण्ड** इति । त्रिपुष्करे सोपकरणे । **दिवौकसो** मेघा मन्द्रगम्भीरशब्दसिद्धये । इत्येवं सर्वत्र दृष्टमपि सदृशोपलक्षणान्तं प्रयोजनमुत्प्रेक्ष्यम् । सर्वथा तदलाभे नियमादृष्टमेव । **वर्णा** इति । तदधिष्ठातारो देवताविशेषाः । **स्तम्भान्तरेष्विति** । वर्णस्तम्भचतुष्कादिरित्येषु न अन्येषु स्तम्भेष्वित्यर्थः । (८४-८६)

शालास्विति । स्तम्भद्वयमष्टकोेश्मनि गवाक्षनेपथ्यगृहद्वितीयभूमिसन्निवेशादिति । **नागमुख्याविति** । अनन्तगुलिकौ । **द्वारपत्रं** कवाटात्मकम् । द्वारबहुत्वाच्च बहुवचनम् । **देहल्यामिति** । द्वाराधस्तनकाष्ठे । **तस्येति** । **शूलमिति** । एतेन प्रक्रान्तद्वारमेव परामृष्टम् । तेनोर्ध्वकाष्ठे उत्सङ्गशब्दवाच्ये त्रिशूलमित्यर्थः । **पार्श्वे स्वयमिति** । राजादेस्तत्स्थानमित्युक्तम् । चकारात्स्वदिशि अंशेनावस्थानमनुस्मृतम् । **विद्युदिति** । वज्रायुधरूपा । स्तम्भेष्वपि चतुर्षु यथाक्रमं तद्भूतादयः । ते च नाटचतत्त्वविदः । अत एव विघ्नैः सह ये(ते) नयेन मिलिता इति द्रष्टव्यम् । एतेन सिद्धिविघातका भेदाख्येनाप्युपायेन दुर्बलीकर्तव्या इति सूचितम् । **प्रतिष्ठित** इति । सदैव सन्निहितो वास्तुमध्य इत्यर्थः । कोणेश्च सन्निधानं सूचितम् ।

अधस्तादिति । येन सुरङ्गाखननादि विघ्नकरणं निवार्यत इत्यर्थः । प्राधनपात्राणि पृथग्रक्षणीयानीत्याह—**नायकमिति** । हास्यशृङ्गाराङ्गत्वाद्विदूषकमित्युक्तम् । अत एव दशरूपकप्रयोगसूचनमेतत् । समवकारे विदूषकाभावात् । हर इति । बहुमूर्तिप्रथमत्वात् । देवता एव दैवतम् । (८७-९८)

---

१ G.O.S. N.S. विघ्नानुवाच ह K.S.S. M.G. वचनमब्रवीत् ।

२. K.S.S. अलं वो मन्युना दैत्या विषादं त्यजतानघाः G.O.S. M.G. कस्माद् भवन्तो नाटचस्य विनाशाय समुत्थिताः N.S. विनाशार्थम् मुपस्थिताः ।

३ K.S.S. N.S. वचः G.O.S. M.G. ततः ।

तन्नैतदेवं कर्तव्यं त्वया लोकपितामह ।
यथा देवास्तथा दैत्यास्त्वत्तः सर्वे[1] विनिर्गताः ॥ १०४ ॥

विघ्नानां[2] वचनं श्रुत्वा ब्रह्मा वचनमब्रवीत् ।
अलं वो मन्युना दैत्या विषादं त्यजतानघाः[3] ॥ १०५ ॥

अथ नाट्यतत्त्वजाते तन्निरूपणार्थमुपक्रमते—एतस्मिन्निति । नाशक्तस्य सामाङ्गीकरोति दुर्जन इति पूर्वं रक्षाकरणम् । इत्युक्तद्वय (सर्वैरुक्त) इति । कविरनुविधेयवचनो भवतीति दर्शयति । सामादिप्रयोगे तावच्छब्दसूचितं क्रमं स्फुटयति—पूर्वं सामेत्यादि । तत इति । सर्वोपायप्रतिहताविति यावत् । तत्र ज्ञाताभिप्रायः प्रतिसमाधातुं सुशक इत्यभिप्रायेणाह देवानामिति । सुरार्थमित्यस्यैव दाढर्यायोक्तं सुरेच्छयेति । प्रत्यादेश इति खलीकार इत्यर्थः । भवतेति । यस्यानुचितमेतदित्यर्थः । अनौचित्यमेव लोकपितामहेत्यामन्त्रणेनाह । तदेव पितामहत्वं दर्शयति—यथेति । आ(त्मनोभ) वा देवा दैत्याश्चेत्याह—सर्व इति । (९९-१०४)

वचनमिति । सुपरिहरमेतत् । नात्र भूयान्प्रयास इत्येकवचनेन दर्शयति । अत एव सिद्धवदुपक्रमते—अलं व इति मिथ्याज्ञानगृहीतसर्पत्रासवद्यो भ्रान्तिमात्रकृत इत्यर्थः । दैत्यानामशुभकारिता लोकप्रसिद्धा । कुरु(कृत) रङ्गविभागञ्चैषां चेष्टितमस्तु । देवानां तद्विपर्यय इति नाट्यस्य न तात्पर्यं येन भवतां मन्युः । किं तर्हीत्याह । शुभकारिणः शुभं फलमशुभकारिणोऽशुभं फलमित्येतावदेवास्माकं प्रतिसाक्षात्कारकल्पे नाट्ये प्रदर्शनीयम् । न तत्र देवेषु दैत्येषु वा कश्चिद्भरः अत एव भवतामपि धर्मादौ यः सदुपायः सोऽपि शुभविपाकत्वेनैव दर्शितः । अत एव शुभग्रहणमेकतरपक्षशैथिल्यदर्शनाय दैत्यसम्बन्धनार्थं प्रथममुपात्तम् । शुभमशुभं च धर्माधर्मरूपं सुखदुःखफलत्वेन विभेदेन कल्पयत्यध्यवसाययति नाट्यवेदः । कीदृक्—कर्मभावान्वयापेक्षीति । तद्यथा—धर्मो दानं स्नानमित्यादिः । अधर्मो हिंसा स्तेयमित्यादिः । भाव आशयः स्त्री(स्व) प्रसङ्गोदिता स्वार्थतापरार्थताद्यभिसन्धिरित्यादिः । अन्वयोऽभिजनः आर्यावर्तादिर्ब्राह्मण्यञ्चेति । तानपेक्षते सहकारितया ।

१, G.O.S. M.G. सर्वे N.S. पूर्वविनिर्गताः ।

२, K.S.S. देवानां G.O.S. विघ्नानां N.S. M.G. विरुपाक्षवचः ।

३, K.S.S. G.O.S. M.G. (Same as above) N.S. त्यजतामयम् ।

भवतां देवतानां च शुभाशुभविकल्पकः[1] ।
कर्मभावान्वयापेक्षी[2] नाट्यवेदो मया कृतः ॥ १०६ ॥

नैकान्ततोऽत्र भवतां देवानां चा[3]नुभावनम् ।
त्रैलोक्यस्यास्य सर्वस्य नाट्यं भावानुकीर्तनम् ॥ १०७ ॥

क्वचिद्धर्मः क्वचित्क्रीडा क्वचिदर्थः क्वचिच्छ्रमः ।
क्वचिद्धास्यं क्वचिद्युद्धं क्वचित्कामः क्वचिद्वधः ॥ १०८ ॥

एतदुक्तं भवति—अस्मिन्देशेऽस्मिन्काले ईदृशेन कर्मणा यः शुभमशुभं चार्जयति स एवंविधफलभागी भवतीति न तावदिहोपदिश्यते । विकल्पक इति द्वौ णिचौ । (१०१-१०६)

ननु चैवमप्यस्मत्पृष्ठे किमेतद्योजितमित्याह—**नैकान्तत** इति । अयं भावः--न युष्मत्पृष्ठे केनचिदेतद्योजितम् । देवासुरस्य बहिर्यथास्वस्थमवस्थानम् । अत्रेति-नाट्यवेदे । न देवासुराणामेकान्तेनानुभावनम् । नैव तेऽनुभाव्यन्ते केनचित्प्रकारेण ।

तथाहि—तेषु न तत्त्वेन धीः । न सादृश्येन यमलकवत् । न भ्रान्तत्वेन रूप्यस्मृतिपूर्वकशुक्तिरूप्यवत् । नारोपेण सम्यग्ज्ञानबाधानन्तरमिथ्याज्ञानरूपेण मुखंचन्द्र इतिवत् । न तदध्यवसायेन गौर्वाहीकवत् । नोत्प्रेक्ष्यमाणत्वेन चन्द्रमुखवत् । न तत्प्रतिकृतित्वेन चित्रपुस्तवत् । न तदनुकारेण गुरुशिष्यव्याख्याहेवाकवत् । न तात्कालिकनिर्माणेनेन्द्रजालवत् । न युक्तिविरचिततदाभासतया हस्तलाघवादिमायावत् । सर्वेष्वेतेषु पक्षेष्वसाधारणतया द्रष्टुरौदासीन्ये रसास्वादायोगात् । कवेश्च नियतवर्णनीयनिश्चितत्वे काव्यस्यैवासम्पत्तेरनौचित्यावर्जनयोगात् । लौकिकमिथुनदृशीव सांसारिकहर्षक्रोधान्वयितापत्तेरुभयदर्शनाकुलतया मुख्यदृष्टौ प्रयोक्तृदृष्टौ तद्धि सम्पत्त्य(द्विसंवित्त्य)भावात् ।

किं तर्ह्येतत् । आह—**त्रैलोक्यस्येति** । एतदुक्तं भवति—एतादृशं तै(ते) रामादयो न कदाचन प्रमाणपथमवतार्यन्ते यदाऽऽगमेन वर्ण्यन्ते । तदा तद्विशेषबुद्धिः यद्यपि रामायणप्रायादेकस्मान्महावाक्यादुल्लसति, तथापि वर्तमानतयैव

---

१. N,S. विकल्पकैः G.O.S. M.G. K.S.S. विकल्पकः ।

२. K.S.S. M.G. पेक्षो N.S. G.O.S. पेक्षी ।

३. G.O.S. चानुभावनम् N.S. चापिभावनम K.S.S. M.G. चात्रभावनम् ।

विशेषाणां सम्भाव्यमानार्थक्रियासामर्थ्यात्मकसालक्षण्यपर्यवसानात् । न च तेषां वर्तमानतेत्युपगता तावद्विशेषबुद्धिः । काव्येष्वपि हृदयमेव एव (हृदय एव) तावत्साधारणीभावो विभावादीनां जाता(तः) । तत्रापि कथामात्रे साधारणीभावः सम्भवति यद्यपि तथापि 'एवं ये कुर्वन्ति तेषामेतद्भवति' इति वाक्यवद्रञ्जनातिशयाभावान्न चित्तवृत्ते(त्ति)र्निर्णयगता भवति ।

काव्ये तु गुणालङ्कारमनोहरशब्दार्थशरीरे लोकोत्तररसप्राणके हृदयसंवादवशात् निमग्नाकारिका तावद्भवति चित्तवृत्तिः । किन्तु सर्वस्य प्रत्यक्ष साक्षात्कारकल्पा तत्र न धीरुदेति ।

नाट्ये तु पारमार्थिकं किञ्चिदद्य मे कृत्यं भविष्यतीत्येवंभूताभिसन्धिसंस्काराभावात्सर्वपरिषत्साधारणप्रमोदसारापर्यन्तविरसना (समा) दरणीयलोत्तरदर्शनश्रवणयोगी भविष्यामीत्यभिसन्धिसंस्कारदुचितगीतातोद्यचर्वणाविस्मृत सांसारिकभावतया विमलमुकुरकल्पीभूतनिजहृदयः, सूच्याद्यभिनयावलोकनोद्भिन्नप्रमोदशोकादितन्मयीभावः, पाठ्याकर्णनपात्रान्तरप्रवेशवशात् समुत्पन्ने देशकालविशेषावेशानालिङ्गिते सम्यङ् मिथ्यासंशयसम्भावनादिज्ञानविज्ञेयत्वपरामर्शानास्पदे, रामरावणादिविषयाध्यवसाये, तत्संस्कारानुवृत्तिकारणभूततत्सहचरहृद्यवस्तुरूपगीतातोद्यप्रमदानुभवसंस्कारसूचितसमनुगततदुक्तरूपरामाध्यवसायसंस्कार एव भवन् पञ्चषैर्दिवसैः सचमत्कारतदीयचरितमध्यप्रविष्टस्वात्मरूपमतिः स्वात्मद्वारेण विश्वं तथा पश्यन् प्रत्येकं सामाजिको देशकालविशेषणापरामर्शेन एवंकारिणामिदमिति लीढा(लिङा)त्मकविधिसमर्पितं संविज्जातीयमेम संविद्विशेषरञ्जकप्राणवल्लभाप्रतिमरसास्वादसहचररम्यगीतातोद्यादिसंस्काररसानुभव) वशेन हृदयाभ्यन्तरनिखातं तत एवोत्पुङ्खशतैरपि म्लानिमात्रमप्यभजमानं भजंस्तत्तच्छुभाशुभप्रेप्साजिहासासततस्यूतवृत्तित्वादेव शुभमाचरत्यशुभं समुज्झति । इदानीमुपायसंवेदनालाभात् तदिदमनुकीर्तनमनुव्यवसायविशेषो नाट्यापरपर्यायः । नानुकार इति भ्रमितव्यम् । अनेन भाण्डेन राजपुत्रस्यान्यस्य वानुकृतेऽन्या (कृतावन्या)दिबुद्धेरभावात् । तद्धि विका(क)रणमिति प्रसिद्धं हासमात्रफलं मध्यस्थानाम् । यदभिप्रायेण मुनिर्वक्ष्यति—

परचेष्टानुकरणाद्धासस्समुपजायते (अ. ७-१०) इति ॥

तत्पक्षीयाणान्तु तदेव द्वेषासूयानि(नु)वृत्त्यादिफलम् । तद्बुद्ध्यैव हि दैत्यानां हृदयक्षोभः 'एवम्भूता वयमुपहासभाजनम्' इति । उपहास्यताभीरवश्च निवर्तन्ते ततः । न तूपदेशेन ।

नन्वेवं तावता नियतानुकारो माभूत् । अनुकारेण तु किमपराद्धम् । न किञ्चिदसम्भवादृते । अनुकार इति हि सदृशकरणम् । तत्कस्य । नतावद्रामादेः । तस्याननुकार्यत्वात् । एतेन प्रमदादिविभावानामनुकरणं पराकृतम् ।

न चिरावृत्तीनां शोकक्रोधादिरूपाणाम् । न हि नटो रामसदृशं स्वात्मनः शोकं करोति । सर्वथैव तस्य तत्राभावात् । भावे वाननुकारत्वात् । न चान्यद्वस्त्वस्ति यच्छोकेन सदृशं स्यात् । अनुभावांस्तु करोति । किन्तु सजातीयानेव । न तु तत्सदृशान् । साधारणरूपस्य कः केन सादृश्यार्थः । त्रैलोक्यवर्तिनः सदृशत्वन्तु न विशेषात्मना यौगपद्येनोपपद्यते । कदाचित्क्रमेण नियत एवानुकृतः स्यात् । सामान्यात्मकत्वे कोऽनुकारार्थः । तस्मादनियतानुकारो नाट्यमित्यपि न भ्रमितव्यम् । **अस्मदुपाध्यायकृते काव्यकौतुके**ऽप्ययमेवाभिप्रायो मन्तव्यः । न त्वनियतानुकारोऽपि ।

तेनानुव्यवसायवत् विशेषविषयीकार्यं नाट्यम् । तथा चाहार्यविशेषादिना निवृत्ते तद्देशकालचैत्रमैत्रादिनटविशेषप्रत्यक्षाभिमाने विशेषलेशोपक्रमेण च विना प्रत्यक्षाप्रवृत्तेरायाते रामादिशब्दस्यात्रोपयोगात् प्रसिद्धतदर्थतयाऽऽदरणीयचरितवाचकस्यासम्भावनामात्रनिराकरणेनानुव्यवसायस्य प्रत्यक्षकल्पनाट्ये हृद्यगीताद्यनुस्यूततया चमत्कारस्थानत्वाद्धृदयानुप्रवेशयोग्यत्वमभिनयचतुष्टयेन स्वरूपप्रच्छादनं, प्रस्तावनादिना नटज्ञानजसंस्कारसाचिव्यं, तेन रञ्जकसामग्रीमध्यानुप्रविष्टेन प्रच्छादितस्वस्वभावेन प्राक्प्रवृत्तलौकिकप्रत्यक्षानुमानादिजनितसंस्कारसहायेन सहृदयसंस्कारसचिवेन हृदयसंवादतन्मयीभावनासहकारिणा प्रयोक्त्रा दृश्यमानेन योऽनुव्यवसायो जन्यते सुखदुःखाद्याकारतत्तच्चित्तवृत्तिरूपरूषितनिजसंविदानन्दप्रकाशमयः अत एव विचित्रो रसनास्वादनचमत्कारचर्वणनिर्वेशभोगाद्यपरपर्यायः तत्र यदवभासते वस्तु तन्नाट्यम् । तच्च ज्ञानाकारमात्रमारोपितं स्वरूपं सामान्यात्मकं तत्कालनिर्मितरूपं चान्यद्वा किञ्चिदस्तु । नात्राप्रस्तुतलेखनेनात्मनो दर्शनान्तरकथापरिचयप्रकटनफलेन प्रकृतवस्तुनिरूपणविघ्नमाचरन्तः सहृदयान्खेदयामः ।

तस्मादनुव्यवसायात्मकं कीर्तनं रूषितविकल्पसंवेदनं नाट्यम् । तद्वेदनवेद्यत्वात् । न त्वनुकरणरूपम् । यदि त्वेवं मुख्यलौकिककरणानुसारितयाऽनुकरणमित्युच्यते तन्न कश्चिद्दोषः । स्थिते वस्तुतो भेदे शब्दप्रवृत्तेरविवादास्पदत्वात् । एतच्च यथावसरं वितनिष्यत इत्यास्तां तावत् ।

यतश्चेदं नानुकरणं ततो यत्कैश्चिच्चोदितं तदनवकाशम्—'न च गीतवाद्ययुक्तः सर्वावस्थासु कश्चिदनुकार्यः' इति न त्वनुकार्यत्वेन गीतादय इत्युक्तम् । परिहारोऽपि य उक्तः 'आसनगमनस्नानस्वापप्रतिबोधभोजनाद्यासु गीतवाद्यं लोके चेष्टास्वतिप्रथितम्' इत्यादि, तदप्यनुपपन्नम् । न हि गमनादौ तद्ध्रुवातालादिरूपेण गीतादि लोकेऽस्ति मङ्गलमात्रत्वादृते । गायनवादनादिष्वपि चानुकारबुद्ध्यापत्तेरित्यलम् । (१०७)

ननु त्रैलोक्यस्य ये भावास्तेषां यद्यनुकीर्तनं नाट्यं तदेकत्रैव रूपके एकत्रैव चाङ्कादौ सर्वमेव दृश्येतेत्याशङ्कानिराकरणपूर्वकं पूर्वप्रयोजनेन सप्रयोजनत्व-

धर्मो धर्मप्रवृत्तानां कामः कामो[1]पसेविनाम् ।
निग्रहो दुर्विनीतानां विनीतानां[2] दमक्रिया ॥ १०९ ॥

क्लीबानां धार्ष्ट्यजन[3]नमुत्साहः शूरमानिनाम् ।
अबु[4]धानां विबोधश्च वैदु[5]ष्यं विदुषामपि ॥ ११० ॥

मुपसंहरति—**क्वचिद्धर्म** इत्यादिना **'लोकोपदेशजननं नाट्यमेतद्भविष्यति'** इत्यन्तेन श्लोकाष्टकेन । एतच्च कैश्चिद्भिन्नवाक्यतया प्रतिश्लोकं व्याख्यातम् । तच्च पौनरुक्त्याध्याहारपरस्परासङ्गत्यादिदोषोपहतं स्यादित्युपेक्ष्यमेव । तस्मादित्थमत्र योजना—नानाप्रकारैर्भावैः स्थायिव्यभिचारिविभावादिभिरुपसम्पन्नं सर्वतो व्याप्तम् । तेषां च भावादीनां देशकालप्रवृत्त्यवस्थान्तरभिन्नस्वभावत्वात्तदपि नानावस्थात्मकम् । अत एवाहोत्तमाधमेति । एवम्भूतमेतद्भविष्यति । काले विश्रान्तिजननं हितोपदेशजननं च भविष्यतीति सम्बन्धः ।

के के नानाप्रकारा भावा इत्याह—**क्वचिद्धर्म** इत्यादि । यथायोगं धर्मादयः शब्दास्तदुचितस्थायिव्यभिचारादिसूचकाः । तेन धर्मोऽर्थ इत्युत्साहादिः । क्रीडेति विस्मयादिः । शम इति निर्वेदादिः । हास्यमिति हासादिः । युद्धमिति रौद्रादिः । काम इति रत्यादिः । वध इति क्रोधभयजुगुप्साशोकादिः । अमीभिश्च समुचितव्यभिचार्यनुभावाः स्वीकृताः । क्वचिदिति शब्देन दशरूपकान्यतममुच्यते । त(य)था नाटकाद्यनेकरूपकगतो विशेषस्तथैकं ना(कना)टकादिविशेषे । को विभागः । एतदुक्तं भवति—किञ्चिद्धर्मप्रधानं रूपकं यथा नाटकम् । प्रकरणं वा क्रीडाप्रधानम् । तथा प्रसिद्धानां यथा भाणः । अर्थप्रधानत्वं प्रकरणादौ । एवं दशरूपकलक्षणानुसारेण सर्वमनुसरणीयम् । तथा क्वचिन्नाटके धर्मः प्रधानम्—यथा **छलितरामे** रामस्याश्वमेधयागः । क्वचित्क्रीडा—यथा **स्वप्नवासवदत्तायाम्** । एवमन्यत्राप्यनुसरणीयम् । तथैकत्रापि नाटके क्वचिदंशे धर्मो यथाऽ**भिज्ञानशाकुन्तले**—"अपि नाम कुलपतेरियमसवर्णक्षेत्रसम्भवा स्यात्" (अङ्क-१) । एवं प्रतिनाटकमेकदेशेषु सुलक्षा एव क्रीडादय इति ग्रन्थविस्तरभीरुभिरस्माभिन परिवर्णिताः ।

---

१. N.S. कामार्थ G.O.S. K.S.S. M.G. कामोप ।
२. N.S. मत्तानां G.O.S. K.S.S. M.G. विनीतानां ।
३. M.G. K.S.S. करणम् N.S. G.O.S. जननं ।
४. N.S. अबोधनां G.O.S. K.S.S. M.G. अबुधानां ।
५. G.O.S. M.G. K.S.S. वैदुष्यम् N.S. वैदग्ध्यम् ।

ईश्वराणां विलासश्च स्थैर्यं दु:खार्दितस्य च।

अर्थोपजीविनामर्थो धृति[1]रुद्विग्नचेतसाम् ॥ १११ ॥

नानाभावोपसम्पन्नं नानावस्थान्तरात्मकम् ।

लोकवृत्तानुकरणं नाट्यमेतन्मया कृतम् ॥ ११२ ॥

उत्तमाधममध्यानां नराणां कर्मसंश्रयम् ।

हितोपदेशजननं धृतिक्रीडासुखादिकृत् ॥ ११३ ॥

(एतद्रसेषु भावेषु सर्वकर्मक्रियास्वथ ।

सर्वोपदेशजननं नाट्यं लोके भविष्यति ॥)

दु:खार्तानां श्रमार्तानां शोकार्तानां तपस्विनाम् ।

विश्रान्ति[3]जननं काले नाट्यमेतद्भवि[4]ष्यति ॥ ११४ ॥

नन्ववस्थादेशकालप्रकृतिविशेषसमुचितभावानुकीर्तनमात्रमेव कर्तव्यम् । किं रामाय(दि) रावणेत्यादिसमाश्रयेणेत्याशङ्क्याह—**धर्म** इति । **चो** हेतौ । यस्माल्लोकवृत्तानुसारेण करणं प्रयोगरूपं नाट्यं मया कृतमेतदित्येतस्मात्कारणाद्धर्मप्रवृत्तानां रामयुधिष्ठिरादीनां सम्बन्धित्वेन धर्म उक्तः । **निग्रह** इति वधः । विनीतानां जितेन्द्रियाणां सम्बन्धित्वेन दमस्य शमस्य क्रिया योजना । विनयो हीन्द्रियजयः । एवं क्लीबानामुपहास्यानां **धाष्ट्यर्जननमिति** विभागेन हासोऽत्रोक्तः । धाष्टर्याज्जननं जन्म यस्य हास्यवस्तुनः । यद्वक्ष्यति —"विकृतपरवेषालङ्कारधाष्ट्यार्दिभिः" (अ-६.) इत्यादि । **विबोध** इति ण्यन्तस्य रूपम् । अबुद्धत्वेन प्रसिद्धानां सम्बन्धित्वेन बोधनमुपायोपदेशेन व्युत्पाद्यत्वम् । **विदुषां** भीष्मादीनाम् । उपायव्युत्पाद्यत्वेन **वैदुष्यम्** । अनेन स्मृतिमतिप्रभृतीनां निरूपणम् । **विलास** इति क्रीडा । **स्थैर्यमिति** व्यवसायात्मकमुत्साहरूपमेव । **चशब्द** एवकारार्थे । दुःखार्दितत्वेन यः प्रसिद्धस्तस्यैव सम्बन्धित्वेनेत्यर्थः । **धृतिर्धैर्यम्** । एतदुक्तं भवति—लोकवृत्तानुसारेण यत इयं

१. K.S.S. वृत्ति G.O.S. N.S. M.G. धृति ।

२. G.O.S. N.S. M.G. (Same as above) K.S.S. नाट्यमेतद्भविष्यति ।

३. K.S.S. M.G. विश्राम G.O.S. N.S. विश्रान्ति ।

४. N.S. मया कृतम् G.O.S. M.G. K.S.S. भविष्यति ।

धर्म्यं यशस्यमायुष्यं हितं बुद्धिविवर्धनम्।
लोकोपदेशजननं नाट्यमेतद्भविष्यति॥ ११५॥
न तज्ज्ञा[1]नं न तच्छिल्पं न सा विद्या न सा कला।
नासौ[2] योगो न तत्कर्म नाट्येऽ[3]स्मिन् यन्न दृश्यते॥ ११६॥

नाट्यक्रिया लोके च धर्मादयो ना(नाना)श्रयाः न संवेदनयोग्याः तेन धर्मादिविषये यो यथा प्रसिद्धो रामादिः स शब्दमात्रोपयोगित्वेन मुख्यया प्रणालिकया गृहीतः।

एवंभूतं यन्नाट्यं तत्प्रेक्षकाणां दुःखेन व्याध्यादिकृतेन श्रमेणाध्वक्लेशादिजेन शोकेन बन्धुमरणादिकृतेनार्तानां पीडितानां तथा तपस्विनामनवरतकृच्छ्रचान्द्रायणाद्याचरणकलितदौर्बल्यातिशयपरिखिन्नहृदयानां **विश्रान्तिजननं** दुःखप्रसरणविघातकम्। प्रतिहतदुःखानां चाह्लादात्मकधृत्यादिकारणं यथायोगम्। तद्यथा—शोकार्तस्य धृतिर्व्याध्यार्तस्य क्रीडा। श्रमार्तस्य सुखम्। आदिग्रहणेन तपस्विनो मतिविबोधादय इति मन्तव्यम्। नचैतावदेव यावत्कालान्तरेऽपि (रवि)परिपाकं सुखमुपदेशजं जनयतीत्येवं दुखितानां तत्प्रशमसुखवितरणकालान्तरसुखलाभाः प्रयोजनम्। ये पुनरदुःखिताः सुखभूयिष्ठवृत्तय एव राजपुत्राद्यास्तेषां लोकवृत्ते धर्माद्युपायवर्गे उपदेशकार्येतन्नाट्यम्। लोकशब्देन लोकवृत्तम्।

ननु किं गुरुवदुपदेशं करोति। नेत्याह। किन्तु बुद्धिं विवर्धयति। स्वप्रतिभामेव तादृशीं वितरतीत्यर्थः न च सा दुष्टा प्रतिभेत्याह—**हितम्**—हितप्रतिभाजनकत्वात्। अत्र हेतुमाह—यतो धर्मादनपेतम्। यशश्शब्देन लोकप्रसिद्धिहेतुभूतमद्भुतकारि वस्तूच्यते, यथा रामस्य सप्तसालव्यथनादि। तदुपदेशे साधु। आयुर्वृद्धिहेतव आचारा आयुः। तेषु साधु। एवं दुःखितानामदुःखितानां चेदमुपादेयमित्युक्तम्। दुखं च शारीरं मानसं वा। शारीरमपि दैवकृतं स्वयंकृतमपि दृष्टं फलो(ष्टफलो)द्देशेनान्येन चेत्येतावानेव दुःखितवर्ग इति दुःखार्तानामित्यादिभेदोपादानस्य फलम्।

केचित्तु धर्मो धर्मप्रवृत्तानामित्यादि सामाजिकविषयत्वेन व्याचक्षते हृदयसंवादयोग्यतातात्पर्येण। अन्ये त्वकारप्रश्लेषादिव्याख्याप्रकारेणाधर्मप्रवृत्तानामि-

१. N.S. श्रुतम् G.O.S. K.S.S. M.G. ज्ञानम्।
२. N.S. M.G. K.S.S. स G.O.S. असौ।
३. K.S.S. G.O.S. M.G. (Same as above) N.S. यन्नाट्येऽस्मिन्न दृश्यते।

तन्नात्र मन्यु: कर्तव्यो भवद्भिरमरान्प्रति ।
सप्तद्वीपानुकरणं नाट्यमेतद्भविष्यति ॥ ११७ ॥
(येनानुकरणं नाट्यमेतत्तद्यन्मया कृतम् ॥)

देवानामसुराणां[2] च राज्ञामथ कुटुम्बिनाम् ।
ब्रह्मर्षीणां च विज्ञेयं नाट्यं वृत्तान्तदर्शकम्[3] ॥ ११८ ॥

योऽयं स्वभावो लोकस्य सुखदु:खसमन्वित: ।
सोऽङ्गाद्यभिनयोपेतो नाट्यमित्यभिधीयते ॥ ११९ ॥

त्यादिविपरीतत्वेन व्याचक्षते उपदेश्यत्वाभिप्रायेण । उभयमपि चैतद्धर्म्यं यशस्यमित्यादे: पुनरुक्तम् । (१०८-११५) ।

न चानेन प्रधानमात्र एवोपदेश: कृत: पुरुषार्थोपायमात्रे वा । यावत्तदुपायोपेयादिष्वपीति दर्शयति—तदिति । अस्मिन्निति । सप्तद्वीपगतभावानुकीर्तनरूपे नाट्ये दृश्यमाने यन्न दृश्यते न हृदयगोचरमेति तादृग्ज्ञानादिकं नास्तीति शेष: । ज्ञानमित्युपादेयमात्मज्ञानादि ।

यथा वेणीसंहारे—"आत्मारामा विहितरतयो निर्विकल्पे समाधौ" (१-२३) इत्यादि । शिल्पमिति । मालाचित्रपुस्तादियोजनम् ।

यथा "वेष्टितग्रथितगुम्फसंहतैराततैश्च कुसुमैस्सपल्लवै:" इत्यादौ । विद्या दण्डनीत्यादि ।

यथा "शमव्यायामाभ्यां प्रतिविहिततन्त्रस्य नृपते: ।" (बाल. रा. १-२४) इत्यादौ । कला गीतवाद्यादिका ।

यथा "व्यक्तिर्व्यञ्जनधातुना" (नागानन्द १-१४) इत्यादौ ।

---

१. K.S.S. M.G. नाट्ये ह्यस्मिन् प्रतिष्ठितम् G.O.S. N.S. (Same as above)

२. K.S.S. ऋषीणाम् M.G. G.O.S. N.S. असुराणां ।

३. G.O.S. N.S. (Same as above) M.G. K.S.S. कृतानुकरणं लोके नाट्यमित्याभिधीयते ।

योगो योजनं तेषामेव ज्ञानादीनां कलान्तानां स्वभेदैरन्योन्यस्वभेदैः । यथा

"मेघाशङ्किशिखण्डिताण्डवविधावाचार्यकं कल्पय-
न्निर्ह्रादो मुरजस्य मूर्च्छतितरां वेणुस्वनापूरितः ।
वीणायाः कलयन् लयेन गमकानुग्राहिणीं मूर्च्छनां
कर्षत्येष च कालकूटितकलारम्यश्रुतिं षाडवे ।।

(हेज्जल-राधाविप्रलम्भ) इत्यादौ । तत्रेहातोद्यनिचयगीतयोजना कृता ।

अन्योन्यं यथा—

"आविलपयोधराग्रं लवलीदलपाण्डुकोमलच्छायम्" (किक्रमो ५-८) इत्यादौ अत्र हि शृङ्गारस्य वैद्यकविद्यया योजना ।

कर्मेति युद्धनियुद्धादिर्व्यापारः । यथा—

"आलीढस्थितटङ्कितस्य निमितां दृष्टित्रयीं तन्वतः
पुङ्खाग्रक्रमसर्पणेन विशिखप्रान्तादथोच्चैस्तमाम् ।
चक्रीभूतशरासनस्य न मनाल्ल(क् ल)क्ष्यादमी विच्युता-
श्चित्रं चित्रमुमाधवस्य युगपत्सर्वे सुरेन्द्रद्विषः ।।" इति ।।

एवं सप्रयोजनत्वमभिधाय प्रकृतमेव पुराकल्पमनुबध्नाति—**तन्त्रात्रेति** । **तदिति** । तस्मात् । अत्र नाट्येऽमरान्प्रति न मन्युः कार्यः । तेऽपि तत्र न केचित् ।

एतदेवाह—**सप्तद्वीपानुकरण**मयी हि क्रिया (नटक्रिया) रङ्गे दृश्यते । न च सागरद्वीपादीनां कश्चित्तत्र (त्रा) सम्भव इति भावः (११६-११७) ।

ननु किमर्थमेषां नामानि गृहीतानीत्याशङ्क्याह—**देवानामित्यादि** । एतेषामेवाधिकारिपुरुषत्वात् निराधारस्य वृत्तस्य दर्शयितुमशक्यत्वात् । एतच्चोक्तं पूर्वम् । अत एव यत्र निर्व्याजसहजौदार्यधर्मादिविषये बलिप्रह्लादप्रभृतेः प्रसिद्धिस्तत्र सोऽपि चरित आश्रयत्वेन । तदाह—**असुराणामिति** । न च भवद्वैरिण एवात्र वर्णिताः अपि तु ब्रह्मादयोऽपि । अनेन 'प्रत्यादेशोऽयमस्माकम् । सुरार्थम् ।' इत्याशङ्काद्वयमपि परिहृतम् । एतत्तात्पर्येणोपसंहरति—**योऽयमिति** । **अयमिति**-प्रत्यक्षकल्पानुव्यवसायविषयः । लोकप्रसिद्धसत्यासत्यादिविलक्षणत्वात् **यच्छब्दवाच्यः** । लोकस्य सर्वस्य साधारणतया स्वत्वेन भाव्यमानश्चर्व्यमाणोऽर्थो **नाट्यम्** । स च सुखदुःखरूपेण विचित्रेण समनुगतः । न तु तदेकात्मा ।

तथा हि—रतिहासोत्साहविस्मयानां सुखस्वभावत्वम् । तत्र तु चिरकालव्यापिसुखानुसन्धिरूपत्वेन विषयौन्मुख्यप्राणतया तद्विषयाशंसाबाहुल्येनापायभीरुत्वाद् दुःखांशानुवेधो रतेः । हासस्य सानुसन्धानस्य, विद्युत्सदृशतात्कालि-

(वेदविद्येतिहासानामाख्यानपरिकल्पनम् ।
विनोदकरणं[1] लोके नाट्यमेतद्भविष्यति ॥

श्रुतिस्मृतिसदाचारपरिशेषार्थकल्पनम् ।
विनोदजननं लोके नाट्यमेतद्भविष्यति ॥)

एतस्मिन्नन्तरे देवान् सर्वानाह पितामहः ।
[2]क्रियता[3]मद्य विधिवद्यजनं नाट्यमण्डपे ॥ १२० ॥

बलिप्रदानैर्होमैश्च मन्त्रौषधिसमन्वितैः ।
[4]भोज्यैर्भक्ष्यैश्च पानैश्च[5] बलिः समुपकल्प्यताम् ॥ १२१ ॥

मर्त्यलोकगताः सर्वे शुभां पूजामवाप्स्यथ[6] ।
अपूजयित्वा रङ्गं तु नैव प्रेक्षां प्रवर्तये[7]त् ॥ १२२ ॥

कालपदुःखरूपसुखानुगतौ । उत्साहस्य तात्कालिकदुःखायासरूपनिमज्जनानुसन्धाना यदि(नाऽपि)भाविबहुजनोपकारिचिरतरकालभाविसुखसञ्चिकीर्षात्मना सखरूपता । विस्मयस्य निरनुसन्धानतडित्तुल्यसुखरूपता ।

क्रोधभयशोकजुगुप्सानां तु दुःखस्वरूपता । तत्र चिरकालदुःखानुसन्धिप्राणो विषयगतामन्तिकानां (तात्यन्तिकनाश)भावनाकांक्षाप्राणतया सुखदुःखानुवेधवान् क्रोधः । निरनुसन्धितात्कालिकदुःखप्राणतया तदपगमाकांक्षोत्प्रेक्षितसुखानुसम्भिन्नं भयम् । द्वैकालिकस्त्वभीष्टविषयनाशजः प्राक्तनसुखस्मरणानुविद्धः सर्वथैव दुःखरूपः शोकः । उत्पाद्यमानसुखानुसन्धानजीवितविषयात्प(या प)लायनपरायणरूपान्नि(पा नि) षिध्यमानशङ्कितसुखानुविद्धा जुगुप्सा । समस्तम (त) त्पूर्वदुःखसञ्चयसंस्मरणप्राणितः (तोऽ)सम्भावितदुपरमबहुलसुख (दुःख)

---

१. M.G. जननं K.S.S. N.S. G.O.S. करणं ।

२. K.S.S. N.S. G.O.S. क्रियताम् M.G. कुरुध्वम् ।

३. G.O.S. N.S. अद्य M.G. अत्र K.S.S. नाट्ये ।

४. G.O.S. N.S. भोज्यैः K.S.S. M.G. जप्यैः ।

५. G.O.S. M.G. N.S. पानैः K.S.S. भोज्यैः

६. G.O.S. M.G. N.S. (Same as above) K.S.S. मर्त्यलोकेष्वयं वेदः शुभां पूजामवाप्स्यति ।

७. G.O.S. M.G. N.S. प्रवर्तयेत् K.S.S. प्रवर्तते ।

अपूजयित्वा रङ्गं तु यः प्रेक्षां कल्पयिष्यति ।
निष्फलं तस्य तत् [1]ज्ञानं तिर्यग्योनिं च यास्यति ॥ १२३ ॥
यज्ञेन संमितं ह्येतद्रङ्गदैवतपूजनम् ।
तस्मात्सर्वप्रत्नेन कर्तव्यं नाटचयोक्तृभिः[2] ॥ १२४ ॥
नर्तकोऽर्थपतिर्वापि यः पूजां न करिष्यति ।
न कारयिष्यत्यन्यैर्वा प्राप्नोत्यपचयं तु सः[3] ॥ १२५ ॥
यथाविधि यथादृष्टं[4]यस्तु पूजां करिष्यति ।
स लप्स्यते शुभानर्थान् स्वर्गलोकं च यास्यति[5] ॥ १२६ ॥

मयो निर्वेदः । एवं व्यभिचारिप्रभृतिष्वपि वाच्यम् । संवित्स्वभावाः सुखादय इति च दर्शने न तत्स्वभावत्वम् । अन्येत्व(तैस्त्व)त्र तद्वेदनरूपत्वमेव तेषां मन्तव्यम् । एवं लौकिका ये सुखदुःखात्मानो भावा तत्सदृशस्तत्संकारानुविद्धो नाटचलक्षणोऽर्थः समुदायरूपस्तस्यैव भागानुसमयः ।

एवं दयारत्यादिरूपानुसरणभूतो (एवंभूतो) नाटचलक्षणोऽर्थः कथं प्रतीतिगोचरीभवतीत्याह—अङ्गादीति । येऽभिनयाः आङ्गिकादयः न च ते लिङ्गसङ्केतादिरूपाः । अपि तु प्रत्यक्षसाक्षात्कारकल्पलौकिकसम्यङ्मिथ्याज्ञानादिरूपः । तस्यैव भावाः शृङ्गारादयो रत्यादिविलक्षणास्वादपर्यायप्रतीत्युपयोगिनः । अत एवाभिमुख्यनयनहेतुत्वादन्यलोकशास्त्राप्रसिद्धेनाभिनयशब्देन व्यपदेश्याः । तथाऽङ्गानि शाखानृत्तगीतानि आदयः प्रधाना येषां तेऽङ्गादयः । तथाऽङ्गानि व्यभिचारिणो भावाः आदयो हेतुरूपा विभावाः । अभिनयाः अनुभवाः । त एते रसाभिमुख्यनयनहेतवः । यद्वक्ष्यते—"विभावानुभावव्यभिचारिसंयोगाद्रसनिष्पत्तिः" इति । (अ-६.) तैरुपेतः । उप समीपमितः त्सविद्र्पणमभिसङ्-

१. K.S.S. M.G. N.S. तस्य तन्निष्फलं ज्ञानम् G.O.S. निष्फलं तस्य तत् ज्ञानम् ।

२. G.O.S. N.S. नाटचयोक्तृभिः K.S.S. रङ्गःपूजनम् M.G. Omits this.

३. G.O.S. M.G. N.S. (Same as above) except M.G. N.S. Read प्राप्स्यति K.S.S. कारयिष्यति वा चैव प्राप्स्यत्यपचयंतु सः ।

४. G.O.S. M.G. N.S. यथा दृष्टम् K.S.S. यथाशास्त्रम् ।

५. G.O.S. M.G. N.S. यास्यति K.S.S. गमिष्यति ।

एवमुक्त्वा[1] तु भगवान्[2]द्रुहिणः सह दैवतैः ।

रङ्गपूजां कुरुष्वेति मामेवं समचोदयत् ॥ १२७ ॥

क्रान्तः । एवंभूतोऽर्थो नाट्यं नटनीयं नर्तनम् । तथा गमनीयं यत्नेन स्वरूपतो हृदयेनानुप्रवेष्टव्यम् । तथा नाटकानां (नटानां) पारम्पर्यात्मकं वृत्तं नाट्यं धर्माम्नायरूपं च । तच्च सुखदुःखाभ्यां फलरूपाभ्यां सम्यगन्वितम् । तेषां पश्चाद्भावित्वात् । तेन हेयोपादेयव्युत्पत्तिः फलम् । एतच्च वितत्याग्रे भावस्वरूपं निरूपयिष्यामः । (११८-११९) ।

एवं सान्त्वेनापसारितेष्वपि विघ्नेषु दिव्यनिदेशनानाममोघत्वात् पूर्वविनियुक्तदेवतांशानां तत्र तत्र सन्निधानाद्यजनमवश्यकार्यमिति प्रदर्शयितुमुक्तमेवेतिहासमनुसन्दधन्निरूपयति—**एतस्मि**न्निति । **अन्तर** इति समये । **विधिवदि**ति व्याचष्टे—**बलिप्रदानै**रित्यादि । बल्यन्ते आप्याय्यन्ते देवता अनेनेति बलिः । विचित्रवर्णतण्डुलादिरचनाविशेषः । तिलादयश्चाग्नौ हूयन्त इति **होमाः** । उभयत्र विशेषणं **मन्त्रौषधी**ति । मन्त्रा वक्ष्यमाणाः । ओषधयो वचाबलाजमोदप्रभृतयः । प्रशस्तानि धान्यानि च । खरविशदं शष्कुलीमोदकादि भोज्यं भक्ष्यमुच्यते । भक्षणीयन्तु भक्ष्यं पायसकृसरादि । पानानि क्षीरेक्षुद्राक्षारसादीनि । वलिः पूर्वोक्तो रचनाविशेषः । एतैर्विच्छिन्नियोजितैर्विविधतया कल्प्यताम् । शोभाप्रधानं हि नाट्यं सर्वम् ।

ननु देवानां देवपूजाकरणे किं फलमित्याह—**मर्त्यलोकगता** इत्यादि । यद्यदाचरति श्रेष्ठ इति न्यायादिति भावः । **प्रवर्तये**दिति । देवानुष्ठिताचारानुवर्तित्वात् । लोक इति शेषः । (१२०-१२२) ।

ननु यदि लोकः सदाचारं नानुवर्तेत ततः किमित्याह—**अपूजयित्वे**ति । **निष्फल**मिति । **तस्ये**ति । नाट्याचार्यस्य । पारलौकिकमपि प्रत्यवायमाह—**तिर्यग्योनिं** चेति । (१२३) ।

ननु यद्यपूजने प्रत्यवायस्तर्हि पूजने किं तन्निवृत्तिमात्रं फलम् । नेत्याह—**यथाविधी**ति । यथा देवैर्विहिता । कथमेतज्ज्ञायत इत्याह—**यथादृष्ट**मिति शास्त्रदृष्टोऽसौ विधिरित्यर्थः । **अर्थान् शुभा**निति । ऐहलौकिकधनमानप्रसिद्धिलाभ उक्तः । (१२४-१२६)

एवं मर्त्यान्प्रत्यभिधाय प्रकृतमेव पुराकल्पमनुसन्धत्ते—**एवमुक्त्वे**ति । नाट्याचार्यस्यैव देवयजनेऽधिकारः । तस्यैव फललाभः । कवेः प्रेक्षाप्रवर्तयितुश्च

---

१. G.O.S. M.G. N.S. एवमुक्त्वा तु K.S.S. एवं भवत्विति ।

२. G.O.S. M.G. N.S. भगवान् K.S.S. प्राह ।

तत्प्रयोक्तृत्वमित्यनेनोक्तम् । रज्यतेऽनेनेति रङ्गो नाट्यम् । तदाधारत्वान्मण्डपः । तदधिष्ठातृत्वाच्च देवता अपीति मण्डपाध्यायस्य द्वितीयस्योपोद्धातं करोतीति विशेषः । (१२७)

त्रिणेत्रपादाब्जसदास्तवो (समाश्रयो) ल्लस

त्प्रसादभाक्स्फुटमिह नाट्यशासने ।

प्रवर्तितेयं हृदये महाधियां

प्रकाशतामभिनवगुप्तभारती ॥

इति श्रीमहामाहेश्वराभिनवगुप्ताचार्यविरचितायामभिनवभारत्यां भारतीयनाट्यशास्त्रविवृतौ नाट्योत्पत्तिः प्रथमोऽध्यायः ॥

द्वितीयोऽध्यायः ।

भरतस्य वचः श्रुत्वा पप्रच्छु[1]र्मुनयस्ततः[2] ।

भगवन् श्रोतुमिच्छामो यजनं रङ्गसंश्रयम् ॥ १ ॥

अथवा याः क्रियास्तत्र लक्षणं यच्च पूजनम् ।

भविष्यद्भिर्नरैः कार्यं कथं[3]तन्नाटचवेश्मनि ॥ २ ॥

संसारनाटचजननधातृबीजलताजुषीम् ।
जलमूर्ति शिवां पत्युः सरसां पर्युपास्महे ॥ १ ॥

वृत्तेऽध्याये यथातत्त्वमिति (१-५) वचनवशात् भरतमुनिर्यजनादेः पाठ्यादिवदन्तरङ्गतां पश्यन्परमार्थनिर्णयेन कुर्यात्कातुकथा (पश्यति परमार्थ-निर्णयेन । द्वितीये तु कथम्) मण्डपलक्षणं स्यात् । अत एव मुनिः 'गानं रङ्गश्च सङ्ग्रहः' (६-१०) इति रङ्गं सर्वं पश्चाद्वक्ष्यति । तस्मात्कदाचिदे(त्कथमे) तदित्याशङ्कमाना(नानां) 'मुनयः पप्रच्छुः' इति परमात्मानं परिकल्प्य मुनिराह —**भरतस्य वच** इति । ब्रह्मेव कविः, शंक्र इव प्रयोजयिता, भरत इव नाटचा-चार्यः, कोहलादय इव नटाः, अप्सरस इव सुकुमारोपकरणं, स्वातिरिवानद्ध-वित्, नारदवद्गीतज्ञः, सुरक्षितो मण्डपः, इन्द्रोत्सवसदृशः प्रयोगकालः, प्रशान्त-रागद्वेषादिकाः सामाजिकाः, देवतापूजनपूर्वकः प्रयोग इत्येव सङ्ग्रहेण पूर्वा-ध्यायनिरूपितमर्थमवधार्येत्यर्थः । **(यजनमिति)** 'रङ्गपूजां कुरुष्व' इति वृत्तो-ऽध्याये निरूपितमिति सङ्गतिः । देवविषये मण्डपस्य क्रियां विना न निष्पत्ति-रिति प्रथमं क्रियाप्रश्नस्तेषां विस्मृतोऽपि झटिति स्मृतिं गत इत्यभिप्रायेण दर्शयति—**अथ वेति** । पूर्वप्रश्नार्थोपमर्दनाय । अत एव **पूजनमिति** पुनर्वचनम् । **क्रियाः** कर्तव्यता । **लक्षणं** सन्निवेशपरिमाणादि । अतीतेषूपदेशो व्यर्थ इति **भविष्यद्भिरि**त्युक्तम् । देवानां मनसा सम्पत्तेः **नरैरिति** । ननु लक्षणं किं कार्यम् । लक्ष्यत इति लक्षणं सन्निवेश इत्यदोषः । अथ वा भाविभिर्यत्कार्यं नाटचवेश्म तत्र यत्क्रियालक्षणं पूजनं तत्कथमिति सम्बन्धः । (१-२)

---

१. N.S. K.S.S. M.G. प्रत्यूचुः G.O.S. पप्रच्छुः ।

२. G.O.S. M.G. N.S. ततः K.S.S. तदा ।

३. K.S.S. वै G.O.S. N.S. M.G. तत ।

इहादिर्नाट्ययोग[1]स्य नाट्यमण्डप एव हि[2] ।
तस्मात्तस्यैव तावत्त्वं लक्षणं वक्तुमर्हसि ॥ ३ ॥

तेषां तु वचनं श्रुत्वा मुनीनां भरतोऽब्रवीत् ।
लक्षणं पूजनं चैव श्रूयतां नाट्यवेश्मनः ॥ ४ ॥

दिव्या[3]नां मानसी सृष्टिर्गृहेषूपवनेषु च ।
(यथाभावाभिनिर्वर्त्याः सर्वे भावास्तु मानुषाः) ।
नराणां यत्नतः कार्याः लक्षणाभिहिताः क्रियाः ॥ ५ ॥

श्रूयतां तद्यथा यत्र[4] कर्तव्यो नाट्यमण्डपः ।
तस्य वास्तु च पूजा च यथा योज्या प्रयत्नतः[5] ॥ ६ ॥

पूर्वकृते प्रश्नपञ्चके निर्णयं कृत्वेदं प्रश्नान्तरं निर्णयेदित्याशङ्कमाना मुनयः पुनराहु**रिहादिरि**ति । नाट्यस्य योग उत्पत्तिः । **तावदि**त्यनेन पूर्वप्रश्नितस्यात्याग उक्तः । एवकारो लक्षणशब्दानन्तरम् । इतिकर्तव्यतायाः तदङ्गत्वात् । यजनस्य च तन्निष्पत्यनन्तरत्वात् । **तेषामिति** । अन्यथा तु न ब्रूयादेवोक्ताद्धेतोः । अनेन श्लोकेन लक्षणपूजनज्ञानं देवानामप्युपयोगि । सङ्कल्पितस्यापि निर्माणस्य ज्ञानापेक्षित्वादित्युक्तम् । अत एवात्र क्रियेति नोक्तम् । (३-४)

ननु किं क्रियै(या नै)वोच्यत इत्याह—**दिव्यानामिति** । श्रूयतामित्यनुवर्तते । नराणां कार्या क्रिया इतिकर्तव्यता च श्रूयताम् । चकाराल्लक्षणपूजने । शास्त्रेणोक्ता नराणामेव कस्मादित्याह—**दिव्यानामिति** । सृज्यमानत्वेन कर्मणोऽपि विषयत्ववि(त्वमेव) यत्र जन्मक्रमनियतप्ररोहकुसुमफलानि बहुविचित्रतरुलतास्थलीसरोवराक्रीडमयान्युपवनान्यपि मानसानि, तत्र गृह का सम्भावनेति । **श्रूयतामिति** । **तदिति** । यतो नराणां यत्नतः कार्यताप्रकारः । **यत्रेति** देशकालौ । **वास्त्विति** । गृहभूमिगतं परिमाणमिह मन्तव्यम् । (पूजा) लक्षणोक्तेत्युक्तम् । (५-६)

---

१. K.S.S. वेदस्य G.O.S. M.G. N.S. योगस्य ।

२. G.O.S. N.S. नाट्यमण्डप एव हि K.S.S. M.G. कीर्तितो नाट्यमण्डपः ।

३. G.O.S. K.S.S. M.G. दिव्यानां N.S. देवानाम् ।

४. G.O.S. N.S. M.G. यत्र K.S.S. तत्र ।

५. G.O.S. N.S. M.G. (Same as above) K.S.S. तस्य दैवतपूजा च यथा योज्या च वास्तुष ।

इह प्रेक्षागृहं[1] दृष्ट्वा धीमता[2] विश्वकर्मणा ।
त्रिविधः सन्निवेशश्च शास्त्रतः परिकल्पितः ॥ ७ ॥

विकृष्टश्चतुरश्रश्च त्र्यश्रश्चैव तु[3] मण्डपः ।
तेषां त्रीणि प्रमाणानि ज्येष्ठं मध्यं तथाऽवरम् ॥ ८ ॥

प्रमाणमेषां निर्दिष्टं हस्तदण्डसमाश्रयम् ।
शतं चाष्टौ चतुःषष्टिर्हस्ता द्वात्रिंशदेव च[4] ॥ ९ ॥

तत्र किं तल्लक्षणमित्याह—इह प्रेक्षागृहमिति । इह नाटचमण्डपे । सन्निवेशः । चशब्दात्प्रमाणमेतत् । विश्वकर्मणा परिकल्पितः । किं स्वबुद्धचा । न । अपि तु शास्त्रतः प्रेक्षागृहं विचार्य । शक्तश्चासौ विचार इत्याह—धीमतेति । ज्ञायत इत्याह । शास्त्रं कृतं तदप्यपरशास्त्रमूलमिति प्रवाहानादित्वमुक्तम् । कोऽसौ त्रिविध इत्याह—विकृष्टश्चेति । विभागेन कृष्टो दीर्घो न तु चतसृषु दिक्षु साम्येन । तिस्त्रोऽश्रयो यस्य, त्र्यश्रि तदस्मिन्निति मत्वर्थी योऽच् । एतान्येव त्रीणि ज्येष्ठादीनीति केचित् । अन्ये तु प्रत्येकं त्रित्वमिति नवैतेऽत्र भेदा इत्याहुः । एतदेव युक्तम् । तथा चाह—तेषामिति । प्रमाणं हस्तदण्डाश्रयं ज्येष्ठादित्वम् न तु सन्निवेशाश्रयमिति यावत् ।

'शतंचाष्टौ चतुःषष्टिर्द्वात्रिंशच्चेति निश्चयात् ।'

इति केचित्पठन्ति । तेषां चास्ति(पि)हस्तदण्डसमाश्रयत्वं वाचकं भवति । एतच्च सर्वं सम्भवमात्रेणोच्यते । अनु(नानु)वादकतया । न त्वियन्तो भेदा उपयोगिनः । एवं चाष्टादश भेदास्तावच्छास्त्रे दृष्टाः । ते चान्यत्वे(द्यत्वे) यद्यप्यनुपयोगिनः तथापि च सम्प्रदायाविच्छेदार्थं निर्दिष्टाः । केषाञ्चित्कदाचिदुपयोगी भविष्यतीति । यथोक्तम्—'अप्रयुक्ते दीर्घसत्रवत्' इति । (७-९)

इदन्त्विहोपयोगीति दर्शयति—अष्टाधिकं शतमित्यादि । इष्यत इति । अन्यत्वेऽपीत्याशयः । देवानामिति । यत्र देवासुरप्राया एव नायकप्रतिनायकास्तत्र डिमादावारभटीप्रधाने विततरङ्गपीठोपयोगात् भाण्डवाद्यप्रधानत्वाच्च परिक्रमणादेरुच्चतरदीर्घतरदीर्घतालपरिग्रहादियोगाच्च व्यक्तभावरयासम्भवादष्टोत्तरशतहस्तो मण्डप इत्यर्थः । यस्तु व्याचष्टे प्रेक्षका अत्र देवादयो विवक्षिता न

---

१. G.O.S., NS., प्रेक्षागृहं दृष्ट्वा K.S.S. M.G. प्रेक्षागृहाणांतु ।

२. G.O.S., K.S.S., M.G. धीमता N.S. श्रीमता ।

३. K.S.S. M.G. हि G.O.S: N.S., तु ।

४. G.O.S. N.S. (Same as above) M.G. द्वात्रिंशच्चेति निश्चितः K.S.S. द्वात्रिंशच्चेति निश्चितम. ।

अष्टाधिकं शतं ज्येष्ठं चतुःषष्टिस्तु मध्यमम् ।
कनीयस्तु तथा वेश्म हस्ता द्वात्रिंशदिष्यते[1] ॥ १० ॥

देवानां तु भवेज्ज्ये[2]ष्ठं नृपाणां मध्यमं भवेत् ।
शेषाणां प्रकृतीनां तु कनीयः संविधीयते ॥ ११ ॥

(प्रेक्षागृहाणां सर्वेषां प्रशस्तं मध्यमं स्मृतम् ।
तत्र पाठ्यं च गेयं च सुखश्राव्यतरं भवेत् ॥

प्रेक्षागृहाणां सर्वेषां त्रिप्रकारो विधिः स्मृतः ।
विकृष्टश्चतुरस्रश्च त्र्यस्रश्चैव प्रयोक्तृभिः ॥

कनीयस्तु स्मृतं त्र्यस्रं चतुरस्रं तु मध्यमम् ।
ज्येष्ठं विकृष्टं विज्ञेयं नाट्यवेदप्रयोक्तृभिः ॥)

प्रमाणं यच्च निर्दिष्टं लक्षणं विश्वकर्मणा ।
प्रेक्षागृहाणां सर्वेषां तच्चैव[3] हि निबोधत ॥ १२ ॥

अणू रजश्च वालश्च लिक्षा यूका यवस्तथा ।
अङ्गुलं च[4] तथा हस्तो दण्डश्चैव[5] प्रकीर्तितः ॥ १३ ॥

तु प्रयोज्याः । तेषां नियतसंख्याकत्वादिति । तस्यास्मदभिप्रायो न स्मृतिपथमागतः सन्नपि दशरूपकादौ । स चानन्तरमेव दर्शयिष्यते । (१०-११)

प्रमाणं लक्षणं यन्निर्दिष्टमितिजातावेकवचनम् ।

कानि प्रमाणानीत्याह—**अणू रजश्चे**त्यादिना । तेषां लक्षणान्याह—**अणबोऽष्टावि**त्यादि । यतः प्रभृति दृश्यता प्रवर्तते सोऽणुः । अणुः प्रसिद्धोऽणुपरिमाणः । द्व्यणुकद्वयपरमाणुद्वयारब्धा अणव एव वा महत्त्वयुक्ताः । परमाणुद्वयारब्धे तु द्व्यणुकेऽणुपरिमाणमस्तु । कोऽत्र विरोध इत्यलमवान्तरेण । अनेनै-

---

१. G.O.S. N.S. M.G. (Same as above) K.S.S. द्वात्रिंशत् करमिष्यते ।
२. G.O.S. N.S. (Same as above) M.G. K.S.S. देवानां भवनं ज्येष्ठम् ।
३. G.O.S. N.S. एव K.S.S. M.G. एवं ।
४. G.O.S. N.S. च तथा हस्तः K.S.S. M·G. चैव हस्तश्च ।
५. G.O.S. N.S. M.G. (Same as above) K.S.S. दण्डश्च परिकीर्तितः ।

अणवोऽष्टौ रजः प्रोक्तं तान्यष्टौ वाल उच्यते ।
वालास्त्वष्टौ भवेल्लिक्षा यूका लिक्षाष्टकं भवेत् ॥ १४ ॥

यूकास्त्वष्टौ यवो ज्ञेयो[1] यवास्त्वष्टौ तथाङ्गुलम् ।
अङ्गुलानि तथा हस्तश्चतुर्विंशतिरुच्यते ॥ १५ ॥

चतुर्हस्तो भवेद्दण्डो निर्दिष्टस्तु प्रमाणतः ।
अनेनैव प्रमाणेन वक्ष्याम्येषां विनिर्णयम् ॥ १६ ॥

वेति । 'देवानान्तु भवेत्' इत्यनेन यदुक्तम् । मण्डपाः—तद्यथा ज्येष्ठप्रमाणं डिमप्राये । यद्वक्ष्यति—

निर्घातोल्कापातैरुपरागेणेन्दुसूर्ययोर्युक्तः ।
युद्धनियुद्धाघर्षणसंम्फेटकृतश्च विज्ञेयः ॥
देवभुजगेन्द्रराक्षसयक्षपिशाचावकीर्णश्च ।
षोडशनायकबहुलः सात्त्वत्यारभटिकायुतस्तु डिमः ॥ (ना. शा. १८.) इति ।

तथा मध्यमप्रमाणं नृपतिप्रायप्रयोज्ये नाटकादौ । यद्वक्ष्यति —

निर्घातोल्कापातैरुपरागेणेन्दुसूर्ययोर्युक्तः ।
युद्धनियुद्धाघर्षणसम्भवकृतश्च विज्ञेयः ॥
नृपतीनां यच्चरितम् । (ना. शा. १८.) इत्यादि ।

शेषास्तु प्रकृतयो भाणप्रहसनादौ । यच्च वक्ष्यति—

विविधाश्रयो हि भाणो विज्ञेयस्त्वेकहार्यस्तु । (ना. शा. १८.)

तथा "भगवत्तापसविप्रैरन्यैरपि च (ना. शा. १८.) इत्यादि । एवंभूतप्रकृतिप्रधाने प्रयोगे कनीयःप्रमाणो मण्डपः इति । एषां मण्डपानां मध्ये यो विनिर्णय एव सर्वसाधारणः मध्यमे मण्डपे नाटकभाणप्रयोगात् कनीयसि च, डिमरूपे एव (ष)मण्डपं(पः)तं वक्ष्यामीति । अयमभिप्रायः—ज्येष्ठमाने नाटकादिप्रयोगसौकर्याभवान्मध्यम एव युक्तः । स एव निर्णयः । विविधोऽपि दिव्यनृपप्रकृता(त्या)दिस्वभावो निश्चयाभिमुख्यमभिनयप्रयोगद्वारेण नीयते यत्रेति । (१२-१६)

---

१. G.O.S. N.S. M.G. ज्ञेयो K.S.S. प्रोक्तः ।

चतुःषष्टिकरान्कुर्याद्दीर्घत्वेन तु मण्डपम् ।
द्वात्रिंशतं च विस्तारान्मर्त्यानां यो भवेदिह[1] **॥ १७ ॥**

अत ऊर्ध्वं न कर्तव्यः कर्तृभिर्नाट्यमण्डपः ।
यस्मादव्यक्तभावं हि तत्र नाट्यं व्रजेदिति[2] **॥ १८ ॥**

मण्डपे विप्रकृष्टे तु पाठ्यमुच्चारितस्वरम्[3] **।**
अनिस्सरणधर्मत्वाद्विस्वरत्वं भृशं व्रजेत्[4] **॥ १९ ॥**

तं दर्शयति—**चतुष्षष्टि** करानित्यादि । प्रयोक्तुः पुरस्तात्पृष्ठतश्च मण्डपेऽस्मिन् सति (पोऽस्मिन्नसति) करणार्हो न भवतीत्यर्थः । **कर्तृभिरिति** । किं तेषां वृथा प्रयासोत्पादनेनेति यावत् । **तत्रेति** । अतोऽधिकप्रमाणे अत्यन्तं न्यूनप्रमाणे चेत्यर्थः । **नाट्यमिति** । सकलावान्तरभेदे प्रभेदं दर्शयितुम् । नाट्यतोऽभि (ट्य यतोऽभि) व्यक्तं भवतीति समुदायाभिप्रायेण मन्तव्यम् । तदेव दर्शयति—**मण्डप** इति । दीर्घत्वम् । पार्श्वयोर्विस्तारः । मर्त्यानामित्यनेन मण्डपकरणात् किमित्यकारणं प्रयोगेणैव (गो नैव) वेद्यत इत्याशयः । एतदेवाह—**अत ऊर्ध्वं नेति** । अत इत्येवंविधो यतो मध्यमोऽस्ति ततो हेतोरित्यर्थः । **ऊर्ध्वमिति** । प्रमाणस्याधिक्यं न्यूनातिरेकाभ्यामिति मन्तव्यम् । **कर्तव्य इति** । प्रकर्षः प्रकृष्टं तदतिक्रान्तो **विप्रकृष्टः** । किन्नियोगमानैः तस्मिश्च तत्र ज्येष्ठे । पाठ्यं यन्मुख्ये (ख्यं) "नाट्यस्यैषा तनूस्स्मृता" (ना. शा. १४-२) इति दर्शयिष्यते । **तद्विस्वरत्वं** विशेषेणोपतापकत्वं निकटवर्तिनः प्रति व्रजेत् । अत्र हेतुः उच्चं कृत्वा चारितोऽतिक्लेशेन सम्पादितः स्वरः काक्वा (कखा) दिविभागो यत्र । तथा दूरवर्तिनः सामाजिकान्प्रति विस्वरत्वं विगतशब्दकत्वमनाकर्णनीयत्वं **व्रजेत्** । अत्र हेतुः **अनिस्सरणधर्मत्वात्** । निरन्तरे देशे सरणं द्वितीयशब्दारम्भः । स यस्य धर्मो नास्ति शब्दान्तरप्रसराभावादित्यर्थः । तथाऽतिकनीयसि मण्डपे पाठ्यमुच्चरितस्वरं सदनिस्सरणधर्मत्वादनुरणनात्मकमधुरशब्दान्तरानारम्भात् विनष्टः स्वरो मधुरो यस्य तादृशत्वं व्रजेत् । अनुरणनं हि स्वरस्य पाठ्य-

---

१. G.O.S N.S. (Same as above) M.G द्वात्रिंशतं च विस्तारं मर्त्यान् योजयेदिह K.S.S. द्वात्रिंशेन तु ।

२. G.O.S. N.S. M.G. व्रजेदिति K.S.S. भवेदिति ।

३. G.O.S. K.S.S. उच्चारित M.G. N.S. उच्चरित ।

४. G.O.S. N.S. M.G. (Same as above) K.S.S. अनभिव्यक्त वर्णत्वाद् विस्वरत्वं भृशं भवेत् ।

यश्चाप्यास्यगतो भावो नानादृष्टिसमन्वितः[1]।
स वेश्मनः प्रकृष्टत्वाद्व्रजेदव्यक्ततां पराम् ॥ २० ॥
प्रेक्षागृहाणां सर्वेषां तस्मान्मध्यममिष्यते।
यावत्पाठ्यं च गेयं च तत्र श्रव्यतरं भवेत्[2] ॥ २१ ॥

सिद्धिरूपमिति गेयाधिकारे वक्ष्यामः। अनेन समानयोगक्षेमत्वात् अधिकातोद्यविस्त्ररत्वमपि लक्षितं भवति। तथा चोपसंहरिष्यति गेयं चेति। विस्वरत्वमिति, 'स्वृ शब्दोपतापयोः' इत्यस्य रूपम्। (१७-१८)

प्रधानस्य पाठ्यस्य प्रधानानुरणनभूतस्य च गीतातोद्यादेर्विनाशं प्रतिपाद्याभिनयवर्गस्यापि प्रतिपादयति—**यश्चापीति**। **आस्यगतो** मुखगतो भावः योऽनुभावलक्षणो दृष्टिबाष्पस्वेदवैवर्ण्यादिः तथा मकुटप्रतिशीर्षादिः। चकारादाङ्गिकः। **स वेश्मनः प्रकृष्टत्वाद**तिविस्तीर्णत्वादव्यक्ततां गच्छेत्। तथा प्रगतं कृष्टं कर्षण दैर्घ्यं यस्य तस्य भावः। ततः कनीयस्त्वाद्धेतोः परां द्वितीयामव्यक्ततामतिसामीप्यकृतां व्रजेत्। प्रथमं ह्यतिदूरत्वं कृत्वा सोक्ता। एवमुभयमण्डपाभिप्रायेणेदं व्याख्येयम्। अन्यथा तस्मान्मध्यममिष्यत इत्युपसंहारो न श्लिष्यति। तदाह—**प्रेक्षागृहाणामि**त्यादि। मध्ये भवं मध्यमम्। तदिष्यते यतः सर्वेषां रूपाणां सम्बन्धि यत्पाठ्यं प्रधानं तनूरूपप्राणोपरञ्जकरूपं च गीतं चकारादातोद्यं च श्रव्यतरं भवति। द्वितीयचकारादभिनयान्तरमपि दृश्यतरं भवतीत्यर्थः। (२०-२१)

ननु यद्येवंभूतः प्रयोगक्रमस्तर्हि हस्तसमाश्रयेणैव विधिर्वक्तव्यः। सोऽपि यत्र परिपूर्णो नोपकारी तत्र दण्डसमाश्रयेणातोद्यमानेन। अथ कदाचिद्दिव्यप्रकृतिप्रेक्षकाभिप्रायेण तदुच्यते तत्रापि कः स्तोकान्तरत्वेनेति न्यायेन का इति (ह) सम्भावनेत्याशङ्कां पराकर्तुं श्लोको भावी। अत एव पूर्वश्लोकेन सह नात्र पौनरुक्त्यं शङ्कितव्यम्। तस्यान्यथोपक्षेपात्। तच्छ्लोकमाह—**देवानामि**त्यादि। मनसस्तदीयस्य सत्त्वबहुलत्वात् तत्कृत इन्द्रियविसर्जनलक्षणे व्यापारोऽतिरूपव्यापी। उपवनेष्वपि विततविततेषु। का कथा मण्डपविषये। अत एव

---

१. G.O.S. N.S. (Same as above) M.G. यश्चाप्यास्यगतो रागो भावसृष्टिरसाश्रयः। K.S.S. यश्चाप्यस्य।

२. G.O.S. N.S. (Same as above) K.S.S. यस्माद् वाद्यं च गेयं च सुखं श्राव्यतरं भवेत्। M.G. यस्मात् पाठ्यं च गेयं च सुखं श्रव्यतरं भवेत।

(प्रेक्षागृहाणां सर्वेषां त्रिप्रकारो विधिः स्मृतः ।
विकृष्टश्चतुरस्रश्च त्र्यस्रश्चैव प्रयोक्तृभिः ॥
कनीयस्तु स्मृतं त्र्यस्रं चतुरस्रं च मध्यमम् ।
ज्येष्ठं विकृष्टं विज्ञेयं नाट्यवेश्म प्रयोक्तृभिः ॥)

देवानां मानसी सृष्टिर्गृहे[1]षूपवनेषु च ।
यत्नभावा[2]भिनिष्पन्नाः सर्वे भावा हि[3] मानुषाः ॥ २२ ॥
तस्माद्देवकृतैर्भावैर्न विस्पर्धेत मानुषः ।
मानुषस्य[4] तु गेहस्य सम्प्रवक्ष्यामि लक्षणम् ॥ २३ ॥
भूमेर्विभागं पूर्वं तु परीक्षेत प्रयोजकः[5] ।
ततो वास्तु प्रमाणेन[6] प्रारभेत शुभेच्छया ॥ २४ ॥

गृहेष्विति बहुवचनमुपात्तम् । तेन तदपेक्षया ते मण्डपा उक्ता इत्यर्थः । न त्वेवं मानुषाणां राजसानां मनः । तदाह—**देवकृतैरिति** । यत एवं तस्मान्मा-**नुषस्यैव गेहस्य** लक्षणं सम्यक्प्रवक्ष्यामि । तुशब्द एवकारार्थे । (२२-२३)

सम्यगिति यदुक्तं तदाह—**भूमेरित्यादि** । विभागो हेयोपादेयत्वेन । **वास्त्विति** । ग्रहणं प्रमाणं चेत्युपलक्ष्यमाणरूपेण प्रारभेत । कर्तुमिति शेषः ।

तं विभागमाह—**समेत्यादि** । समा स्वभावान्नातिनिम्नोन्नतेत्यर्थः । **स्थिरा** अचलनस्वभावा । **कठिना** अनूषरा । **कृष्णा गौरीचेति** । चो वार्थे । अन्ये तु व्यामिश्रितत्वमाहुः । **कर्तव्य** इति करणार्हः । कथमित्याह—**प्रथममित्यादि** । **शोधनमुपरिगताशुचिशर्कराद्यपसारणम्** । ततो हलेनोद्धृतगुल्मपाषाणादिकां कुर्यात् । एतदेवाह—**अस्थीत्यादिना** ।

एवं बाह्याभ्यन्तरतो भूमिशुद्धिं निरूप्यानन्तरकरणीयमाह—**शोधयित्वेति** । कथं प्रमाणनिर्देश इत्याह—**पुष्येति** । शुक्लसूत्रत्वं तावत्पिष्टरञ्जनादिना ।

---

१. G.O.S. M.G. K.S S. गृहेषु च N.S. वनेषु ।

२. K.S.S. M.G. N.S. यत्नभावाद् विनिष्पन्नाः G.O.S. यत्नभावाभि निष्पन्ना ।

३. K.S.S. तु G.O.S. N.S. M.G. हि ।

४. K.S.S. मनुष्यस्य G.O.S. M.G N.S. मानुषस्य ।

५. G.O.S. N.S. प्रयोजकः K.S.S. विचक्षणः ।

६. K.S.S. M.G. वास्तु प्रमाण G.O.S, N.S. वास्तुप्रमाणेन ।

समा स्थिरा तु कठिना कृष्णा गौ[1]री च या भवेत् ।
भूमिस्तत्रैव[2] कर्तव्यः कर्तृभिर्नाट्यमण्डपः ॥ २५ ॥

प्रथमं शोधनं कृत्वा लाङ्गलेन समुत्कृषेत् ।
अस्थिकीलकपालानि तृणगुल्मांश्च शोधयेत् ॥ २६ ॥

शोधयित्वा वसुमतीं प्रमाणं निर्दिशेत्ततः ।
(त्रीण्युत्तराणि सौम्यं च विशाखापि च रेवती ॥

हस्ततिष्यानुराधाश्च प्रशस्ता नाटयकर्मणि ।)
पुष्यनक्षत्रयोगेन[3] शुक्लं सूत्रं प्रसारयेत् ॥ २७ ॥

कार्पासं बाल्बजं वापि मौञ्जं वाल्कलमेव च[4] ।
सूत्रं बुधैस्तु कर्तव्यं यस्य च्छेदो न विद्यते ॥ २८ ॥

चर्मकृतं मानसूत्रं न कार्यमिति च तात्पर्यम् । **स्वामिनः** प्रेक्षापतेः । **प्रयोक्तु** र्नाटयाचार्यस्य । **प्रयत्नेन रज्जुग्रहणमि**त्यच्छेद्यानुभरणीया । तादृशी च सावधानतयावष्टम्भवियोगाद्युभयथा तथा प्रयत्नतो योज्यम् । **नित्यमिति** । न केवलमत्र प्रथमपरिग्रहे यावदन्यभाविस्तम्भविनिवेशाय भूभागमानग्रहणादावित्यर्थः । **प्रयत्नेन** मानमित्यूनाधिकादिदोषवर्जनायायं यत्न इत्यपौनरुक्त्यम् । **मुहूर्तो** ब्राह्मादिः । **तिथि**र्हदा(र्नन्दा)दिः । **करणं** विष्टयादिरहितम् (२४-३२) ।

सूत्रप्रसारणेन यत्कृत्य तदाह—**चतुष्षष्टिरि**त्यादि । चतुष्षष्टिर्हस्तदैर्घ्याद्विस्ताराच्च द्वात्रिंशत्करं क्षेत्रं गृहीत्वा मध्ये सूत्रं विस्तारेण दद्यात् । तत्र यत्प्रयोक्तुः पृष्ठगं भविष्यति तदेव पृष्ठम् । तस्य मध्ये विस्तारेण सूत्रं दद्यात् । ततः षोडशहस्तौ द्वौ भागौ भवतः । पृष्ठगतं भागमर्धेन विभज्याष्टहस्तं रङ्गशिरः । प्रविशतां पात्राणां चान्तस्स्थानम् । नाटचमण्डपस्य ह्युत्तानसुप्तवदवस्थितस्य रङ्गपीठं मुख्यम् । तदष्टहस्तं शिरः । तत्पृष्ठे तु दैर्घ्याद्धि षोडशहस्तं नेपथ्यगृहं भवति । विस्तारात्तु द्वात्रिंशत्करमेव तत् । नैपथ्यादिकं

---

१. M.G· कृष्णाऽगौरी G.O.S. N.S. K.S.S. कृष्णा गौरी ।

२. K.S.S. M.G. तु G.O.S. N.S. एव ।

३. K.S.S. M.G. योगे तु G.O.S. N.S. योगेन ।

४. K.S.S. वादरं चापि वाल्कलं मौञ्जमेव च G.O.S. M.G. N.S. (Same as above) But M.G. Reads चापि ।

अर्धच्छिन्ने भवेत्सूत्रे स्वामिनो मरणं ध्रुवम् ।
त्रिभागच्छिन्नया रज्ज्वा राष्ट्रकोपो विधीयते ॥ २९ ॥
छिन्नायां तु चतुर्भागे प्रयोक्तुर्नाश उच्यते ।
हस्तात्प्रभ्रष्टया[1] वापि कश्चित्त्वपचयो भवेत् ॥ ३० ॥
तस्मान्नित्यं प्रयत्नेन रज्जुग्रहणमिष्यते ।
कार्यं चैव प्रयत्नेन मानं नाट्यगृहस्य तु ॥ ३१ ॥
मुहूर्तेनानुकूलेन तिथ्या सुकरणेन च[2] ।
ब्राह्मणांस्तर्पयित्वा तु[3] पुण्याहं वाचयेत्ततः ॥ ३२ ॥
शान्तितोयं ततो दत्वा ततः सूत्रं प्रसारयेत्[4] ।
चतुष्षष्टिकरान्कृत्वा द्विधा कुर्यात्पुनश्च तान् ॥ ३३ ॥
पृष्ठतो यो भवेद्भागो द्विधाभूतस्य तस्य तु[5] ।
सममर्धविभागेन रङ्गशीर्षं प्रकल्पयेत्[6] ॥ ३४ ॥
पश्चिमे च विभागेऽथ[7] नेपथ्यगृहमादिशेत् ।

तत्र गृह्यते । तदाह—**पश्चिमे चेति** । तत्र रङ्गपीठं विस्तारतः षोडश दैर्घ्यतस्त्वष्टहस्ता इति केचित् । अन्ये त्वेतदेव विपर्यासयन्ति । सर्वथा तावद्रङ्गपीठस्यापि विकृष्टत्वं विधेयमिति तात्पर्यम् । यद्वक्ष्यते—रङ्गो विकृष्टो भरतेन कार्यः (ना.शा. १२-२०) इत्यादि । (३३-३५)

एवं मानविधिमभिधायेष्टकास्थापनरूपे निवेशने विधिमाह—**शुभे नक्षत्रयोग इत्यादिना** । दशसु तिर्यगूर्ध्वाधोरूपासु दिक्षु बलिः कार्य इत्युक्त्वा चतसृषु

---

१. M.G. K.S.S हस्तप्र...टया G.O.S. N.S. हस्तात् प्रभ्रष्टया ।
२. K.S.S. M.G. तिथ्या च करणेन च G.O.S. N.S. तिथ्या सुकरणेन च ।
३. K.S.S. च G.O.S. N.S. M.G. तु ।
४. K.S.S. N.S. शान्तितो यत्नतो धृत्वा तत्र सूत्रं प्रसारयेत् N.S. Reads ततः in place of तत्र G.O.S. M.G. (Same as above) except M.G. Reads तत्र in place of ततः ।
५. K.S.S. द्विधाभूतो भवेच्च सः G.O.S. M.G. N.S. द्विधाभूतस्य तस्य तु ।
६. K.S.S. तस्यार्धेन विभागेन रङ्गशीर्षं प्रयोजयेत् G.O.S. M.G. (Same as above) N.S. तस्याप्यर्धार्धभागे तु रङ्गशीर्षं प्रकल्पयेत् ।
७. K.S.S. M.G. तु पुनर्भागे N.S. अथ विभागे च G.O.S. च विभागेऽथ ।

विभज्य[1] भागान्विधिवद्यथावदनुपूर्वशः ॥ ३५ ॥
शुभे नक्षत्रयोगे च[2] मण्डपस्य निवेशनम् ।
शङ्खदुन्दुभिनिर्घोषैर्मृदङ्गपणवादिभिः ॥ ३६ ॥
सर्वातोद्यैः प्रणुदितैः[3] स्थापनं कार्यमेव तु[4] ।
उत्सार्याणि त्वनिष्टानि पाषण्ड्या[5]श्रमिणस्तथा ॥ ३७ ॥
[6]काषायवसनाश्चैव विकलाश्चैव ये नराः ।
निशायां च बलिः कार्यो नानाभोजनसंयुतः[7] ॥ ३८ ॥
गन्धपुष्पफलोपेतो दिशो दश समाश्रितः ।
पूर्वेण शुक्लान्नयुतो नीलान्नो दक्षिणेन च[8] ॥ ३९ ॥
पश्चिमेन बलिः पीतो रक्तश्चैवोत्तरेण तु ।
यादृशं दिशि यस्यां तु दैवतं परिकल्पितम्[9] ॥ ४० ॥
तादृशस्तत्र दातव्यो बलिर्मन्त्रपुरस्कृतः ।
स्थापने ब्राह्मणेभ्यश्च दातव्यं घृतपायसम्[10] ॥ ४१ ॥

दिक्षु बलि विधिरुक्तो नान्यथेत्यभिप्रायेण व्यापकं विधिमाह—**यादृशमित्यादिना**। तेनाग्नेये रक्तवर्ण इत्याद्यूह्यम् । मन्त्रा वरणपूजाविधौ वक्ष्यमाणाः ।

---

१. G.O.S. K.S.S. M.G. विभज्य N.S. विकल्प्य ।
२. K.S.S. M.G. तु N.S. G.O.S. च ।
३. K.S.S. सर्वतूर्यनिनादैश्च M.G. सर्वातोद्यनिनादैश्च G.O.S. N.S. (Same as above)
४. M.G. K.S.S. च G.O.S. N.S. तु ।
५. K.S.S. M.G. पाषण्डा G.O.S. N.S. पाषण्ड्याः ।
६. N.S. कषाय G.O.S. K.S.S. M.G. काषाय ।
७. N.S. संश्रयः G.O.S. K.S.S. M.G. संयुतः ।
८. K.S.S. M.G. नीलः स्याद् दक्षिणेन च G.O.S. N.S. (Same as above) ।
९. K.S.S. M.G. यस्यां यच्चाधिदैवं तु दिशि संपरिकीर्तितम् । G.O.S. N.S (Same as above) ।
१०. K.S.S. M.G. दातव्यो घृतपायसः G.O.S. N.S. (Same as above) ।

मधुपर्कस्तथा राज्ञे कर्तृभ्यश्च गुडौदनम् ।
नक्षत्रेण तु कर्तव्यं मूलेन स्थापनं बुधैः ॥ ४२ ॥
मुहूर्तेनानुकूलेन तिथ्या सुकरणेन च[1] ।
एवं तु स्थापनं कृत्वा भित्तिकर्म प्रयोजयेत् ॥ ४३ ॥
भित्तिकर्मणि निर्वृत्ते स्तम्भानां स्थापनं ततः ।
तिथिनक्षत्रयोगेन शुभेन करणेन च ॥ ४४ ॥
स्तम्भानां स्थापनं कार्यं रोहिण्या श्रवणेन वा ।
आचार्येण सुयुक्तेन त्रिरात्रोपोषितेन च ॥ ४५ ॥
स्तम्भानां स्थापनं कार्यं प्राप्ते सूर्योदये शुभे ।
प्रथमे ब्राह्मणस्तम्भे सर्पिस्सर्षपसंस्कृतः[2] ॥ ४६ ॥
सर्वशुक्लो विधिः कार्यो दद्यात्पायसमेव च ।
ततश्च क्षत्रियस्तम्भे वस्त्रमाल्यानुलेपनम् ॥ ४७ ॥
सर्वं रक्तं प्रदातव्यं द्विजेभ्यश्च गुडौदनम् ।
वैश्यस्तम्भे विधिः कार्यो दिग्भागे पश्चिमोत्तरे ॥ ४८ ॥
सर्वं पीतं प्रदातव्यं द्विजेभ्यश्च घृतौदनम्[3] ।
शूद्रस्तम्भे विधिः कार्यः सम्यक्पूर्वोत्तराश्रये ॥ ४९ ॥

ते च कर्मशंसोप (सं) योगिनोहेन युक्ता विधेयाः । 'मन्त्रेण स्मृतं कर्म करोति' इति हि स्मृतिः । अन्ये तु तद्देवताकैः श्रुतिमन्त्रैरेव बलिकर्मेत्याहुः । तल्लिङ्गैरित्यन्ये । चकारो भिन्नक्रमः । न केवलं मानोपक्रमे ब्राह्मणतर्पणं यावत्स्थापनेऽपीत्यर्थः । (३६-४३)

एवं मानविधिं स्थापनविधिं च कृत्वा स्तम्भविधिः कार्य इति दर्शयति —**भित्तिकर्मणीति** । स्थापनमुच्छ्रयणम् । प्रथमं त्वाग्नेयः कोणः । तस्य विशेषणैः अनुवादलिङ्गविधिकल्प्यं (लिङ्गविधिः कल्प्यः) । **शुभं** (क्लं) सर्वत्र । **पायसमिति**—द्विजेभ्य इति प्रकरणात् । विध्यनुसारेणैव भोजनं शुक्लादिवर्णमिति मन्तव्यम् । **ततश्चेति** । तैरन्त(तदन्त) इत्यर्थः । (४४-५४)

---

१. K.S.S. M.G. तु G.O.S. N.S. च ।

२. N.S. K.S.S. संस्कृते G.O.S. M.G. संस्कृतः ।

३. K.S.S. घृतोदनम् G.O.S. N.S. M.G. घृतौदनम् ।

नीलप्रायं प्रय[1]त्नेन कृसरं[2] च द्विजाशनम् ।
पूर्वोक्त[3]ब्राह्मणस्तम्भे शुक्लमाल्यानुलेपने ॥ ५० ॥
निक्षिपेत्कनकं मूले कर्णाभरणसंश्रयम् ।
ताम्रं चाधः[4] प्रदातव्यं स्तम्भे क्षत्रियसंज्ञके ॥ ५१ ॥
वैश्यस्तम्भस्य मूले तु रजतं सम्प्रदापयेत् ।
शूद्रस्तम्भस्य मूले तु दद्यादायसमेव च ॥ ५२ ॥
सर्वेष्वेव[5] तु निक्षेप्यं स्तम्भमूलेषु[6] काञ्चनम् ।
स्वस्तिपुण्याहघोषेण जयशब्देन चैव हि ॥ ५३ ॥
स्तम्भानां स्थापनं कार्यं पुष्प[7]मालापुरस्कृतम् ।
रत्नदानैः सगोदानैर्वस्त्रदानैरनल्पकैः ॥ ५४ ॥
ब्राह्मणांस्तर्प[8]यित्वा तु स्तम्भानु[9]त्थापयेत्ततः ।
अचलं चाप्यकम्पञ्च तथैवावलितं[10] पुनः ॥ ५५ ॥
स्तम्भस्योत्थापने सम्यग्दोषा ह्येते प्रकीर्तिताः ।
अवृष्टिरुक्ता चलने वलने मृत्युतो[11] भयम् ॥ ५६ ॥

अचलमिति । स्थानान्तरानिवेशलक्षणमनेनोक्तम् । अविद्यमाना चलना यस्येति । **अकम्प्यमिति** । तत्रैव स्थानशिथिलता येन न भवति । **अवलितमिति** । वलयाकृत्यादिना परिवर्तनं यस्य करणीयं न भवति । दोषसूचकत्वाद्दोषकारित्वाच्च दोषाः । तान्दोषानाह—**अवृष्टिरित्यादि** । (५५-५७)

---

१. K.S.S. M.G. प्रदातव्यं G.O.S. N.S. प्रयत्नेन ।
२. N.S. कृशरा G.O.S. K.S.S. M.G. कृसरं ।
३. K.S.S. M.G. पूर्वे तु N.S. G.O.S. पूर्वोक्त ।
४. K.S.S. चापि G.O.S. M.G. N.S. चाधः ।
५. K.S.S. M.G. N.S. शेषेष्वपि च G.O.S. सर्वेष्वेव ।
६. M.G. G.O.S. K.S.S. स्तम्भमूलेषु N.S. स्तम्भमूले तु ।
७. K.S.S. M.G. पर्ण G.O.S. N.S. पुष्प ।
८. K.S.S. स्थापयित्वा G.O.S. N.S. M.G. तर्पयित्वा ।
९. G.O.S. स्तम्भान् N.S. K.S.S. M.G. स्तम्भम् ।
१०. K.S.S N.S. तथैवाचलितम् G.O.S. M.G. (Same as above)
११. N.S. M.G. मृतितो G.O.S. K.S.S. मृत्युनो ।

कम्पने परचक्रात्तु भयं भवति[1] दारुणम् ।
दोषैरेतैर्विहीनं तु स्तम्भमुत्थापयेच्छिवम् ॥ ५७ ॥
पवित्रे[2] ब्राह्मणस्तम्भे दातव्या दक्षिणा च गौः ।
शेषाणां भोजनं कार्यं स्थापने कर्तृसंश्रयम्[3] ॥ ५८ ॥
मन्त्रपूतं[4] च तद्देयं नाट्याचार्येण धीमता ।
पुरोहितं नृपं चैव भोजयेन्मधुपायसैः[5] ॥ ५९ ॥
कर्तृनपि तथा सर्वान्कृसरां लवणोत्तराम्[6] ।
सर्वमेवं[7] विधिं कृत्वा सर्वातोद्यैः प्रवादितैः ॥ ६० ॥
अभिमन्त्र्य यथान्यायं स्तम्भान्[8]उत्थापयेच्छुचिः ।
यथाऽचलो गिरि[9]र्मेरुर्हिमवांश्च महाबलः[10] ॥ ६१ ॥
जयावहो नरेन्द्रस्य तथा त्वमचलो भव ।
स्तम्भद्वारं च भित्तिं च नेपथ्यगृहमेव च ॥ ६२ ॥
एवमुत्थापयेत्तज्ज्ञो विधिदृष्टेन कर्मणा ।
रङ्गपीठस्य पार्श्वे[11] तु कर्तव्या मत्तवारणी ॥ ६३ ॥

दातव्येति । द्विजायेति दातव्यबलाल्लोभ्यते । **अभिमन्त्र्येति** सूचितो यः मन्त्रस्तमाह—**यथेति** । प्रणवनमस्कारमध्यवर्ती चायं पठितव्य इति वास्तु-

---

१. K.S.S. M.G. वदति G.O.S. भवति ।
२. N.S. K.S.S. पवित्रं M.G. G.O.S. पवित्रे ।
३. M.G. शेषाणां स्थापने कार्यं भोजनं कर्तृसंश्रयम् K.S.S. N.S. G.O.S. (Same as above)
४. K.S.S. M.G. मंत्रपूर्वं G.O.S. N.S. मन्त्रपूतं ।
५. G.O.S. N.S. पायसैः M.G. K.S.S. पायसम् ।
६. K.S.S. N.S. M.G. कृसरं लवणोत्तरम् G.O.S. कृसरां लवणोत्तराम् ।
७. N.S. सर्वमेव M.G. K.S.S. G.O.S. सर्वमेवं ।
८. K.S.S. N.S. M.G. स्तम्भम् G.O.S. स्तम्भान् ।
९ K.S.S. गुरुः G.O.S. N.S M.G. गिरिः ।
१०. M.G. यथाचलः G.O.S. K.S.S. N.S. महाबलः ।
११. K.S.S. पश्चात् G.O.S. N.S. M.G. पार्श्वे ।

चतुःस्तम्भसमायुक्ता रङ्गपीठप्रमाणतः ।
अध्यर्धहस्तोत्सेधेन कर्तव्या मत्तवारणी ॥ ६४ ॥

ऊत्सेधे[1]न तयोस्तुल्यं कर्तव्यं रङ्गमण्डपम् ।
तस्यां माल्यं च धूपं च गन्धं वस्त्रं तथैव च[2] ॥ ६५ ॥

नानावर्णानि देयानि तथा भूतप्रियो बलिः ।
आय[3]सं तत्र दातव्यं स्तम्भानां कुशलैर[4]धः ॥ ६६ ॥

भोजने कृसरा[5]श्चैव दातव्यं ब्राह्मणाशनम् ।
एवं विधिपुरस्कारैः कर्तव्या मत्तवारणी ॥ ६७ ॥

रङ्गपीठं ततः कार्यं विधिदृष्टेन कर्मणा ।
रङ्गशीर्षन्तु कर्तव्यं षड्दारुकसमन्वितम् ॥ ६८ ॥

विद्याविदः । अचालो भवेति पू(अपू)र्वविधिः । न तेन) तदनुवादेन जयावहो भवेत्यस्य न पौनरुक्त्यम् (?) । एवमिति । तेन भित्तौ स्त्रीत्वेन गृहे नपुंसकत्वेनोहः कार्यः । पार्श्व इति । विशेषानुपादानात्तयोस्तुल्यम् (ना. शा. २-६५) इति च द्विवचनाल्लिङ्गाद्वाविनोर्द्वयोः पार्श्वयोरिति लभ्यते (५८-६३)

स्तम्भाश्चत्वारः बहिर्मण्डपान्निष्कासनं कृत्वा ध्रियन्ते मण्डपक्षेत्राद्बहिः । तेन भित्तिच्छदावधौ स्तम्भद्वयम् । ततोऽपि बहिर्भित्तेरष्टहस्तान्तरस्तम्भापेक्षयाऽप्यष्टहस्तान्तरं स्तम्भद्वयमित्येतावदित्यष्टहस्तविस्तारा समचतुरश्रा मत्तवारणी भवति । आयामस्तु प्रमाणमिति ये वदन्ति तेषां मते दैर्घ्यादष्टहस्तं विस्तारात् षोडशहस्तमित्येवं विकृष्टता रङ्गपीटस्य भवति । अन्येषां हस्तमानोऽत्र (मानमत्र) यथा रङ्गपीठापेक्षया च सार्धहस्तपरिमाण उच्छ्रायः कार्यो मत्तवारण्याः । तयोरिति द्विवचनं ज्ञापकमेतच्चरितार्थमितीह नापेक्षित इति । तस्या एव यावानुत्सेधस्तावान् रङ्गपीठस्य । तेन ब्रध्नभूभागापेक्षया सार्धहस्त

---

१. K.S.S. N S. M.G. उत्सेधेन G.O.S. ऊत्सेधेन ।

२. K.S.S. तस्य माल्यञ्च वस्त्रञ्च गन्धमाल्यं तथैव च G.O.S. N.S. M.G. (Same as above.)

३. K.S.S. M.G. पायसं चात्र G.O.S. N.S. आयसं तत्र ।

४. M.G. कुशलाय तु N.S. G.O.S. K.S.S. कुशलैरधः ।

५. K.S.S. M.G. कृसरं चैव N.S. G.O.S. कृसराश्चैव ।

कार्यं द्वारद्वयं चात्र नेपथ्यगृहकस्य तु ।
पूरणे मृत्तिका चात्र कृष्णा देया प्रयत्नतः ॥ ६९ ॥
लाङ्गलेन समुत्कृष्य निर्लोष्टतृणशर्करम्[१] ।
लाङ्गले शुद्धवर्णौ तु धुर्यौ योज्यौ प्रयत्नतः ॥ ७० ॥
कर्तारः पुरुषाश्चात्र[२] येऽङ्गदोषविवर्जिताः ।
अहीनाङ्गैश्च वोढव्या मृत्तिका पिटकैर्नवैः[३] ॥ ७१ ॥
एवंविधैः[४] प्रकर्तव्यं रङ्गशीर्षं प्रयत्नतः ।
कूर्मपृष्ठं[५] न कर्तव्यं मत्स्यपृष्ठं तथैव च ॥ ७२ ॥
शुद्धादर्शतलाकारं रङ्गशीर्षं प्रशस्यते ।
रत्नानि चात्र देयानि पूर्वे[६] वज्रं विचक्षणैः ॥ ७३ ॥
वैडूर्यं दक्षिणे पार्श्वे[७] स्फटिकं पश्चिमे तथा ।
प्रवालमुत्तरे चैव मध्ये तु कनकं भवेत् ॥ ७४ ॥

प्रमाणोन्नतं रङ्गपीठमित्युक्तं भवति । तेन मत्तवारण्यालोकेन नात्यर्थं रङ्गपीठस्य दुष्प्रेक्षता । एतच्चोत्सेधेनेत्येकवचनेन सूचितम् । अन्यथोत्सेधाभ्यामित्युच्येत ।

माल्यधूपाद्यत्र निर्माणकाल एव देयम् । तदधिष्ठातृणां भूतादीनामुग्रत्वेन यत्नोपचरणीयत्वात् । तदाह—विधिपुरस्कारैरिति । पुरस्कारशब्देन विधिर्वास्तुशास्त्रोक्तः । (६४-६७) ।

रङ्गपीठे कार्ये रङ्गशिरस्तावदाह-रङ्गशीर्षमिति । नेपथ्यगृहभित्तिलग्नौ स्तम्भावष्टहस्तान्तरावन्योन्यं निवेश्य तयोर्यन्मुखं तदपेक्षया चतुर्हस्तान्तरं स्तम्भद्वयम् । तेषामधस्तनं काष्ठमुपरितनं चेति षड् दारूणि । यत्र षड्दारूणि तत्षड्दारुकम् । संज्ञायां कन् । तत्तेन विचित्ररचनोपेतत्वं लभ्यते । अत्र नेपथ्य-

---

१. M.G. K.S.S. शर्करा G.O.S. N.S. शर्करम् ।
२. K.S.S. तत्र M.G. N.S. G.O.S. चात्र ।
३. K.S.S. M.G. पीठकैः G.O.S. N.S. पिटकैः ।
४. M.G. K.S.S. एवंविधैश्च कर्तव्यम् G.O.S. N.S. एवंविधैः प्रकर्तव्यम्
५. K.S.S. पूर्वं G.O.S. M.G. कर्तव्यम् N.S. पृष्ठम् ।
६. K.S.S. M.G. पूर्वं G.O.S. N.S. पूर्वे ।
७. K.S.S. M.G. चैव N.S. G.O.S. पार्श्वे ।

एवं रङ्गशिरः कृत्वा दारुकर्म प्रयोजयेत्[१] ।
ऊहप्रत्यूहसंयुक्तं नानाशिल्पप्रयोजितम् ॥ ७५ ॥
नानासञ्जवनोपेतं बहुव्यालोपशोभितम् ।
[२]ससालभञ्जिकाभिश्च समन्तात्समलङ्कृतम् ॥ ७६ ॥
निर्व्यूहकु[३]हरोपेतं नानाग्रथितवेदिकम् ।
नानाविन्याससंयुक्तं [४]चित्रजालगवाक्षकम् ॥ ७७ ॥
सुपीठधारिणी[५]युक्तं कपोतालीसमाकुलम् ।
नानाकुट्टिमविन्यस्तैः स्तम्भैश्चाप्युपशोभितम् ॥ ७८ ॥
एवं काष्ठविधिं कृत्वा भित्तिकर्म प्रयोजयेत्[६] ।
स्तम्भं वा नागदन्तं वा वातायनमथापि वा ॥ ७९
कोणं वा सप्रतिद्वारं [७]द्वारविद्धं न कारयेत् ।

गृहस्य द्वारद्वयं कार्यम् । एकं दक्षिणतः । अपरमुत्तरतः । तच्च द्वारद्वयमापादितं कूर्पराभिन(म)त्या भवति । तत्पात्राणां विश्रान्त्यै आगच्छतां च गुप्त्यै रङ्गस्य शोभायै रङ्गशिरः कार्यम् ।

अन्ये तु—

पार्श्वद्वयोर्ध्वाधरदारुमण्डितं स्तम्भद्वयोपेतमिहाच्छपातकम् ।

इति षड्दारुकमाहुः । अन्ये (अत्र) तूहः स्तम्भशिरसो दूरं निर्गतं काष्ठम् । प्रत्यूहस्ततो विनिर्गता तुला आकाशे भित्त्याकारोच्छ्रितकाष्ठः संजवनोपेतः व्यूहः । स्तम्भाश्रिताः सिंहादयो व्यालानुबन्धाश्च निर्यूहास्तुलान्तान्निस्सृताः फलकभित्तिमयाः । कुहराणि पर्वतपुरनिकुञ्जगह्वररूपाणीति षड्दारुकम् । सर्वत्र च पक्षे दक्षिणोत्तरगतं द्वारद्वयं पात्राणां प्रवृत्तिभेदकृतात्प्रदक्षिणाप्रदक्षिणप्रवेशत्वात् । **शुद्धवर्णौ** । शुक्लौ । **धुर्यौ** दान्तौ । (६८-७१)

---

१. K.S.S. M.G. प्रवर्तयेत् N.S. G.O.S. प्रयोजयेत् ।
२. N.S. K.S.S. अट्टाल G.O.S. ससाल M.G. भवेयुश्चात्र विन्यस्ता विविधाः सालभञ्जिकाः ।
३. K.S.S. M.G. निर्यूह G.O.S. N.S. निर्व्यूह ।
४. K.S.S. यन्त्र G.O.S. N.S. M.G. चित्र ।
५. K.S.S. धरणी G.O.S. N.S. M.G. धारिणी ।
६. K.S.S. M.G. प्रवर्तयेत् G.O.S. N.S. प्रयोजयेत् ।
७. K.S.S. दारु G.O.S. N.S. M.G. द्वार ।

कार्यः शैलगुहाकारो द्विभूमिर्नाट्यमण्डपः ॥ ८० ॥
मन्दवातायनोपेतो निर्वातो धीरशब्दवान्[1] ।
तस्मान्निवातः कर्तव्यः कर्तृभिर्नाट्यमण्डपः ॥ ८१ ॥
गम्भीरस्वरता येन कुतपस्य भविष्यति ।[2]
भित्तिकर्मविधिं कृत्वा भित्तिलेपं प्रदापयेत् ॥ ८२ ॥
सुधाकर्म बहिस्[3]तस्य विधातव्यं[4] प्रयत्नतः ।
भित्तिष्वथ[5] विलिप्तासु[6] परिमृष्टासु सर्वतः ॥ ८३ ॥
समासु जातशोभासु चित्रकर्म प्रयोजयेत्[7] ।
चित्रकर्मणि चालेख्याः पुरुषाः स्त्रीजनास्तथा ॥ ८४ ॥
लताबन्धाश्च कर्तव्याश्चरितं चात्मभोगजम् ।
एवं विकृष्टं कर्तव्यं नाट्यवेश्म प्रयोक्तृभिः[8] ॥ ८५ ॥

कूर्मपृष्ठमिति । समन्ततो निम्नं मध्ये च वर्तुलरूपं मन्दम् । तत्तादृगेव मध्ये दीर्घरूपं मत्स्यपृष्टम् । तदुभयं नात्र कार्यम् । समं तुल्यं कार्यम् । रत्नानि तदायुधं तद्वर्णानुरूपत्वेन यथायोगम् । **कृत्वेति** । पूर्वं विभज्य बुद्ध्येति यावत् । दारुकर्मेत्युक्तं विभजति – **ऊहप्रत्यूहसंयुक्तमित्यादिना** । **स्तम्भैश्चाप्युपशोभितमि**त्यन्तेन । अनेकसालभञ्जिकाः काष्ठमय्यः कान्ता(न्त)प्रकृतयः । नानाकृतिभिर्ग्रथिताः वेदिकाश्चतुरश्रिकाः यत्र । **चित्राणि जालानि** चतुरश्राष्टाश्रच्छिद्ररूपाणि **गवाक्षाणि** च वर्तुलच्छिद्रात्मकानि यत्र । **पीठानि** स्तम्भोपरि । तेषु

१. K.S.S. M.G. धीरशब्दभाक् G.O.S. N.S. धीरशब्दवान् ।
२. K.S.S. गाम्भीर्यं सुस्वरत्वं च कुतुपस्य भवेदिति G.O.S. M.G. N.S. (Same as above)
३. K.S.S. M.G. तथैवास्य N.S. G.O.S. बहिस्तस्य ।
४. K.S.S. M.G. कुर्याद् बाह्य N.S. G.O.S. विधातव्यं ।
५. K.S.S. अपि M.G. N.S. G.O.S. अथ ।
६. K.S.S. M.G. च लिप्तासु G.O.S. N.S विलिप्तासु ।
७. K.S.S. M.G. प्रवर्तयेत् G.O.S. N.S. प्रयोजयेत् ।
८. K.S.S. नाट्यवेश्मप्रयोक्तृभिः G.O.S. N.S. M.G. (Same as above.)

पुनरेव[1] हि वक्ष्यामि चतुरश्रस्य लक्षणम् ।
समन्ततश्च[2] कर्तव्या हस्ता द्वात्रिंशदेव तु ॥ ८६ ॥
शुभभूमिविभागस्थो नाट्यज्ञैर्नाट्यमण्डपः ।
यो विधिः पूर्वमुक्तस्तु लक्षणं मङ्गलानि[3] च ॥ ८७ ॥
विकृष्टे तान्यशेषाणि चतुरश्रेऽपि कारयेत्[4] ।
चतुरश्रं समं कृत्वा सूत्रेण प्रविभज्य च ॥ ८८ ॥
बाह्यतः सर्वतः कार्या भित्तिः श्लिष्टेष्टका दृढा ।
तत्राभ्यन्तरतः कार्या रङ्गपीठोपरि[5] स्थिताः ॥ ८९ ॥

धारिण्यस्तुलाः । कपोताली विटङ्कपाली । कुट्टिमस्य नानात्वं रङ्गशिरो-रङ्गपीठमत्तवारणीद्वयभेदात् । सर्वत्र तथाविधदारुकम् । रक्तसितनीलपीतादि-भेदाद्वा । अत्रोहप्रत्यूहावन्वयव्यतिरेकतर्कोपयोगिनौ केचिदाहुः । (७२-७८)

प्रतिद्वारमवान्तरद्वारं द्वारेण विद्धं परस्परसंमुखीभूतमध्यं न कुर्यात् । नागदन्तं स्तम्भोर्ध्वनीचस्थांशकं(नीडस्थाङ्ककं) पुत्रिकाधारणार्थं गजमुखमिति केचित् । द्वे भूमी रङ्गपीठस्याधस्तनोपरितनरूपेणेति केचित् । मत्तवारणी बहिर्निर्गमनप्रमाणेन सर्वतो द्वितीयभित्तिनिवेशेन देवप्रसादाद्धा (दद्वा)रिका (देवप्रासादाट्टालिका) प्रदक्षिणसदृशी द्वितीया भूमिरित्यन्ये । उपरि मण्डपा-न्तरनिवेशनादित्यपरे । अद्विभूमिरित्येके । उपाध्यायास्तु वीप्सागर्भं व्याचक्षते । द्वे द्वे भूमी निम्नाते (निम्नोन्नते) ततोऽप्युन्नता इति निक्रमेण (निम्नो-न्नतक्रमेण) यत्र रङ्गपीठनिकटात्प्रभृति द्वारपर्यन्तं यावद्रङ्गपीठोत्सेधतुल्योत्सेधा भवति । एवं हि परस्परानाच्छादनं सामाजिकानाम् । शैलगुहाकारत्वं (त्वात्) स्थिरशब्दादित्वं च भवति । मन्दत्वं वातायनानां जलकपान(जालकपाट) योगात्कार्यम् । कुतपः सफेटकगायनवादकसमूहः । कुर्नाट्यभूमिस्तां तपति उज्ज्वलयतीति कृत्वा । कुतं शब्दं पातीत्यन्ये । गम्भीरत्वं तत्रैव शब्दस्य

---

१. K.S.S. M.G. अतः परं G.O.S. N.S. पुनरेव हि ।
२. K.S.S. M.G. तु G.O.S. N.S. च ।
३. K.S.S. मण्डलानि G.O.S. N.S. M.G. मङ्गलानि ।
४. K.S.S. M.G. चतुरस्रस्य तान्येव कारयेन्नाट्यवेश्मनः G.O.S. N.S. (Same as above.)
५. K.S.S. M.G. रङ्गपीठे यथादिशम् G.O.S. N.S. रङ्गपीठोपरि ।

दश प्रयोक्तृभिः स्तम्भाः शक्ता[1] मण्डपधारणे।
स्तम्भानां बाह्यतश्चापि[2] सोपानाकृति पीठकम्॥ ६०॥
इष्टकादारुभिः कार्यं प्रेक्षकाणां निवेशनम्।
हस्तप्रमाणैरुत्सेधैर्भूमिभागसमुत्थितैः॥ ६१॥
रङ्गपीठावलोक्यं तु[3] कुर्यादासनजं[4] विधिम्।
षडन्यानन्तरे[5] चैव पुनः स्तम्भान्यथादिशम्[5]॥ ६२॥

भ्रमणादन्योन्यप्रतिश्रुतिकारसमारम्भसम्पूर्णाच्च। **भित्तिलेपो** भङ्ग(शङ्ख) वालुकाशुक्तिकालेपः। **लताबन्धा** द्रुमलतादिबन्धसन्निवेशा वा मालत्यादिलतागतातोद्यवेष्टनवैचित्र्यप्रकार वक्ष्यमाणपिण्डीबन्धप्रकारविशेषाश्च। एतदुपसंहरति—**एवं विकृष्टमिति** (७९-८५)।

यद्यपि समचतुरश्रोऽत एव शक्य ऊहितुं तथापि विस्पष्टार्थं वक्ष्यामीत्याशयेन पुनःशब्देनोपक्रमते-**पुनरेवेति**। ननु विकृष्टे स्तम्भविभागरङ्गयोजनादि. नोक्तं तत्कथं प्रतिपत्तव्यमित्याशङ्कायामावृत्याऽनेनैवोत्तरं—चतुरश्र सम्बन्धि यल्लक्षणं तत्पुनर्यस्माद्वक्ष्यामो घटस्य (यदस्य) विकृष्टस्य सम्बन्धित्वेन तस्मान्नापूर्णं विकृष्टलक्षणम्। तथा यदस्य लक्षणमुक्तं तच्चतुरश्रेऽपि सञ्चारणीयमिति पुनश्शब्देन दर्शयति। तेनातिदेशा(शम)नागतापेक्षणाख्यं तत्र युराति (योजयति)। चतुरश्रमाह-**समन्तत** इति। सर्वेष्वन्तेषु चतसृष्वपि दिक्ष्वित्यर्थः। **प्रविभज्य** चेति। पूर्ववदेवेत्यर्थः। यदि बाह्यतो भित्तिरभ्यन्तरे किमित्याह **तत्राभ्यन्तर** इति। अष्टभिर्भागैः सर्वतः क्षेत्रं विभजेत्। येन चतुरङ्गफलकवच्चतुष्षष्टिकोष्ठं भवति। तत्र मध्यमकोष्ठकचतुष्के रङ्गपीठं सर्वतोऽष्टहस्तम्। तस्य पश्चिमे भागे प्राक्पश्चिमं द्वादशहस्तं दक्षिणोत्तरतो द्वात्रिंशत्करं तत्क्षेत्रमवशिष्यते। (अत्र यद्रङ्गपीठेन स्वीकृतं तद्धि हस्ताष्टकमेव।) यदवशिष्टं क्षेत्रं तन्मध्याद्रङ्गपीठनिकटगतं प्राक्पश्चिमतश्चतुर्हस्तं विस्तारेण द्वात्रिंशद्धस्त क्षेत्रांशाद्विभज्य तावत्प्रमाणमेव पश्चिमभागेऽपि ष(ड्दारु) कसंस्थान रङ्गशिरः कुर्यात्। ततोऽपि पश्चिमे तावदेव नेपथ्यग्रहणम् (गृहम्)। एवं स्थिते रङ्गपीठं लक्षयित्वा दश स्तम्भाः षड्दारुकस्तम्भव्यतिरिक्ता देयाः। तत्र

---

१. N.S. शस्ता M.G. G.OS. K.S.S. शक्ता।
२. K.S.S. स्थाप्यम् M.G. G.O.S. N.S. चापि।
३. K.S.S. M.G. च G.O.S. N.S. तु।
४. K.S.S. आसनिकं G.O.S. M.G. N.S. आसनजं।
५ K.S.S. सुन्दरान् दद्यात् G.O.S. N.S. M.G. अन्तरे चैव।

विधिना स्थापयेत्तज्ज्ञो[१][२] दृढान्मण्डपधारणे ।
अष्टौ स्तम्भान्पुनश्चैव तेषामुपरि कल्पयेत्[३] ॥ ६३ ॥

स्थाप्यं चैव ततः[४] पीठमष्टहस्तप्रमाणतः ।
विद्धास्यमष्टहस्तं च पीठं तेषु ततो न्यसेत्[५] ॥ ६४ ॥

कोणचतुष्टये तावच्चत्वारः । तत्राग्नेयस्तम्भाच्चतुर्हस्तान्तरो दक्षिणदिश्येकः स्तम्भः । तथैव नैर्ऋतस्तम्भाद् द्वितीयः । एवमुदीच्यामपि स्तम्भद्वयम् । पूर्वभागे ऐशानाग्निगतात्स्तम्भद्वयाच्चतुर्हस्तान्तरं स्तम्भद्वयमिति षट् । कोणगाश्चत्वार इति ये दश त एव । बहिः समाजिकासनानि सर्वेभ्यो वा बहिः । अतिसामीप्ये दृष्टिविघातात् । अत एवाह रङ्गपीठावलोकने साधुभूतमिति । अनेन द्विभूमित्वमेवानुसंहितम् ।

अन्तरे स्तम्भविधिमाह—**षडन्यानिति** । रङ्गपीठस्य दक्षिणतो निवेशितस्तम्भद्वयाच्चतुर्हस्तान्तरौ अन्योन्यमष्टहस्तान्तरौ द्वौ । तत आग्नेयस्तम्भसम्मुखो योऽन्यस्तु पूर्वः स्तम्भः ततश्चतुर्हस्तान्तरं दक्षिणस्तम्भं कुर्यादिति पूर्वन्यस्तानां दक्षिणस्तम्भानां दक्षिणभित्तेश्चान्तराले स्तम्भत्रयम् । एवमुत्तरस्यामपि ।

तेषामुपरीति । अधिकानष्टौ दद्यात् । तत्र दक्षिणभित्तेरुदग्भागे चतुर्हस्तान्तरं पूर्वस्थापितस्तम्भाद्भित्तेश्चैकं स्तम्भं दद्यात्पूर्वम् । एवमुत्तरभित्तेर्दक्षिणदिग्भागे । ततः पूर्वभित्तेश्चतुर्हस्तान्तरौ रङ्गभागद्वयानुसारेण द्वौ (द्वौ द्वौ) ततोऽपि चतुर्हस्तान्तरौ द्वावित्यष्टौ ।

विद्धमास्यं मुखं यस्य तत् पद्मादिविरचितं मुखं स्तम्भेष्वष्टहस्तं पीठं निक्षिपेत् । विद्धास्यस्योपरि हस्तप्रमाणधारिणीनां तुलानां धारकाःआश्रया स्तम्भा इति चतुरश्रे स्तम्भविधिः ।

तमेव विकृष्टे त्रिकोणेषु स्वबुद्ध्या योजयेदिति श्रीशङ्कुकाद्याः । अन्ये तु—'अष्टौ स्तम्भान्पुनश्च' इति नेपथ्यगृहविषयानेतानाहुः ।

---

१. N.S. धारयेत् K.S.S. G.O.S. M.G. स्थापयेत् ।

२. K.S.S. प्राज्ञो G.O.S. M.G. N.S. तज्ज्ञो ।

३. K.S.S. कारयेत् G.O.S. M.G. N.S. कल्पयेत् ।

४. N.S. Omits this hemistich. M.G. K.S.S. संस्थाप्यं च पुनः G.O.S. स्थाप्यं चैव ततः ।

५. M.G. K.S.S. Both Omit this hemistich. G.O.S. N.S Retain it

तत्र स्तम्भाः प्रदातव्यास्तज्ज्ञैर्मण्डपधारणे ।
धारणीधारणास्ते[1] च शालस्त्रीभिरलङ्कृताः ॥ ६५ ॥

नेपथ्यगृहकं[2] चैव ततः कार्यं प्रयत्नतः[3] ।
द्वारं चैकं भवेत्तत्र रङ्गपीठप्रवेशनम्[4] ॥ ६६ ॥

जनप्रवेशनं चान्यदा[5]भिमुख्येन कारयेत् ।
रङ्गस्याभिमुखं कार्यं द्वितीयं द्वारमेव तु ॥ ६७ ॥

वार्तिककृत्तु—

"अन्तर्नेपथ्यगृहं स्तम्भौ द्वौ पीठकाश्च चत्वारः ।
दिक्ष्वन्ये चत्वारो दशैवमुक्ता भवन्त्येते ॥

भित्तेः स्तम्भानां च स्यादन्तरमष्टहस्तमेवान्ते । " इति ।
दत्तोऽद्यवाताथः, सोऽथा नानाभवेदुक्तः (?) ।
चत्वारः पीठगताः पश्चादग्रे च याविह द्वौ द्वौ ॥
षट् सान्तरास्तथान्ये कार्या इति शास्त्र (तात्पर्यम्,
......पीठगताः पश्चादग्रे च याविह द्वौ द्वौ ॥ (?)
तेषामष्टावन्येऽप्युपरि निवेश्या य उद्दिष्टाः ।
तैरुत्क्षिप्तैरिह तले स्यादालोकः समस्तरङ्गस्य ॥
सोपानाकृति पीठकमत्र विधेयं समन्ततो रङ्गे ।
येनालोकेनसुविधा येष्युपरि गतेषु काष्ठेषु ॥ इति ॥

अन्येऽपि चैवंविधा बहवः प्रवादा ग्रन्थविस्तरभयान्न लिखिताः ।

अयं चन्द्रसोदर(चात्र सार)इत्युपाध्यायाः । इह प्रेक्षामण्डपस्य त्रिधा कल्पना कृता । अधोभूमिः रङ्गपीठं रङ्ग इति । तेषु चायं स्तम्भविन्यासविधिविच्छेद उक्तः ।

---

१. K.S.S. M.G. धारिताः N.S. G.O.S. धारणाः ।

२. K.S.S. M.G. नैपथ्य N.S. G.O.S. नेपथ्य ।

३. G.O.S. N.S. प्रयत्नतः K:S.S. M.G. प्रयोक्तृभिः ।

४. K.S.S. M.G. तस्य रङ्गपीठप्रवेशने G.O.S. N.S. तत्र रङ्गपीठप्रवेशनम् ।

५. K.S.S. M.G. चैवम् G.O.S. N.S. चान्यत् ।

अष्टहस्तं तु कर्तव्यं रङ्गपीठं प्रमाणतः ।
चतुरश्रं समतलं वेदिकासमलङ्कृतम् ॥ ९८ ॥

पूर्वप्रमाणनिर्दिष्टा कर्तव्या मत्तवारणी ।
चतुःस्तम्भसमायुक्ता वेदिकायास्तु पार्श्वतः ॥ ९९ ॥

समुन्नतं समं चैव रङ्गशीर्षं[1] तु कारयेत् ।
विकृष्टे तू[2]न्नतं कार्यं चतुरश्रे समं तथा ॥ १०० ॥

एवमेतेन विधिना चतुरश्रं गृहं भवेत् ।
अतः परं प्रवक्ष्यामि त्र्यश्रगेहस्य लक्षणम्[3] ॥ १०१ ॥

त्र्यश्रं त्रिकोणं कर्तव्यं नाट्यवेश्म प्रयोक्तृभिः ।
मध्ये त्रिकोणमेवास्य रङ्गपीठं तु कारयेत् ॥ १०२ ॥

द्वारं तेनैव[4] कोणेन कर्तव्यं तस्य[5] वेश्मनः ।
द्वितीयं चैव कर्तव्यं रङ्गपीठस्य पृष्ठतः ॥ १०३ ॥

तथा हि—अधोभूमौ स्तम्भानाह—तत्राभ्यन्तरत इति । विस्तारे द्वादशहस्तायाममेवं च चतुर्हस्तान्तरा दातव्याः । द्वौ स्तम्भौ भित्तिद्वयापेक्षया द्वादशहस्तान्तरावन्योन्यापेक्षया चाष्टहस्तान्तरौ । अन्योन्यं तयोरन्तरं तथा कार्यं येन द्वारविद्धता न भवति । इत्येवं पञ्चतुलासु दश ।

एतत्स्तम्भदशकव्यतिरिक्तायां भूमावासनविधिरित्याह—स्तम्भानां बाह्यतश्चापीत्यादि । पूर्ववद्व्याख्येयम् । अथ रङ्गपीठे स्तम्भन्यासमाह—षडन्यानित्यादि । उपरि रङ्गपीठमुखोपलक्षितस्य वा(?)नेपथ्यगृहस्य वारुणकोण इत्युक्तं भवति । रङ्गपीठस्य यत्पृष्ठं रङ्गशिरस्तत्र द्वितीयमिति राश्यपेक्षयैकवचनम् । तेन द्वारद्वयमेव रङ्गशिरसि नेपथ्यगतपात्रप्रवेशाय कर्तव्यम् । चकारादन्य(प्रवेशा)र्थम् । जनप्रवेशनद्वारम् । त्रीणि वा कार्याणि मतान्तरे

---

१. M.G. रङ्गपीठं G.O.S. N.S. K.S.S. रङ्गशीर्षं ।

२. K.S.S. अपि M.G. N.S. G.O.S. तु ।

३. K.S.S. M.G. Read त्र्यस्रस्य मण्डपस्यापि संप्रवक्ष्यामि लक्षणम् G.O.S. N.S. (Same as above) ।

४. M.G. एकेन K.S.S. N.S. G.O.S. तेनैव ।

५. M.G. K.S.S. तु प्रवेशने G.O.S. N.S. तस्य वेश्मनः ।

विधिर्यश्चतुरश्रस्य भित्तिस्तम्भसमाश्रयः[1] ।
स तु सर्वः प्रयोक्तव्यस्त्र्यश्रस्यापि प्रयोक्तृभिः ॥ १०४ ॥

एवमेतेन विधिना कार्या नाट्यगृहा[2] बुधैः ।
पुनरेषां[3] प्रवक्ष्यामि पूजामेवं[4] यथाविधि ॥ १०५ ॥

इति भारतीये नाट्यशास्त्रे मण्डपविधानो नाम द्वितीयोऽध्यायः ।

इति सङ्गृहीतं भवति । सर्वग्रहणादन्यूनाधिकत्वमत्र दर्शयन् विकृष्टे स्तम्भानामाधिक्यमभ्यनुजानीते । (८६-९४)

त्र्यश्ररङ्गपीठे तु प्रतिरङ्गमध्य इति । रङ्गोऽत्र तच्छिरः । ततः पीठस्य पृष्ठतः रङ्गं यावत् परितोऽभितः परि कर्मप्रवचनीयो वर्जन (न) द्योतकः । रङ्गपीठं वर्जयित्वा तदभ्यन्तरमण्डपस्य । तत्र द्वात्रिंशद्धस्तेषु रङ्गपीठे प्रतिकोणस्तम्भा इत्यष्टहस्तान्तराश्चत्वारः । तदनन्तरं स्तम्भद्वयमिति षडप्येतेऽष्टहस्तान्तरं ततो द्वादशहस्तायामं यदवशिष्यते तत्र चतुर्हस्तायामं द्वात्रिंशद्धस्तविस्तारं यद्रङ्गशिरस्तत्र द्वे तुले दातव्ये । प्रतितुलं चाष्टहस्ता (न्तरं स्तम्भचतुष्टयं) वर्जयित्वेत्यष्टौ भवन्ति । अत एव हि विद्धास्यमष्टहस्तं चतुर्हस्तान्तरालेऽपि तिरश्चीनं देयम् । येन तुलितं चित्रं भवति । एतदाहाष्टौ स्तम्भानित्यादि । रङ्गपीठस्य यदुपरि शिरोरूपमित्यर्थः । तथा च विकृष्टमण्डपे रङ्गपीठापेक्षया रङ्गशिर उन्नतं वक्ष्यते । तत्र नियमादष्टस्तम्भा न्यस्यन्ते । अपि तु दृढा न्यसनीया इति दर्शयति—**तत्र स्तम्भा** इति । अथावशिष्टेषु हस्तेषु विधिमाह—**नेपथ्यगृहकमिति । रङ्गपीठप्रवेशनमिति** वचनेनेदमाह—कक्ष्याविभागेन तावत् द्वे द्वारे तेन द्वारमिति जातावेकवचनम् एकशब्दश्च राश्यभिप्रायेण । राशिकरणे च निमित्तंपात्रप्रवेशोपायनम् । तथा च कक्ष्याध्याये वक्ष्यति—

"ये नेपथ्यगृहद्वारे मया पूर्वं प्रकीर्तिते । तयोर्भाण्डस्य विन्यासः ।" (ना. शा. १३-२) इति । (जन)प्रवेशनं च तृतीयद्वारनेपथ्यगृहस्य । येन भार्यामादाय नटपरिवारः प्रविशति । अन्यत्तु द्वारमाभिमुख्येन पूर्वस्यां दिशि कुर्यात् । द्वारवृत्त्या सामाजिकजनप्रवेशार्थम् । ननु किमपेक्षमाभिमु(ख्यम् । कक्ष्यापे)क्षयैव पूर्वादिभिरित्युक्तम् । यद् वक्ष्यति च—

---

१. K.S.S. Omits this hemistich G.O.S. N.S. M.G. Retain it.

२. K.S.S. M.G. कार्यं नाट्यगृहं G.O.S. N.S. कार्या नाट्यगृहा ।

३. K.S.S. M.G. अत ऊर्ध्वम् G.O.S. N.S. पुनरेषां ।

४. K.S.S. M.G. एषां G.O.S. N.S. एवं ।

'यतो मुखं भवेद्भाण्डद्वारं नेपथ्यकस्य तु ।
सा मन्तव्या तु दिक् पूर्वा नाट्ययोगे विपश्चिता ॥' (ना. शा. १३-११)
इति । एवं चतुर्द्वारं नाट्यगृहम् ।

अन्ये त्वाद्यद्वार(द्वयमि)वाद्येन हेतुनाऽन्यद्वारद्वयं पार्श्वस्थितं कुर्यादालोकसिद्ध्यर्थमिति षड्द्वारं नाट्यगृहमाचक्षते । अथ रङ्गपीठरङ्गशिरसोर्वक्तव्यशेषं निरूपयति—**अष्टहस्तन्त्विति**। वेदिके शोभायुक्ते कार्ये । **पूर्वप्रमाणम्** । अध्यर्धहस्तोत्सेधत्वम् । **समुन्नतमिति** । रङ्गपीठापेक्षया । एतच्चेह प्रसङ्गात्सूचयन् विकृष्टे तेनैव प्रकारेण स्तम्भत्रय्यधिका कर्तव्या । अन्तरमप्यत्रैव दर्शितम् । (९५-१०१)

अथ त्र्यश्रस्यातिदेशद्वारेण लक्षणं कर्तुमुपक्रममाह—**त्र्यश्रमिति** । **त्रिकोणमिति** लक्षणम् । उभयानुग्रहाच्च विकृष्टचतुरश्रमानद्वयमेव भवति । मध्ये च त्रिकोणमेव रङ्गपीठम् । तथैव रङ्गशिरसः । नेपथ्यगृहं च **तेनैव कोणेनेति** । वारुणीगतेन । **द्वारं** जनप्रवेशनम् । येन तस्मिन्नेव कोणे द्वारे कर्तव्ये । सङ्गतिं सूचयति—**एवमेतेनेति** । एतेन विधिना **बहवो** नाट्यमण्डपाः, न तु पूर्वोक्ताष्टादशभेदकलनयेत्यर्थः । **बुधै**रित्यूहापोहविद्भिः । **पुनरिति** । यद्यपि गदिताः सर्वे शुभदाः । **पूजामिति** । तथापि **वक्ष्यामीति** पुनश्शब्दार्थः । तत्र हि विधाने(नं)नोक्तम् । तदाह—**यथाविधीति** । **एषामिति** । मण्डपस्था देवताः । अनेनोपचारादुक्ताः । (१०२-१०५)

इति श्रीमहामाहेश्वराभिनवगुप्ताचार्यविरचितायामभिनवभारत्यां
भारतीयनाट्यशास्त्रविवृतौ मण्डपाध्यायो द्वितीयः ॥

तृतीयोऽध्यायः ।

सर्वलक्षणसम्पन्ने कृते नाट्यगृहे शुभे ।
गावो वसेयुः सप्ताहं सह जप्यपरैर्द्विजैः ॥ १ ॥
ततोऽधिवासयेद्वेश्म रङ्गपीठं तथैव च ।
मन्त्रपूतेन तोयेन प्रोक्षिताङ्गो निशागमे ॥ २ ॥
यथास्थानान्तरगतो दीक्षितः प्रयतः शुचिः ।
त्रिरात्रोपोषितो भूत्वा नाट्याचार्योऽहताम्बरः[1] ॥ ३ ॥
नमस्कृत्य महादेवं सर्वलोकोद्भवं[2] भवम् ।
जगत्पितामहं[3] चैव विष्णुमिन्द्रं गुहं तथा ॥ ४ ॥
सरस्वतीं च लक्ष्मीं च सिद्धिं मेधां धृतिं स्मृतिम्[4] ।
सोमं सूर्यं च मरुतो लोकपालांस्तथाश्विनौ ॥ ५ ॥
मित्रमग्निं सुरा[5]न्वर्णान्[6] रुद्रान्कालं कलिं तथा ।
मृत्युं च नियतिं चैव कालदण्डं तथैव च ॥ ६ ॥

यदाप्यायपरा लोकाः स्वे स्वे कर्मणि संगताः ।
प्राप्नुवन्ति फलं वन्दे तत्तेजोवपुरैश्वरम् ॥

निष्पन्ने मण्डपे पूजाऽवश्यं कर्तव्येति सङ्गतिः । तत्र प्रयोगक्रमोऽयम् । त (अत)थात्वेऽध्या (गताध्या)यानन्तरं पूर्वरङ्गाभिधानापत्तेः । तस्मान्मण्डपविधानशेष ए(व दर्शयि)ष्यते । अवश्यपूज्यत्वात् । **जप्यपरैरिति** । ये रक्षोघ्ना मन्त्रास्तज्जापकैरित्यर्थः । **तत** इति । सप्ताहादनन्तरम् । **अधिवासयेदिति** ।

---

१. N.S. नायकोऽहतवस्त्रधृक् M.G. K.S.S. G.O.S. ह नाट्याचार्योऽहताम्बरः ।

२ K.S.S. M.G. सर्वलोकेश्वरंभवम् N.S. सर्वलोकोद्भवोद्भवम् G.O.S. (Same as above).

३. K.S.S. M.G. पद्मयोनिसुरगुरू N.S. G.O.S. जगत्पितामहं चैव ।

४. K.S.S. M.G. स्मृतिं मतिं N.S. धृतिं मतिम् G.O.S. धृतिं स्मृतिम् ।

५. K.S.S. N.S. स्वरान् M.G. G.O.S. सुरान् ।

६. M.G. K.S.S. रुद्रान्वर्णान् G.O.S. N.S. वर्णान रुद्रान् ।

विष्णुप्रहरणं चैव नागराजं च वासुकिम्[1] ।
वज्रं विद्युत्समुद्रांश्च गन्धर्वाप्सरसो मुनीन् ॥ ७ ॥
भूतान् पिशाचान् यक्षांश्च गुह्यकांश्च महेश्वरान्[2] ।
असुरान्नाट्यविघ्नांश्च तथाऽन्यान्दैत्यराक्षसान्[3] ॥ ८ ॥
तथा नाट्यकुमारीश्च महाग्रामण्यमेव च ।
यक्षांश्च गुह्यकांश्चैव भूतसङ्घांस्तथैव च ॥ ९ ॥
एतांश्चान्यांश्च देवर्षीन्प्रणम्य[4] रचिताञ्जलिः ।
यथास्थानान्तरगतान्समावाह्य ततो वदेत् ॥ [5]१० ॥
भवद्भिर्[6]नो निशायां तु कर्तव्यः सम्परिग्रहः ।
साहाय्यं चैव दातव्यमस्मिन्नाट्ये सहानुगैः ॥ ११ ॥
सम्पूज्य सर्वानेकत्र[7] कुतपं सम्प्रयुज्य च ।
जर्जराय प्रयुञ्जीत पूजां नाट्यप्रसिद्धये ॥ १२ ॥
त्वं महेन्द्रप्रहरण सर्वदानवसूदन ।
निर्मितस्सर्वदेवैश्च सर्वविघ्ननिबर्हण[8] ॥ १३ ॥

देवता मण्डपमधिवसन्त्यागच्छन्ति । नाट्याचार्यो धर्म(र्यंकृतमुपरि)तनदेवतोपनिमन्त्रणमधिवासनं वेश्मनः । दीक्षितो गृहीतव्रतः । नायको नाट्याचार्यः । नमस्कृत्यावाह्य । वदेदिति सम्बन्धः : परमेश्वरस्मरणं च प्रथममुचितमिति

---

१. K.S.S. खगेश्वरं N.S. G.O.S. M.G. वासुकिम् ।

२. K.S.S. महोरगान् G.O.S. महेश्वरान् ।

३. M.G. N.S. Omit whole verse.

४. M.G. K.S.S. प्रणिपत्य कृताञ्जलिः G.O.S. N.S. प्रणम्य रचिताञ्जलिः ।

५. K.S.S. M.G. यथास्थानस्थितान् देवान् निमन्त्र्यैतद्वचोऽवदत् G.O.S. N.S. (Same as above).

६. N.S. भवद्भिर्निशायां नः G.O.S. K.S.S. M.G. (Same as above)

७. K.S.S. M.G. सम्पूज्य देवताः सर्वाः G.O.S. N.S. सम्पूज्य सर्वानेकत्र ।

८. K.S.S. निवारणम् M.G. निबर्हणम् G.O.S. N.S. निबर्हण ।

नृपस्य विजयं शंस[1] रिपूणां च पराजयम् ।
गोब्राह्मणशिवं[2] चैव नाट्यस्य च विवर्धनम् ॥ १४ ॥
एवं कृत्वा यथान्यायमुपास्यं[3] नाट्यमण्डपे ।
निशायां तु[4] प्रभातायां पूजनं प्रक्रमेदिह[5] ॥ १५ ॥
आर्द्रायां वा मघायां वा याम्ये पूर्वेषु[6] वा त्रिषु ।
आश्लेषामूलयोर्वापि कर्तव्यं रङ्गपूजनम् ॥ १६ ॥
आचार्येण तु युक्तेन[7] शुचिना दीक्षितेन च ।
रङ्गस्योद्योतनं[8] कार्यं देवतानां[9] च पूजनम् ॥ १७ ॥
दिनान्ते वारुणे घोरे मुहूर्ते यम[10] दैवते ।
आचम्य तु यथान्यायं देवता वै[11] निवेशयेत् ॥ १८ ॥
रक्ताः प्रतिसराः सूत्रं[12] रक्तगन्धाश्च पूजिताः ।
रक्ताः सुमनसश्चैव यच्च रक्तं फलं भवेत् ॥ १९ ॥
यवैस्सिद्धार्थकैर्लाजैरक्षतैः शालितण्डुलैः[13] ।
नागपुष्पस्य चूर्णेन वितुषाभिः प्रियङ्गुभिः ॥ २० ॥

महादेवमिति । महाग्रामणीर्गणपतिः । अन्यांश्चेति । प्रथमाध्यायोक्तान् । (१-१०)

---

१. K.S.S. नृपाय विजयं देहि G.O.S. N.S. M.G. नृपस्य विजयं शंस ।
२. K.S.S. हितम् G.O.S. N.S. M.G. शिवम् ।
३. K.S.S. M.G. उषित्वा G.O.S. N.S. उपास्यं ।
४. G.O.S. N.S. तु K.S.S. M.G. च ।
५. K.S.S. बुधः G.O.S. M.G. N.S. इह ।
६. K.S.S. M.G. G.O.S. पूर्वेषु N.S. पूर्वासु ।
७. K.S.S. M.G. सुयुक्तेन G.O.S. N.S. तु युक्तेन ।
८. K.S.S. N.S. उद्यापनं G.O.S. M.G. उद्योतनं ।
९. G.O.S. N.S. देवतानाम् K.S.S. M.G. दैवतानां ।
१०. K.S.S. N.S. M.G. भूत G.O.S. यम ।
११. K.S.S. M.G. दैवतानि G.O.S. N.S. देवता वै ।
१२. K.S.S. M.G. तत्र N.S. G.O.S. सूत्रम् ।
१३. K.S.S. लक्षितैर्लाजतण्डुलैः G.O.S. N.S. M.G. अक्षतैः शालितण्डुलैः

एतैर्द्रव्यैर्युतं कुर्या[१]द्देवतानां निवेशनम् ।
आलिखेन्मण्डलं पूर्वं यथास्थानं यथाविधि ॥ २१ ॥
समन्ततश्च[२] कर्तव्यं[३] हस्ताः षोडश मण्डलम्[४] ।
द्वाराणि चात्र कुर्वीत विधानेन[५] चतुर्दिशम् ॥ २२ ॥
मध्ये चैवात्र कर्तव्ये द्वे रेखे तिर्यगूर्ध्वगे ।
तयोः कक्ष्याविभागेन दैवतानि निवेशयेत् ॥ २३ ॥
पद्मोपविष्टं ब्रह्माणं तस्य[६] मध्ये निवेशयेत् ।
आदौ निवेश्यो भगवान्सार्धं भूतगणैः शिवः[७] ॥ २४ ॥
नारायणो महेन्द्रश्च स्कन्दः सूर्यो[८]ऽश्विनौ शशी ।
सरस्वती च लक्ष्मीश्च श्रद्धा मेधा च पूर्वतः ॥ २५ ॥
पूर्वदक्षिणतो वह्निर्निवेश्यः स्वाहया सह ।
विश्वेदेवाः सगन्धर्वा रुद्राः सर्पगणास्तथा[९] ॥ २६ ॥
दक्षिणेन निवेश्यस्तु[१०] यमो मित्रश्च सानुगः ।
पितॄन्पिशाचानुरगान् गुह्यकांश्च निवेशयेत् ॥ २७ ॥

एकत्रेति । स्थण्डिलभूभागे । कुतपमिति । चतुर्विधातोद्यभाण्डानि । एकत्र निवेशनं जर्जरस्य पूजार्थमवस्थापनम् । निवसत्यय (उपास्य) मिति भावे कृत्यः । **याम्यं** भरणीनक्षत्रम् । **पूर्वेष्विति** नक्षत्रापेक्षानिर्देशः । तानि पूर्वफल्गुनी पूर्वाषाढा पूर्वा भाद्रपदा च । (**उद्योतनमिति** ।) ज्वलितदर्भोल्मुकेन स्प(द)र्शनं

---

१. K.S.S. N.S. M.G. कार्यं G.O.S. कुर्यात् ।
२. K.S.S. M.G. तु N.S. G.O.S. च ।
३. G.O.S. N.S. कर्तव्यं K.S.S. M.G. वर्तव्या ।
४. G.O.S. N.S. मण्डलम् K.S.S. मण्डलैः, M.G. मण्डले ।
५. G.O.S. N.S. M.G. विधानेन K.S.S. नियोगेन ।
६. K.S.S. रङ्ग G.O.S. M.G. N.S. तस्य ।
७. G.O.S. K.S.S. शिवः M.G. N.S. भवः ।
८. G.O.S. N.S. स्कन्दः सूर्यः K.S.S. M.G. स्कन्दार्कौ ।
९. G.O.S (Same as above) K.S.S. M.G. विश्वेदेवाश्च गन्धर्वा रुद्राश्च ऋषयस्तथा । N.S. विश्वेदेवाः सगन्धर्वा रुद्रा सर्वगणास्तथा ।
१०. G.O.S. N.S. तु K.S.S. M.G. च ।

नैर्ऋत्यां राक्षसांश्चैव[1] भूतानि[2] च निवेशयेत् ।
पश्चिमायां समुद्रांश्च वरुणं यादसां पतिम्[3] ॥ २८ ॥
वायव्यायां[4] दिशि तथा सप्त वायून्[5]निवेशयेत् ।
तत्रैव विनिवेश्यस्तु गरुडः पक्षिभिः सह[6] ॥ २९ ॥
उत्तरस्यां दिशि तथा धनदं संनिवेशयेत्[7] ।
नाट्यस्य मातृश्च तथा यक्षानथ सगुह्यकान्[8] ॥ ३० ॥
तथैवोत्तरपूर्वायां नन्द्याद्यांश्च[9] गणेश्वरान् ।
ब्रह्मर्षिभूतसंघांश्च यथाभागं निवेशयेत् ॥ ३१ ॥
स्तम्भे सनत्कुमारं तु दक्षिणे दक्षमेव च ।
ग्रामण्यमुत्तरे[10] स्तम्भे पूजार्थं संनिवेशयेत्[11] ॥ ३२ ॥
अनेनैव विधानेन यथास्थानं यथाविधि ।
सुप्रसादानि सर्वाणि दैवतानि निवेश[12]येत् ॥ ३३ ॥
स्थाने स्थाने यथान्यायं विनिवेश्य तु देवताः ।
तासां प्रकुर्वीत ततः पूजनं तु यथार्हतः[13] ॥ ३४ ॥

---

१. K.S.S. नैऋतांश्चैव G.O.S. N.S. M.G. राक्षसांश्चैव ।
२. G.O.S. N.S. भूतानिच K.S.S. M.G. सर्वभूतान् ।
३. K.S.S. च निवेशयेत् G.O.S. N.S. M.G. यादसां पतिम् ।
४. G.O.S. वायव्यायां N.S. M.G. K.S.S. वायव्यां वै ।
५. G.O.S. N.S. M.G. वायून् K.S.S. वायुं ।
६. G.O.S. N.S. (Same as above) K.S.S. M.G. निवेशयेच्च तत्रैव गरुडं पक्षिभिः सह ।
७. G.O.S. N.S. M.G. (Same as above) K.S.S. उत्तरस्यां कुबेरं च सर्वैरनुचरैः सह ।
८. GOS N.S. M.G. सगुह्यकान् K.S.S. च गुह्यकान् ।
९. G.O.S. N.S. नन्द्याद्यांश्च K.S.S. M.G. नन्दिनं च ।
१०. G.O.S. N.S. उत्तरे K.S.S. M.G. चोत्तरे ।
११. G.O.S. N.S. M.G. संनिवेशयेत् K.S.S. विनिवेशयेत् ।
१२. G.O.S. N.S. (Same as above) K.S.S. M.G. वर्णरुपान्विताः सर्वा देवताः संनिवेशयेत् ।
१३. G.O.S. N.S. (Same as above) K.S.S. M.G. प्रकुर्वीत ततस्तासां पूजनं तु यथार्हतः ।

देवताभ्यस्तु[1] दातव्यं सितमा[2]ल्यानुलेपनम् ।
गन्धर्ववह्निसूर्ये[3]भ्यो रक्तमाल्यानुलेपनम् ॥ ३४ ॥
गन्धं माल्यं च धूपं च यथावदनुपूर्वशः ।
दत्वा ततः प्रकुर्वीत बलिं पू[4]जां यथाविधि ॥ ३६ ॥
ब्रह्माणं[5] मधुपर्केण पायसेन सरस्वतीम् ।
शिवविष्णुमहेन्द्राद्याः सम्पूज्या मोदकैरथ ॥ ३७ ॥
घृतौदनेन हुतभु[6]क्सोमार्कौ तु गुडौदनैः ।
विश्वेदेवाः सगन्धर्वा मुनयो मधुपायसैः ॥ ३८ ॥
यममित्रौ च सम्पूज्या[7]वपूपै[8]र्मोदकैस्तथा ।
पितॄन्पिशाचानुरगान् सर्पिःक्षीरेण तर्पयेत् ॥ ३९ ॥
पक्वान्नेन[9] तु मांसेन सुरासीधुफलासवैः ।
अर्चयेद्भूतसंघांश्च चणकैः पललाप्लुतैः ॥ ४० ॥
अनेनैव विधानेन सम्पूज्या मत्तवारणी ।
पक्वामेन[10] तु मांसेन सम्पूज्या रक्षसां गणाः ॥ ४१ ॥
सुरामांसप्रदानेन दानवा[11]न्प्रतिपूजयेत् ।
शेषान्देवगणांस्तज्ज्ञ[12]: सापूपोत्कारिकौदनैः ॥ ४२ ॥

---

१. G.O.S. N.S. देवताभ्यस्तु K.S.S. M.G. दैवतेभ्यस्तु ।
२. G.O.S. N.S. सितमाल्या...K.S.S. M.G. सितं माल्या...
३. G.O.S. N.S. (Same as above) K.S.S. M.G. वह्निगन्धर्व...
४. G.O.S. N.S. बलिं पूजां K.S.S. बलिपूजां ।
५. G.O.S. N.S. ब्रह्माणं K.S.S. M.G. द्रुहिणं ।
६. G.O.S. N.S. हुतभुक् K.S.S. M.G. वह्निश्च ।
७. G.O.S. N.S. च सम्पूज्यौ K.S.S. M.G. समभ्यर्च्यौ ।
८. G.O.S. N.S. M.G. अपूपैर्मोदकैस्तथा K.S.S. मोदकैः सूपमिश्रितैः
९. G.O.S. N.S. पक्वान्नेन K.S.S. M.G. पक्वामकेन ।
१०. G.O.S. पक्वामेनतु मांसेन N,S. पक्वान्नेन तु मात्स्येन K.S.S. M.G. पक्वामकेन मांसेन ।
११. G.O.S. M.G. N.S. दानवान् K.S.S. विधिना ।
१२. G.O.S. N.S. तज्ज्ञः K.S.S. M.G. प्राज्ञः

मत्स्यैश्च पिष्टभक्ष्यैश्च सागरान्सरितस्तथा ।
सम्पूज्य[1] वरुणं[2] चापि दातव्यं[3] घृतपायसम् ॥ ४३ ॥
नानामूलफलैश्चापि मुनीन्सम्प्रतिपूजयेत् ।
वायूंश्च पक्षिणश्चैव विचित्रै[4]र्भक्ष्यभोजनैः ॥ ४४ ॥
मातॄर्नाट्यस्य सर्वास्ता[5] धनदं च सहानुगैः ।
अपूपैर्लाजिकामिश्रै[6]र्भक्ष्यभोज्यैश्च पूजयेत्[7] ॥ ४५ ॥
एवमेषां बलिः कार्यो नानाभोजनसंश्रयः ।
पुनर्मन्त्रविधानेन बलिकर्म चवक्ष्यते[8] ॥ ४६ ॥
देवदेव महाभाग सर्वलोकपितामह[9] ।
मन्त्रपूतमिमं सर्वं प्रतिगृह्णीष्व मे [10]बलिम् ॥ ४७ ॥
देवदेव महादेव गणेश त्रिपुरान्तक ।
प्रगृह्यतां बलिर्देव मन्त्रपूतो मयोद्यतः ॥ ४८ ॥

नीराच(राज)नमिति प्रसिद्धम् । प्रतिसरा इति । सूत्रविनिर्मिता ग्रन्थिमन्तः कङ्कणविशेषाः । मण्डपस्य रङ्गपीठादेश्चोपर्युक्तं सर्वं निवेश्यते । सूत्रमिति समन्ततो...रित्येतत्सर्वं शेष(षम् ।) निवेशनमित्यावाहनकालेऽर्घ्यदानमित्यर्थः । अन्ये तन्नि(तु नि-)वेशनमित्यधिकरणे ल्युट् । मण्डलविशेषणं चैतत् । मण्डलं च यवादिभिरित्यादि । नागपुष्पं नागदन्तः । (११-२१)

---

१. G.O.S. N.S. सम्पूज्य K.S.S. M.G. अभ्यर्च्य ।
२. G.O.S. N.S. वरुणं K.S.S. M.G. वरुणः ।
३. G.O.S. दातव्यं K.S.S. M.G. दातव्यः ।
४. G.O.S. N.S. विचित्रैः K.S.S. M.G. विविधैः ।
५. G.O.S. N.S. (Same as above) K.S.S. M.G. नाट्यस्य च तथा मातॄः ।
६. G.O.S. लाजिकामिश्रैः N.S. लेपिकामिश्रैः K.S.S. लोपिकाभिस्तैः M.G. लोचिताभिस्तैः ।
७. G.O.S. N.S. पूजयेत् K.S.S. M.G. प्रयत्नतः ।
८. G.O.S. च वक्ष्यते K.S.S. N.S. M.G. प्रवक्ष्यते ।
९. G.O.S. N.S. (Same as above) K.S.S. M.G. पद्मयोने पितामह ।
१०. G.O.S. N.S. (Same as above) K.S.S. M.G. बलिं देव गृहाण नः ।

नारायणामितगते पद्मनाभ सुरोत्तम ।
प्रगृह्यतां बलिर्देव मन्त्रपूतो[1] मयार्पितः ॥ ४९ ॥

पुरन्दरामरपते वज्रपाणे शतक्रतो ।
प्रगृह्यतां बलिर्देव विधि[2]मन्त्रपुरस्कृतः ॥ ५० ॥

देवसेनापते स्कन्द[3] भगवन् शङ्करप्रिय ।
बलिः प्रीतेन मनसा[4] षण्मुख प्रतिगृह्यताम् ॥ ५१ ॥

(महादेव महायोगिन्देवदेव सुरोत्तम ।
संप्रगृह्य बलिं देव रक्ष विघ्नात्सदोत्थितात्[5] ॥)

षोडशहस्तं यथा भवति तथा कार्यमिति । अतः चतुर्हस्तं रङ्गपीठपृष्ठ एव मण्डलमित्युक्तं भवति । तेन **शङ्कुकादिभिः** षोडशहस्तावकाशाभावः आसनस्तम्भादिवशात् । तस्मादकृत एव रङ्गपीठे इत्यादि वृथैव बहुतर मुपन्यस्तम् । **द्वे रेखे** इति । प्राक्तने । तिर्यग्गतैका दक्षिणोत्तरगता । पृष्ठे द्वितीया पूर्वपश्चिमगता । **तयोः** रेखयोः । **कक्ष्या** स्थानान्तराणि । तेषु विभागेन भावितानि । **तस्येति** । मण्डलस्य । **पद्मोपविष्टमिति** । मध्ये पद्मं कार्यमित्यर्थः । **आदाविति** । तेन आदिदेशे ऐशानकोणे । प्रथमावसरे च तथैवावाहनस्योक्तत्वात् । पद्मोपम(पविष्टिमि)मिति प्रतिदिशः सम्बन्ध नीयत्वेन(सम्बन्धीनि । तेन) नवपद्ममण्डलमित्युक्तं भवति । दक्षिणपूर्वे आग्नेयस्तम्भ इति । उत्तरपूर्वे ऐशानस्तम्भ इत्यर्थः । **सुप्रसादानीति** । तथा ध्यानेन निवेशितानीत्यर्थः । **यथार्हतः** तत्तदागमेषु यो यस्यां विधिर्दृश्यते देवतायां तेन क्रमेण । (२२-३४ ।)

१. G.O.S. N.S. (Same as above) K.S.S. M.G. मन्त्रसंस्कार-संस्कृतः ।

२. G.O.S. N.S. विधि K.S.S. M.G. बलि ।

३. G.O.S. M.G. N.S. (Same as above) K.S.S. देवसेनापति-स्कन्द ।

४. G.O.S. N.S. M.G. (Same as above) K.S.S. प्रीतेन मनसा देव ।

५. G.O.S. उत्थितात् K.S.S. N.S. उत्थितान् M.G. Omits whole verse.

देवि देव[1] महाभागे सरस्वति हरिप्रिये ।
प्रगृह्यतां बलिर्मातर्मया भक्त्या समर्पितः ॥ ५२ ॥

नानानिमित्तसम्भूताः पौलस्त्याः सर्व एव तु ।
राक्षसेन्द्रा महासत्त्वाः प्रतिगृह्णी[2]त मे बलिम् ॥ ५३ ॥

लक्ष्मीः सिद्धिर्मतिर्मेधा सर्वलोकनमस्कृताः ।
मन्त्रपूतमिमं देव्यः प्रतिगृह्णन्तु मे बलिम् ॥ ५४ ॥

सर्वभूतानुभावज्ञ लोकजीवन मारुत ।
प्रगृह्यतां बलिर्देव मन्त्रपूतो मयोद्यतः[3] ॥ ५५ ॥

देववक्त्र सुरश्रेष्ठ धूमकेतो हुताशन ।
भक्त्या समुद्यतो देव बलिः सम्प्रतिगृह्य[4]ताम् ॥ ५६ ॥

सर्वग्रहाणां प्रवर तेजोराशे दिवाकर ।
भक्त्या मयोद्यतो देव बलिः सम्प्रति गृह्यताम् ॥ ५७ ॥

सर्वग्रहपते सोम द्विजराज जगत्प्रिय ।
प्रगृह्यतामेष बलिर्मन्त्रपूतो मयोद्यतः[5] ॥ ५८ ॥

महागणेश्वराः सर्वे नन्दीश्वरपुरोगमाः ।
प्रगृह्यतां बलिर्भक्त्या मया सम्प्रति चोदितः[6] ॥ ५९ ॥

माल्यानुलेपनम् । (उभय)त्रापि सुरादिप्रधानो बलिरित्यर्थः । अत्र पूजित-
ापितस्य कुम्भस्य विनियोगो भविष्यति ।

---

1. G.O.S. देवि देव K.S.S. M.G. देवि देवि N.S. देवदेवि ।
2. G.O.S. N.S. प्रतिगृह्णीत K.S.S. M.G. प्रतिगृह्णन्त्विमं ।
3. K.S.S. M.G. G.O.S. उद्यतः N.S. अर्पितः ।
4. G.O.S सम्प्रति गृह्यताम् K.S.S. M.G. N.S. सम्प्रतिगृह्यताम् ।
5. G.O.S. M.G. N.S. मयोद्यतः K.S.S. पुरस्कृतः ।
6. G.O.S. N.S. (Same as above) K.S.S. M.G. प्रतिगृह्णन्त्विमं भक्त्या बलिं सम्यङ् मयोदितम् ।

नमः पितृभ्यः सर्वेभ्यः प्रतिगृह्णन्त्विमं बलिम् ।
(भूतेभ्यश्च नमो नित्यं येषामेष बलिः प्रियः ।)
कामपाल नमो नित्यं यस्यायं ते विधिः[१] कृतः ॥ ६० ॥
नारदस्तुम्बुरुश्चैव विश्वावसुपुरोगमाः ।
परिगृह्णन्तु मे सर्वे गन्धर्वा बलिमुद्यतम्[२] ॥ ६१ ॥
यमो मित्रश्च भगवानीश्वरौ लोकपूजितौ ।
इमं मे प्रतिगृह्णीतां बलिं मन्त्रपुरस्कृतम् ॥ ६२ ॥
रसातलगतेभ्य[३]श्च पन्नगेभ्यो नमोनमः ।
दिशस्तु सिद्धिर्नाटचस्य पूजिताः पापनाशनाः[४] ॥ ६३ ॥
सर्वाम्भसां पतिर्देवो वरुणो हंसवाहनः ।
पूजितः प्रीतिमानस्तु ससमुद्रनदीनदः ॥ ६४ ॥
वैनतेय महासत्त्व सर्वपक्षिपते विभो[५] ।
प्रगृह्यतां बलिर्देव मन्त्रपूतो मयोद्यतः ॥ ६५ ॥
धनाध्यक्षो यक्षपतिर्लोकपालो धनेश्वरः ।
सगुह्यकस्सयक्षश्च[६] प्रतिगृह्णातु मे बलिम् ॥ ६६ ॥
नमोऽस्तु नाटचमातृभ्यो ब्राह्म्याद्याभ्यो नमोनमः ।
सुमुखीभिः प्रसन्नाभिर्बलिरद्य[७] प्रगृह्यताम् ॥ ६७ ॥
रुद्रप्रहरणं सर्वं[८] प्रतिगृह्णातु मे बलिम् ।
विष्णुप्रहरणं[९] चैव विष्णुभक्त्या मयोद्यतम् ॥ ६७ ॥
तथा कृतान्तः कालश्च सर्वप्राणिवधेश्वरौ[१०] ।
मृत्युश्च नियतिश्चैव प्रतिगृह्णातु मे बलिम् ॥ ६९ ॥

---

१. G.O.S. N.S. विधिः K.S.S. M.G. बलिः ।
२. G.O.S. N.S. M.G. उद्यतम् K.S.S. उत्तमम् ।
३. G.O.S. N.S. गतेभ्यः K.S.S. M.G. चरेभ्यः ।
४. G.O.S. पापनाशनाः K.S.S. M.G. N.S. पवनाशनाः ।
५. G.O.S. N.S. विभो K.S.S. M.G. प्रभो ।
६. G.O.S. N.S. (Same as above) K.S.S. M.G. सगुह्यकैश्च यक्षैश्च ।
७. G.O.S. अद्य प्रगृह्यताम् N.S. M.G. K.S.S. सम्प्रतिगृह्यताम् ।
८. G.O.S. N.S. सर्वं K.S.S. M.G. चैव ।
९. G.O.S. N.S. M.G. विष्णुप्रहरणं K.S.S. विष्णुः प्रहरणं ।
१०. G.O.S. M.G. N.S. वधेश्वरौ K.S.S. वशेश्वरौ ।

याश्चास्यां मत्तवारण्यां संश्रिता वास्तुदेवताः ।
मन्त्रपूतमिमं सम्यक्प्रतिगृह्णन्तु मे बलिम् ॥ ७० ॥

अन्ये ये देवगन्धर्वा दिशो दश समाश्रिताः ।
दिव्यान्तरिक्षभौमाश्च[1] तेभ्यश्चायं बलिः कृतः ॥ ७१ ॥

कुम्भं सलिलसम्पूर्णं[2] पुष्पमालापुरस्कृतम्[3] ।
स्थापयेद्रङ्गमध्ये तु सुवर्णं चात्र दापयेत् ॥ ७२ ॥

(आतोद्यानि तु सर्वाणि कृत्वा वस्त्रोत्तराणि तु ।
गन्धैर्माल्यैश्च धूपैश्च भक्ष्यैर्भोज्यैश्च पूजयेत् ॥)

पूजयित्वा तु सर्वाणि दैवतानि यथाक्रमम् ।
जर्जरस्त्वभि[4]संपूज्यः स्यात्ततो विघ्नजर्जरः ॥ ७३ ॥

श्वेतं शिरसि वस्त्रं स्यान्नीलं रौद्रे च पर्वणि ।
विष्णुपर्वणि वै[5] पीतं रक्तं स्कन्दस्य पर्वणि ॥ ७४ ॥

मृड[6]पर्वणि चित्रं तु देयं वस्त्रं हितार्थिना[7] ।
सदृशं च प्रदातव्यं धूपमा[8]ल्यानुलेपनम् ॥ ७५ ॥

आतोद्यानि च सर्वाणि वासोभिरवगुण्ठयेत्[9] ।
गन्धैर्माल्यैश्च धूपैश्च भक्ष्यभोज्यैश्च पूजयेत्[10] ॥ ७६ ॥

सर्वमेव[11] विधिं कृत्वा गन्धमाल्यानुलेपनैः ।
विघ्नजर्जरणार्थं तु जर्जरं त्व[12]भिमन्त्रयेत् ॥ ७७ ॥

माल्यानुलेपनम् । उभयत्रापि सुरादिप्रधानो बलिरित्यर्थः । अत्र पूजितस्थापितस्य कुम्भस्य विनियोगो भविष्यति ।

---

१. G.O.S. N.S. M.G. (Same as above) K.S.S. दिव्यान्तरिक्ष-भौमाश्च ।
२. G.O.S. N.S. सम्पूर्णं K.S.S. M.G. पूर्णं ।
३. G.O.S. N.S. पुष्प K.S.S. पर्ण ।
४. G.O.S. N.S. अभि K.S.S. M.G. प्रति ।
५. G.O.S. वै पीतं M.G. N.S. K.S.S. स्यात् ।
६. K.S.S. N.S. M.G. मूल G.O.S, मृड ।
७. K.S.S M.G. हितार्थिनाम् G.O.S. N.S. हितार्थिना ।
८. G.O.S. N S. (Same as above.) M.G. K.S.S. माल्यधूप ।
९. M.G. कृत्वा वस्त्रोत्तराणि तु K.S.S. G.O.S. N.S. ((Same as above) ।
१०. G.O.S. N.S. M.G. पूजयेत् K.S.S. भोजयेत् ।
११. G.O.S. N.S. सर्वमेव K.S.S. M.G. सर्वमेव ।
१२. G.O.S. M.G. N.S. तु K.S.S. च ।

अत्र विघ्नविनाशार्थं पितामहमुखैस्सुरैः[१] ।
निर्मितस्त्वं महावीर्यो वज्रसारो महातनुः ॥ ७८ ॥

शिरस्ते रक्षतु ब्रह्मा सर्वैर्देवगणैः सह ।
द्वितीयं च हरः पर्व तृतीयं च[२] जनार्दनः ॥ ७९ ॥

चतुर्थं च कुमारस्ते पञ्चमं पन्नगोत्तमः ।
नित्यं सर्वेऽपि[३]पान्तु त्वां सुरा[४]र्थे च शिवो भव ॥ ८० ॥

नक्षत्रेऽभिजिति त्वं हि प्रसूतोऽहितसूदन[५] ।
जयं चाभ्युदयं चैव पार्थिवस्य समावह[६] ॥ ८१ ॥

जर्जरं पूजयित्वैवं बलिं सर्वं निवेद्य च ।
अग्नौ होमं ततः कुर्यान्मन्त्राहुतिपुरस्कृतम् ॥ ८२ ॥

हुताश[७] एव दीप्ताभिरुल्काभिः परिमार्जनम् ।
नृपतेर्नर्तकीनां च कुर्याद्दीप्त्यभिवर्धनम् ॥ ८३ ॥

अभिद्योत्य सहातोद्यैर्नृपतिं नर्तकीस्तथा ।
मन्त्रपूतेन तोयेन पुनरभ्युक्ष्य तान्वदेत् ॥ ८४ ॥

महाकुले प्रसूता स्थ[८] गुणौघैश्चाप्यलङ्कृताः ।
यद्वो जन्मगुणोपेतं तद्वो भवतु नित्यशः ॥ ८५ ॥

एवमुक्त्वा ततो वाक्यं नृपतेर्भूतये बुधः ।
नाट्ययोगप्रसिद्ध्यर्थमाशिषस्सम्प्रयोजयेत् ॥ ८६ ॥

सरस्वती धृतिर्मेधा ह्रीः श्रीर्लक्ष्मीस्स्मृतिर्मतिः[९] ।
पान्तु वो मातरः सौम्या[१०]स्सिद्धिदाश्च भवन्तु वः ॥ ८७ ॥

---

१. G.O.S. N.S. (Same as above) K.S.S. M.G. विघ्नानां शमनार्थं हि देवैर्ब्रह्मपुरोगमैः ।

२. N.S. तु K.S.S. M.G. G.O.S. च ।

३. G.O.S. N.S. अपि K.S.S. M.G. हि ।

४ G.O.S. सुरार्थे K.S.S. M·G. सुरास्त्वं N.S. पुनस्त्वं ।

५. G.O.S. अहितसूदन K.S.S. M:G. N.S. रिपुसूदनः ।

६. G.O.S. N.S. पार्थिवस्य समावह । K.S.S. M.G. पार्थिवाय प्रयच्छ नः ।

७. G.O.S. N.S. हुताश एव K.S.S. M.G. हुत्वा स एव ।

८. G.O.S. N.S. प्रसूताःस्थ K.S.S. M.G. प्रसूताश्च ।

९. K.S.S. M.G. मतिः स्मृतिः G.O.S. N.S. स्मृतिर्मतिः ।

१०. G.O.S. N.S. सौम्याः K.S.S. M.G. सर्वाः ।

होमं कृत्वा यथान्यायं हविर्मन्त्रपुरस्कृतम् ।
भिन्द्यात्कुम्भं ततश्चैव नाट्याचार्यः प्रयत्नतः ॥ ८८ ॥
अभिन्ने तु भवेत्कुम्भे स्वामिनः शत्रुतो भयम् ।
भिन्ने चैव तु विज्ञेय[1]: स्वामिनः शत्रुसंक्षयः ॥ ८९ ॥
भिन्ने कुम्भे ततश्चैव नाट्याचार्यः प्रयत्नतः[2] ।
प्रगृह्य दीपिकां दीप्तां सर्वं रङ्गं प्रदीपयेत् ॥ ९० ॥
क्ष्वेडितैः स्फोटितैश्चैव वल्गितैश्च प्रधावितैः ।
रङ्गमध्ये तु तां दीप्तां सशब्दां सम्प्रयोजयेत् ॥ ९१ ॥
शङ्खदुन्दुभिनिर्घोषैर्मृदङ्गपणवैस्तथा ।
सर्वातोद्यैः प्रणदितै रङ्गे युद्धा[3]नि कारयेत् ॥ ९२ ॥
तत्र च्छिन्नं च भिन्नं च दारितं च सशोणितम् ।
क्षतं[4] प्रदीप्तमाय[5]स्तं निमित्तं सिद्धि[6]लक्षणम् ॥ ९३ ॥
सम्यगिष्टस्तु रङ्गो वै स्वामिनः शुभमावहेत् ।
पुरस्याबालवृद्धस्य तथा जनपदस्य च ॥ ९४ ॥
दुरिष्टस्तु तथा रङ्गो दैवतैर्दुरधिष्ठितः ।
नाट्यविध्वंसनं कुर्यान्नृपस्य च तथाऽशुभम्[7] ॥ ९५ ॥

आहुतिराहवनम् ।-हुत्वा हवनं तथा सत्याहुतिः स्यात् । दीप्ताभिः...। कुम्भस्य विनियोगमाह—**भिन्द्यादिति** ।

उद्विग्नमानस इत्यनवधानरूपं लक्ष्यते । **नवे नाट्यगृह** इति मण्डपशेषत्वमेवोक्तम् । **प्रेक्षायां चेति** । **नवायामिति** केचित्संबन्धयन्ति । तेन...पूजा

---

१. N.S. भवेत् भिन्ने तु कुम्भे K.S.S. अभिन्नेतु भवेत् कुम्भे G.O.S. M.G. भिन्ने चैव तु विज्ञेयः ।
२. G.O.S. N.S. प्रयत्नतः K.S.S. M.G. अपेतभीः ।
३. N.S. रङ्गयुद्धानि G.O.S. M.G. K.S.S. रङ्गे युद्धानि ।
४. N.S. कृत्तं K.S.S. G.O.S. M.G. क्षतं ।
५. G.O.S. M.G. N.S. आयस्तं K.S.S. आयत्तम् ।
६. G.O.S. N.S. M.G. सिद्धि K.S.S. सिद्ध ।
७. G.O.S. N.S. M.G. तथाऽशुभम् K.S.S. तथा शुभम् ।

य एवं विधिमुत्सृज्य यथेष्टं सम्प्रयोजयेत् ।
प्राप्नोत्यपचयं शीघ्रं तिर्यग्योनिं च गच्छति ॥ ९६ ॥

यज्ञेन सम्मितं ह्येतद्रङ्गदैवतपूजनम् ।
अपूजयित्वा रङ्गं तु नैव प्रेक्षां प्रयोजयेत् ॥ ९७ ॥

पूजिताः पूजयन्त्येते मानिता मानयन्ति च ।
तस्मात्सर्वप्रयत्नेन कर्तव्यं रङ्गपूजनम् ॥ ९८ ॥

न तथा प्रदहत्यग्निः[1] प्रभञ्जनसमीरितः ।
यथा ह्यपप्रयोगस्तु प्रयुक्तो दहति क्षणात् ॥ ९९ ॥

शास्त्रज्ञेन विनीतेन शुचिना दीक्षितेन च ।
नाट्याचार्येण शान्तेन कर्तव्यं रङ्गपूजनम् ॥ १०० ॥

स्थानभ्रष्टं तु यो दद्याद्बलिमुद्विग्नमानसः ।
मन्त्रहीनो यथा होता प्रायश्चित्ती भवेत्तु सः ॥ १०१ ॥

इत्ययं[2] यो विधिर्दृष्टो रङ्गदैवतपूजने ।
नवे नाट्यगृहे कार्यः प्रेक्षायां च प्रयोक्तृभिः ॥ १०२ ॥

कार्येति । अन्य प्रेक्षारम्भे सर्वथा(दा)पूजा कार्येत्याहुरिति शिवम् ॥ (३५-१०२) ॥

इत्थं तृतीयमध्यायं ग्रन्थिस्थानेषु योजये(यन्) ।
बुद्ध्याऽभिनवगुप्तोऽहं शिवतातरवबृंहितः ॥

इति श्रीमहामाहेश्वराभिनवगुप्तविरचितायां भारतीयनाट्यशास्त्रविवृतावभिनवभारत्यां रङ्गदैवतपूजनं नाम तृतीयोऽध्यायः समाप्तः ॥

१. K.S.S. M.G. न तथाऽऽशु दहत्यग्निः G.O.S. N.S. (Same as above).

२. G.O.S. N.S. इत्ययं यो K.S.S. M.G. एवमेव ।

चतुर्थोऽध्यायः ।

एवं तु पूजनं कृत्वा मया प्रोक्तः पितामहः ।

आज्ञापय विभो[1] क्षिप्रं कः प्रयोगः प्रयुज्यताम् ॥ १ ॥

स्वविलासैरिदं विश्वं यो दर्शयति सन्ततम् ।
(समीरमूर्ति तं वन्दे गिरिराजसुताप्रियम् ॥)

एवन्त्विति । प्रथमाध्यायोक्ताभिप्रायेणेदमुच्यते तथा हि—

"मर्त्यलोकगताः सर्वे शुभां पूजामवाप्स्यथ ।" (१-१२२)

इत्येवमवश्यकार्या पूजा । तत्र च—

"रङ्गपूजां कुरुष्वेति मामेवं समचोदयत् । " (१-१२७)

इति वचनानुसारेण वा इदं **प्रोक्तमित्येवमिति** । **(मयेति)** द्रुहिणाज्ञप्तेन सतेत्यर्थः । मध्ये तु,

"अथवा या क्रियास्तत्र लक्षणं यच्च पूजनम् ।
भविष्यद्भिर्नरैः कार्यं कथं तन्नाटचवेश्मनि ॥ " (२-२)

इति मुनप्रश्नितपूजा कथं कृतेति प्रसङ्गादेवमङ्गस्य यथासंभवं पूरकम् । सर्वात्मना दिव्ये नाटचगृहे भोजनदानलाङ्गलोत्कर्षणादिविधेः समस्तस्यास- म्भवादिति । प्रथमाध्यायानन्तर्यमेवास्य तु कर्तव्यम् । **क्षिप्रमिति** । अनन पूजानन्तरं प्रयोगेण न चिरायितव्यमित्युक्तं भवति । प्रयुज्यत इति प्रयोगो दशरूपकान्यतमम् । यद्यपि च सम्फेटविद्रवकृता प्रस्तावना बद्धेत्युक्तं (१-५८) तथापि प्रयोगो विघ्नैः स्तम्भित इति नाटचमण्डपे विघ्नसान्त्वनदैवतपूजने च कृतेऽन्त्य एवायमुपक्रम इति युक्त एव प्रश्नः । **कः प्रयोगः प्रयुज्यतामिति** । अत्रोत्तरं श्लोकद्वयेनाह—**ततोऽस्मीति** । **योजयेति** । स्वपुत्रानटा (त्रान्नटां)

---

१. G.O.S. N.S. विभो K.S.S. M.G. प्रभो ।

ततोऽस्म्युक्तो भगवता योजयामृतमन्थनम् ।

एतदुत्साहजननं सुरप्रीतिकरं तथा[1] **॥ २ ॥**

योऽयं समवकारस्तु धर्मकामार्थसाधकः ।

मया प्रा[२]**ग्ग्रथितो विद्वन्स प्रयोगः प्रयुज्यताम् ॥ ३ ॥**

तस्मिन्समवकारे तु प्रयुक्ते देवदानवाः ।

हृष्टाः समभवन्सर्वे कर्मभावानुदर्शनात् ॥ ४ ॥

स्तं प्रयोगं पुनरनुसन्धानशिक्षयेत्यर्थः । **यो धर्मकामार्थो**पायोपदेशको मया प्राङ् नाट्यवेदनिर्माणनान्तरीयकदशरूपकनिर्माणविधौ ग्रथितः । **अयमिति** च गुणनिकया त्वया सम्यक्साक्षात्कारकल्पत्वं नयनयोग्यत्वं कृतोऽमृतमन्थनं नाम समवकाराख्यः प्रयोगः, सह (स) विद्वन्ननुप्रयोज्यतामिति श्लोकद्वये सङ्गतिः ।

तुर्हेतौ । यस्मादेतदुत्साहजननं चतुर्विधनायकस्थायिभावोत्साहप्रभववीररसात्मकम् । **तथेति** । तेन प्रकारेण सुराणां सर्वेषां प्रीतिं रसनारूपां चर्वणालक्षणां करोति । उत्साहो जननो यस्येति समासः । तेन च प्रीतिप्रकारेणोत्साहस्य त्रिवर्गोपायविषयस्य जननम् । एतेन दृश्यं श्रव्यत्वमित्यनुसंहितम् । सङ्गतं महावाक्यार्थाभिप्रायेणापि किञ्चिच्छब्दोन्मीलनाभिप्रायेणात्र कार्यं तेन सम (समम) वकीर्यतेऽर्थो यत्र स समवकारः । सङ्गतिश्च—

"देवासुरबीजकृतः प्रख्यातोदात्तनायकश्चैव ॥" (१८-६३)

इत्यनेन दर्शितः (ता) । "अङ्कोऽङ्कस्त्वन्यार्थः कर्तव्यः" (१८-६९) इत्यनेन चावकीर्णता । एष च प्रयोगः समये (?) सुखभूयिष्ठतया एकरसे वस्तुन्युद्वेगशीलाः एकानुसन्धानप्रयासभीरवश्च देवतुल्याः ।

अमृतमथनं समवकार इति भिन्नलिङ्गसामानाधिकरण्यसूचनद्वारेण तदेव तदिति साक्षात्कारकल्पनाद्व्यवधान (नमध्यवसान) विषय......स्याह । तत एव विक्रमोर्वशीयस्वप्नवासवदत्ता (त्तं) नाटकमिति कवयो व्यवहरन्ति । (१-४)

एवमितिहासस्य परिसमाप्ति पश्यन्सकलप्रयोगप्राणभूतकैशिकीसर्वस्वभूतनृत्तप्रयोगप्रस्तावनायेतिहासमनुसन्धत्ते—**कस्यचित्त्विति** । यावता कालेन गतेन

---

1. G.O.S. N.S. तथा K.S.S. M.G. महत् ।
२. G.O.S. प्राग् ग्रथितः K.S.S. N.S. M.G. प्रग्रथितः ।

कस्यचित्त्वथ कालस्य मामाहाम्बुजसम्भवः ।
नाट्यं सन्दर्शयामोऽद्य त्रिनेत्राय महात्मने ॥ ५ ॥

ततः सार्धं सुरैर्गत्वा वृषभाङ्कनिवेशनम् ।
समभ्यर्च्य शिवं पश्चादुवाचेदं पितामहः ॥ ६ ॥

मया समवकारस्तु योऽयं सृष्टः सुरोत्तम ।
श्रवणे दर्शने चास्य प्रसादं कर्तुमर्हसि ॥ ७ ॥

पश्याम इति देवेशो द्रुहिणं वाक्यमब्रवीत् ।
ततो मामाह भगवान् सज्जो भव महामते ॥ ८ ॥

ततो हिमवतः पृष्ठे नानानगसमाकुले[1] ।
बहुभूत[2]गणाकीर्णे रम्यकन्दरनिर्झरे ॥ ९ ॥

पूर्वरङ्गः कृतः पूर्वं तत्रायं द्विजसत्तमाः ।
तथा त्रिपुरदाहश्च डिमसंज्ञः प्रयोजितः ॥ १० ॥

शिक्षणं सम्पद्यते तावता कालेन गतेन हेतुनेत्यर्थः । एतेन नाट्यप्रयोगस्तद्विदे प्रथमं दर्शनीय इति दर्शयति । तेन यद्बलात्प्रयोगो ब्रह्मणे दर्शित इति व्याख्यातं तदसदेव । न चोपयुक्तं वस्तु भगवते प्रदर्शयितुमु (द्यो) योजयेदिति चासङ्गतं स्यात् । सन्दर्शयाम इति चानेन कवेस्तन्मध्ये प्रवेशसूचनेनोत्प्रेक्षकत्व-सूचनं स्यादित्यलमनेन ।

महात्मशब्देन तस्यैवात्र प्रेक्षणे सम्यगौचित्यमित्याह । **श्रवणे दर्शने चे**त्यनु-सन्धत्ते । तथा पूर्वं परीक्षकः कविना श्रावयितव्य इति श्रवण इत्यनेनोक्तम् । सामाजिकास्तु श्रावयितव्या इति नातीव समञ्जसम् । तावत्तेषां प्रवृत्त्ययोगात् । श्रवणादेव चोपदेशसिद्धौ प्रयोगवैकल्यात् । परमेश्वरस्य परीक्षकत्वात् परितोष्यत्वाच्च ज्ञानातिशयेन रसचर्वणात्मकमहाभोगसमर्पणेन च । (५-६)

तत्र पूर्वरङ्गपूर्वकत्वं प्रयोगक्रमस्य दर्शयति—**पूर्वरङ्ग** इत्यादिना । **अयमिति** समवकारः । परमेश्वरचरितप्राधान्येन च त्रिपुरदाहसंबन्धो(ज्ञको) डिमः । प्रयुक्त इत्यनेन परीक्षकपरितोषनिमित्तं प्रयोक्तृभिः किञ्चित्प्रयोज्य-मित्याह । परितोषं फलतः प्रकटयति —**मयापीदमिति** । अननेदमाह—भरत-

---

1. G.O.S. N.S. समाकुले K.S.S. M.G. समावृते ।
२. G.O.S. K.S.S. भूत M.G. N.S. चूत ।

ततो भूतगणा हृष्टाः कर्मभावानुकीर्तनात् ।
महादेवश्च सुप्रीतः पितामहमथाब्रवीत् ॥ ११ ॥
अहो नाट्यमिदं सम्यक् त्वया सृष्टं महामते ।
यशस्यं च शुभार्थं च पुण्यं बुद्धिविवर्धनम् ॥ १२ ॥
मयाऽपीदं स्मृतं नृत्यं¹ सन्ध्याकालेषु नृत्यता ।
नानाकरणसंयुक्तैरङ्गहारैर्विभूषितम् ॥ १३ ॥

मुनिना तावद्भगवन्नृत्तकैशिकीदर्शनात्तत्प्रयोगार्थमनुस्मृत्य किञ्चिन्नियोजितम् । तत्तु सम्यगुपदेशाभावान्नातीव सुश्लिष्टमिति । अत एव वक्ष्यति—**सम्यगिति**। **स्मृत**मित्यनादित्वमस्य दर्शयति । बहुवचनेनादरविषयतामिति । अङ्गहार एव नृत्तं प्रयोगफलं प्रसूते । तदङ्गानि तु करणादीनि । द्वात्रिंशन्नृत्तकर्मणि प्रधानानीत्याशयेन विशेषणयोगमाह—**नानेति** । विनियोगमस्य निरूपयति—**पूर्वरङ्गविधाविति** । क(र)तिस्थाने रङ्गे नाट्यप्रयोगे यः पूर्वो भागस्त्वया शुद्धो वैचित्र्यरहितः प्रयुक्तः स एतेन नृत्तेन मिश्रितश्चित्रो नामेति प्रासिद्धयात् भरत इत्येष भविष्यति ? । भरतमुनिना प्रत्याहाराद्यन्तर्यवनिकागतमङ्गनवकं गीतकविरच (विधानादिप्ररोच) नान्तकमङ्गदशकं यत्प्रयोगे नृत्तविरहितमेव प्रयुक्तं कर्तव्यमात्रेण, न तु कृतमङ्गदशकं यत्प्रयुक्तं तद्दृष्टादृष्टोभयप्रयोजनमपि यथा तत्र रञ्जकत्वं किञ्चित् । अनेन तु विमिश्रं विचित्रं दृष्टादृष्टात्मकफलं सम्यग्वितरतीत्यभिप्रायो महावाक्यस्य । **अस्मिन्निति** । त्वं प्र(त्वत्प्र ?)युयुक्षितप्रयोगोचितोद्धतपूर्वरङ्गप्रयोगविधौ । तत्प्रयुक्ता इमे करणाङ्गहाराः । सुकुमारपूर्वरङ्गे तु दैवी(देव्या)कृता अनुद्धता अङ्गहारा इत्यभिप्रायात् । महागीतं च यद्गीतकवर्धमानमनादिरूपं तत्र सम्यग्वर्धमानादिक्रमेण, तथा वाक्यार्थाभिनये यथायोगं योज्यमानाङ्गहारपिण्डीबन्धक्रमेण येनाभिनेतुं शक्ष्यसि । **आचक्ष्व भरतायेति**—अनेन मुनिः परमेश्वरप्रसादपात्रमात्मानं बहुमन्यमानो-मामेव प्रति देवेनैवेदं निरूपितं **प्रयोजितस्त्वयाभिनेतुं** शक्ष्यसीति (कथ)यता । प्रधानसन्निधौ तु नैव प्रतिवक्तव्यमित्याशयेन "श्रुत्वा महेश्वरवचः प्रत्युक्तं तु स्वयम्भुवा" इत्युक्तमिति दर्शयति । **तण्डुं समाहूयेति** । सर्वत्र पाठे तण्डुशब्द एव युक्तः, ताण्डवशब्दव्युत्पत्तिवशात् । तण्डुमुनिशब्दौ (नन्दिभर) (?) तयोरपरनामनी । **य** इति । आत्रेयप्रभृतीन्प्रति मुनिरेतदाह--**सकरणान्सरेचकानिति** । विशेषणत्वादङ्गहाराणामेव प्राधान्यम् । तत एव

---

१. N.S. G.O.S. नृत्यं K.S.S. M.G. नृत्तं ।

पूर्वरङ्गविधावस्मिंस्त्वया सम्यक्प्रयोज्यताम् ।
वर्धमानकयोगेषु[1] गीतेष्वासारितेषु[2] च ॥ १४ ॥

महागीतेषु चैवार्थान्सम्यगेवाभिनेष्यसि ।
यश्चायं पूर्वरङ्गस्तु त्वया शुद्धः प्रयोजितः ॥ १५ ॥

एभिर्विमिश्रितश्चायं चित्रो नाम भविष्यति ।
श्रुत्वा महेश्वरवचः प्रत्युक्तस्तु स्वयम्भुवा ॥ १६ ॥

प्रयोगमङ्गहाराणामाचक्ष्व सुरसत्तम ।
ततस्तण्डुं समाहूय प्रोक्तवान् भुवनेश्वरः[3] ॥ १७ ॥

प्रयोगमङ्गहाराणामाचक्ष्व भरताय वै ।
ततो ये[4] तण्डुना प्रोक्तास्त्वङ्गहारा[5] महात्मना ॥ १८ ॥

तान्वः[6] करणसंयुक्तान्व्याख्यास्यामि सरेचकान् ।
स्थिरहस्तोऽङ्गहारस्तु तथा पर्यस्तकः स्मृतः ॥ १९ ॥

तेषामेव पूर्वमुद्देशः । उपायत्वात् । तत्र करणानां पूर्वं लक्षणं तत्सञ्चयात्मकत्वात्तेषां । (१०-१९)

तत्राङ्गहारोद्देशमाह—स्थिररहत इत्यादिना । द्वात्रिंशदेत इति (त्यन्तेन) । अयं भावः—अष्टोत्तरे करणशते ज्ञाते चतुष्षष्टिकरणयोजनया त्रुटिताङ्गत्या (ङ्गतरीत्या) यद्यप्यानन्त्यमङ्गहाराणां तथापि प्राधान्याद्दृष्टफलं प्रत्यधिकोपरक्ततया द्वात्रिंशन्नामतो निर्दिष्टाः । न तु परिगणनमेतत् । अङ्गानां देशान्तरे प्रापणप्रकारोऽङ्गहारः । हरस्य चायं हारः प्रयोगः । अङ्गनिर्वर्त्यो हारोऽङ्गहारः । यद्वक्ष्यति—"महेश्वरस्य चरितं य इदम्" इति । (ना. शा. ४-३३०) (१९२७)

---

1. G.O.S. योगेषु N.S. M.G. K.S.S. योगेन ।
२. G.O.S. M.G. N.S. आसारितेषु K.S.S. आसादितेषु ।
३. G.O.S. N.S. भुवनेश्वरः K.S.S. M G. सुरसत्तमः ।
४. G.O.S. N.S. ये K.S.S. M.G. वै ।
५. G.O.S. M.G. N.S. अङ्गहारा K.S.S. अङ्गहारान् ।
६. G,O,S, तान्वः M.G, N.S, K.S.S. नाना ।

सूचीविद्धस्तथा चैव ह्यपविद्धस्तथैव च[१] ।
आक्षिप्तकोऽथ[२] विज्ञेयस्तथा चोद्धट्टितः स्मृतः ॥ २० ॥
विष्कम्भश्चैव सम्प्रोक्तस्तथा चैवापराजितः ।
विष्कम्भापसृतश्चैव मत्ताक्रीडस्तथैव च ॥ २१ ॥
स्वस्तिको रेचितश्चैव पार्श्वस्वस्तिक एव च ।
वृश्चिकापसृतः[३] प्रोक्तो भ्रमरश्च[४] तथापरः ॥ २२ ॥
मत्तस्खलितकश्चैव मदाद्विलसितस्तथा ।
गतिमण्डलको ज्ञेयः[५] परिच्छिन्नस्तथैव च ॥ २३ ॥
परिवृत्तचितोऽथ स्यात्त[६]था वैशाखरेचितः ।
परावृत्तोऽथ विज्ञेयस्तथा चैवाप्यलातकः ॥ २४ ॥
पार्श्वच्छेदोऽथ सम्प्रोक्तो विद्युद्भ्रान्तस्तथैव च ।
ऊरुद्वृत्तस्तथा चैव स्यादालीढस्तथैव च ॥ २५ ॥
रेचितश्चापि विज्ञेयस्तथैवाच्छुरितः स्मृतः ।
आक्षिप्तरेचितश्चैव सम्भ्रान्तश्च तथापरः ॥ २६ ॥

तत्र निर्दिष्टानामेषां लक्षणं वाच्यमित्याशङ्क्याह—**एतेषान्त्वित्यादि** । करणेषूक्तेष्वेव ते लक्षयितुं शक्यन्ते । ननु किं करणक्रमपाठ एव तेषां लक्षणं भविष्यति । नेत्याह—**हस्तपादप्रचारश्चेति** । अङ्गहारप्रयोगेषु कर्तव्येषु यानि करणानि तद्विषये करणात्करणान्तरसञ्चारे हस्तपादादेरङ्गस्य ःयः संहिता-

---

१. K.S.S. सूचीविद्धस्तथा च स्यात् सूपविद्धस्तथैव च M.G G.O.S N.S. (Same as above).

२. N.S. तु G.O.S. M.G. K.S.S. अथ ।

३. K.S.S. M.G. N.S. वृश्चिकश्चैव संप्रोक्तो G.O.S. वृश्चिकापसृतः प्रोक्तो ।

४. N.S. G.O.S. M.G. भ्रमरः K.S.S. चमरः ।

५. N.S. M.G. K.S.S. गतिमण्डलोऽथ विज्ञेयः G.O.S. गतिमण्डलको ज्ञेयः ।

६. N.S. M.G. परिवृत्तरेचितः स्यात् K.S.S. परिवृत्तरेचितोऽथ स्यात् G.O.S. परिवृत्तचितोऽथ स्यात् ।

अपसर्पस्तु[1] विज्ञेयस्तथा चार्धनिकुट्टकः ।
द्वात्रिंशदेते सम्प्रोक्ता अङ्गहारास्तु नामतः ॥ २७ ॥

एतेषां तु प्रवक्ष्यामि प्रयोगं करणाश्रयम्[2] ।
हस्तपादप्रचारश्च यथा योज्यः प्रयोक्तृभिः ॥ २८ ॥

अङ्गहारेषु वक्ष्यामि करणेषु च वै द्विजाः[3] ।
सर्वेषामङ्गहाराणां निष्पत्तिः करणैर्यतः[4] ॥ २९ ॥

तान्यतः[5] सम्प्रवक्ष्यामि नामतः कर्मतस्तथा ।
हस्तपादसमायोगो नृत्यस्य[6] करणं भवेत् ॥ ३० ॥

कार्यकल्पप्रयोगः तमपि वक्ष्यामि । चशब्दात्क्वचिन्नवक्ष्यामि । ऊहप्रदर्शनार्थम् । वैशब्दः आगमप्रयोगद्योतकस्तु (कः) । अङ्गहारविषये वक्तव्ये पूर्वं किं निरूपणार्हमित्याह—**सर्वेषामिति** । तत्र करणानामङ्गहाराणां च सामान्यलक्षणं कर्तुमाह—**हस्तपादेत्यादिना** । क्रिया करणम् । कस्य क्रिया । नृत्तस्य । गात्राणां विलासक्षेपस्य । हेयोपादेयविषयक्रियादिभ्यो व्यतिरिक्ता या तत्क्रिया करणमित्यर्थः । नृत्यस्येति । व्यपदेशिवत्त्वेन षष्ठी । तस्याः क्रियायाः स्वरूपमाह—**हस्तपादसमायोगः** । हस्तोपलक्षितस्य पूर्वकायवर्तिशाखाङ्गोपाङ्गादेः पादोपलक्षितस्य चापरकायगतपार्श्वकटयूरुजङ्घाचरणादेः सङ्गततयाऽत्रुटितत्वेन वृत्तियोजने । पूर्वक्षेत्रसंयोगत्यागेन समुचितक्षेत्रान्तरप्राप्तिपर्यन्तत्या एका क्रिया तत्करणमित्यर्थः । उत्तरसंयोगान्तं हि सर्वत्र कर्म । स चाप्यभिलषितोत्तरसंयोग एव क्रियावधित्वेन लोके प्रसिद्ध इति नापूर्वमेतत् । एतावदेवेहाधिकं (यत्) सौन्दर्यानुप्रवेशेन सविलासत्वं नाम । अत एव नृत्तशब्देन विशेषणं नृत्तकरणमिति । एकदेशाभिप्रायेण तु करणशब्दस्य प्रयोगो भीमसेने भीम इतिवत् ।

---

१. M.G. N.S. G.O.S. तु K.S.S. अथ ।
२. M.G. K.S.S. एषां चैव प्रवक्ष्यामि प्रयोगं करणाश्रितम् G.O.S. N.S. (Same as above).
३. K.S.S. M.G. तथाऽहं द्विजसत्तमाः G.O.S. N.S. करणेषु च वै द्विजाः ।
४. G.O.S. N.S. यतः M.G. K.S.S. भवेत् ।
५. M.G. K.S.S. अहम् G.O.S. N.S. अतः ।
६. K.S.S. M.G. नृत्तस्य G.O.S. N.S. नृत्यस्य ।

द्वे नृत्तकरणे चैव भवतो नृत्तमातृका[1] ।

द्वाभ्यां त्रिभिश्चतुर्भिर्वाप्यङ्गहारस्तु मातृभिः[2] ॥ ३१ ॥

त्रिभिः कलापकं चैव चतुर्भिः षण्डकं भवेत्[3] ।

पञ्चैव करणानि स्युः सङ्घातक इति स्मृतः ॥ ३२ ॥

षड्भिर्वा सप्तभिर्वापि अष्टभिर्नवभिस्तथा ।

करणैरिह संयुक्ता अङ्गहाराः प्रकीर्तिताः[4] ॥ ३३ ॥

एवं तावत्करणस्य सामान्यलक्षणम् । तत्राङ्गहारस्य विशेषलक्षणं विरचयितुं पीठबन्धमाह—**द्वे नृत्तकरणे** इति । नृत्तमातृकेति । नृत्तस्याङ्गहारात्मनो मातृका उत्पत्तिकारणम् । नृत्तशब्देन विशेषणात् "यानि स्थानानि" इत्यादिना (ना. शा. ४-५६) याः करणमातृका वक्ष्यन्ते ततो विशेषं दर्शयति । करणद्वयप्रयोगेण च क्विनिवृत्ता (विनिर्वृत्तनृत्ता) भिमानो नास्ति । ततः परन्तु नृत्यतीत्यभिमानात्करणद्वयं नृत्तमातृकेत्युक्तम् । एवग्रहणादन्यूनाधिकसङ्ग्रहः । नृत्तमातृकालक्षणेनाङ्गहारसामान्यलक्षणेन च करणद्वयमूहिताङ्गहारान्तरं च पिण्डीबन्धोपयोगि प्रयोज्यानुजानीते—**एतेषामिति** । अङ्गहाराणामेव संबन्धित्वेन हस्तपादविकल्पनं करणं वक्ष्यामि । जातावेकवचनम् ।

ननु स्थानकचार्यादीनां प्राक् लक्षणं वाच्यम् । नैवम् । तेषां नाट्यज्ञानादेव मुनिं प्रति विदितत्वात् । नृत्तहस्ता अपि वर्तनात्मानोऽस्य विदिता एव । यत उक्तम् 'इदं नृत्तम्' इति । तत एवाङ्गिके(ना. शा. १०)तेषामभिधास्यमानता । करणान्येव त्विव......वाच्यम् । (त्विह वाच्यानि) (२८-३३)

तत्र नामतः **कर्मतश्चेत्युक्तम्** । नामतस्तावदाह **तलपुष्पपुटमित्यादि ।**

अष्टाधिकं शतमुक्तं यदङ्गहारोपयोगित्वे नियतसमप्रत्यस्तमयमिति किमनेन संख्यानिरूपणेनेत्याशङ्क्याह—**अष्टोत्तरशतमित्यादिना** । अभिनये वस्तुत्वेन यन्नृत्तं वक्ष्यतेऽभिनयान्तरालवर्तिच्छिद्रप्रच्छादनादेतत्प्रयुज्यते । शस्त्रादियुद्धे चाङ्गप्रयोगसौष्ठवार्थमपि प्रयुज्यते । पृथक्तया गत्यध्याय—(ना. शा. १३)

१. K.S.S. नृत्तमातृकाः G.O.S. M.G. नृत्तमातृका N.S. नृत्यमातृका ।

२. G.O.S. M.G. (Same as above) K.S.S. N.S. द्वाभ्यां त्रिचतुराभिर्वाप्यङ्गहारस्तु मातृभिः ।

३. K.S.S. त्रिभिः कलापको ज्ञेयः चतुर्भिर्मण्डकस्तथा M.G. षण्डकः N.S. त्रिभिः कलापकं चैव चतुर्भिर्मण्डकं भवेत् G.O.S. षण्डकं ।

४. K.S.S. G.O.S. M.G प्रकीर्तिताः N.S. इति स्मृताः ।

एतेषामेव[1] वक्ष्यामि हस्तपादविकल्पनम् ।
तलपुष्पपुटं पूर्वं[2] वर्तितं वलितोरु[3] च ॥ ३४ ॥
अपविद्धं समनखं लीनं स्वस्तिकरेचितम् ।
मण्डलस्वस्तिकं[4] चैव निकुट्टकमथापि च ॥ ३५ ॥
तथैवार्धनिकुट्टं च कटिच्छिन्नं तथैव च ।
अर्धरेचितकं चैव वक्षःस्वस्तिकमेव च ॥ ३६ ॥
उन्मत्तं स्वस्तिकं चैव पृष्ठस्वस्तिकमेव च ।
दिक्स्वस्तिकमलातं च तथैव च[5] कटीसमम् ॥ ३७ ॥
आक्षिप्तरेचितं चैव विक्षिप्ताक्षिप्तकं तथा ।
अर्धस्वस्तिकमुद्दिष्टमञ्चितं च तथापरम् ॥ ३८ ॥
भुजङ्गत्रासितं प्रोक्तमूर्ध्वजानु तथैव च ।
निकुञ्चितं च मत्तल्लि त्वर्धमत्तल्लि चैव हि ॥ ३९ ॥
स्याद्रेचकनिकुट्टं च तथा पादापविद्धकम् ।
वलितं घूर्णितं चैव ललितं च तथापरम्[6] ॥ ४० ॥
दण्डपक्षं तथा चैव भुजङ्गत्रस्तरेचितम् ।
नूपुरं चैव सम्प्रोक्तं तथा वैशाखरेचितम् ॥ ४१ ॥
भ्रमरं चतुरं चैव भुजङ्गाञ्चितमेव च ।
दण्डरेचितकं चैव तथा वृश्चिककुट्टितम्[7] ॥ ४२ ॥
कटिभ्रान्तं तथा चैव लतावृश्चिकमेव च ।
छिन्नं च करणं प्रोक्तं तथा वृश्चिकरेचितम् ॥ ४३ ॥

---

१. K.S.S. M.G. इह G.O.S. N.S. एव ।
२. K.S.S. M.G. चैव G.O.S. N.S. पूर्वं ।
३. K.S.S. M.G. चलितोरू G.O.S. N.S. वलितोरू ।
४. K.S.S M.G. मण्डलं स्वस्तिकं चैव G.O.S. N.S. मण्डलस्वस्तिकं चैव ।
५. K.S.S. M.G. तथा चैव G.O.S. N.S. तथैव च ।
६. K.S.S. M.G. घूर्णितं चैव ललितं च तथापरम् G.O.S. N.S. (Same as above).
७. N.S. वृश्चिककुट्टनम् G.O.S. M.G. K.S.S. वृश्चिककुट्टितम् ।

वृश्चिकं व्यंसितं चैव तथा पार्श्वनिकुट्टकम्[1] ।
ललाटतिलकं क्रान्तं कुञ्चितं चक्रमण्डलम् ॥ ४४ ॥
उरोमण्डलमाक्षिप्तं तथा तलविलासितम् ।
अर्गलं चाथ[2] विक्षिप्तमावृत्तं दोलपादकम्[3] ॥ ४५ ॥
विवृत्तं विनिवृत्तं च पार्श्वक्रान्तं निशुम्भितम् ।
विद्युद्भ्रान्तमतिक्रान्तं विवर्तितकमेव च ॥ ४६ ॥
गजक्रीडितकं चैव तलसंस्फोटितं तथा ।
गरुडप्लुतकं चैव गण्डसूचि तथापरम् ॥ ४७ ॥
परिवृत्तं समुद्दिष्टं पार्श्वजानु तथैव च ।
गृध्रावलीनकं चैव सन्नतं सूच्यथापि च ॥ ४८ ॥
अर्धसूचीति करणं सूचीविद्धं तथैव च ।
अपक्रान्तं च सम्प्रोक्तं मयूरललितं तथा ॥ ४९ ॥
सर्पितं दण्डपादं च हरिणप्लुतमेव च ।
प्रेङ्खोलितं नितम्बं च स्खलितं करिहस्तकम् ॥ ५० ॥
प्रसर्पित[4]कमुद्दिष्टं सिंहविक्रीडितं तथा ।
सिंहाकर्षितमुद्वृत्तं तथोपसृतमेव[5] च ॥ ५१ ॥
तलसङ्घट्टितं चैव जनितं चावहित्थकम् ।
निवेशमेलकाक्रीडमू[6]रूद्वृत्तं तथैव च ॥ ५२ ॥
मदस्खलितकं चैव विष्णुक्रान्तमथापि च[7] ।
सम्भ्रान्तमथ विष्कम्भमुद्घट्टितमथापि च ॥ ५३ ॥
वृषभक्रीडितं चैव लोलितं च तथापरम् ।

१. K.S.S. पादनिकुट्टनम् M.G. N.S. G.O.S. पार्श्वनिकुट्टकम् ।
२. K.S.S. M.G. चापि G.O.S. N.S. चाथ ।
३. K.S.S. पादुकम् G.O.S. N.S. M.G. पादकम् ।
४. K.S.S. प्रसर्पितं समुद्दिष्टं M.G. समर्पितं समुद्दिष्टं G.O.S. N.S. प्रसर्पितकमुद्दिष्टं ।
५. K.S.S. M.G. तथाऽपसृतमेव च G.O.S. N.S. तथोपसृतमेव च ।
६. K.S.S. निवेशं मौलिकाक्रीडम् M.G. G.O.S. N.S. निवेशमेलकाक्रीडम् ।
७. K.S.S M.G. तथैव च G.O.S. N.S. अथापि च ।

नागापसर्पितं चैव शकटास्यं तथैव च ॥ ५४ ॥
गङ्गावतरणं चैवेत्युक्तमष्टाधिकं शतम् ।
अष्टोत्तरशतं ह्येतत्करणानां मयोदितम्[1] ॥ ५५ ॥
नृत्ते युद्धे नियुद्धे च तथा गतिपरिक्रमे ।
गतिप्रचारे वक्ष्यामि युद्धचारीविकल्पनम् ॥ ५६ ॥
यत्र तत्रापि संयोज्यमाचार्यैर्नाट्यशक्तितः ।
प्रायेण करणे कार्यो वामो वक्षःस्थितः करः ॥ ५७ ॥
चरणस्यानुगश्चापि दक्षिणस्तु भवेत्करः ।
हस्तपादप्रचारन्तु कटिपार्श्वोरुसंयुतम् ॥ ५८ ॥
उरःपृष्ठोदरोपेतं वक्ष्यमाणं[2] निबोधत ।
यानि स्थानानि याश्चार्यो नृत्तहस्तास्तथैव च ॥ ५९ ॥

वक्ष्यमाणासु च गतिषु ये परिक्रमाः परिक्रमणानि तत्र पृथक् तेन पृथक्त्वेन प्रयोगदर्शनादष्टोत्तरशतत्वं न नोपयोगि । एष च यथा विनियोगो भविष्यति तथा समनन्तरमेव वक्ष्यामः । अत्र 'अष्टोत्तरशतम्' इत्यादि श्लोकं केचिन्न पठन्ति । अन्ये (न्ते) ततोऽप्यधिकं—

"हस्तपादप्रचारन्तु कटिपार्श्वोरुसंयुतम्" ॥

इति श्लोकं पठन्ति (३४-५८) ।

तत्र महासामान्यरूपं करणमाह—**यानि स्थानानीति** । इहावस्थानं गतिश्चेति द्वयनिर्वर्त्यं करणम् । तत्रावस्थाने करकार्योपयोगि स्थानकम् । गतौ तु चार्यः पूर्वकाये तु गतौ नृत्तहस्ता दृष्टयश्च । स्थितौ पताकाद्याः । एतच्चकारेण सङ्गृहीतम् । तेन गतिस्थितिसंमिलिते (तं) करणमित्यानन्त्यं यद्यपि करणं (णानां) तथाप्यङ्गहारोपयोगित्वादेतावदुक्तमिति श्लोकस्य तात्पर्यम् ।

(१) तलपुष्पपुटम् ।

तत्रोद्देशक्रमेण लक्षणान्याह—**वाम इत्यादिना** ।

"यस्तु सर्पशिराः प्रोक्तस्तस्याङ्गुलिनिरन्तरः ।

---

१. K.S.S. M.G. Omit this hemistich N.S. G.O.S. Retain it.
२. K.S.S. M.G. नृत्तमार्गं G.O.S. N.S. वक्ष्यमाणं ।

सा मातृकेति विज्ञेया तद्योगात्करणं[1] भवेत् ।
कटी कर्णसमा यत्र कोर्परांसशिरस्तथा ॥ ६० ॥
समुन्नतमुरश्चैव सौष्ठवं नाम तद्भवेत्[2] ।
वामे पुष्पपुट[3]: पार्श्वे पादोऽग्रतलसञ्चर: ॥ ६१ ॥

द्वितीयः पार्श्वसंश्लिष्टः स तु पुष्पपुटः करः ॥ " (ना. शा. ९-१५०)
"उत्क्षिप्ता तु भवेत्पार्ष्णिः प्रसृतोऽङ्गुष्ठकस्तथा ।
अङ्गुल्यश्चाञ्चिताः सर्वाः पादेऽग्रतलसञ्चरे ॥ " (ना. शा.९-२७३)
"कटी भवेच्च व्याभुग्ना पार्श्वमाभुग्नमेव च ।
तथैवापसृतांसं च किञ्चित्पार्श्वं नतं स्मृतम् ॥ " (ना. शा. १२-३५)

एषां योजनोच्यते ।

तत्र नृत्ते समपादतला हस्तद्वयपूर्वकं तत्ता (लता) वत्प्राचुर्यें सर्वत्र । ततश्चाद्यर्धिकया चार्या (ना. शा. १०-१७) दक्षिणपादनिष्क्रमणेन समकालं व्यावर्तितेन करयुगलेन दक्षिणपार्श्वे समं नीतेन परिवर्तितकरणवशादानीतेन वामपार्श्वे सौष्ठवेन वामस्तनक्षेत्रे पुष्पपुटहस्तबन्ध इति । अग्रतलपादपुष्पपुटयोगादेकदेशसूचनं नामेदं तलपुष्पपुटमिति । एवमन्यत्रापि नामवासना ऊह्याः ।

तत्र (यत्र) क्वचिद्वाक्यार्थाभिनय एव प्राधान्येन दर्शिते (दृश्यते) तत्र करणानामेव प्राधान्यम् । यत्रापि पदार्थाभिनयाः क्रियन्ते तत्राप्येकवाक्यानुप्रवेशप्राधान्यप्रख्यापनायामवश्यमादौ मध्येऽन्ते वा यथावसरं करणमित्युपनिषत् । अत एव वक्ष्यति—

"अस्य शाखा च नृत्तं च तथैवाङ्कुर एव च ।
वस्तून्यभिनयस्येह । " इति । (ना. शा. ८-१५)

वर्तनानुप्रवेशो हि शाखयैव गतार्थः स्यात् । तत्रैव च शाखान्ते भेदं वक्ष्यति । "आङ्गिकश्च भवेच्छाखा" (ना. शा. ८-१६) इत्युक्तम् । "अङ्गहारवि-

---

१. M.G. करणानि तु K.S.S. G.O.S. N.S. करणं भवेत् ।

२. K.S.S. करौ कर्णसमौ यत्र कूर्पराङ्गशिरस्तथा । समुन्नतमुखं चैव सौष्ठवं नाम तद्भवेत् G.O.S. N.S. (Same as above) M.G. कटिजानुसमं यत्र कूर्परांसशिरस्तथा ।

३. K.S.S. M.G. पुष्पपुटं N.S. G.O.S. पुष्पपुटः ।

तथा च सन्नतं पार्श्वं तलपुष्पपुटं भवेत् ।
कुञ्चितौ मणिबन्धे तु व्यावृत्त¹परिवर्तितौ ॥ ६२ ॥

निष्पन्नं नृत्तं तु करणाश्रयम्" (ना, शा, ८-१६) एतत्स्फुटं तत्रैव व्याख्यास्यत इत्यास्तां तावत् । अत्रोदाहरणं दिक्प्रदर्शनाय "अभिजअइ मळविमुक्ककमळासणउदितस्स" इत्यादावनेन वाक्यार्थाभिनये, नाट्येऽपि "पादाग्रस्थितया (रत्ना १-१) इत्यादावुपसंहारवाक्यार्थाभिनये इय(द) मेव युक्तं करणम् । न नृ (यन्नृ) त्यस्य पादाग्रस्थितत्वस्य कुसुमाञ्जलिक्षेप: । स चानेनैव सम्पन्नेन चतुरश्रीभूतत्वादङ्गादनन्तरं यदा प्रयुज्यते तदा हस्तयो: स्वे स्वे पार्श्वे आवेष्टितकरणं (ना. शा. ६-२१५) कृत्वा तत: उद्वेष्टितकरणेन (ना. शा. ६-२१६) पुष्पपुटप्रयोग: ।

यदा तु करा(रणा)न्तरसन्निवेशानन्तरमिदं करणं प्रयुज्यते तदा त्यक्तव्यतदीयहस्तपादापेक्षया आदातव्यकरणगतहस्तपादाद्यपेक्षया च यथा वर्तनाक्रमेण स्वयमेव त्यागोपादाने अत्रुटिततया वा सम्पद्यते तथा कर्तव्यमित्यलं नृत्ताचार्यैगोपिता (र्योपयोगि) नाऽनेन । एतच्च यथावसरं दर्शयित्वा सर्वं निरूपयिष्याम: ।

"सव्यस्य पृष्ठतो वामश्चरणस्तु यदा भवेत् ।
तस्यापसर्पणं चैव सा ज्ञेयाऽर्ध्यधिका बुधै: ॥ (ना. शा. १०-१७)
"आवर्तन्ते कनिष्ठाद्या अङ्गुल्योऽभ्यन्तरेण तु ॥ (ना. शा. ६-२१७)
"उद्वर्तन्ते कनिष्ठाद्या बाह्यत: क्रमशो यदा ॥ " (ना. शा. ६-२१८)

इति व्यावृत्तपरिवर्तिते । एवं तर्जन्यादित: आवेष्टितपरिवेष्टिते । (५६-६१)

(२) **वर्तितम्** ।

कुञ्चिताविस्यादि । वक्ष:क्षेत्रे उन्मुखं स्वस्तिकवदश्लिष्टमेव मणिबन्धनमतं करयुगलं कृत्वा तत्रैव विहस्तौ समकालं व्यावृत्तपरिवर्तौ (वृत्तौ) विधायोत्तानावेव यथास्वमूर्वो: पातनीयौ । असूयावाक्यार्थाभिनये चोत्तानौ पताकौ । यथा "तुज्झ कए सरिवं ररामर उण मरापरागुण अआविद्धत्तनआ" । तावेव पताकावधोमुखघृष्टमुखपातैरेतैर्यदा तदा रोषवाक्यार्थाभिनये यथा—"सब... डओ गु महिलो नु" इत्यादौ । एवं कटकामुखशुकतुण्डादयोऽपि यथायथमत्र योजयितव्या: । तत एवात्र मुनिना हस्तावशेषो न निरूपित: । अग्रतलसञ्चर एवात्र पाद इति केचित् । तद्धस्तौचित्यानुसारी पादयोग इति नृत्ताचार्या: । (६२)

---

१. M.G. व्यावृत K.S.S. G.O.S. N.S. व्यावृत्त ।

हस्तौ निपतितौ चोर्वोर्वर्तितं करणं तु तत् ।
शुकतुण्डौ यदा हस्तौ व्यावृत्तपरिवर्तितौ ॥ ६३ ॥
ऊरू च वलितौ यस्मिन्वलितोरुकमुच्यते[1] ।
आवर्त्य शुकतुण्डाख्यमूरुपृष्ठे निपातयेत् ॥ ६४ ॥

---

(३) वलितोरुकम् ।

शुकतुण्डावित्यादि ।

"आद्या धनुर्नता कार्या कुञ्चितोऽङ्गुष्ठकस्तथा ।
शेषा भिन्नोर्ध्ववलिता ह्यरालेऽङ्गुलयः करे ॥" (ना. शा. ९-४६)
"अरालस्य यदा वक्रानामिका त्वङ्गुलिर्भवेत् ।
शुकतुण्डः स तु करः" (ना. शा. ९-५३)
"भवेदभ्यन्तरं जानु यत्राहुर्वलितं तु तत् ।" (ना. शा. ९-२५२)

योजना तु—वक्षःक्षेत्रात्समकालं हस्तौ व्यावर्तितौ कृत्वा आक्षिप्तया पादचार्या सह पततः । परिवर्तनानुनीय वक्षःप्रदेशे शुकतुण्डावधोमुखौ स्थापयेत् । बद्धया च चार्या स्थितिः ।

एतन्मुग्धाविषयं च । यथा—"दुल्लणुल्लीति तुहिगुह् णंविळुळिअ अह्न हुदौ मुणाहि दिडात्तमहि" ।

'त्रिपताका तर्जनी वक्रतया शुकतुण्डः' इत्यतान्त्रिर्कालिखितमुपेक्ष्यमेव ।

"अन्योन्यजङ्घासंवेधात् कृत्वा तु स्वस्तिकं ततः ।
ऊरुभ्यां वलनं यत्स्यात् सा बद्धा चार्युदाहृता ॥" (ना. शा. १०-२१) (६३)

(४) अपविद्धम् ।

"वक्षसोऽष्टाङ्गुलस्थौ तु प्राङ्मुखौ कटकामुखौ ।" (ना. शा. ९-१८४)

इति चातुरश्र्येण स्थित्वा ततो हस्तमावर्तितेन निष्क्रमय्य ततः समकालमाक्षिप्तिकां चारीं कृत्वा तमेव हस्तं शुकतुण्डीकृतं तस्योर्वोः(रोः)पृष्ठे निपातयेत् । वामहस्तश्च कटकामुखः । "स तु वक्षस्येवेति दक्षिणस्य करपादस्यापर्यवसानात्तदुपलक्षितवेगनिस्सरणादपविद्धमिति नाम्नैव वर्तनायाश्चातुर्यं सूचितम् । असूयाकोपवाक्यार्थाभिनये चेदम् ।

---

१. M.G. K.S.S. यत्र वलितोरु तदुच्यते G.O.S. N.S. (Same as above).

वामहस्तश्च वक्षःस्थोऽ[1]प्यपविद्धं तु तद्भवेत् ।
श्लिष्टौ समनखौ पादौ करौ चापि प्रलम्बितौ ॥ ६५ ॥

देहः स्वाभाविको यत्र भवेत्समनखं तु तत् ।
पताकाञ्जलि वक्षःस्थं प्रसारितशिरोधरम् ॥ ६६ ॥

यथा—

"विमाळकाळतुज्ञ" इत्यादौ ।

मुनिविषयस्त्वस्यैव कैश्चित्प्रयोगो लिखितः तत्पात्रान्तरपरिवर्तनदोषात्स्वयमलक्ष्यत्वाच्चेत्युपेक्ष्यम् ।

"कुञ्चितं पादमुत्क्षिप्य व्याक्षिप्तं त्वञ्चितं न्यसेत् ।
जङ्घा स्वस्तिकसंयुक्ता चाक्षिप्ता नाम सा स्मृता ॥" (ना. शा. १०-३७) (६४)

(५) समनखम् ।

प्रलम्बितौ कराविति लताहस्तौ मन्तव्यौ । न तु दोलाहस्तौ । तयोरेकविषययोरत्र वर्तनायाश्चातुरश्र्यभङ्गहेतुत्वात् ।

"तिर्यक्प्रसारितौ चैव पार्श्वसंस्थौ लताकरौ ।" (ना. शा. ९-१९८)
एतच्च प्रथमप्रवेशे नृत्ते दृश्यते । जप्य(य)मङ्गलादिविषये तु नास्य प्रयोगो युक्तः यथा कैश्चिदिष्टः । (६५)

(६) लीनम् ।

"पताकाभ्यां तु हस्ताभ्यां संश्लेषादञ्जलिः स्मृतः ।" (ना. शा. ९१२८)
प्रसारितसमाः सर्वा यस्याङ्गुल्यो भवन्ति हि ।
कुञ्चितश्च तथाङ्गुष्ठः स पताक इति स्मृतः ॥ (ना. शा. ९-१८)
रेचितग्रीवा ।

"रेचिता विस्तृतभ्रान्ता भावे मथननृत्तयोः ॥" (ना. शा. ८-१७६)
इति केचित् । तदसत् । औचित्यायोगात् । तेन प्रणामापसारिता गमिता नतं (नता) स्याद्ग्रीवा ।

---

१. K.S.S. M.G. वक्षःस्थो वामहस्तश्च G.O.S. N.S. वामहस्तश्च

निहञ्चितांसकूटं च तल्लीनं करणं स्मृतम्[1] ।
स्वस्तिकौ रेचिताविद्धौ[2] विश्लिष्टौ कटिसंश्रितौ[3] ॥ ६७ ॥
यत्र तत्करणं ज्ञेयं बुधैः स्वस्तिकरेचितम् ।
स्वस्तिकौ तु करौ कृत्वा प्राङ्मुखोर्ध्वतलौ समौ ॥ ६८ ॥

"उत्क्षिप्तबाहुशिखरं निकुञ्चितशिरोधरम् ।
निकुञ्चितं शिरः ।" (ना. शा. ८-३२)

तद्योगादंसकूटयोर्निहञ्चितत्वम् ।

योजना तूर्ध्वमण्डलिनौ (ना. शा. ६-२०३) नृत्तहस्तौ प्राक्प्रयुज्य तद्वर्तनाक्रमेण वक्षोदेशेऽञ्जलिं रचयेत् । एतदेव पताकाग्रहणस्य प्रयोजनम् । अञ्जलेर्नलिनीपद्मकोशवर्तनया सम्पादनं माभूत् । अपि तूर्ध्वमण्डलवर्तनया । तथा पताकयोः स्फुटप्रयोगोत्पत्तिः । तथाऽप्यव्यभिचारात् पताकाग्रहणमफलमेव । लौकिकाञ्जलिशङ्काशमनं तु सति तान्त्रिके तुच्छफलम् ।

एतच्च प्रियप्रार्थनावाक्यार्थाभिनये । यथा—"पुरिपडाळपळदु०ळडासं लिबिल्लइ दुंदु" । न तु देवताप्रणामे वक्षःस्थोऽप्यञ्जलिरत्र । देवताप्रणामे तु शिरःस्थ इति वक्ष्यामः । (६६)

(७) स्वस्तिकरेचितम् ।

पूर्वं रेचितौ तत आविद्धौ वक्रौ ततो देहक्षेत्रमागतौ स्वस्तिकौ । ततोऽपि विश्लिष्टौ विप्रकीर्णौ । ततः कटिसंस्थौ पक्षप्रद्योतपक्षवञ्चितकाख्यौ । एवं नृत्तहस्तषट्कात्मकमेतत्करणम् । तत्र—

"रेचितावपि विज्ञेयौ हंसपक्षौ द्रुतभ्रमौ ।" (ना. शा. ६-१९३)

"समाः प्रसारितास्तिस्रः तथा चोर्ध्वा कनीयसी ।
अङ्गुष्ठः कुञ्चितश्चैव हंसपक्ष इति स्मृतः ॥" (ना. शा. ६-१०६)

"भुजांसकूर्पराग्रैस्तु कुटिलावर्तितौ करौ ।
पराङ्मुखतलाविद्धौ ज्ञेयावाविद्धवक्रकौ" ॥ (ना. शा. ६-१९०)

---

१ K.S.S. M.G. निकुञ्चितांसकूटं G.O.S. N.S. निहञ्चितांसकूटं ।
२. K.S.S. N.S. रैचितौ विद्धौ G.O.S. M.G. रेचिताविद्धौ ।
३. M.G. K.S.S N.S. संस्थितौ G.O.S. संश्रितौ ।

तथा च मण्डलं स्थानं मण्डलस्वस्तिकं तु तत् ।
निकुट्टितौ यदा हस्तौ स्वबाहुशिरसोऽन्तरे ॥ ६६ ॥

"तावेव मणिबन्धान्ते स्वस्तिकाकृतिसंस्थितौ ।
स्वस्तिकाविति विज्ञेयौ विच्युतौ विप्रकीर्णकौ" ॥ (ना. शा. ६-१८७)
"कटिशीर्षनिविष्टाग्रौ त्रिपताकौ यदा करौ ।
पक्षवञ्चितकौ ।" (ना. शा. ६-२००)
"तावेव तु परावृत्तौ पक्षप्रद्योतकौ स्मृतौ ।" (ना. शा. ६-२०१)

योजना तु—चातुरश्रचान्तरे रेचितवर्तनया पक्षौ विधाय व्यावर्तितकरणेन शिरःक्षेत्रादधरगमनोपरिगमने च या आविद्धवक्रवर्तना तया वक्षःक्षेत्रस्वस्तिकौ विधाय तावेव विप्रकीर्णौ कृत्वा पुनःपक्षवञ्चितौ पुनः पक्षप्रद्योताविति तद्योगा-त्स्वस्तिकरेचितम् ।

अत्र च तत्र तत्र नृत्तहस्ते प्रयोगवशादा(ला)(त) चार्या शतचार्याविदन्ते (अवहित्थकाद्) बहिर्मण्डलसंस्थानकृतेन समनखौ पादावनुवर्तत इत्यसत् । एतच्च यत्र नृत्तमेव प्राधान्येनाभिनेयं तावत्कालं प्रहर्षादियोगे तत्र तत्र प्रयुज्यते ।

यथा "घण्णिइ घण्णिइ घणहिए अणुराहिणव्वहरासु । महुरकण्णे जितिसअ-उदाणवकुळिणिणोसु ।" (६७)

(८) मण्डलस्वस्तिकम् ।

स्वस्तिकावृत्त(वृक्त)लक्षणौ । करौ । प्राङ्मुखौ चतुरश्रौ ऊर्ध्वतलौ । ऊर्ध्वमण्डलिनौ ।

"वक्षसोऽष्टाङ्गुलस्थौ तु प्राङ्मुखौ कटकामुखौ ।
समानकूर्परांसौ च चतुरश्रौ प्रकीर्तितौ ॥" (ना. शा. ६-१८४)
"ऐन्द्रे तु मण्डले पादौ चतुस्तालान्तरस्थितौ ।
त्र्यश्रौ वक्षःस्थितौ चैव कटी जानुसमा तथा ॥" (ना. शा. १०-६५)

योजना तु—चतुरश्रहस्ताभ्यां स्थित्वा ततो विच्यवाप्रयोगसमकालमुद्वेष्टित-वर्तनया गत्वा तत ऊर्ध्वमण्डलिवर्तनिकया स्वस्तिकौ कुर्यात् । मण्डलस्थानकं च बध्नीयादिति । इति मण्डलस्वस्तिकम् ।

"विच्यवात्समपादाया विच्यवां सम्प्रयोजयेत् ।
निकुट्टयंस्तलाग्रेण पादस्य धरणीतलम् ॥" (ना. शा. १०-१६)

पादौ निकुट्टितौ चैव ज्ञेयं तत्तु निकुट्टकम्[1] ।
अञ्चितौ बाहुशिरसि[2] हस्तस्त्वभिमुखाङ्गुलिः ॥ ७० ॥

तलाग्रोऽग्रतलसञ्चरः । निकारवाक्यार्थाभिनये । यथा—"उव्वेळा वि अगत्थि अवळआ वाह्लिअएहिँशि । जळचरिउ ससक्कसुणिममंमदउ" । इत्यादौ । (६८)

(९) निकुट्टकम् ।

"उन्नमनं विनमनं स्यादङ्गस्य निकुट्टनम् ।"

इति कोहलः ।

तेन हस्तस्यालपल्लवस्य कनिष्ठाङ्गुलिपतनोत्पतनप्रकारो निकुट्टनम् । इहापि वक्ष्यते । अञ्चित इति पादस्याप्युद्घट्टितरूपता ।

"स्थित्वा पादतलाग्रेण पार्ष्णिं भूमौ निपातयेत् ।
यस्य पादस्य करणे भवेदुद्घट्टितस्तु सः ॥" (ना. शा. ९-२६६)

चकारेण मण्डलस्थानकमुच्यते । स्वबाहुशिरस इत्येकवचनाद्धस्ताविति द्विवचनाच्च पर्यायेणाङ्गद्वयेन प्रयोगः । एवकाराद्दक्षिणेन प्रयोगे दक्षिण एव पादः वामेन वामः । तेन मण्डलस्थानके स्थित्वा चातुरश्र्यादनन्तरमुद्वेष्टितकरणेन हस्तं नीत्वा स्कन्धशिरसि निकुट्टयेत् । तमेव पादमुद्घट्टितं कुर्यात् । वामं तु हस्तं यथावस्थितं पुनराविद्धवक्रवर्तनतया तं हस्तं चतुरश्रीकुर्यात् । तत्समकालं चोक्तविधिना द्वितीयमङ्गं निकुट्टयेदिति योजना ।

अस्य च पुनः पुनरात्मसम्भावनाप्रधाने वाक्यार्थेऽभिनेतव्ये प्रयोगः । यथा—"भीउणजाणमिहउसू भवउकज्जी ॥" (६९)

(१०) अर्धनिकुट्टकम् ।

चरममेवार्धं लक्षणम् । आद्येन तु निकुट्टितस्य हस्तस्य युक्त्या लक्षणं कृतम् । अलपल्लव इति वक्तव्ये कुञ्चितग्रहणं क्रियाविशिष्टत्वप्रदर्शकम् ।

"आवर्तिन्यः करतले यस्याङ्गुल्यो भवन्ति हि ।
पार्श्वगास्ता विकीर्णाश्च स हस्तस्त्वलपल्लवः ॥" (ना. शा. ९-९१)

शङ्कुकादिभिस्त्वञ्चनं देहाभिमुख्येन पृष्ठभागेन मभागलक्षणमिति व्याख्यायित नाम्ना न सङ्गतमित्यास्ताम् ।

---

१. N.S. निकुट्टनम् G.O.S. M.G. K.S.S. निकुट्टकम् ।
२. G.O.S. M.G. बाहुशिरसि K.S.S. N.S. बाहू शिरसि ।

निकुञ्चितार्धयोगेन भवे'दर्धनिकुट्टकम् ।

पर्यायशः कटिश्छिन्ना बाह्वोः[२] शिरसि पल्लवौ ॥ ७१ ॥

अस्य च प्रयोगः, स्वात्मसम्भावनाविषय एवाप्ररूढे वाक्यार्थे । यथा—"हउपरपरिवध उद्घटइघ" (७०) ।

(११) कटिच्छिन्नम् ।

"कटिमध्यस्य वलनाच्छिन्ना ।" (ना. शा. ६-२४५)

पर्यायश इत्युभयशेषः ।

"मणिबन्धनमुक्तौ तु पताकौ पल्लवौ स्मृतौ ।" (ना. शा. ६-१६६)

योजना तु—भ्रमरिकया (ना. शा. १०-४५) चार्या पर्यायेण पार्श्वद्वयभ्रमणं कृत्वा मण्डलस्थानके (ना. शा. १०-६५) स्थित्वा बाहुशिरसि च पल्लवं पताकालपल्लवच्छायाद्वितीयं पर्यायेण बिभ्रद्विधेयः । पुनरपरेणाङ्गेनैवमिति । त्रिश्चतुर्वैषैव क्रिया ।

"अतिक्रान्तक्रमं कृत्वा त्रिकं तु परिवर्तयेत् ।
द्वितीयपादभ्रमणात्तलेन भ्रमरी स्मृता ॥" (ना. शा. १०-४५)

"कुञ्चितं पादमुत्क्षिप्य पुरतः सम्प्रसारयेत् ।
उत्क्षिप्य पातयेच्चैनमतिक्रान्ता तु सा स्मृता ।" (ना. शा. १०-३०)

विस्मयप्रधानवाक्यार्थाभिनये चास्य प्रयोगः । यथा—"एभि उ० वि० खु गिडत्थ गिळित्थ उ० वोरु० वदाणहुणं भूकुळावणइ" । विस्मयप्राधान्यख्यापनायैवात्रपल्लवस्यादौ प्रयोगः "अद्धक्खि आ" इत्यादौ ॥ (७१)

(१२) अर्धरेचितकम् ।

"हस्तौ तु सर्पशिरसौ मध्यमाङ्गुष्ठकौ यदा ।
तिर्यक्प्रसारितास्यौ च तदा सूचीमुखौ स्मृतौ ॥" (ना. शा. ६-१६१)

मण्डल एव स्थानके स्थित्वा करो वक्षसि कटकामुखः सूचीमुखेन हस्तेनापगमपूर्वकं विद्धो निकटयोजितः चपटचावसरे (तदपसारणे) च पार्श्वं सम्यक्सौष्ठवेन नतं पादश्च निकुट्टितस्तदा कायार्धस्य पर्यायेण रेचनाद्बहिर्गमनादर्धरेचितम् । एतच्चासमञ्जसचेष्टाप्रधानवाक्यार्थाभिनये : यथा—"गिरिगिइळ०वमुं चोळउकज्जनुकारण" इत्यादौ । (७२) ।

---

१. K.S.S. M.G. निकुञ्चितश्च पादः स्यात् G.O.S. N.S. (Same as above) ।

२ N.S. K.S.S. M.G. बाहू G O S बाह्वोः ।

पुनःपुनश्च करणं कटिच्छिन्नं तु तद्भवेत् ।
अपविद्धकरः[1] सूच्या पादश्चैव निकुट्टितः[2] ॥ ७२ ॥
सन्नतं यत्र पार्श्वं च तद्भवेदर्धरेचितम् ।
स्वस्तिकौ चरणौ यत्र करौ वक्षसि रेचितौ[3] ॥ ७३ ॥
निकुञ्चितं तथा वक्षो वक्षस्स्वस्तिकमेव तत्[4] ।
अञ्चितेन तु पादेन रेचितौ तु करौ यदा ॥ ७४ ॥

---

(१३) वक्षःस्वस्तिकम् ।

वक्षसि तौ हस्तौ चतुरश्रौ स्थितौ तौ रेचितौ कृत्वा व्यावृत्तकरणेनानीय निकुञ्चिते आभुग्ने वक्षसि स्वस्तिकौ कार्यौ । हस्तस्वस्तिकानुसारेण च पादावन्योन्यं जङ्घानुगुल्फवलनेन स्वस्तिकौ कार्यौ ।

"निम्नमुन्नतपृष्ठं च व्याभुग्नांसं श्लथं क्वचित् ।
आभुग्नं तदुरः । " (ना. शा. ९-२२४)

अत्र च नृत्तयोगात्सौष्ठवप्राधान्यमिति । भुग्नांसमिति । अंसौ हस्तापेक्षया । लज्जितजातानुतापप्रधाने वाक्यार्थे एवास्य प्रयोजनम् । यथा—"भुंजइ सदेसदेसं धावंति बहिः णि अमित एव वंसतिण्णववसिः अनु अन्नअविरंहीम ।" (७३)

(१४) उन्मत्तकम् ।

"पार्ष्णिर्यत्र स्थिता भूमावूर्ध्वमग्रतलं तथा ।
अङ्गुल्यश्चाञ्चिताः सर्वाः स पादोऽञ्चित उच्यते ॥" (ना. शा. ९-२७५) आविद्धचार्या चास्य प्रयोगः ।

"स्वस्तिकस्याग्रतः पादः कुञ्चितस्तु प्रसारितः ।
निपतेदञ्चिताविद्धमाविद्धा नाम सा स्मृता ॥" (ना. शा, १०-३८)

एकवचनद्विवचनाभ्यामङ्गपर्यायः सूच्यते । एतस्यातिसौभाग्यादिजनितगर्वविषयः प्रयोगः । यथा—"इतिइएण इहहि कह विमाखरिततवसिइ ।" (७४)

---

१. M.G. अपविद्धः करः K.S.S G.O.S. N.S. अपविद्धकरः ।
२. K.S.S. M.G. निकुट्टकः G.O.S. N.S. निकुट्टितः ।
३. N.S. वक्षःस्थरेचितौ G.O.S. M.G. K.S.S. वक्षसि रेचितौ ।
४. K.S.S. M.G. च N.S. G.O.S. तत् ।

उन्मत्तं करणं तत्तु विज्ञेयं नृत्तकोविदैः ।
हस्ताभ्यामथ पादाभ्यां[1] भवतः स्वस्तिकौ यदा ॥ ७५ ॥
तत्स्वस्तिकमिति प्रोक्तं करणं करणार्थिभिः ।
विक्षिप्ताक्षिप्तबाहुभ्यां स्वस्तिकौ चरणौ यदा ॥ ७६ ॥

---

(१५) स्वस्तिकम् ।

उद्वेष्टितवर्तनवामहस्तो निष्क्रमस्य(निष्कास्य) व्यावर्तितस्य करणसमकालमुत्प्लुत्य युगपदेव हस्तापादस्य स्वस्तिकं रचयेत् । **करणार्थिभिरिति** वाक्यार्थाभिनयलक्षणा । नृत्ताङ्गहाररूपा गतिपरिक्रमादिस्वभावाश्च क्रिया येऽर्थयन्त इति मध्ये तेन भङ्गिवचनेन सर्वेषां करणानां प्रयोजनं सूचितम् । तत्र युक्त्या द्वे (न्वे) षणनिषेधरहस्ये (राभस्ये ?)च वाक्यार्थेऽभिनेतव्येऽस्य प्रयोगः । यथा "मणिचारिं ते मत्थिअरुअं गढजांवणयेणवंति हिअंभुळणए किं त कंमणएण" ॥ (७५)

(१६) पृष्ठस्वस्तिकम् ।

"ऊरुभ्यां वलनं कृत्वा कुञ्चितं पादमुद्धरेत् ।
पार्श्वे विनिक्षिपेच्चैनमपक्रान्ता तु सा स्मृता ॥" (ना. शा. १०-३१)
"कुञ्चितं पादमुत्क्षिप्य जानूर्ध्वं सम्प्रसारयेत् ।
पातयेच्चाग्रयोगेन सा सूची परिकीर्तिता ॥" (ना. शा १०-३४)

ऊर्ध्व (अर्ध) शब्देन द्वितीयस्मिन्पादे सूची कार्या । न तु तस्मिन्नेव पर्यायेणेत्याह । तेनेत्थं योजना—उद्वेष्टितक्रियया बाहुद्वयविक्षेपसमकालमपक्रान्ता चारी । तया अपवेष्टितकरणसमकालं द्वितीयेन पादेन सूचीं विधाय स्वस्तिकं पादाभ्यां तथा हस्ताभ्यां कुर्यादिति । पृष्ठे पाश्चात्ये समे यत्स्वस्तिकं तथा दक्षिणपृष्ठे वामपादेन स्वस्तिकं त्रिकवलनया च पराङ्मुखीभूय स्वस्तिकमिति पृष्ठस्वस्तिकम् । प्रयोगोऽस्योक्तविषय एव । अन्ये तु पृष्ठविषये हस्ताभ्यां स्वस्तिकमिच्छन्तो युद्धविषये परिक्रमेऽस्य प्रयोगमाहुः । (७६)

(१७) दिक्स्वस्तिकम् ।

हस्ताभ्यामथेत्यादिना यत्पश्चात्स्वस्तिकाख्यं करणमुक्तं तदेव यदा पार्श्वयोरग्रे चकारात्पृष्ठे चतुर्दिङ्मुखेषु (षु) त्रुटितेना (ङ्गेन) क्रियतेऽत एवाङ्ग

---

1. M.G. K.S.S. उभाभ्यां हस्तपादाभ्याम् G.O.S. N.S. हस्ताभ्यामथ पादाभ्यां ।

ऽपक्रान्तार्धसूचिभ्यां तत्पृष्ठस्वस्तिकं भवेत् ।

पार्श्वयोरग्रतश्चैव यत्र श्लिष्टः करो भवेत्[1] ॥ ७७ ॥

स्वस्तिकौ[2] हस्तपादाभ्यां तद्दिक्स्वस्तिकमुच्यते ।

ऽलातं चरणं कृत्वा व्यंसयेद्दक्षिणं करम् ॥ ७८ ॥

ऊर्ध्वजानुक्रमं कुर्यादलातकमिति स्मृतम्[3] ।

स्वस्तिकापसृतः पादः करौ नाभिकटिस्थितौ ॥ ७९ ॥

श्लिष्ट इति । तदा दिक्स्वस्तिकमिति । अनेन मध्ये निरूपितेन सर्वेषां करणानामित्थं प्रयोगमनुजानीते । प्रयोगश्चास्य गीतपरिवर्तेषु । यद्वक्ष्यति "यदा गीत(ति)वशादङ्गं भूयो भूयो निवर्तते" (ना. शा. ४-३०६) । इत्यादि । (७७)

(१८) अलातकम् ।

पृष्ठे प्रसारितः पादो वलितेनान्तरीकृतः ।

पार्ष्णिप्रपतिता चैवमलाता सा प्रकीर्तिता ॥" (ना. शा. १०-४१)

अंसाद्विनिष्क्रमणं व्यंसयेदिति । तं च नृत्तहस्तं (नितम्बहस्तं) दक्षिणेन रचयति । यत्—

"कुञ्चितं पादमुत्क्षिप्य जानुस्तनसमं न्यसेत् ।

द्वितीयं च क्रमं तूर्ध्वमूर्ध्वजानुः प्रकीर्तिता ॥" (ना. शा. १०-३३)

ततश्चारीनिवेशाच्च पादस्याप्यलातादिसंज्ञा । एवं सर्वत्र ।

"बाहुशीर्षाद्विनिष्क्रान्तौ नितम्बाविति कीर्तितौ ।" (ना. शा. ८-१९६)

योजना तु—दक्षिणपादेनालातां चारीं प्रयुञ्जानो दक्षिणहस्तेन नितम्बं कृत्वा चतुरश्रमेव कुर्यात् । वामेन पादेनोर्ध्वजानुं ततो वामेनाप्यङ्गेन । एवमेतेऽध्वलातचार्या द्वि(द्विः)प्रयोगात्तन्नामधेयमेवेदं करणम् । प्रयोगश्चास्य ललितनृत्तविषये । यथा—"देवं हं उणवशंमि" इत्यादौ । (७८)

---

१. N.S. यत्र श्लिष्टकृतो भवेत् K.S.S. यत्र श्लिष्टः कृतो भवेत् । M.G. यत्र श्लिष्टः गतो भवेत् G.O.S. यत्र श्लिष्टः करो भवेत् ।

२. N.S. K.S.S. M.G. स्वस्तिको G.O.S. स्वस्तिकौ ।

३. K.S.S. M.G. चैव अलातकरणं भवेत् G.O.S. N.S. (Same as above) ।

पार्श्वमुद्वाहितं चैव करणं तत्कटीसमम् ।

हस्तो हृदि भवेद्वामः सव्यश्चाक्षिप्तरेचितः ॥ ८० ॥

(१९) कटीसमम् ।

स्वस्तिकादनन्तरमपसृत इत्यनेन आक्षिप्तायाश्चार्या अनन्तरमपक्रान्ताया-श्चार्याः प्रयोगमाह । चकारेण करौ च स्वस्तिकाववधृतौ । तत एको नाभिस्थः खटकः । एवमपरः कट्यामर्धचन्द्रः । तदेव पार्श्वं नतमपरमुद्वाहितं द्वितीये-नाङ्गेन ।

"कुञ्चितं पादमुत्क्षिप्य आक्षिप्य त्वञ्चितं न्यसेत् ।
जङ्घास्वस्तिकसंयुक्तमाक्षिप्ता नाम सा स्मृता ॥" (ना. शा. १०-३७)

"उत्क्षिप्तचक्रा तु यदाऽनामिका सकनीयसी ।
अस्यैव तु कपित्थस्य तदासौ खटकामुखः ॥" (ना. शा. ९-६१)

"यस्याङ्गुल्यस्तु विनताः सहाङ्गुष्ठेन चापवत् ।
सोऽर्धचन्द्रः " (ना. शा. ९-४३)
"उद्वाहितं तूर्ध्वगतमुरो ज्ञेयम्" इति । (ना. शा. ९-२३१)

तत्पार्श्वमप्युद्वाहितम् । वैष्णवं चात्र स्थानकं कटिसमं तरवबन्धाल्लभ्यते ।

"द्वौ तालावर्धतालश्च पादयोरन्तरं भवेत् ।
तयोः समस्थितस्त्वेकः त्र्यश्रः पक्षस्थितोऽपरः ॥
किञ्चिदञ्चितजङ्घं च सौष्ठवाङ्गपुरस्कृतम् ।
वैष्णवं स्थानमेतद्धि विष्णुरत्राधिदैवतम् ॥ " (ना. शा. १०-५२-५३)

जर्जराभिमन्त्रणावसरे सूत्रधारेणायं प्रयोक्तव्यः । (७९)

(२०) आक्षिप्तरेचितम् ।

हृदयक्षेत्रे वामः सव्यश्च यो हस्तः स आसमन्तादित्यूर्ध्वे पार्श्वद्वये च व्यावर्तितकरणेन क्षिप्तः स रेचितो हंसपक्षद्रुतभ्रमात्मा । (ना. शा. ९-१९३) । तत एक आक्षिप्तः स्ववक्षोदेशमधोमुख आनीतोऽञ्चितश्च रेचितः सन्नपविद्धश्च । गात्रक्षेत्रान्निष्क्रामित इत्याक्षिप्तरेचितं करणम् । पादावत्र प्रयोगानुसारेण अञ्चितसूचीरूपेण । त्यागोपादानपरस्प (म्प) रात्मनि च वाक्यार्थेऽभिनेतव्येऽस्य प्रयोगः । यथा "हुण्डे चिसुणइ एइं वइउ वण" इत्यादौ ॥ (८०)

रेचितश्चापविद्धश्च तत्स्यादाक्षिप्तरेचितम् ।
विक्षिप्तं हस्तपादं च[1] तस्यैवाक्षेपणं पुनः ॥ ८१ ॥
यत्र तत्करणं ज्ञेयं विक्षिप्ताक्षिप्तकं द्विजाः ।
स्वस्तिकौ चरणौ कृत्वा करिहस्तं च दक्षिणम् ॥ ८२ ॥

(२१) विक्षिप्ताक्षिप्तकम् ।

एकस्य हस्तस्य व्यावर्तनकरणकाले पादस्य बहिर्निष्क्रमणलक्षणो विक्षेपः । द्वितीयहस्तस्तु चतुरश्र एव । पुनः परिवर्तितकरणेन तस्य हस्तपादस्याक्षेपो द्वितीयस्य विक्षेपः । गमनागमनप्रधाने वाक्यार्थे चास्य प्रयोगः ।

यथा—"आवर्तउजंतउ पुणं रगइदम्" इत्यादाविति केचित् ।

उपाध्यायास्त्वाहुः—अभिनयहस्ता ये वक्ष्यन्ते तत्प्रधानस्य करणस्य वाक्यार्थाभिनये प्रयोगः । न तु केवलवर्तनाप्रधानस्य केवलनृत्तहस्तप्रधानस्य वा तस्य तु नृत्ते प्रयोगः प्राधान्येन । अन्ये तु कदाचिदङ्गस्य मोदरक्षणा (यै) यथायोगमभिनयान्तराले गतिपरिक्रम(मे ?)तालान्तरसन्धाने युद्धनियुद्धचारीस्थानके सञ्चारे वा प्रयोग इति । एतच्च सर्वत्रानुसरणीयम् । (८१)

(२२) अर्धस्वस्तिकम् ।

"समुन्नतो लताहस्तः पार्श्वात्पार्श्वं तु दोलितः ।
त्रिपताकोऽपरः कर्णे करिहस्तः प्रकीर्तितः ॥"
"तिर्यक्प्रसारितौ चैव पार्श्वसंस्थौ लताभिधौ ।" (ना. शा. ९-१९८-१९९) ।

"कटिहस्तम्" इति केचित्पठन्ति । तत्र व्याख्या कट्यां यो हस्तोऽर्धचन्द्रः पक्षप्रद्योतकवञ्चितकौ । **वाममिति** खटकास्यम् (ना. शा. ९-६१) पादाभ्यामेव स्वस्तिकयोगादर्धस्वस्तिकम् । एतत्करणमभिनयहस्तरहितमेव । (८२)

(२३) अञ्चितम् ।

स एवेति योऽर्धस्वस्तिककरणे करिहस्त उक्तः स एव व्यावर्तितकरणेन यदा नासाक्षेत्रे अलपल्लवाकृतित्वादञ्चितोऽञ्चितसारणानुकारि तदञ्चितम् । एतस्य संमुखीनात्मविषये स्वातिशयकौतुके(क)प्रधाने वाक्यार्थे प्रयोगः । यथा—एवउवेम्मकुहेउको इति । (८३)

---

१. K.S.S. M.G. तु G.O.S. N.S. च ।

वक्षःस्थाने तथा वाममर्धस्वस्तिकमाविशेत् ।
व्यावृत्तपरिवृत्तस्तु स एव तु करो यदा ॥ ८३ ॥

अञ्चितो नासिकाग्रे तु तदञ्चितमुदाहृतम् ।
कुञ्चितं पादमुत्क्षिप्य त्र्यश्रमूरुं विवर्तयेत्[1] ॥ ८४ ॥

कटिजानुविवर्ताच्च[2] भुजङ्गत्रासितं भवेत् ।
कुञ्चितं पादमुत्क्षिप्य जानुस्तनसमं[3] न्यसेत् ॥ ८५ ॥

---

(२४) भुजङ्गत्रासितम् ।

नृत्तस्थानादिसिद्धत्वात्करणमिदमुक्तरूपमाशङ्कितदृष्टनिकटतः सर्पत्रासाविष्टस्येव गतिसंवर्ते भुजङ्गत्रासितं करणम् । हस्तौ तु पादवशाद्व्यावर्तितपरिवर्तितौ भवतः । क्रमेणैको दोलाहस्तः (ना. शा. ९-१४१) परः खटकास्य इति करणम् । एतत्सादृश्यात्तु भुजङ्गत्रासितचारी (ना. शा. १०-४२) वक्ष्यते । एवं करणतुल्यं नाम सर्वचारीषु वाच्यम् । (८४)

(२५) ऊर्ध्वजानु ।

"उत्क्षिप्ता यस्य पार्ष्णिः स्यादङ्गुल्यः कुञ्चितास्तथा ।
तथा कुञ्चितमध्यश्च स पादः परिकुञ्चितः ॥" (ना. शा. ९-२७७)

ऊर्ध्वजानु एवं भविष्यति—कुञ्चितसमकालं स एव हस्त एव कुञ्चितस्तनसमजानूपरि वोर्ध्वमुखोऽलपल्लवोऽरालो वा । तत्रापरस्तु वक्षःस्थखटकामुखः । (८५)

(२६) निकुञ्चितम् ।

वृश्चिकाख्ये करणे यः पादो वक्ष्यते "पादः पृष्ठाञ्चितस्तथा" इति (ना. शा. ४-१०८) (स) वृश्चिकशब्देनेहोच्यते । तेन पश्चात्प्रसारितं चरणं

---

१. K.S.S. ऊरू विवर्तयेत् M.G. ऊरू निवर्तयेत् G.O.S. N.S. ऊरू विवर्तयेत् ।

२. N.S. कटिजानू विवर्तौ च K.S.S. कटिजानु विवृत्तं च M.G. कटिजानू निवृत्तौ च G.O.S. कटिजानुविवर्ताच्च ।

३. K.S.S. जानुमूर्ध्वं प्रसारयेत् M.G. जानुहस्तं समं न्यसेत् G.O.S. N.S. जानुस्तनसमं न्यसेत् ।

प्रयोगवशगौ हस्तावूर्ध्वजानु प्रकीर्तितम् ।
वृश्चिकं चरणं[1] कृत्वा करं पार्श्वे निकुञ्चयेत् ॥ ८६ ॥
नासाग्रे दक्षिणं चैव ज्ञेयं तत्तु[2] निकुञ्चितम् ।
वामदक्षिणपादाभ्यां घूर्णमानो[3]पसर्पणैः ॥ ८७ ॥
उद्वेष्टितापविद्धैश्च हस्तैर्मत्तल्ल्यु[4]दाहृतम् ।
स्खलितापसृतौ पादौ वामहस्तश्च रेचितः ॥ ८८ ॥

कृत्वा तदेकं च हस्तं शिरःपार्श्वक्षेत्रेऽरालं द्वितीयं च नासाग्रक्षेत्रानुसारि वक्षस्थरालमेव कुर्यात् । अन्ये त्वाहुः—नासाग्रे एकः पताकः अन्यश्च सूच्यास्य इति । एतच्चाकाशगमनोन्मुखवितर्कप्रणिधानादिप्रधानवाक्यार्थाभिनये । यथा हनूमतः 'एषोऽस्मि व्योममार्गे प्रसभमभिचरन्किं विलम्बैः' । इत्यादौ ॥ (८६)

(२७) मत्तल्लि ।

चार्यप्येवंरूपैव(ना. शा. १०-२८)भविष्यति । घूर्णमानस्य ततो यान्युपसर्पणानि पादस्य तैरुपलक्षिताभ्यां पादाभ्याम् । घूर्णनं च पादस्य द्वितीयपादगुल्फस्वस्तिकोपसर्पणम् । तत्समकालं च हस्तौ नितम्बाख्यावुद्वेष्टितौ तदोपसर्पणकालेऽपविद्धोपवेष्टने (द्वावपवेष्टितौ) । एवं द्वितीयेनाङ्गेन । बहुवचनं पुनः पुनरित्थं क्रियेति सूचयति । मदनं मत्त तनोतीति मत्तल्लि मदोत्कलस्य वीप्सायोगेन करणेन । तन्मत्तल्लित्रये विक्षेपः । मत्तशेखरकादिविषयोऽस्याः प्रयोगः । (८७)

(२८) अर्धमत्तल्लि ।

(वामः) रेचितो हंसपक्षो द्रुतभ्रमः । स्खलित इति षट् (कट्यां ?) द्वितीयः पादनिकटं प्राप्तः । तरुणमदविषयः (प्रयोगः) । (८८)

(२९) रेचितनिकुट्टितम् ।

सव्य इति दक्षिण एव । निकुट्टित इत्युद्घट्टितक्रियया ।

---

१. K.S.S. M.G. करणं वृश्चिकं कृत्वा G.O.S. N.S. वृश्चिकं चरणं कृत्वा ।
२. G.O.S. N.S. ततस्तु K.S.S. M.G. तद्धि ।
३. G.O.S. N.S. M.G. घूर्णमान K.S.S. पूर्णमान ।
४. G.O.S. N.S. K.S.S. मत्तल्ली M.G. मल्ली ।

सव्यहस्तः कटिस्थः स्यादर्धमत्तल्लि तत्स्मृ[1]तम् ।

रेचितो दक्षिणो हस्तः पादः सव्यो निकुट्टितः ॥ ८९ ॥

दोला चैव भवेद्वामस्ताद्[2]रेचिता निकुट्टितम् ।

कार्यौ नामितटे हस्तौ प्राङ्मुखौ खटका[3]मुखौ ॥ ९० ॥

"स्थित्वा पादतलाग्रेण पार्ष्णिर्भूमौ निपात्यते ।" (ना. शा. ६-२४८) स उद्घट्टितः ।

"अंसौ प्रशिथिलौ मुक्तौ पताकौ तु प्रलम्बितौ ।

यदा भवेतां करणे स दोल इति संज्ञितः ॥" (ना. शा. ६-१३५) स्त्रीलिङ्गयोगेन दोलाहस्तस्य प्रेङ्खोलितं यद्वर्तनया गमनागमने सूचयति । (८९)

(३०) पादापविद्धकम् ।

नाभिक्षेत्रे पराङ्मुखौ । सूच्याख्येन पादने द्वितीयं पादं विद्धं विधाय स एव सूचीपादोऽपक्रान्तचारीयुक्तः कार्यः । एवं द्वितीयोऽपि ।

"उत्क्षिप्ता तु भवेत्पार्ष्णिरङ्गुष्ठाग्रेण संस्थितः ।"

सूचीपादः । (ना. शा. ६-२७६)

"ऊरुभ्यां वलनं कृत्वा" इत्यपक्रान्ता (ना. शा. १०-३१) पादात् पादान्तरमपविद्धमपसारितं यत्र तदिदं करणम् । (९०)

(३१) वलितम् ।

"हस्तौ तु सर्पशिरसौ" (ना. शा. ६-१६१) इति सूचीमुखो हस्तः । स देहक्षेत्रादपसृतः कार्यः । तत्समकालं सूचीपादोऽप्यसृतः । ततो भ्रमरिकां चारीं कृत्वा—

"अतिक्रान्तकमं कृत्वा त्रिकं तु परिवर्तयेत् ।

द्वितीयपादभ्रमणात्तलेन भ्रमरी स्मृता ॥" (ना. शा. १०-४८) तदिदं त्रिकवलनाद्वलितम् । (९१)

---

१. K.S.S. M G. अर्धमत्तल्लिमादिशेत् G.O.S. N.S. अर्धमत्तल्लि तत्स्मृतम् ।

२. K.S.S. M.G. रेचक G.O.S. N.S. रेचित ।

३. K.S.S. M.G. कटका G.O.S. N.S. खटका ।

सूचीविद्धावपक्रान्तौ पादौ पादापविद्धके[1] ।
अपविद्धो भवेद्धस्तः सूचीपादस्तथैव च ॥ ६१ ॥
तथा त्रिकं विवृत्तं च वलितं नाम तद्भवेत् ।
वर्तिताघूर्णितः[2] सव्यो हस्तो वामश्च दोलितः ॥ ६२ ॥
स्वस्तिकापसृतः पादः करणं घूर्णितं तु तत् ।
करिहस्तो भवेद्वामो दक्षिणश्च विवर्तितः[3] ॥ ६३ ॥

---

(३२) घूर्णितम् ।

पार्श्वक्षेत्रादूर्ध्वव्यावर्तितेनाधोमुखपरिवर्तितेन यदा दोलाहस्तत्वाद्-घूर्णितम् । (६२)

(३३) ललितम् ।

"समुन्नतो लताहस्तः पार्श्वात्पार्श्वंलोलितः ।

इत्ययं वामः । (ना. शा. ६-१६६)

दक्षिणं विविधं कृत्वा बहुशो वर्तितः ।

"बाहुशीर्षाद्विनिष्क्रान्तौ नितम्बौ । " (ना. शा. ६-१६६)

"केशदेशाद्विनिष्क्रान्तौ परिपार्श्वोत्थितौ तथा ।

विज्ञेयौ केशबन्धौ ॥ " (ना. शा. ६-१६७)

इत्येवंप्रकारनृत्तहस्तयोजनया वर्तितः । चकाराद्वर्तनान्ते "त्रिपताकोऽपरः कर्णे" (ना. शा. ६-१६६) इति करिहस्तः । पादश्च हस्तानुसारेण निकुट्टितः पुनः पुनरन्येनाङ्गेन । तदिति सविलासनृत्तविषयमेतत् । अत एव ललितं नाम करणम् । (६३)

(३४) दण्डपक्षम् ।

'कुञ्चितं पादमुत्क्षिप्य जानुस्तनसमम्' इति (ना. शा. १०-३३) ऊर्ध्व-जानुचारीं कुर्वन् "तिर्यक्प्रसारितौ" (ना. शा. ६-१६८) इति लताहस्तौ

---

१. K.S.S. पादापविद्धको G.O.S. N.S. M.G. पादापविद्धके ।

२. K.S.S. M.G. वर्तितो घूर्णितः G.O.S. N.S. वर्तिताघूर्णितः ।

३. N.S. अपवर्तितः G.O.S. M.G. K.S.S. विवर्तितः ।

बहुशः कुट्टितः पादो ज्ञेयं तल्ललितं बुधैः ।
ऊर्ध्वजानुं विधायाथ[1] तस्योपरि लतां न्यसेत् ॥ ६४ ॥
दण्डपक्षं तु तत्प्रोक्तं करणं नृत्तवेदिभिः ।
भुजङ्गत्रासितं कृत्वा यत्रोभावपि रेचितौ ॥ ६५ ॥
वामपार्श्वस्थितौ हस्तौ भुजङ्गत्रस्तरेचितम् ।
त्रिकं सुवलितं कृत्वा लतारेचितकौ करौ ॥ ६६ ॥

विधायैकं लताहस्तं तस्य जानुन उपरि क्षिपेत् । पुनर्द्वितीयेनाङ्गेनैवमित्येकत्र पार्श्वे दण्डवद्बाहुसमवस्थानाद्दण्डपक्षं करणम् । (६४)

(३५) **भुजङ्गत्रस्तरेचितम् ।**

तदित्यध्याहारः ।

"कुञ्चितं पादमुत्क्षिप्य त्र्यश्रमूरुं विवर्तयेत् ।" (ना. शा. १०-४२) इति विधाय द्वावपि हंसपक्षौ द्रुतभ्रमौ (ना. शा. ९-१९३) वामक्षेत्रगौ हस्तौ नेयौ । (६५)

(३६) **नूपुरम् ।**

पृष्ठतोऽञ्चितं कृत्वा पादमग्रतलेन तु ।
द्रुतं निपातयेद् भूमौ चारी नूपुरपादिका ॥" (ना. शा. १०-३५)

तेन भ्रमरिकया चार्या (ना. शा. १०-४५) त्रिकवलनं कृत्वा ततो नूपुरपादिकां चारीं येन पादेन करोति तद्दिक्केनैव हस्तेन (**रेचितम्** । द्वितीयो लताहस्तः) । (६६)

(३७) **वैशाखरेचितम् ।**

रेचितौ नृत्तहस्तौ हंसपक्षौ द्रुतभ्रमाविति । तदनुकारेण पादग्रीवाकटिगतं रेचितं ज्ञेयम् । यथोक्तं **राहुलकेन**—

"ग्रीवायां करयोः कट्यां पादयोश्च पृथक्पृथक् ।
भ्रमणं रेचितं विद्यात् ।" इति ।

---

१. N.S. ऊर्ध्वजानु विधायातः G.O.S. ऊर्ध्वजानुं विधायाथ K.S.S. ऊर्ध्वं जानु विधायाथ M.G. ऊर्ध्वजानु विधायाथ ।

नूपुरश्च तथा पादः[1] करणे नूपुरे न्यसेत् ।
रेचितौ हस्तपादौ च कटी ग्रीवा च[2] रेचिता ॥ ९७ ॥
वैशाखस्थानकेनैतद्भवेद्वैशाखरेचितम् ।
आक्षिप्तः स्वस्तिकः पादः करौ चोद्वेष्टितौ तथा ॥ ९८ ॥
त्रिकस्य वलनाच्चैव[3] ज्ञेयं भ्रमरकं तु तत् ।
अञ्चितः स्यात्करो वामः सव्यश्चतुर एव तु[4] ॥ ९९ ॥

"तालास्त्रयोऽर्धतालश्च पादयोरन्तरं भवेत् ।
तालांस्त्रीनर्धतालं च निषण्णोरु प्रकल्पयेत् ॥
त्र्यश्रौ पक्षस्थितौ पादौ ॥" (ना. शा. १०-६१-६२)

वैशाखं स्थानम् । एतत्करणमभिवाहने । (९७)

(३८) भ्रमरकम् ।

अनेन पादेनाक्षिप्ता चारी सूचिता ।

"कुञ्चितं पादमुत्क्षिप्य व्याक्षिप्य त्वञ्चितं न्यसेत् ।
जङ्घास्वस्तिकसंयुक्तमाक्षिप्ता नाम सा स्मृता ॥" (ना. शा. १०-३७) तेनैवं योजना—स्वस्तिकानन्तरं पादमाक्षिप्य तत्समकालमुद्वेष्टय "तर्जन्याद्या बहिर्मुखम्" (ना. शा. ९-२१९) इत्युद्वेष्टितमेकं हस्तं कृत्वा त्रिकवलनं कृत्वा पुनर्द्वितीयेनाङ्गेन तथैव । चकारात्तद्वलनानन्तरं स्वस्तिक एव पादः । एकवचनद्विवचनाभ्यां पर्यायेण प्रयोगोऽत्र सूचितः । यदि वोद्वेष्टितशब्देनोल्बणौ नृत्तहस्तावुपलक्षितौ ।

"करावुद्वेष्टिताग्रौ तु प्रविधायालपल्लवौ ।
ऊर्ध्वं प्रसारिताविद्धौ कर्तव्यावुल्बणौ ॥" इति (ना. शा. ९-२०८)

तदा युगपदेव प्रयोगं कृत्वा पादस्वस्तिकभ्रमणाद्धेस्य साक्षात्कृतः । संज्ञायां कन् । एतदुद्धतपरिभ्रमणविषये प्रयोक्तव्यम् । (९८)

---

१. M.G. K.S.S. N.S. नूपुरं च तथा पादं G.O.S. नूपुरश्च तथा पादः ।
२. K.S.S. M.G. कटिग्रीवौ च रेचितौ N.S. G.O.S. कटी ग्रीवा च रेचिता ।
३. N.S. वलनं चैव G.O.S. K.S.S. M.G. वलनाच्चैव ।
४. K.S.S. M.G. N.S. च G.O.S. तु ।

दक्षिणः कुट्टितः पादश्चतुरं तत्प्रकीर्तितम् ।
भुजङ्गत्रासितः पादो दक्षिणो रेचितः करः[1] ॥ १०० ॥
लताख्यश्च करो वामो भुजङ्गाञ्चितकं भवेत् ।
विक्षिप्तं हस्तपादं तु समन्ताद्यत्र दण्डवत् ॥ १०१ ॥

(३९) चतुरम् ।

अञ्चित इत्यलपल्लवः (ना. शा. ६-६१)

"तिस्रः प्रसारिता यत्र तथा चोर्ध्वा कनीयसी ।

तासां मध्ये तथाङ्गुष्ठः स करश्चतुरः स्मृतः ॥" (६-६३) एवकारेण वक्षःक्षेत्राद् द्वयोरप्यलम् । तु शब्देन सन्निवेशाधिक्यं केवलमिति सूच्यते । **कुट्टित** इति ।

"स्थित्वा पादतलाग्रेण पार्ष्णिर्भूमौ निपात्यते ।" (ना. शा. ६-२६६) इत्युद्धट्टिताङ्गरूपः । एतद्विदूषकस्य सविस्मयसूच्याभिनयादौ । यथा "सानुरे खण्डदासवर्येमिसासा । (६६)

(४०) भुजङ्गाञ्चितकम् ।

("कुञ्चितं पादम् । " (ना. शा. १०-४२) इत्यादि भुजङ्गत्रासितचार्यां पादः । "हंसपक्षौ द्रुतभ्रमौ ।" (६-१०३) इति दक्षिणो रेचितः । "तिर्यक्प्रसारितौ" इति (ना. शा. ६-१६८) वामो लताख्यो नृत्तहस्तः ।). (१००)

(४१) दण्डकरेचितम् ।

दण्डवद्धस्तविक्षेपेण रेचनेन च दण्डपक्षौ सूच्येते । पादविक्षेपेण तु दण्डपादाचारी ।

"हंसपक्षकृतौ हस्तौ व्यावृत्तपरिवर्तितौ ।

तथा प्रसारितभुजौ दण्डपक्षाविति स्मृतौ ॥" (ना. शा. ६-२०२)

"नूपुरं चरणं कृत्वा पुरतः सम्प्रसारयेत् ।

क्षिप्रमाविद्धकरणं दण्डपादा तु सा स्मृता ॥" (ना. शा. १०-४४) तत्प्रमोदविषयं करणम् । उद्धतविषये चास्य प्रयोगः (इत्यन्ये) । (१०१)

---

१. K.S.S. M.G. रेचितो दक्षिणः करः C.O.S. N.S. दक्षिणो रेचितः करः ।

रेच्यते तद्धि करणं ज्ञेयं दण्डकरेचितम् ।

वृश्चिकं चरणं[1] कृत्वा द्वावप्यथ निकुट्टितौ ॥ १०२ ॥

विधातव्यौ करौ तत्तु[2] ज्ञेयं वृश्चिककुट्टितम् ।

सूचीं कृत्वा[3]पविद्धं च दक्षिणं चरणं न्यसेत् ॥ १०३ ॥

रेचिता च कटिर्यत्र कटिभ्रान्तं तदुच्यते ।

अञ्चितः पृष्ठतः पादः कुञ्चितोर्ध्वतलाङ्गुलिः ॥ १०४ ॥

---

(४२) वृश्चिककुट्टितम् ।

पृष्ठभागे रेचितजङ्घमुत्तानतलं वृश्चिकोपलक्षितं चरणं कृत्वा द्वावपि हस्तौ स्वबाहुशिरस्यलपल्लवौ निकुट्टितौ पर्यायेण विदध्यादिति । एतच्च विस्मयाकाशगमनेच्छादिप्रधाने वाक्यार्थविषये प्रयुज्यते । यथा, "पडिविधारिअं उवक्खंहिआ" इत्यादौ । (१०२)

(४३) कटिभ्रान्तम् ।

"कुञ्चितं पादमुत्क्षिप्य जानूर्ध्वं सम्प्रसारयेत् ।

पातयेदग्रयोगेन सा सूची परिकीर्तिता ॥" (ना. शा. १०-३४) वाम द्रुतमपसारितं कृत्वा पार्श्वे दक्षिणं पादं न्यसेत् । समकालं पृष्ठपरावर्तनक्रमेण कटिं रेचयेत् । भ्रमरिकया वा चार्या (ना. शा. १०४५) करयोश्च प्रयोगवशगत्वेन (कटि) भ्रमणकाले तयोरपि व्यावर्तनपरिवर्तनकरणं योजनान्ते चतुरश्रावस्थानम् । गतिपरिक्रमेऽस्य तालाकारादि (लान्तरालादि) यतिपरिपूरणविषये प्रयोगः । (१०३)

(४४) लतावृश्चिकम् ।

प्रथमार्धेन वृश्चिकं । वामं चरणं भूमौ । आकाशादवपतनेऽस्य प्रयोगः । (१०२)

---

१. K.S.S. M.G. करणं G.O.S. N.S. चरणं ।

२. K.S.S. M.G. तद्धि G.O.S. N.S. तत्तु ।

३. N.S. दत्त्वा K.S.S. M.G. G.O.S. कृत्वा ।

लताख्यश्च करो वामस्तल्लतावृश्चिकं भवेत् ।
अलपद्मः कटीदेशे छिन्ना पर्यायशः कटी ॥ १०५ ॥
वैशाखस्थानकेनेह तच्छिन्नं करणं भवेत् ।
वृश्चिकं चरणं कृत्वा स्वस्तिकौ च करावुभौ ॥ १०६ ॥
रेचितौ विप्रकीर्णौ च करौ वृश्चिकरेचितम्[1] ।
बाहुशीर्षाञ्चितौ हस्तौ पादः पृष्ठाञ्चितस्तथा ॥ १०७ ॥

(४५) छिन्नम् ।

क्रमेण पार्ष्ण्योर्नमनोन्नमनाभ्यां (ना. शा. ६-२५१, २३५) यदा कटिच्छेदः । पार्ष्ण्योर्नमनोन्नमने पर्यायेण । तथैव च कटिपार्श्वक्षेत्र एव ।

"आवर्तिन्यः करतले यस्याङ्गुल्यः ।" (ना. शा. ९-९१)

इत्येवंभूतोऽलपल्लवः । ईषद्गतागतपर्यायेण द्वाभ्यां हस्ताभ्यां प्रयुज्यते । वैशाखस्थानकेन "तालास्त्रयोऽर्धतालश्च" (ना. शा. १०-६१) इति "निष्क्रान्तौ" इति च लक्षणेन तदा कटिच्छेदयोगि छिन्नं नाम । अङ्गप्रतिसारणतालभञ्जनादिविषये चास्य प्रयोगः । (१०५)

(४६) वृश्चिकरेचितम् ।

"तावेव मणिबन्धान्ते ।" इति (ना. शा. ९-१८७) स्वस्तिकौ । विप्रकीर्णकौ रेचितौ हंसपक्षौ द्रुतभ्रमौ । एतदाकाशयानके प्रयोज्यम् । (१०६)

(४७) वृश्चिकम् ।

द्विवचनैकवचने अङ्गस्यापरिहारं सूचयतः । हस्तस्य बाहुशिरस्यञ्चनेन करिहस्तप्रयोगः सूच्यते ।

"समुन्नतो लताहस्तः पार्श्वात्पार्श्वं विलोलितः ।
त्रिपताकोऽपरः कर्णे करिहस्तः ॥" (ना. शा. ९-१९९)

दूरसन्नतपृष्ठत्वं वृश्चिकप्रयोगनान्तरीयं(कं) सर्वत्र वृश्चिकप्रयोगेषु मन्तव्यम् । वृश्चिकपुच्छस्थानीयचरणं वृश्चिकमेतत्करणम् । तदुपलक्षितपादो वृश्चिकः । अस्याकाशगतौ च ऐरावणादिविषये प्रयोगः । यथा—"श्वेताभ्रभ्रान्तिकारी समवतरति खादभ्रमूवल्लभोऽयम्" इति । (१०७)

---

१. K.S.S. M.G. रेचितापसृतौ चैव कार्यं वृश्चिकरेचितम् G.O.S. N.S. (Same as above).

दूरसन्नतपृष्ठं च वृश्चिकं तत्प्रकीर्तितम् ।
आलीढं स्थानकं[1] यत्र करौ वक्षसि रेचितौ ॥ १०८ ॥

ऊर्ध्वाधोविप्रकीर्णौ च व्यंसितं करणं तु तत्[2] ।
हस्तौ तु स्वस्तिकौ पार्श्वे तथा पादो निकुट्टितः ॥ १०९ ॥

---

(४८) **व्यंसितम् ।**

"मण्डले दक्षिणं पादं पञ्चतालान्प्रसार्य तु ।
आलीढं स्थानकं कुर्यात् ॥" (ना. शा. १०-६७)

एकस्य तर्जन्याद्युद्वेष्टितेन (ना. शा. ६-२१६) करणेनाधो विप्रकीर्णता। द्वितीयस्तर्जन्यादिपरावर्तितकरणेनोर्ध्वगतः, क्षेत्रपर्यायेणैक उत्तानो हंसपक्षो द्रुतभ्रमलक्षणो रेचकम् । अव(प)रोऽधोमुख ऊर्ध्वाध इत्येकीकरणम् । तच्च करणमुभयत्र सम्बध्यते । एतच्च विभ्रमादि(हनुमदादि ?)परिक्रमविषयम् । (१०८)

(४९) **पार्श्वनिकुट्टकम् ।**

"तावेव मणिबन्धान्ते" इति (ना. शा. ६-१८७) स्वस्तिकौ । तथाशब्देन पार्श्वे तयोर्निकुट्टितत्वं पर्यायेणोच्यते । तस्य तलमेव च पादस्य निकुट्टितत्वम् । पुनर्द्वितीयेनाङ्गेनेति पार्श्वगतहस्तनिकुट्टितयोगात् पार्श्वनिकुट्टितम् । प्रकाशनसंवरणाहार(भ्यास ?)प्रधाने वाक्यार्थे चास्य प्रयोगः । यथा "पुण्णाव उडेहराभुइं कुहुएहमं......पेताहं (महंसिपित") इत्यादौ । (१०९)

(५०) **ललाटतिलकम् ।**

पादस्य तस्यैव पश्चाद्भागादितरस्याङ्गुष्ठेन तिलकं तिलकक्रियाहेतुभूतत्वेन लक्षितं संश्लेषं कुर्यादित्यासि(दि)कमेतत्करणं विद्याधरगतिविषये प्रयुज्यते । (११०)

(५१) **क्रान्तकम् ।**

"कुञ्चितं पादमुत्क्षिप्य पुरतः सम्प्रसारयेत् ।

---

१. K.S.S. आलीढस्थानके M.G. N.S. G.O.S. आलीढं स्थानकं ।
२. M.G. ऊर्ध्वाधौ विप्रकीर्णौ च व्यंसितं तद्विदुर्बुधाः K.S.S. ऊर्ध्वाधो विप्रकीर्णौ .........G.O.S. N.S. (Same as above).

यत्र तत्करणं ज्ञेयं बुधैः पार्श्वनिकुट्टितम्[1] ।
वृश्चिकं चरणं कृत्वा पादस्याङ्गुष्ठकेन तु ॥ ११० ॥
ललाटे तिलकं कुर्याल्ललाटतिलकं तु[2] तत् ।
पृष्ठतः कुञ्चितं कृत्वा व्यतिक्रान्तक्रमं ततः[3] ॥ १११ ॥
आक्षिप्तौ च करौ कार्यौ क्रान्तके करणे द्विजाः ।
आद्यः पादो नतः[4] कार्यः सव्यहस्तश्च कुञ्चितः ॥ ११२ ॥

उत्क्षिप्य पातयेच्चैनमतिक्रान्ता ॥" इति (ना. शा. १०-३०) चारीं तां कृत्वा पात्यमानं चरणं कुञ्चितं स्थापयेत् । पृष्ठतः कुञ्चितं च समादाय क्रियान्तपरिक्रमेण प्रसारयेत् । हस्तौ विचार्य (ल्य ?) व्यावर्तितकरणेन देहक्षेत्रान्निष्क्रान्तः पुनः परिवर्तितकरणेनाक्षिप्तः स (व)क्षसि खटकामुखः । पुनरपरेणाङ्गेन प्रयोगः । उद्धतपरिक्रमेऽस्य प्रयोगः । (१११)

(५२) कुञ्चितम् ।

आद्यो नत इति जानुगमनेन भूतलसञ्चरो लक्ष्यते । दक्षिणहस्तश्च कुञ्चितः उत्तानालपल्लवरूपो वामपार्श्वे विधेयः । तदेतन्निर्भरानन्दपूर्णदेवस्याभिनयविषये प्रयोक्तव्वम् । यथा "देहसुभाइउं मकरकलिअणुकापालविर्द्धं इचळणं घिआइ" इत्यादौ । (११२)

(५३) चक्रमण्डलम् ।

अड्डिता चात्रादौ चारी ।

"अग्रतः पृष्ठतो वाऽपि पादोऽग्रतलसञ्चरः ।
द्वितीयपादनिर्घृष्टो यस्यां स्यादड्डिता तु सा ॥" (ना. शा. १०-२३)

उद्धतपरिक्रमपरिष्करणा (रिक्रमा)दिविषये चैतत् । (११३)

---

१. K.S.S. निकुट्टनम् M.G. निकुट्टकम् G.O.S. N.S. निकुट्टितम्
२. G.O.S. N.S. तु K.S.S. M.G. च ।
३. K.S.S. M.G. पृष्ठतः कुञ्चितं कुर्यादतिक्रान्तं समन्ततः G.O.S. M.G. (Same as above).
४. K.S.S. M.G. अञ्चितः G.O.S. N.S. नतः ।

उत्तानो वामपार्श्वस्थ[1]स्तत्कुञ्चितमुदाहृतम् ।
प्रलम्बिताभ्यां बाहुभ्यां यद्गात्रेणानतेन च ॥ ११३ ॥
अभ्यन्तरापविद्धः[2] स्यात्तज्ज्ञेयं चक्रमण्डलम् ।
स्वस्तिकापसृतौ पादा[3]वपविद्धक्रमौ यदा ॥ ११४ ॥
उरोमण्डलकौ[4] हस्तावुरोमण्डलिकन्तु तत् ।
आक्षिप्तं हस्तपादं[5] च क्रियते यत्र वेगतः ॥ ११५ ॥

---

(५४) उरोमण्डलम् ।

"भूमिघृष्टेन पादेन कृत्वाभ्यन्तरमण्डलम् ।
पुनरुत्सारयेदन्यं स्थितावर्ता तु सा स्मृता ॥" (ना. शा. १०-१५)

इत्यनया चार्याऽप्रसारणं स्वस्तिकस्य कार्यम् । बद्धाचार्यत्वादादाववस्थानमित्युक्तं भवति ।

"अन्योन्यजङ्घासंवेधात्कृत्वा तु स्वस्तिकं ततः ।
ऊरुभ्यां वलनम्" इति (ना. शा. १०-२१)

तस्या रूपं स्वस्तिकसंस्थानाक्षिप्तम् ।

उद्वेष्टितो भवेदेको द्वितीयश्चापवेष्टितः ।
भ्रमितावुरसः स्थाने ह्युरोमण्डलिनौ स्मृतौ ॥" (ना. शा. ४-२०६) (११०)

(५५) आक्षिप्तम् ।

"कुञ्चितं पादमुत्क्षिप्याञ्चितम्" । इति (ना. शा. १०-३७)

---

१. K.S.S. M.G. पार्श्वश्च G.O.S. N.S. पार्श्वस्थः ।
२. N.S. अपविद्धम् K.S.S. अपविद्धाः M.G. G.O.S. अपविद्धः ।
३. K.S.S. पादावर्धक्रमौ यदा G.O.S. M.G. N.S. (Same as above).
४. K.S.S. M.G. उरोमण्डलिको हस्तः N.S. Same except मण्डलकः G.O.S. (Same as above) ।
५. K.S.S. M.G. आक्षिप्तहस्तपादं च G.O.S. N.S. आक्षिप्तं हस्तपादं च ।

आक्षिप्तं नाम करणं विज्ञेयं तत्द्विजोत्तमाः[1]।

ऊर्ध्वाङ्गुलितलः पादः पार्श्वेनोर्ध्वं प्रसारितः॥ ११६॥

प्रकुर्यादञ्चिततलौ हस्तौ तलविलासिते।

पृष्ठतः प्रसृतः पादो द्वौ तालावर्धमेव[2] च॥ ११७॥

आक्षिप्तया पादचार्या पार्श्वस्य किञ्चिन्नमनेन हस्तस्य चतुरश्रस्य खटकामुख्या क्षेपः इति विदूषकगतिविषयमाक्षिप्तकरणम्। (११५)

(५६) तलविलसितम्।

तेनैवोर्ध्वगतेन पादेन सहाञ्चिततलो वा श्लिष्टतलत्वात्कर्तव्यः। द्विवचनात्पर्यायेण द्वितीयेनाङ्गेन प्रयोगोऽभ्यासेन वा। पताकौ हस्तौ परस्परोपसंश्लिष्टाविति पादतलस्य हस्ततलस्य च विकृष्टे देशे आकाशे लसितं श्लेषण यत्र तलविलसितम्। पादोद्धारसंज्ञया सूत्रधारादिविषये नाट्याचार्या योजयन्ति। (११६)

(५७) अर्गलम्।

द्वितीयचरणकनिष्ठाभङ्गे साधन्तालाह्वजङ्घः सन् पादः प्रसृतो भवति। एतत्समकालं च हस्तबाहुर्द्वितीयं पार्श्वक्षेत्रं किञ्चिदग्रप्रसृतोऽलपल्लवाकारः तदन्तर्ज(र्ग)लमर्गलयेत्। देहस्य नयम्यन्त्रणात् (नियन्त्रणात्?) अर्गलम्)। परिक्रमे चैतदङ्गदप्रभृतीनां भवति।

(५८) विक्षिप्तम्।

वाग्रहणं चार्थे। तेन विद्युद्भ्रान्तादण्डपादाभ्यां (ना. शा. १०-४०-४६) चारीभ्यामुद्वेष्टितापवेष्टितरेचकवर्तनया पार्श्वयोः पृष्ठेऽग्रे च हस्तपादविक्षेपः। (इद) मुद्धतगतिपरिक्रमसूचनादिविषयम्। (११८)

(५९) आवर्तम्।

"पादः प्रसारितः सव्यः पुनश्चैवापसर्पितः।

वामः सव्योपसर्पी च चाषगत्याम्। इति॥" (ना. शा. १०-१८)

चाषगत्या चार्या प्रयोगः। हस्तौ च किञ्चिदुद्वेष्टितापवेष्टितरूपौ दोलावेवेति।

---

१. M.G. K.S.S. तद्विज्ञेयं द्विजर्षभाः N.S. G.O.S. तत् द्विजोत्तमाः।

२. K.S.S. द्वौ तलावूर्धमेवच G.O.S. M.G. N.S. द्वौ तालावर्धमेव च।

तस्यैव चानुगो[1] हस्तः पुरतस्त्वर्गलं तु तत् ।

विक्षिप्तं हस्तपादं च पृष्ठतः पार्श्वतोऽपि वा[2] ॥ ११८ ॥

एकमार्गगतं यत्र तद्विक्षिप्तमुदाहृतम् ।

प्रसार्य कुञ्चितं पादं पुनरावर्तयेत् द्रुतम् ॥ ११९ ॥

प्रयोगवशगौ हस्तौ तदावर्त[3]मुदाहृतम् ।

कुञ्चितं पादमुत्क्षिप्य पार्श्वात्पार्श्वं तु डोलयेत्[4] ॥ १२० ॥

आ ईषत् वर्तनं हस्तपादस्य यत्र तदिदमावर्तकरणम् । एतन्नायकोपसर्पणे सागरिकापाशबन्धाद्यवसरे प्रयोज्यम् । (११९)

(६०) डोलापादम् ।

पूर्वमूर्ध्वजानुचारी । (ना. शा. १०-३३) ततो दोलापादा ।

"(कुञ्चितं पादमुत्क्षिप्य पार्श्वात्पार्श्वं विलोलयेत् ।
पातयेदञ्चितं चैव दोलापादा ॥") (ना. शा. १०-३६)

डोलाहस्तावेव (ना. शा. ९-१४८) प्रयोगवशगौ इति डोलापादं करणम् ।

(६१) विवृत्तम् ।

आक्षिप्य वाम(पाद)माक्षिप्य स्वदेहक्षेत्रादपसारितवृत्त्याऽऽवर्त्य हस्तं च व्यावर्तितपरिवर्तिताभ्यां तथैवाक्षिप्य त्रिकं भ्रमरिकया (ना. शा. १०-४५) वलयेत् । तद्रेचितौ च हंसपक्षौ द्रुतभ्रमौ हस्ताविति त्रिकविवर्तनयोगात् विवृत्तम् । अस्योद्धतगतिपरिक्रमे प्रयोगः । (१२१)

(६२) विनिवृत्तम् ।

"कुञ्चित पादमुत्क्षिप्य जानूर्ध्वं सम्प्रसारयेत् ।
पातयेच्चाग्रयोगेन सा सूची ॥" इति (ना. शा. १०-३४)

---

१. M.G. K.S.S. तस्यैवानुगतो G.O.S. N.S. तस्यैव चानुगो ।

२. K.S.S. M.G. अथवा G.O.S. N.S. अपिवा ।

३. K.S.S. M.G. आवृत्तम् G.O.S. N.S. आवर्तम् ।

४ K.S.S. M.G. दोलयेत् G.O.S. N.S. डोलयेत् ।

प्रयोगवशगौ हस्तौ डोलापादं तदुच्यते[1] ।
आक्षिप्तं हस्तपादं च त्रिकं चैव विवर्तयेत्[2] ॥ १२१ ॥

रेचितो च तथा हस्तौ विवृत्ते करणे द्विजाः ।
सूचीविद्धं विधायाथ त्रिकं तु विनिवर्तयेत् ॥ १२२ ॥

चार्या द्वितीयं पादं पार्ष्णिभागे स्वस्तिकयोजनया विद्धा (द्ध्वा) त्रिकस्यैकपार्श्वे विवर्तनस्य प्रत्यावर्तनक्रमेण निवृत्तिं कुर्यात् । "अन्योन्ययोन्यजङ्घावेधेन बद्धया" (ना. शा. १०-२४) वा चार्योरुवलनं कुर्यात् । हस्तौ च रेचितौ हंसपक्षौ द्रुतभ्रमौ । उक्त एवास्य प्रयोगः (विवृत्तवत्) । (१२२)

(६३) पार्श्वक्रान्तम् ।

"कुञ्चितं पादमुत्क्षिप्य पार्श्वस्थाने स्थितं न्यसेत् ।" (ना. शा. १०-३२)

इति पार्श्वक्रान्ता चारी । तयाऽग्रे चरणं पातयेत् । हस्तयोश्च पादप्रयोगानुसारेण पर्यायेण पुरः प्रसारणम् । यदि वा प्रयुज्यत इति प्रयोगः गतिप्रचारयुद्धादिः । तत्र पादावुचितौ हस्तावित्येवं सर्वत्र । एतच्च रौद्रप्रधाने भीमसेनादेः परिक्रमे । (१२३)

(६४) निस्तम्भितम् ।

द्वितीयपादस्य पृष्ठे पार्ष्णिभागे कुञ्चितः । समुन्नतमिति । निर्भुग्नं स्तब्धं च निम्नपृष्ठं चेति । खटकामुखः कर इति तदेतद्देशो मध्यमाङ्गुलिरूपो ललाटे तिलकवदिति । पादेन भुव आघातान्निस्तम्भितं महेश्वराभिनयविषयम् । वश्चिकोऽत्र पाद इत्येके । (१२४)

(६५) विद्युद्भ्रान्तम् ।

पृष्टत ऊरुमूलदेशात्प्रभृति वलितं चक्रवद्भ्रामितं तत एव प्रयोक्तुः शिरःक्षेत्रेण श्लिष्टं सर्वतो मण्डलगत्या आख्या(ख्यया)आविद्धं चतुरं कृत्वा प्रसारयेत् । प्रकर्षेण स सर्वादिषु (सर्वदिक्षु) पर्यायेण सारयेत् । तत्पदस्य विद्युत उद्भ्रमणाद्विद्युद्भ्रान्तमुद्धतगतिपरिक्रमादिविषयम् । (१२५)

---

१. K.S.S. M.G. दोलापादं प्रकीर्तितम् G.O.S. N.S. दोलापादं तदुच्यते ।
२. K.S.S. M.G. विर्वातितम् G.O.S. N.S. विवर्तयेत् ।

करौ च[1] रेचितौ कार्यौ विनिवृत्ते द्विजोत्तमाः ।
पार्श्वक्रान्तक्रमं[2] कृत्वा पुरस्तादथ पातयेत् ॥ १२३ ॥
प्रयोगवशगौ हस्तौ पार्श्वक्रान्तं तदुच्यते[3] ।
पृष्ठतः कुञ्चितः पादो[4] वक्षश्चैव समुन्नतम् ॥ १२४ ॥
तिलके च करः स्थाप्यस्तन्निस्तम्भित[5]मुच्यते ।
पृष्ठतो वलितं पादं शिरोघृष्टं प्रसारयेत् ॥ १२५ ॥

---

(६६) अतिक्रान्तम् ।

अतिक्रान्ता चारी (ना. शा. १०-३०) व्याख्याता । **पुरस्तादिति स्वदेहस्याग्रेण** । एतदपि गतिपरिक्रमादिविषयमेव । एवमन्यस्यापि यस्याभिनयविषयो नोपयोगस्तस्य विषयो मन्तव्यः । (१२६)

(६७) विवर्तितकम् ।

आक्षिप्तहस्तापेक्षया द्वितीयो हस्तः । तं हंसपक्षद्रुतभ्रमक्रमं कुर्यात् । (१२७)

(६८) गजक्रीडितकम् ।

"समुन्नतो लताहस्तः पार्श्वात्पार्श्वं विलोलितः ।" (ना. शा. ९-१९९)

इति यः करिहस्तो लक्ष्यते वृत्तमध्ये तस्यैव यदा त्रिपताकोऽसावञ्चितक्रियाविष्टो डोलापादचारी तदा गजक्रीडितकम् । क्रियाविष्टत्वाच्चाङ्गपर्यायोऽत्र लभ्यते । प्रयोगश्चास्य नामोचित एव विषये । यथा "अरुवद्रणा" इत्यादौ । (१२८)

(६९) तलसंस्फोटितम् ।

अतिक्रान्तया (ना. शा. १०-३०) चार्या दण्डपादया (ना. शा. १०-४४) वा चरणमुत्क्षिप्याक्षिप्तं कृत्वा तथैवाग्रे निपातयेत् । तत्समकालं च पताकौ

---

१. K.S.S. M.G. तु G.O.S. N.S. च ।
२. K.S.S. पार्श्वजानुक्रमं M.G. N.S. G.O.S. पार्श्वक्रान्तक्रमं ।
३. K.S.S. M.G. उदाहृतम् G.O.S. N.S. तदुच्यते ।
४. K.S.S. M.G. कुञ्चितौ पादौ G.O.S. N.S. कुञ्चितः पादः ।
५. N.S. M.G. निशुम्भितम् K.S.S. निसुम्भितम् G.O.S. निस्तम्भितम् ।

सर्वतो मण्डलाविद्धं[1] विद्युद्भ्रान्तं तदुच्यते ।
अतिक्रान्तक्रमं[2] कृत्वा पुरस्तात्संप्रसारयेत् ॥ १२६ ॥
प्रयोगवशगौ हस्तावतिक्रान्ते प्रकीर्तितौ ।
आक्षिप्तं हस्तपादं च त्रिकं चैव विवर्तितम् ॥ १२७ ॥
द्वितीयो रचितो हस्तो[3] विवर्तितकमेव तत् ।
कर्णेऽञ्चितः करो वामो लताहस्तश्च दक्षिणः ॥ १२८ ॥
दोलापादस्त[4]था चैव गजक्रीडितकं[5] भवेत् ।
द्रुतमुत्क्षिप्य चरणं पुरस्तादथ पातयेत् ॥ १२९ ॥

हस्तौ संश्लेषितशब्दादभिहितौ इति तलसंस्फोटितम् । तस्यैतद्विषय एव प्रयोगो, यथा "तालाद्देवी सुसुखसुभसइ जणु" इत्यादौ । (१२९)

(७०) गरुडप्लुतकम् ।

वृश्चिकवच्चरणम् । एकोऽलातहस्तः (लताहस्तः) । द्वितीयो रेचितः । प्रयोगोऽस्य नामोचित एव विषये । (१३०)

(७१) गण्डसूची ।

"उत्क्षिप्ता तु भवेत्पार्ष्णिरङ्गुष्ठाग्रेण संस्थितः ।
वामश्चैव स्वभावस्थः ॥" (ना. शा. ९-२८०)

इति सूचीपादः । अञ्चितोऽलपल्लवो गण्डक्षेत्रे । अन्ये तु सूचीपादं गण्डक्षेत्रप्राप्तमिच्छन्ति । अन्ये तु सूचीमुखं नृत्तहस्तं गण्डाञ्चितं पुनः क्रियाविष्टमाहुः ।

"हस्तौ तु सर्पशिरसौ मध्यमाङ्गुष्ठकौ यदा ।
तिर्यक्प्रसारितास्यौ" (ना. शा. ९-१९९) इति ।

अन्ये तु सूच्यास्यमभिनयहस्तमाहुः ।

---

१. K.S.S. M.G. हस्तौ च मण्डलाविद्धौ G.O.S. N.S. सर्वतो मण्डला विद्धम् ।
२. G.O.S. M.G. K.S.S. अतिक्रान्तक्रमं N.S. अतिक्रान्तं क्रमं ।
३. K.S.S. M.G. पुनश्च रेचयेद्धस्तम् G.O.S. N.S. द्वितीयो रेचितो हस्तो ।
४. G.O.S. N.S. तथा K.S.S. M.G. तदा ।
५. N.S. K.S.S. M.G. गजक्रीडितके G.O.S. गजक्रीडितकं ·

तलसंस्फोटितौ हस्तौ तलसंस्फोटिते मतौ[1] ।

पृष्ठप्रसारित: पाद:[2] लतारेचितकौ करौ ॥ १३० ॥

समुन्नतं शिरश्चैव गरुडप्लुतकं भवेत्[3] ।

सूचीपादो नतं[4] पार्श्वमेको वक्ष:स्थित: कर: ॥ १३१ ॥

द्वितीयश्चाञ्चितो गण्डे गण्डसूची[5] तदुच्यते ।

ऊर्ध्वापवेष्टितौ[6] हस्तौ सूचीपादो विवर्तित: ॥ १३२ ॥

"खटकाख्ये यदा हस्ते तर्जनी सम्प्रसारिता ।
हस्त: सूचीमुखो नाम ॥" इति (ना. शा. ९-६५)

अत्र पक्षे गण्डसंश्रयप्रधानभूषणाभिनयविषयोऽस्य प्रयोग: यथा "गंडप्पळीला-वण्णज्जळ एसो फळके अइदाम" इत्यादौ । (१३१)

(७२) **परिवृत्तम् ।**

"ऊर्ध्वमण्डलिनौ हस्तावूर्ध्वदेशविवर्तनात् ।"(ना. शा. ९-२०३) सूचीलक्षणश्च (ना. शा. १०-३४)पादो बद्धाचारी(ना. शा. १०-२१)माश्रित्य विचित्ररूपतया द्वितीयपादे (ना. शा. १०-४५) वर्तित: अन्योन्यजङ्घासंवेधादिति । ततोऽपि भ्रमरिकया त्रिकं परिवर्तितमाहु: । (१३२)

(७३) **पार्श्वजानु ।**

उरुपृष्टजनि(स्थित:) तस्यैव समस्थितपादस्योरो: द्वितीयोऽस्या(पि) हस्त: कटधामर्धचन्द्र इति पार्श्वजानु । पार्श्वं ऊरुपृष्ठ: तस्य पादस्य सम्बन्धि जानु यत्रेति । युद्धनियुद्धविषयमेतत् । (१३३)

---

१. G.O.S. N.S. मतौ K.S.S. M.G. स्मृतौ ।

२. N.S. पृष्ठप्रसारितौ पादौ G.O.S. M.G. G.O.S. पृष्ठप्रसारित: पाद: ।

३. N.S. K.S.S. M.G. समुन्नतमुरश्चैव गरुडप्लुतके भवेत् G.O.S. (Same as above) ।

४. N.S. M.G K.S.S. सूचीपादोन्नतम् G.O.S. सूचीपादो नतं ।

५. G.O.S. N.S. गण्डसूची K.S.S. M.G. गण्डसूचि ।

६. K.S.S. ऊर्ध्वविचेष्टितौ M.G. ऊर्ध्वाववेष्टितौ N.S. G.O.S. ऊर्ध्वापवेष्टितौ ।

परिवृत्तत्रिकं[1] चैव परिवृत्तं तदुच्यते ।
एकः समस्थितः पाद ऊरुपृष्ठे स्थितोऽपरः[2] ॥ १३३ ॥
मुष्टिहस्तश्च वक्षःस्थः पार्श्वजानु तदुच्यते ।
पृष्ठप्रसारितः पादः किञ्चिदञ्चितजानुकः ॥ १३४ ॥

(७४) गृध्रावलीनकम् ।

पार्श्वात्प्रसारिपादोऽङ्गुष्ठभूमिसंश्लेषादञ्चितजानुकः । लताहस्तौ च पार्श्वगौ । तत्पक्षिनिरूपणादौ गृध्रावलीनकम् । (१३४)

(७५) सन्नतम् ।

"कुञ्चितं पादमुत्क्षिप्य समुत्प्लुत्य निपातयेत् ।

जङ्घाञ्चितोपरि क्षिप्ता सा ज्ञेया हरिणप्लुता ॥" (ना. शा. १०-४३) इत्यनया चार्योत्प्लुत्याग्रदेशे पादं स्वस्तिकं कुर्यात् । सन्नतौ च दोलाहस्तौ ।

"अंसौ प्रशिथिलौ हस्तौ पताकौ तु प्रलम्बितौ" (ना. शा ६-१४८) एतदधमप्रकीर्तनादुपसर्पणादिषये । (१३५)

(७६) सूची ।

अग्रतः स्थितमिति । (१३६)

(७७) अर्धसूची ।

शिरःक्षेत्रे हस्तः शिरोहस्तः । तच्चार्यमिव करणमेकेनाङ्गेनेत्यर्धसूची । (१३७)

सूचीविद्धम् ।

प्रविध्यता इति सूचीपादौ । द्वितीय इति पादः पार्ष्णिस्थः क्रियत इत्यर्थः ।

---

१. K.S.S. M.G. परिवृत्तत्रिक G.O.S. N.S. परिवृत्तत्रिकं ।

२. K.S.S. एकः समुत्थितः पाद ऊरुपार्श्वस्थितः परः । M.G. एकः समस्थितः पाद ऊरुपार्श्वे स्थितोऽपरः G.O.S. N.S. (Same as above) ।

यत्र प्रसारितौ बाहू तत्स्यात् गृध्रावलीनकम् ।
उत्प्लुत्य चरणौ कार्यावग्रतः स्वस्तिकस्थितौ ॥ १३५ ॥

सन्नतौ च तथा हस्तौ सन्नतं तद्धुदाहृतम् ।
कुञ्चितं पादमुत्क्षिप्य कुर्यादग्रस्थितं भुवि ॥ १३६ ॥

प्रयोगवशगौ हस्तौ सा सूची परिकीर्तिता[1] ।
अलपद्मः शिरोहस्तः[2] सूचीपादश्च दक्षिणः ॥ १३७ ॥

यत्र तत्करणं ज्ञेयमर्धसूचीति नामतः ।
पादसूच्या यदा पादो[3] द्वितीयस्तु प्रविध्यते[4] ॥ १३८ ॥

कटिस्थितः पक्षवञ्चितकोऽर्धचन्द्रो वा द्वितीयः खटकामुख एव वक्षसि । चिन्ताविषयेऽस्य प्रयोगः । यथा—"कालीकरमिकस्सकहम्" इत्यादौ । (१३८)

अपक्रान्तम् ।

"ऊरुभ्यां वलनं कृत्वा कुञ्चितं पादमुद्धरेत् ।
पार्श्वे विनिक्षिपेच्चैतदपक्रान्ता ॥" (ना. शा. १०-३१)

इत्यपक्रान्तक्रमं कृत्वोरुवलितबद्धां चारोमन्योन्यजङ्घासंयोगात्कृत्वा तु स्वस्तिकमूरुभ्यां वलनमित्येवंभूतां कुर्यात् । (१३९)

मयूरललितम् ।

वृश्चिकं पादं विधाय रेचितौ हंसपक्षौ द्रुतभ्रमौ करौ कृत्वा पादं तमेवोरुदेशे निकुञ्च्य भ्रमरिकां चारीं कुर्यादिति मयूरनृत्तानुकारि मयूरललितम् ।

"अतिक्रान्तक्रमं कृत्वा त्रिकं तु परिवर्तयेत् ।
द्वितीयपादभ्रमणात्तलेन भ्रमरी भवेत् ॥" (ना. शा. १०-४५)
(१४०)

---

१. G.O.S. सा सूची परिकीर्तिता K.S.S. N.S. M.G. तत्सूचि परिकीर्तितम् ।

२. K.S.S. वामः पादः शिरोदेशे M.G. अलपद्मः शिरोदेशे G.O.S. N.S. (Same as above) ।

३. K.S.S. M.G. पादौ G.O.S. N.S. पादः ।

४. K.S.S. G.O.S. N.S. प्रविध्यते M.G. प्रपीड्यते ।

कटिवक्षःस्थितौ हस्तौ सूचीविद्धं तदुच्यते ।
कृत्वोरुवलितं पादमपक्रान्तक्रमं न्यसेत् ॥ १३९ ॥
प्रयोगवशगौ हस्तावपक्रान्तं तदुच्यते ।
वृश्चिकं चरणं[1] कृत्वा रेचितौ च तथा करौ ॥ १४० ॥
तथा त्रिकं विवृत्तं च मयूरललितं भवेत् ।
अञ्चितापसृतौ पादौ शिरश्च परिवाहितम् ॥ १४१ ॥
रेचितौ च तथा हस्तौ[2] तत्सर्पितमुदाहृतम् ।
नूपुरं चरणं कृत्वा दण्डपादं प्रसारयेत् ॥ १४२ ॥
क्षिप्राविद्धकरं[3] चैव दण्डपादं तदुच्यते ।
अतिक्रान्तक्रमं[4] कृत्वा समुत्प्लुत्य निपातयेत् ॥ १४३ ॥
जङ्घाञ्चितोपरि क्षिप्ता तद्विद्याद्धरिणप्लुतम् ।
डोलापादक्रमं कृत्वा समुत्प्लुत्य निपातयेत् ॥ १४४ ॥

---

(८१) सर्पितम् ।

"पार्ष्णी (र्ष्णिः) यस्य स्थितौ (ता) भूमावूर्ध्वमग्रतलं भवेत् ।
अङ्गुल्यश्चाञ्चिताः सर्वाः स पादोऽञ्चित उच्यते ॥" (ना. शा. ९-२७५)

अञ्चितपादः सन्नपसृतो द्वितीयपादनिकटात्पलायितकोऽर्थः (तौ यः तत्) समकालमेव तत्पार्श्वगं शिरः । तथेति तत्पार्श्वग एव हस्तो रेचितः । पुनरयं द्वितीयकरपादस्य विधिः । तत्पार्श्वगतमेव च शिरः । अत एव चपरिवाहितम् । यद्वक्ष्यति—

"पर्यायशः पार्श्वगतं शिरः स्यात्परिवाहितम् ।" (ना. शा. ८-२२७)

एतच्च पादकृतमदोपसर्पणविषयमिति मानं (नाम) बलाद्गम्यते । (१४१)

---

१. K.S.S. M.G. करणं G.O.S. N.S. चरणं ।
२. K.S.S. M.G. च करौ यत्र G.O.S. N.S. रेचितौ च तथा हस्तौ ।
३. K.S.S. M.G. क्षिप्रविद्धं करं G.O.S. N.S. क्षिप्राविद्धकरं ।
४. K.S.S. M.G. N.S. अतिक्रान्तं क्रमं कृत्वा G.O.S. अतिक्रान्तक्रमं कृत्वा ।

परिवृत्तत्रिकं चैव[1] तत्प्रेङ्खोलितमुच्यते ।
भुजावूर्ध्वविनिष्क्रान्तौ हस्तौ चाभि(धो)मुखाङ्गुली ॥ १४५ ॥
बद्धा चारी[2] तथा चैव नितम्बे करणे भवेत् ।
दोला[3]पादक्रमं कृत्वा हस्तौ तदनुगावुभौ ॥ १४६ ॥
रेचितौ घूर्णितौ वापि स्खलितं करणं भवेत्[4] ।
एको[5] वक्षःस्थितो हस्तः प्रोद्वेष्टिततलोऽपरः ॥ १४७ ॥

---

(८२) दण्डपादम् ।

"पृष्ठतोऽभ्यञ्चितं कृत्वा पादमग्रतलेन तु ।
द्रुतं निपातयेद्भूमौ चारी नूपुरपादिका ॥" (ना. शा. १०-३५)

इत्येतदनन्तरमेव दण्डपादादिपुरश्चरणं कृत्वा दण्डपादं प्रसारयेत् ।

"क्षिप्रापविद्धकरणं दण्डपादा तु सा स्मृता ।" (ना. शा. १०-४४)

इत्येतत्सहितमेव पादसहितदण्डत्वरितहस्तं न्यसेदिति साटोपपरिक्रमादि विषयमेतत् । (१४२)

(८३) हरिणप्लुतम् ।

ईदृशस्यैव हरिणप्लुता चारी (ना. शा. १०-४३) भविष्यति । तस्यास्तु करणप्रवेशः प्रागेवोक्त (सन्नतकरणव्याख्यावसरे) । (१४३)

(८४) प्रेङ्खोलितकम् ।

कुञ्चितं पादं पाश्र्वात्पाश्र्वं दोला (ना. शा. १०-३६) । तमेवं कृत्वा द्वितीयेनोत्प्लुत्य भ्रमरिकां (ना. शा. १०-४५) कुर्यात् । (१४४)

(८५) नितम्बम् ।

अभिमुखाङ्गली । अथोर्ध्वाङ्गुलौ पताकौ व्यावर्तितकरणेन शिरोदेशं नीत्वा ततः परिवर्तितकरणेनोर्ध्वक्षेत्रेण निष्क्रान्तौ बाहू कृत्वा यथासमं देशे-

---

१. K.S.S. N.S. M.G. परिवृत्तं त्रिकं चैतत् G.O.S. परिवृत्तत्रिकं चैव ।
२. K.S.S. N.S. M.G. वद्धाचारी G.O.S. बद्धा चारी ।
३. K.S.S. M.G. दोलपादक्रमं G.O.S. N.S. दोलापादक्रमं ।
४. N.S. न्यसेत् K.S.S. G.O.S. M.G. भवेत् ।
५. N.S. M.G. K.S.S. वामः G.O.S. एकः ।

अञ्चितश्चरणश्चैव प्रयोज्यः करिहस्तके ।
एकस्तु रेचितो हस्तो लताख्यस्तु तथा परः[1] ॥ १४८ ॥
प्रसर्पिततलौ[2] पादौ प्रसर्पितकमेव तत् ।
अलातं[3] च पुरःकृत्वा द्वितीयं च द्रुतक्रमम् ॥ १४९ ॥
हस्तौ पादानुगौ चापि सिंहविक्रीडिते स्मृतौ ।
पृष्ठप्रसर्पितः[4] पादस्तथा हस्तौ निकुञ्चितौ[5] ॥ १५० ॥

ऽन्योन्यं वीक्ष्यमाणौ पताकौ स्थापयेत् । ततो देहाभिमुखाङ्गुलिहस्तौ तदनुगावुभौ रेचिताघूर्णितौ चापि नितम्बनृत्तहस्तलक्षणौ कुर्यात् । एतत्त्रिभिर्मुखा (एतदभिमुखा)ङ्गुलित्वं निपातत्रयेण द्योतितम् । "बाहुशीर्षाद्विनिष्क्रान्तौ" (ना. शा. ९-१९६) निमेषा(वेशा)त्तद्योगात्करणान्वितम् । (१४५)

(८६) **स्खलितम् ।**

दोलापादगमनागमनसमकालं हंसपक्षोपलक्षितौ बाहू गमनागमनयुक्त पुनरपरेणाङ्गेनेति । (१४६)

(८७) **करिहस्तकम् ।**

प्रोद्वेष्टनक्रियया परः कर्णस्थः त्रिपताकस्तद्दिक्क एव च पादस्तत्प्रोद्वेष्टनसमकालमञ्चितः सम्प्रयोज्य निष्क्रमणीयः । करिहस्तेन नृत्तहस्तेन सदृशमेतदंश इत्येतत्तन्नामा ।

(समुन्नतो लताहस्तः पार्श्वात्पार्श्वं विलोलितः ।
त्रिपताकोऽपरः कर्णे करिहस्तः) (ना. शा. ९-१९९) (१४७)

(८८) **प्रसर्पितकम् ।**

हंसपक्षो द्रुतभ्रम इति रेचितः । अपरो लताख्यो (ना. शा. ९-१९८, नृत्तहस्तः । रेचितकरस्य दिक्पादः पादान्तरान्मन्दं मन्दं भूमिघर्षणाच्चलेत् । एतस्य खेचरसंचारविषये प्रयोगः (१४८)

---

१. K.S.S. N.S. M.G. तथापरः G.O.S. तथा परः ।
२. M.G. K.S.S. संसर्पिततलौ G.O.S. N.S. प्रसर्पिततलौ ।
३. K.S.S. M.G. अलातकं G.O.S. N.S. अलातं च ।
४. G.O.S. M.G. पृष्ठप्रसर्पितः N.S. पृष्ठप्रसारितः K.S.S. पृष्ठःप्रसर्पितः ।
५. K.S.S. M.G. कुञ्चितावर्तितौ करौ G.O.S. N,S. तथा हस्तौ निकुञ्चितौ ।

पुन[1]स्तथैव कर्तव्यौ सिंहाकर्षितके द्विजाः ।
आक्षिप्तहस्तमाक्षिप्तदेहमाक्षिप्तपादकम्[2] ॥ १५१ ॥
उद्वृत्तगात्रमित्येतदुद्वृत्तं करणं स्मृतम् ।
आक्षिप्तश्चरणश्चैको[3] हस्तौ तस्यैव चानुगौ[4] ॥ १५२ ॥
आनतं च तथा गात्रं तथोपसृतकं भवेत्[5] ।
दोलापादक्रमं कृत्वा तलसङ्घट्टितौ करौ ॥ १५३ ॥

---

(८९) सिंहविक्रीडितम् ।

अलातं चारीमग्रगतां द्रुतं निक्षिप्य तदनुसारेणैव च हस्तं (ना. शा. १०-४१) द्वितीयमपि चक्रमेवंभूतं कुर्यादिति सिंहकरघातसाम्यात्सिंहविक्रीडितं रौद्रगतिविषयम् । (१४९)

(९०) सिंहाकर्षितम् ।

वृश्चिक एकः पादः । निकुञ्चितौ स्वस्तिकेन पद्मकोशोर्णनाभौ (ना. शा. ९-८२-१२०) (दक्षिण) वामहस्तौ । पूर्नद्वितीयेन पादेन यदा वृश्चिकस्तदा तौ क्रियावर्तनावशादपसार्य पुनरपि तादृशावेव हस्ताविति सिंहाद्यभिनयविषयं सिंहाकर्षितकम् । (१५०)

(९१) उद्वृत्तम् ।

आक्षिप्तमासारितानीतं हस्तपादं यत्र । कथं सर्वदेहाक्षेपः । आह-उद्वृत्ता-चारीयुक्तं कृत्वा—

"पादमाविद्धमावेष्टच समुत्प्लुत्य निपातयेत् ।
परिवृत्य द्वितीयं तु सोद्वृत्ता ।" (ना. शा. १०-३९) इति ।

अत एवोद्वृत्तं करणम् । (१५१)

(९२) उपसृतकम् ।

(कुञ्चितं पादमुत्क्षिप्येत्याक्षिप्तां चारीं (ना. शा. १०-३७) वामतो

---

१. M.G. पुरः K.S.S. G.O.S. N.S. पुनः ।
२. M.G. K.S.S. N.S. आक्षिप्तहस्तमाक्षिप्तपादमाक्षिप्तदेहकम् G.O.S. (Same as above) ।
३. K.S.S. M.G. कार्यः G.O.S. N.S. एको ।
४. N.S. हस्तस्यैव वशानुगः M.G. K.S.S. G.O.S. हस्तौ तस्यैव चानुगौ ।
५. K.S.S. M.G. स्मृतम् G.O.S. N.S. भवेत् ।

रेचयेच्च करं वामं तलसङ्घट्टिते सदा[1] ।

एको वक्ष:स्थितो हस्तो द्वितीयश्च प्रलम्बित: ॥ १५४ ॥

तलाग्रसंस्थितः पादो जनिते करणे भवेत् ।

जनितं करणं कृत्वा हस्तौ चाभिमुखाङ्गुली ॥ १५५ ॥

शनैर्निपतितौ चैव ज्ञेयं तदवहित्थकम् ।

करौ वक्ष:स्थितौ कार्यावुरो निर्भुग्नमेव च ॥ १५६ ॥

व्यावृत्य करपरिवर्तनेन गात्रमानम्य दक्षिणमरालतां नयेत् । एताद्विनयोपसर्पणे) यथा "महादेवी विण्णवेदि" इति । (१५२)

(९३) तलसङ्घट्टितम् ।

कुञ्चित पार्श्वात्पार्श्वमिति (ना. शा. १०-३६) दोलपादां चारीं कुर्वंस्तत्समकालं पताकौ सम्यग्घट्टितमन्योन्यतलं ययोस्तादृशौ करौ कृत्वा वैष्णवे स्थानके "तौ तालौ" (ना. शा. १०-५२) इत्यत्र स्थित्वा दक्षिणं हस्तं कटचां च द्वितीयं हंसपक्षद्रुतभ्रमात्मकं रेचकं कुर्यात् । अनुकम्पाप्रधाने वाक्यार्थेऽस्य प्रयोगः । "धाणवगळछिफ......अ० धिअचणारि" इत्यादि । (१५३)

(९४) जनितम् ।

वक्षसि मुष्टिहस्तः । प्रलम्बितो लताख्यः । अन्यासां क्रियाणामारम्भकाल एव तत्सन्निवेशजननयोगाद्यथोचितचारीवशानीतम् । (जनिताचारी ना. शा. १०-२५) (१४५)

(९५) अवहित्थकम् ।

"मुष्टिहस्तश्च वक्षःस्थः करोऽन्यश्च प्रवर्तते ।

तलसञ्चरपादश्च जनिता ॥" (ना. श. १०-२५) इति ।

चारीपादं कृत्वा । तथाप्यभिमुखाङ्गुली इत्यरालालपल्लवतया ललाटवक्षःक्षेत्रगौ हस्तौ विधाय शनैरिति यथाक्रममुद्वेष्टितकरणावधरोर्ध्वक्रमेण पार्श्वगौ कृत्वा पुनरपवेष्टितपरिवर्तितक्रियया रालालपल्लावावन्योन्यं सम्मुखं वक्षोदेशे कुर्यात् । गोपनप्रधाने वाक्यार्थेऽस्य प्रयोगः । इत्यवहित्थकमे तद्यथा—"ऐथगअं गइर्कारि थविफासहसश्व०खे इअं बइसं परिहि" ॥ अन्ये तु (अवहित्थहस्तेन)

---

१. K.S.S. M.G. तथा G.O.S. N.S. मदा ।

मण्डलस्थानकं[1] चैव निवेशं करणं[2] तु तत् ।

तलसञ्चरपादाभ्यामुत्प्लुत्य पतनं भवेत्[3] ॥ १५७ ॥

संनतं वलितं गात्रमेलकाक्रीडितं तु तत् ।

करमावृत्तकरणमूरुपृष्ठेऽञ्चितं न्यसेत् ॥ १५८ ॥

जङ्घाञ्चिता तथोद्वृत्ता ह्यूरूद्वृत्तं तु तद्भवेत्[4] ।

करौ प्रलम्बितौ कार्यौ शिरश्च परिवाहितम् ॥ १५९ ॥

"शुकतुण्डौ करौ कृत्वा वक्षस्यभिमुखाञ्चितौ ।

शनैरधोमुखाविद्धोऽसाववहित्थः ॥ " (ना. शा. ९-१५९)

इत्येतच्चिन्तादौर्बल्यविषयमाहुः । (१५५)

(९६) **निवेशम् ।**

"स्तब्धं च निम्नपृष्ठं च निर्भुग्नांसं समुन्नतम् ।

उरो निर्भुग्नम् । " (ना. शा. ९-२२६)

ऐन्द्रे मण्डले पादौ चतुस्तालान्तरस्थितौ । (गजवा)हनादिविषयेऽनेन निवेशयेत् । गात्रस्याविश्रमणान्निवेशाख्यम् । (१५६)

(९७) **एलकाक्रीडितम् ।**

पतनकाले गात्रस्य नमनं ततो वलनम् । एवं नाम्नैकरूपाचारी (ना. शा. १०-२०) भविष्यति । अधमप्रकृतिगतिविषयमेतत् । (१५७)

(९८) **ऊरूद्वृत्तम् ।**

"तलसञ्चरपादस्य पार्ष्णिर्बाह्योन्मुखी यदा ।

जङ्घाञ्चिता तथोद्वृत्ता ऊरूद्वृत्ता ।" इति (ना. शा. १०-२२)

अनया चार्या सह व्यावर्तितकरणेनारालं खटकं चोरुदेशे पृष्ठे च क्षिपेत् । प्रणयकोपेर्ष्याप्रार्थनादिविषयमेतत्करणम् । (१५८)

---

१. N.S. K.S.S. M.G. मण्डलं स्थानक G.O.S. मण्डलस्थानकं ।

२. N.S. K.S.S. निवेशकरणं M.G. G.O.S. निवेशं करणं ।

३. K.S.S. M.G. N.S. तु यत् G.O.S. भवेत् ।

४. N.S. तदुच्यते K.S.S. तदूरुवृत्तमुच्यते M.G. तदूरुद्वृत्तमुच्यते G.O.S. ह्यूरुद्वृत्तं तु तद्भवेत् ।

पादौ च वलिताविद्धौ मदस्खलितके द्विजाः ।
पुरः प्रसारितः पादः कुञ्चितो गगनो[1]न्मुखः ॥ १६० ॥
करौ च रेचितौ यत्र विष्णुक्रान्तं तदुच्यते ।
करमावर्तितं कृत्वा ह्यूरुपृष्ठे निकुञ्चयेत् ॥ १६१ ॥
ऊरुश्चैव तथा[2]विद्धः सम्भ्रान्तं[3] करणं तु तत् ।
अपविद्धः करः सूच्या पादश्चैव निकुट्टितः ॥ १६२ ॥
वक्षःस्थश्च करो वामो विष्कम्भे करणे भवेत् ।
पादावुद्घट्टितौ कार्यौ तलसङ्घट्टितौ करौ ॥ १६३ ॥

---

(९९) **मदस्खलितकम् ।**

करौ दोलौ । पर्यायशः पार्श्वगतं शिरः । **वलिताविद्धौ** अवनतावनन्तरं स्वस्तिकापसृतौ (पादौ) पर्यायेणेति । मद्यमदविषयमेतत् । (१५९)

(१००) **विष्णुक्रान्तम् ।**

विष्णोरित्थं क्रमणमत्र । तत्तद्विषय एवास्य प्रयोगः । (१६०)

(१००) **सम्भ्रान्तम् ।**

आविद्धायां चार्यां सत्यामूरुस्तथा ।

"स्वस्तिकस्याग्रतः पादः कुञ्चितश्च प्रसारितः ।
निपतेदञ्चिताविद्ध आविद्धा नाम सा स्मृता ॥" (ना. शा. १०-३८)

तच्चारीप्रयोगकाले च व्यावर्तितपरिवर्तितकरणेनालपल्लवमूरुपृष्ठे न्यसेत् । सम्भ्रमपरिक्रमविषयमेतत् । (१६१)

(१०२) **विष्कम्भम् ।**

वामः करो दक्षिणेन हस्तेन सूचीमुखं (ना. शा. ९-१६१) नृत्तहस्तात्मनापगमपूर्वकं विद्धः । स एव पादो निकुट्टितः । चकरात् द्वितीयेनैवाङ्गेन ।

---

१. K.S.S. N.S. M.G. गमन G.O.S. गगन ।

२. K.S.S. M.G. तदा G.O.S. N.S. तथा ।

३. K.S.S. संभ्रान्तकरणं G.O.S. N.S. M.G. सम्भ्रान्तं करणं ।

नतञ्च पार्श्वं कर्तव्यं[1] बुधैरुद्धट्टिते सदा ।

प्रयुज्यालातकं पूर्वं हस्तौ[2] चापि हि रेचयेत् ॥ १६४ ॥

कुञ्चितावञ्चितौ चैव वृषभक्रीडिते सदा[3] ।

रेचितावञ्चितौ हस्तौ लोलितं वर्तितं शिरः ॥ १६५ ॥

एवकारेणेदमाह पुनः सूच्या (ना. शा. १०-३४) चार्योपलक्षितः पादः । परश्च निकुट्टितोऽलपल्लवोऽन्यस्तु वामः । एवं पुनःकरणे सति क्रियाविष्कम्भनाद्विस्तारणाद्विष्कम्भाख्यं करणम् । (१६२)

(१०३) **उद्धट्टितम् ।**

"स्थित्वा पादतलाग्रेण पार्ष्णी भूमौ ।" इति (ना. शा. ६-२६६) पादः । अन्योन्यमनेन तालिकादानोद्यतौ करौ पुनर्द्वितीयपाद उद्धट्टितः पर्यायेण च तथैव पार्श्वयोर्नमनमिति । प्रमोदविषमेतत् । (१६३)

(१०४) **वृषभक्रीडितम् ।**

अलातचारीं (ना. शा. १०-४१)कुर्वन्हस्तौ रेचितौ कुर्यात् । ततः कुञ्चतौ व्यावर्तितकरणेन कृत्वा ततो बाहुशिरस्यलपल्लवाकृती अञ्चितौ विधेयाविति वृषभमङ्गद्वारद्वयप्रयोगात् वृषभक्रीडितम् । (१६४)

(१०५) **लोलितम् ।**

वैष्णवे स्थाने आदौ रेचितं हंसपक्षद्रुतभ्रमरूपं हस्तद्विती(त)यं चाञ्चितं वक्षस्थलपल्लवाकारं कुर्यात् । शिरश्च लोलितम् । सर्वतो लोलितमपि चोभयोः पार्श्वयोर्वर्तितं विश्रमितम् । (१६५)

---

१. M.G. K.S.S नितम्बपार्श्वे कर्तव्यौ N.S. नितम्बपार्श्वं कर्तव्यम् G.O.S. नतञ्च पार्श्वं कर्तव्यम् ।

२. K.S.S. M.G. पादं हस्तौ द्वावपि रेचितौ G.O.S. N.S. (Same as above) ।

३. K.S.S. M.G. स्मृतौ G.O.S. N.S. सदा ।

उभयोः पार्श्वयोर्यत्र तल्लोलितमुदाहृतम्[1] ।
स्वस्तिकापसृतौ पादौ शिरश्च परिवाहितम् ॥ १६६ ॥
रेचितौ च तथा हस्तौ स्यातां नागापसर्पिते[2] ।
निषण्णाङ्गस्तु चरणं प्रसार्य तलसञ्चरम् ॥ १६७ ॥
उद्वाहितमुरः कृत्वा शकटास्यं प्रयोजयेत् ।
ऊर्ध्वाङ्गुलितलौ[3] पादौ त्रिपताकावधोमुखौ ॥ १६८ ॥

(१०६) नागापसर्पितम् ।

परिवाहितं पर्यायशः पार्श्वगतं कुटिलगतियोगान्नागापसर्पितम् । इदं तरुण-मदविषयम् । (१६६)

(१०७) शकटास्यम् ।

निषण्णं निस्समीकृतमङ्गं येन तेन तज्जानुसमस्थिते पदे पुरो गुल्फदेशे कुञ्चितो न तु जानुरेव पादः स एवाध्यर्धतालान्तरसञ्चरः प्रसार्यः । तत्सहितोऽपि हस्तो द्वितीयो वक्षसि खटकः । ईदृश्येवेयं चारी (ना. शा. १०-१६) भविष्यति । अनेन सन्निवेशेन शकटस्यासनं क्षेप इति । तथाविधबाल-क्रीडादिविषये भाणिकादिविषयेऽस्य प्रयोगः । (१६७)

(१०८) गङ्गावतरणम् ।

अत्र केचिदूर्ध्वाङ्गुलितलं इत्यनेन समपादाञ्चितावस्थानमुक्तमित्याहुः । एतच्चायुक्तमशब्दार्थत्वात् । तस्मादञ्चितो न पादः । अन्ये त्वाहुः—अनेन क्रमेणाग्रतलसञ्चारो वृश्चिकहस्तपाद इति । अपरे तु—चकारेण च पादस्य त्रिपताकाहस्तयोश्शिरसश्च सन्नतत्वात्तेन प्रथमं पादोद्धारं स्थित्वा पादमूर्ध्वं विधाय तदुपरि च पताकाहस्तौ तं पादं क्रमेणाग्रतलसञ्चारो वृश्चिकपाद इति । [अपरे तु चकारेण भिन्नक्रमेण च तदास्य त्रिपताकाहस्तयोः शिरसश्च सन्नतत्वात्तेन प्रथमः पादोद्धारः । स्थित्वा पादमूर्ध्वं विधाय तदुपरि च त्रिपताकहस्तौ तं पादं क्रमेण]सन्नमयेत् अवरोधयेत् । तदनुसारेण च त्रिपताका-

---

१. K.S.S. M.G. ज्ञेयं लोलितकं बुधैः G.O.S. N.S. तल्लोलितमुदाहृतम् ।
२. K.S.S. M.G. स्खलितासर्पितौ पादौ तथा हस्तौ च रेचितौ ।
परिवाहितं शिरश्चैव कुर्यान्नागापसर्पिते ॥
G.O.S. N.S. (Same as above) ।
३. N.S. ऊर्ध्वाङ्गुलितलः पादः G.O.S. K.S.S. M.G. ऊर्ध्वाङ्गुलितलौ पादौ ।

हस्तौ शिरस्सन्नतं च गङ्गावतरणं त्विति[1]।
यानि स्थानानि याश्चार्यो व्यायामे कथितानि[2] तु ॥ १६९ ॥
पादप्रचारस्त्वेषां तु करणानामयं भवेत् ।
ये चापि नृत्तहस्तास्तु गदिता नृत्तकर्मणि ॥ १७० ॥
तेषां समासतो योगः करणेषु विभाव्यते ।
प्रायेण करणे कार्यो वामो वक्षःस्थितः करः ॥ १७१ ॥
चरणश्चानुगश्चापि दक्षिणस्तु भवेत्करः ।
चार्यश्चैव तु याः प्रोक्ता नृत्तहस्तास्तथैव च ॥ १७२ ॥
सा मातृकेति विज्ञेया तद्भेदात्करणानि तु ।
अष्टोत्तरशतं ह्येतत्करणानां मयोदितम् ॥ १७३ ॥
अतः परं प्रवक्ष्यामि ह्यङ्गहारविकल्पनम् ।
प्रसार्योत्क्षिप्य च करौ समपादं प्रयोजयेत् ॥ १७४ ॥

हस्तं संनमयेत् । तथैव क्रमेण शिरः । एवमेव त्रिविक्रमपादप्रसरणपूर्वकं गङ्गा-देव्या अवतरणमिति नाम्नैवास्य करणस्य विषयो दर्शितः । इतिशब्दः समाप्तौ । (१६८)

[इत्यष्टोत्तरशतकरणनिरूपणं समाप्तम्]

अङ्गहारलक्षणम् ।

तलपुष्पपुटस्य पूर्वं निर्देशात्सर्वत्र वर्तनाप्राधान्येनोपक्रम इति सूचितं परं प्रयोगमाह । उक्तमुपसंहरन् क्रमप्राप्तानङ्गहारान्यथोद्देशं लक्षणीयत्वेन प्रति-जानीते—अष्टोत्तरशतमित्यादिना । हि यस्मात्करणानामष्टोत्तरशतमुदितं (ततो) हेतोः परं विशिष्टमङ्गहारो (वि) कल्प्यते परस्परतो भेद्यते येन तदङ्गहारेष्वेव विशेषलक्षणं वक्ष्यामीति सम्बन्धः । जातावेकवचनम् । (१७३)

---

१. K.S.S. M.G. च तत् G.O.S. N.S. त्विति ।

२. N.S. गदितानि G.O.S. कथितानि K.S.S. M.G. do not read from यानि स्थानानि V.N. 169b to सा मातृकेति विज्ञेया तद्भेदात् करणानितु V.N. 173a.

व्यंसितापसृतं सव्यं हस्तमूर्ध्वं[1] प्रसारयेत् ।

प्रत्यालीढं ततः कुर्यात्[2] तथैव च निकुट्टकम् ॥ १७५ ॥

ऊरूद्वृत्तं ततः कुर्यादाक्षिप्तं स्वस्तिकं ततः ।

नितम्बं करिहस्तं[3] च कटिच्छिन्नं च योगतः[4] ॥ १७६ ॥

---

(१) स्थिरहस्तः ।

तत्रोद्देशक्रमेण स्थिरहस्तं लक्षयति—**प्रसार्ये**त्यादिना **हरप्रिय** इत्यन्तेन । तत्र प्रसार्योत्क्षिप्य च कराविति त्रिपताकाञ्जलि वक्षःस्थमिति लक्षितस्य लीनाख्यस्य करणस्य (ना. शा. ४-६६) प्रथमेतिकर्तव्यतानिरूपणेनोपलक्षितम् । एतच्च तल्लक्षण एवोक्तमस्माभिः पताकशब्दस्य प्रयोजनं वदद्भिः । इदमिदं करणं योगतोऽन्यादौ ह्यनया जिघृक्षतीत्यक्षिकरणगतहस्तपादाद्यौचित्ययुक्त-वर्तनाचारीयोजनया यदि भवति तत एव चाविच्छिन्ना शुभा च । प्रबन्धा-दलातचक्रवदेकबुद्ध्यनुसंहार्यं तदलम् । स्थिरहस्तो नामाङ्गहार इति सम्बन्धः । एवं सर्वत्र **योगत** इति सर्वाङ्गहारेषु सम्बध्यते ।

अन्ये तु योगात्समाधेरप्ययं भगवतः प्रीतय इति व्याचक्षते ।

समपादमिति समनखं करणम् । "पदं (पादौ) श्लिष्टौ समनखौ" इति (ना. शा. ४-६५) ।

व्यंसिते—

"आलीढं स्थानकं यत्र करौ वक्षसि रेचितौ ।

ऊर्ध्वाधोविप्रकीर्णौ च व्यंसितं करणं तु तत् ॥" (ना. शा. ४-१०८)

इति लक्षिते करणेऽपसृतौ विप्रकीर्णौ यौ हस्तौ तौ द्वावप्यूर्ध्वस्थानस्थितौ कृत्वा आलीढस्य परिवर्तनेन (ना. शा. १०-७०) प्रत्यालीढं स्थानकं कुर्यात् । ततो निकुट्टिते "निकुट्टितौ यदा हस्तौ" (ना. शा. ४-६९) इति नवमं करणम् । ततोऽपि "करमावृत्तकरणमूरुपृष्ठ" (ना. शा. ४-०५९) इत्यष्टनवतितमम् । ततः स्वस्तिकं हस्ताभ्यामथ पादाभ्यामिति (ना. शा. ४-७५) पञ्चदशम् । तत "आक्षिप्तं हस्तपादं चेति" (ना. शा. ४-००५) पञ्चपञ्चाशत् ।

---

१. K.S.S. M.G. ऊर्ध्वं हस्तं G.O.S. N.S. हस्तमूर्ध्वं ।

२. K.S.S. M.G. N.S. कृत्वा G.O.S. कुर्यात् ।

३. G.O.S. N.S. करिहस्तं च K.S.S. M.G. करिहस्तश्च ।

४. G.O. K.S.S. तथैव च G.O.S. N.S. च योगतः ।

स्थिरहस्तो भवेदेष त्वङ्गहारो हरप्रियः ।

तलपुष्पापविद्धे द्वे[1] वर्तितं सनिकुट्टकम्[2] ॥ १७७ ॥

ऊरूद्वृत्तं तथाक्षिप्तमुरोमण्डलमेव च ।

नितम्बं करिहस्तं च कटिच्छिन्नं तथैव च[3] ॥ १७८ ॥

"भुजावूर्ध्वं विनिष्क्रान्तौ हस्तौ चाभिमुखाङ्गुली" (ना. शा. ४-१४६) इति नितम्बगतिः । ततः करिहस्तम्—

"वामो वक्षःस्थितो हस्तः प्रोद्वेष्टिततलोपरि" (ना. शा. ४-०४८) इति सप्ताशीतितमम् । ततः "पर्याशः कटिश्छिन्ना बाहू शिरसि" (ना. शा. ४-७२) इत्येकादशम् ।

इत्येवं करणग्रामसम्यग्योजनया कृतं स्थिरहस्तमङ्गहारं निर्वर्तयति । अतः (त्र) सर्वेष्वङ्गहारेष्वित्यर्थः(हारेषु) करणावयववर्गं सर्वं करणजातं चतुर्दिङ्मुखेषु प्रयोज्यमिति नाट्याचार्या मन्यन्ते । अनागतातीतवे(दी मुनिस्तद)युक्तं मन्यमान एकान्नविंशतितमे हि परिवृत्तकरेचितेऽङ्गहारे (ना. शा. ४-२०१) वक्ष्यति 'पराङ्मुखविधिर्भूय एवमेव भवेत्' इत्यङ्गहारविधावित्यर्थायोगात् । तदाङ्गिकेष्वेव वक्ष्यामः । उद्वेष्टितकरणस्वरूपं निरूपयतः प्रयोगश्चैषामदृष्टार्थ एव । प्रयोगे च तत्तद्वाक्यार्थादूनं विप्रकर्षानुसारेण । एतच्च पूर्वरङ्गे (अ-५) यथोपदेशं वक्ष्यामः । 'युद्धे नियुद्धे च' इत्यादौ(ना. शा. ४-५६) । विषयेणैतेषां (विशेषेणैतेषाम्) कदाचित्प्रयोगः । एवं स्थिरहस्त एव नानिर्व(र्तनं) लक्ष्यत इति न वृथा तन्निर्देशेनायासः । (१७६)

(२) **पर्यस्तकः ।**

तलपुष्पपुटेत्यादि । **केचित्प्रसार्ये**त्यादिना **प्रत्यालीढं** **तः कुर्यादित्यन्तं सर्वेष्वङ्गहारेषु प्रथममितिकर्तव्यतां योजयन्ति प्रथमाङ्गस(ङ्ग)तिकरणयोगः कथमित्यभिप्रायेण । अन्ये तु प्रत्यङ्गहारसमुचिताः साधारणाः स्वयमूह्या इत्याहुः । श्रुतहानौ को गुण इत्यपरे ।

तत्र "वामे पुष्पपुट" (ना. शा. ४-६१) इति प्रथमम् । "आवर्त्य शुकतुण्डाख्यमूरुपृष्ठे" "वामहस्तश्च वक्षःस्थ" (ना. शा. ४-६४) इत्यपविद्धम् । "कुञ्चितौ मणिबन्धे तु" इति(ना. शा. ४-६२) वर्तितम् । "निकुट्टिताविति" (ना. शा. ४-६६) निकुट्टकम् । "करमावृत्तकरणम्" इति (ना. शा. ४-०५६)

---

१. K.S.S. M.G. च G.O.S. N.S. द्वे ।

२. K.S.S. M.G. संप्रसारयेत् N.S. संनिकुट्टकम् G.O.S, सनिकुट्टकम् ।

३. K.S.S Omits this verse.

एषः पर्यस्तको नाम ह्यङ्गहारो हरोद्भवः[1] ।
अलपल्लवसूचीं च कृत्वा विक्षिप्तमेव च ॥ १७९ ॥
आवर्तितं ततः कुर्यात्तथैव च निकुट्टकम् ।
ऊरूद्वृत्तं तथाक्षिप्तमुरोमण्डलमेव[2] च ॥ १८० ॥
करिहस्तं कटिच्छिन्नं सूचीविद्धो भवेदयम् ।
अपविद्धं तु करणं सूचीविद्धं तथैव च[3] ॥ १८१ ॥

ऊरूद्वृत्तम् । (तत "आक्षिप्तं हस्तपादम्" (४-११६) इत्याक्षिप्तम् । 'स्वस्तिकापसृता" विति (४-११५) उरोमण्डलम् । ततो "भुजावूर्ध्वविनिष्क्रान्ता" विति (४-१४६) नितम्बकरणम् । अनन्तरं "वामो वक्षःस्थित" इति (४-१४८) करिहस्तम् । ततः "पर्यायश" इति (४-७२) कटिच्छिन्नम् । एतेन करणदशकेन पर्यस्तकः ।।) (१७८)

(३) सूचीविद्धः ।

अर्ध(ल)पल्लवसूचीं चेति । "अलपद्मः शिरोदेशे (हस्त.) सूचीपादश्च" इति (ना. शा. ४-१३८) अलपल्लवोपलक्षितमर्धसूच्याख्यं सप्तसप्ततितमं करणम्—

'विक्षिप्तं हस्तपादं च पृष्ठतः पार्श्वतोऽपि वा ।
एकमार्गम्". इति (ना. शा. ४-११९) विक्षिप्तम् ।

एकान्नषष्टितमं यदावर्ताख्यं करणं—

"प्रसार्य कुञ्चितं पादं पुरस्त्वा(नरा)वर्तयेद्द्रुतम् ।
प्रयोगवशगो" इति (ना. शा. ४-१२०)

तदेवावर्तितशब्देनोक्तम् । ततो निकुट्टकादीनि षट् करणान्युक्ताङ्गहारवदेव (स्थिरहस्त इव) । (१८०)

(४) अपविद्धः ।

अपविद्धन्त्वित्यादि ।

"आवर्त्य शुकतुण्डाख्यमूरुपृष्ठे निपातयेत् ।
वामहस्तश्च वक्षःस्थोऽप्यपविद्धम् ।। (ना. शा. ४-६४)

---

१. G.O.S. N S. हि K.S.S. M.G. तु ।
२. K.S.S. M.G. उरोमण्डलकं तथा K.S.S. N.S. उरोमण्डलमेव च ।
३. K.S.S. M.G. पुनर्भवेत G.O.S. N.S. तथैव च ।

उद्वेष्टितेन हस्तेन त्रिकं तु परिवर्तयेत् ।

उरोमण्डलकौ हस्तौ कटिच्छिन्नं तथैव च ॥ १८२ ॥

अपविद्धोऽङ्गहारश्च[1] विज्ञेयोऽयं[2] प्रयोक्तृभिः ।

करणं नूपुरं कृत्वा विक्षिप्तालातके पुनः ॥ १८३ ॥

पुनराक्षिप्तकं कुर्यादुरोमण्डलकं तथा ।

नितम्बं करिहस्तं[3] च कटिच्छिन्नं तथैव च ॥ १८४ ॥

"पादसूच्या यदा पादो द्वितीयश्च प्रविध्यते ।

कटिवक्षःस्थितौ हस्तौ सूचीविद्धं तत् ॥ " (ना. शा. ४-१३६)

एवं करणद्वयं कृत्वोद्वेष्टितेन करणेन (ना. शा. ६-२१६) बद्धया चार्या त्रिकं वलितं कृत्वोरोमण्डलहस्तोपलक्षितमुरोमण्डलकरणं ततोऽपि कटिच्छिन्नं विदध्यात् ।

"स्वस्तिकापसृतौ पादावपविद्धक्रमौ यदा ।

उरोमण्डलकौ हस्तावुरोमण्डलकं तु तत् ॥"(ना. शा. ४-११५)

प्रयोक्तृभिरिति ये प्रयोगकुशलास्तैः । स्वयमङ्गस्य गतिः सम्यग्विद्वद्भिर्ज्ञातुं न शक्य इत्यनेनेदमाह । एतेषु करणेषु यदा मध्यवर्तनशिरोभ्रूनेत्रादिकर्मसंहितापि या योजना च सा अंशश्च स्वरूपतत्त्वविदा स्वयमङ्गीकर्तुं शक्यः । अन्यस्य तूक्तापि प्रयोक्तुमशक्या न चापि निरूपयितुं शक्या । गीतवाद्यलययन्ति (ति) वाक्यार्थभेदेन च तस्या एव योजना । योजने चानन्त्यम् । नहि सुशिक्षितोऽपि लक्षणकारो वाक्यानां प्रतिपदं लक्षणं कर्तुं शक्नोति । अस्य पश्चादिदं प्रयोज्यमिति दयापि(ज्ञापि)तेन किञ्चदात्मनो योजना च संहिता कार्या । नियमनमग्रे वक्ष्याम इत्युक्तम् । तेन मण्डलादिस्थाननिरूपणमिह कैश्चित्कृतं निरुपयोगमेवेत्यास्ताम् । (१८२)

(५) **आक्षिप्तकः ।**

करणं नूपुरमित्यादि ।

त्रिकं सुवलितं कृत्वा लतारेचितकौ करौ " (ना. शा. ४-६७) (नू) पुरं च तथा पादकरणे नूपुरे "विक्षिप्तं हस्तपादं च " इति (ना. शा. ४-११६) विक्षिप्तम् ।

---

१. K.S.S. M.G. तु N.S. G.O.S. च ।

२. K.S.S. M.G. तत् G.O.S. N.S. अयम् ।

३. K.S.S. M.G. नितम्बः करिहस्तश्च G.O.S. N.S. नितम्बं करिहस्तं च ।

आक्षिप्तकः स[1] विज्ञेयो ह्यङ्गहारः प्रयोक्तृभिः ।
उद्वेष्टितापविद्धस्तु करः पादो निकुट्टितः ॥ १८५ ॥

पुनस्तेनैव योगेन वामपार्श्वे भवेदथ ।
उरोमण्डलकौ हस्तौ नितम्बं करिहस्तकम्[2] ॥ १८६ ॥

कर्तव्यं सकटिच्छिन्नं नृत्ते तूद्धट्टिते सदा[3] ।
पर्यायोद्वेष्टितौ हस्तौ पादौ चैव निकुट्टितौ ॥ १८७ ॥

"अलातं चरणं कृत्वाऽप्यंसयोर्दक्षिणं करम् ।
ऊर्ध्वजानुक्रमं कुर्यादलातकमिति स्मृतम् ॥ " (ना. शा. ४-७८)

यत्र यत्र पुनर्ग्रहणं तत्र तत्र केचित् द्वियोगमाहुः । द्वितीयाङ्गहारोक्तमाक्षिप्तादिकरणपञ्चकम् । (१८४)

(६) **उद्धट्टितः ।**

उद्वेष्टितापविद्धस्त्विति । अनेन प्रथमश्लोकेन पर्यायशोऽङ्गद्वयप्रयोगं निकुट्टकं करणमाह—"निकुट्टितौ यदा हस्तौ " (ना. शा. ४-६९) इति । उरोमण्डलकादिकरणचतुष्कं द्वितीयाङ्गहारवदेवं । (१८६)

(७) **विष्कम्भः ।**

पर्यायोद्वेष्टिताविति । अनेनार्धेनानन्तराङ्गहारवदेव प्रथममण्डलद्वयेन निकुट्टितं करणमित्याह । **कुञ्चिताविति** । हस्तौ पादौ चेति सम्बन्धः । तेन कुञ्चितस्य करणस्याञ्चितस्य चाङ्गद्वयपर्यायेण प्रयोज्यत्वमुक्तम् ।

"वृश्चिकं चरणं कृत्वा करं पार्श्वे निकुञ्चयेत् । (ना. शा. ४-८७)
नासाग्रे दक्षिणं चैव निकुञ्चितम् ॥"

"स्वस्तिकौ चरणौ कृत्वा करिहस्तं च दक्षिणम् ।
वक्षःस्थाने तथा वाममर्धस्वस्तिकमादिशेत् " ॥ (ना. शा. ४-८३)

---

१. K.S.S M.G. तु G.O.S. N.S. स ।
२. K.S.S. M.G. करिहस्तकः G.O.S. N.S. करिहस्तकम् ।
३. K.S.S. M.G. कर्तव्यः स कटिच्छेदो नृत्ते तूद्घट्टिते बुधैः G.O.S. कर्तव्यं सकटिच्छिन्नं नृत्ते तूद्धट्टिते सदा N.S. Same except नृत्ते तद्घटिते सदा ।

कुञ्चितावञ्चितौ चैव ह्यू[1]रूद्वृत्तं तथैव च ।
चतुरश्रं करं कृत्वा पादेन च निकुट्टकम् ॥ १८८ ॥
भुजङ्गत्रासितं[2] चैव करं चोद्वेष्टितं पुनः ।
परिच्छिन्नं च कर्तव्यं त्रिकं भ्रमरकेण तु ॥ १८९ ॥
करिहस्तं कटिच्छिन्नं विष्कम्भे परिकीर्तितम्[3] ।
दण्डपादं करं चैव विक्षिप्याक्षिप्य चैव हि ॥ १९० ॥
व्यंसितं वामहस्तं च सह पादेन सर्पयेत् ।
निकुट्टकद्वयं कार्यमाक्षिप्तं मण्डलोरसि[4] ॥ १९१ ॥
करिहस्तं कटिच्छिन्नं[5] कर्तव्यमपराजिते ।
कुट्टितं करणं[6] कृत्वा भुजङ्गत्रासितं तथा ॥ १९२ ॥

इत्यनन्तरं

"व्यावृत्तपरिवृत्तस्तु स एव तु करो यदा ।
अञ्चितो नासिकाग्रे तु तदञ्चितम् ॥" (ना. शा. ४-८३)

चतुरश्रमिति अनेनार्धेनार्धनिकुट्टकं दशमं करणमाह—

"अञ्चितौ बाहुशिरसि हस्तस्त्वभिमुखाङ्गुलिः ।
निकुञ्चितार्धयोगेन" (ना. शा. ४-७०) इति ।

द्वितीयो हि तत्र प्राङ्मुखं खटकरूपं चतुरश्रो हस्तः ।

"कुञ्चितं पादमुत्क्षिप्य त्र्यश्रमूरू विवर्तयेत् ।
कटिजानुविवर्तश्च भुजङ्गत्रासितं भवेत् ॥" (ना. शा. ४-८४)

भुजङ्गत्रासितं चतुर्विधम् । अत्रैवकारेण हस्तप्रयोगमनुक्तं निरूपयति—**करं चोद्वेष्टितमिति** । तत्समकालं च भ्रमरकेणाष्टत्रिंशेन (ना. शा. ४-९९)करणेन

---

१. K.S.S. M.G. च ऊरूद्वृत्तं N.S. G.O.S. चैव ह्यूरूद्वृत्तम् ।
२. K.S.S. M.G. भुजङ्गत्रासकं G.O.S. N.S. भुजङ्गत्रासितं ।
३. K.S.S. M.G. N.S. विष्कम्भः परिकीर्तितः G.O.S. विष्कम्भे परिकीर्तितम् ।
४. K.S.S. M.G. उरसा G.O.S. N.S. उरसि ।
५. K.S.S. M G. करिहस्तः कटिच्छेदः G.O.S. N.S. (Same as above)
६. M.G. करणे K.S.S. G.O.S. N.S. करणं ।

रेचितेन तु हस्तेन पताकं हस्तमा[1]दिशेत् ।

आक्षिप्तकं प्रयुञ्जीत ह्यु रोमण्डलकं[2] तथा ॥ १६३ ॥

लताख्यं सकटिच्छिन्नं[3] विष्कम्भापसृते भवेत् ।

त्रिकं [4]सुवलितं कृत्वा नूपुरं करणं तथा ॥ १६४ ॥

भुजङ्गत्रासितं सव्यं तथा वैशाखरेचित[5]म् ।

आक्षिप्तकं ततः कृत्वा परिच्छिन्नं तथैव च ॥ १६५ ॥

बाह्यभ्रमरकं कुर्यादुरोमण्डलमेव च ।

नितम्बं करिहस्तं च कटिच्छिन्नं तथैव च[6] ॥ १६६ ॥

परित इत्युभयाङ्गप्रयोगेण च्छिन्नत्रिकं कुर्यात् । कटिमध्यस्य वलनाच्छिन्ना । यतः—

"आक्षिप्तः स्वस्तिकः पादः करौ चोद्वेष्टितौ तथा ।

त्रिकस्य वलनाच्च ।"

इति भ्रमरकम् । ततः करिहस्तः कटिच्छिन्नश्च पूर्वाङ्गहारवदेव । (२८९)

(८) **अपराजितः ।**

दण्डपादमित्यादि ।

"नूपुरं चरणं कृत्वा दण्डपादं प्रसारयेत् ।

क्षिप्राविद्धकरं चेति दण्डपादम् ॥" (ना. शा. ४-१४३)

यदत्र करणे निरूपितं तदेवेह भङ्क्त्वा दर्शितं **विक्षिप्ये**त्यादिना । "आलीढस्थानकं यत्र" (ना. शा. ४-१०९)इति व्यंसितं प्रथमाङ्गहारोक्तम् । **वामहस्ते**त्यादिना प्रसर्पितमष्टाशीतितमकरणमाह ।

---

१. K.S.S. M.G. पताकाहस्तम् G.O.S. N.S. पताकं हस्तम् ।

२. G.O.S. N.S. ह्यु रोमण्डलकं K.S.S. M.G. उरोमण्डलकं ।

३. G.O.S. N.S. सकटिच्छिन्नम् K.S.S. M.G. सकटिच्छेदम् ।

४. G.O.S. N.S. सुवलितं K.S.S. M.G. तु वलितं ।

५. K.S.S. M.G. चरणं चैव रेचितम् G.O.S. N.S. तथा वैशाखरेचितम् ।

६. K.S.S. M.G. नितम्बः करिहस्तं च कटिच्छेदं तथैव च G.O.S: N.S. (Same as above) except N.S. Reads कटिच्छेदं instead of कटिच्छिन्नं ।

मत्ताक्रीडो भवेदेष ह्यङ्गहारो हरप्रियः[1] ।

रेचितं हस्तपादं च[2] कृत्वा वृश्चिकमेव च ॥ १६७ ॥

पुनस्तेनैव योगेन वृश्चिकं[3] सम्प्रयोजयेत् ।

निकुट्टकं तथा चैव सव्यासव्यकृतं क्रमात्[4] ॥ १६८ ॥

लताख्यः सकटिच्छेदो भवेत्स्वस्तिकरेचिते ।

पार्श्वे तु स्वस्तिकं बध्वा कार्यं त्वथ निकुट्टकम्[5] ॥ १६९ ॥

"एकस्तु रेचितो हस्तः लताख्यश्च तथापरः ।

प्रसर्पितकम् ।" इति (ना. शा. ४-१४६)

निकुट्टकद्वयमिति । निकुट्टमर्धनिकुट्टं च (ना. शा. ४-६९-७०) "**निकुट्टितौ यदा हस्तौ**" इति । "अञ्चितो बाहुशिरसि हस्तस्तु" इति । **मण्डलोरसीत्युरोमण्डले करणे** (ना. शा. ४-११५) सतीत्यर्थः । आक्षिप्तादीनि कटिच्छिन्नान्तानि चत्वारि द्वितीयाङ्गहारवदेव ।

(९) **विष्कम्भापसृतः** ।

कुट्टितमित्यादि । निकुट्टकमर्धनिकुट्टकं चेति द्वे कुट्टितशब्देन साधारण्यात्सङ्गृहीते । "कुञ्चितं पादम्" (ना. शा. ४-८४) इत्यादि भुजङ्गत्रासितं चतुर्विंशतितमम् । **रेचितेभ्यस्त्वि(तेने)**त्यादिनार्धेन पञ्चत्रिंशक (ना. शा. ४-९६) दर्शयतीति ।

"भुजङ्गत्रासितं कृत्वा यत्रोभावपि रेचितौ ।

वामपार्श्वस्थितौ हस्तौ भुजङ्गत्रस्तरेचितम् ॥" (ना. शा. ४-९६)

अस्य चाङ्गपर्यायेण प्रयोग इति पताकाग्रहणेनाह । आक्षिप्तकादित्रयं पूर्वाङ्ग-

---

१. K.S.S. अङ्गहारो भवेत् प्रियः M.G. अङ्गहारो भव प्रियः G.O.S. N.S. ह्यङ्गहारो हरप्रियः ।

२. N.S. तु K.S.S. M.G. G.O.S. च ।

३. K.S.S. M.G. कृत्वा वृश्चिकमेथ तु G.O.S. N.S. वृश्चिकं सम्प्रायोजयेत् ।

४. K.S.S. M.G. सव्यासव्यकृतः G.O.S. N.S. सव्यापसव्यकृतं क्रमात् ।

५. N.S. पार्श्वस्वस्तिकपादौ च कार्यं त्वर्धनिकुट्टकम् K.S.S. पार्श्वे तु स्वस्तिकं बुद्ध्वा कार्यं त्वथ निकुट्टकम् M.G. पार्श्वे तु स्वस्तिकं बध्वा कार्यं त्वर्धनिकुट्टकम् G.O.S. (Same as above) ।

द्वितीयस्य च[1] पार्श्वस्य विधिः स्यादय[2]मेव हि ।
ततश्च करमावर्त्य ह्यूरुपृष्ठे[3] निपातयेत् ॥ २०० ॥
ऊरूद्वृत्तं ततः कुर्यादाक्षिप्तं पुनरेव हि[4] ।
नितम्ब करिहस्तं च कटिच्छिन्नं तथैव च[5] ॥ २०१ ॥
पार्श्वस्वस्तिक इत्येष ह्यङ्गहारः प्रकीर्तितः ।
वृश्चिकं करणं कृत्वा लताख्यं हस्तमेव च ॥ २०२ ॥
तमेव च करं भूयो नासाग्रे सन्निकुञ्चये[6]त् ।
तमेवोद्वेष्टितं कृत्वा नितम्बं परिवर्तयेत्[7] ॥ २०३ ॥
करिहस्तं कटिच्छि[8]न्नं वृश्चिकापसृते भवेत्[9] ।
कृत्वा नूपुरपादं तु तथाक्षिप्तकमेव च ॥ २०४ ॥

हारवदेव । केवलमत्र कटिच्छिन्ने करणे (ना. शा. ४-७१) पर्यायेणैको लताहस्तः ।

(१०) मत्ताक्रीडः .

[**त्रिकं सुवलितं कृत्वेति** । भ्रमरकं करणम् "आक्षिप्तः स्वस्तिकः पाद इत्यादि (ना. शा. ४-६६) । ततो नूपुराख्यं करणं "त्रिकं सुवलितम्'- इति (ना. शा. ४-६७), "कुञ्चितं पादम्" इति (ना.शा. ४-८४) भुजङ्गत्रासितम् । **सव्यमिति** दक्षिणाङ्गेनैव वैशाखरेचितम् (४-६८) । "आक्षिप्तं हस्तपादम्" इति (ना. शा. ४-११६) आक्षिप्तकरणम् । परिच्छिन्नमिति—

"अलपद्मः कटीदेशे च्छिन्ना पर्यायशः कटी" ।

---

१. K.S.S. M.G. तु G.O.S. N.S. च ।
२. K.S.S. M.G. एष G.O.S. N.S. अयम् ।
३. G.O.S. N.S. ह्यूरुपृष्ठे K.S.S. M.G. ऊरुपृष्ठे ।
४. K.S.S. M.G. च G.O.S. N.S. हि ।
५. G.O.S. N.S. (Same as above) K.S.S. M.G. नितम्बं करिहस्तः च कटिच्छेदं तथैव च except that K.S.S. Reads नितम्बः in place of नितम्बं ।
६. G.O.S. N.S. सन्निकुञ्चयेत् K.S.S. M.G. सन्निवेशयेत् ।
७. K.S.S. M.G. नितम्बमथ वर्तयेत् G.O.S. N.S. नितम्बं परिवर्तयेत् ।
८. K.S.S. M.G. कटिच्छेदं G.O.S. N.S. कटिच्छिन्नं ।
९. K.S.S. वृश्चिके सम्प्रयोजयेत् M.G. G.O.S. N.S. वृश्चिकापसृते भवेत् ।

परिच्छिन्नं च कर्तव्यं सूचीपादं तथैव च[१] ।
नितम्बं करिहस्तं[२] चाप्युरोमण्डल[३]कं तथा ॥ २०५ ॥
कटिच्छिन्नं[४] ततश्चैव भ्रमरः सतु संज्ञितः ।
मत्तल्लिकरणं कृत्वा करमावर्त्य[५] दक्षिणम् ॥ २०६ ॥
कपोलस्य प्रदेशे तु कार्यं[६] सम्यङ् निकुञ्चितम् ।
अपविद्धं द्रुतं चैव तलसंस्फोटसंयुतम्[७] ॥ २०७ ॥
करिहस्तं कटिच्छिन्नं मत्तस्खलितके भवेत्[८] ।
दोलैः करैः प्रचलितैः स्वस्तिकापसृतैः पदैः ॥ २०८ ॥

इति च्छिन्नं करणम् (ना. शा. ४-१०६) **बाह्यभ्रमरकमिति** वामभ्रमरकम् । ततो व्यंसितम् "आक्षिप्तः स्वस्तिकः पादः" इति (ना. शा. ४-९९) भ्रमरकम् । व्यंसितं "आलीढं स्थानकं यत्रेति (४-१०९) । उरोमण्डलम्—"स्वस्तिकापसृतौ पादौ" इति (ना. शा. ४-११५)। नितम्बं—"भुजावूर्ध्वौ विनिष्क्रान्तौ" इति (ना. शा. ४-१४६) । करिहस्तं "वामो वक्षःस्थितो हस्त" इति (ना. शा. ४-१४८) । कटिच्छिन्नम् "पर्यायशः कटी च्छिन्ना" इति (ना. शा. ४-४१) । एतानि द्वादश करणानि :

(११) **स्वस्तिकरेचितः ।**

रेचितमिति । रेचितं हस्तपादं चेति वैशाखरेचितम् (ना. शा. ४-९८) । वृश्चिकं "बाहुशीर्षाञ्चितौ" इति (ना. शा. ४-१०८) पुनरिति वैशाखरेचित-

---

१. N.S. कटिच्छिन्नं च कर्तव्यं सूचीविद्धं तथैव च G.O.S. K.S.S. M.G. (Same as above) except K.S.S. M.G.Read कटिच्छिन्नं तु in place of परिच्छिन्नं च ।

२. K.S.S. करिहस्तश्च G.O.S. N.S. M.G. करिहस्तं ।

३. K.S.S. M.G. उरोमण्डलकं G.O.S. N.S. चाप्युरोमण्डलकं ।

४. K.S.S. M.G. कटिच्छेदं G.O.S. N.S. कटिच्छिन्नं ।

५. G.O.S. N.S. आवर्त्य K.S.S. M.G. आवृत्य ।

६. K.S.S. M.G. कर्तव्यं तु G.O.S. N.S. कार्यं सम्यक् ।

७. K.S.S. M.G. अपविद्धं तथा चैव तलसंस्फोटितं तथा G.O.S. N.S. (Same as above).

८. K.S.S. करिहस्तः कटिच्छेदो मत्तस्खलितकं भवेत् G.O.S. N.S. M.G. (Same as above) except M.G. Reads कटिच्छेदं in place of कटिच्छिन्नम् ।

वृश्चिके प्रयोजयेत् । निकुट्टकं "निकुट्टितौ यदा हस्तौ" इति (ना. शा. ४-६६) वामदक्षिणकृतौ लताख्यौ नृत्तहस्तौ (ना. शा. ६-१६८) । ततः कटिच्छिन्नं "पर्यायशः कटी च्छिन्ना" इति (ना. शा. ४-७४) षट् करणानि ।

(१२) पार्श्वस्वस्तिकः ।

पार्श्वयोः स्वस्तिक इति दिक्स्वस्तिकं करणम् । "पार्श्वयोरग्रतश्चैव" इति (ना. शा. ४-७७) । एकाङ्गेनार्धनिकुट्टकम्—"अञ्चितौ बाहुशिरसि" इति (ना. शा. ४-७०)। पुनर्दिक्स्वस्तिकं कृत्वा द्वितीयपार्श्वेनार्धनिकुट्टकं योजयेत् । "करमावर्त्य" इत्यपविद्धम् । "आवर्त्य शुकतुण्डाख्यम्" इति(ना.शा. ४-६४) । ऊरूद्वृत्तम्—"करमाविद्धकरणम्" इति (ना. शा. ४-१५६) । "आक्षिप्तं हस्तपादम्" इति (ना. शा. ४-११६) आक्षिप्तम् । नितम्बादिकरणत्रयं पूर्ववत् ।

(१३) वृश्चिकापसृतः ।

वृश्चिकमिति । वृश्चिकचरणलताहस्तत्वात् लतावृश्चिकम्—"अञ्चितः पृष्ठतः पादः" इति (ना. शा. ४-१०५) । **नासाग्र** इति निकुञ्चितम् 'वृश्चिकं चरणं कृत्वा' इति (ना. शा. ४-८७) । **तमेवोद्वेष्टितमिति** मत्तल्लि "वामदक्षिणपादाभ्याम्" इति(ना. शा. ४-८८) । नितम्बादित्रयं पूर्ववत् । केचिन्नितम्बस्य भ्रमरमाहुः ।

(१४) भ्रमरः ।

कृत्वेति । नूपुरपादं कृत्वेति नूपुरं करणम्—"त्रिकं सुवलितं कृत्वा" इति (ना.शा. ४-६७)। आक्षिप्तकं "आक्षिप्तहस्तपादम्" इति(ना.शा. ४-११६) । परिच्छिन्नम्—

"अलपद्मः शिरोदेशे च्छिन्ना पर्यायशः कटी"

इति (ना. शा. ४-१०६) । सूचीपादम्—'पादसूच्या यदा' इति (ना. शा. ४-१३६) । नितम्बं "भुजावूर्ध्वविनिष्क्रान्तौ" इति (ना. शा. ४-१४६) । करिहस्तं "वामो वक्षःस्थितो हस्तः" इति (ना. शा. ४-१४८) उरोमण्डलं "स्वस्तिकापसृतौ पादौ" इति (ना. शा. ४-११५) । कटिच्छिन्नं "पर्यायशः कटी च्छिन्ना" इति (ना. शा. ४-७२)

(१५) मत्तस्खलितकः ।

मत्तल्लीति । "वामदक्षिणपादाभ्याम्" इति मत्तल्लि (ना. शा. ४-८८) । कपोलस्येति गण्डसूची "सूचीपादोन्नतं पार्श्वम्" इति (ना. शा. ४-१३२) । सम्यङ्निकुञ्चितमिति लीनं नाम करणम्—

अञ्चितैर्वलितैर्हस्तैस्तलसङ्घट्टितैस्तथा ।
निकुट्टितं च कर्तव्यमूरूद्वृत्तं तथैव च ।। २०९ ।।
करिहस्तं कटिच्छिन्नं मदाद्विलसिते भवेत् ।
मण्डलं स्थानकं[1] कृत्वा तथा हस्तौ च रेचितौ ।। २१० ।।
उद्घट्टितेन पादेन मत्तल्लिकरणं भवेत् ।
आक्षिप्तं करणं[2] चैव ह्युरोमण्डलमेव[3] च ।। २११ ।।
कटिच्छिन्नं[4] तथा चैव भवेत्तु गतिमण्डले ।
समपादं प्रयुज्याथ परिच्छिन्नं[5] त्वनन्तरम् ।। २१२ ।।

"पताकाञ्जलिवक्षःस्थं प्रसारितशिरोधरम् ।
निकुञ्चितांसकूटं च तल्लीनम् ।" (ना. शा. ४-६६)

अपविद्धम् "आवर्त्य शुकतुण्डाख्यम्" इति (ना. शा. ४-६४), अपविद्धगतेनैव तलसंस्फोटित "द्रुतं विक्षिप्य चरणम्" इति (ना. शा. ४-१३०), करिहस्तादिद्वयं पूर्ववत् ।

(१६) मदविलसितः ।

दोलैरिति । दोलैः करैरिति मदस्खलितमेकोनशततमं करणम् । स्वस्तिकापसृतैः पदैर्मत्तल्लि सूचितम् । ततस्तलसंघट्टितैरिति तलसंस्फोटितमूनसप्तति करणम् । वलितशब्देन त्रीण्यपि करणानि बहुविधचित्रगुम्फानीति । ततो निकुट्टकादिकरणचतुष्कम् । अत्र केचिद् दोलादिकरणानां त्रयाणां त्रिरभ्यासात् त्रयोदश करणानि वाऽऽहुः । अन्ये तु करणसप्तकस्यापि त्रिरभ्यासादेकविंशतीति ।

(१७) गतिमण्डलः ।

मण्डलमिति । मण्डलस्थानकेन मण्डलस्वस्तिकनिवेशे करणे उद्दिष्टे । तत उन्मत्तं रेचितावित्याह । पादेनोद्घट्टिताख्यं त्र्युत्तरशतम् । आक्षिप्तादीनि त्रीणि चाष्टौ करणानि गतिमण्डले ।

---

१. K.S.S. M.G. N.S. मण्डलस्थानकं G.O.S. मण्डलं स्थानकं ।
२. K.S.S. आक्षिप्तकरणं M.G. G.O.S. N.S. आक्षिप्तं करणं ।
३. K.S.S. M.G. उरोमण्डलकं तथा G.O.S. N.S. ह्युरोमण्डलमेव च ।
४. K.S.S. M.G. कटिच्छेदं G.O.S. N.S. कटिच्छिन्नं ।
५. K.S.S. परिच्छिन्नः M.G. G.O.S. N.S. परिच्छिन्नं ।

आविद्धेन तु पादेन बाह्यभ्रमरकं तथा ।
वाम[1]सूच्या त्वतिक्रान्तं भुजङ्गत्रासितं तथा ॥ २१३ ॥
करिहस्तं कटिच्छिन्नं परिच्छिन्ने विधीयते ।
शिरसस्तूपरि स्थाप्यौ स्वस्तिकौ विच्युतौ करौ[2] ॥ २१४ ॥
ततः सव्यं करं चापि गात्रमानम्य रेचयेत् ।
पुनरुत्थापयेत्तत्र गात्रमुन्नम्य रेचितम् ॥ २१५ ॥
लताख्यौ च करौ कृत्वा वृश्चिकं सम्प्रयोजयेत् ।
रेचितं करिहस्तं च भुजङ्गत्रासितं तथा ॥ २१६ ॥
आक्षिप्तकं प्रयुञ्जीत स्वस्तिकं पाद[3]मेव च ।
पराङ्मुख[4]विधिर्भूय एवमेव भवेदिह[5] ॥ २१७ ॥

---

(१८) परिच्छिन्नः ।

समपादमिति । "श्लिष्टौ समनखौ पादौ" (ना. शा. ४-६५) इति समनखं प्रथमं कुर्यात् । ततश्छिन्नं पञ्चचत्वारिंशत् । आविद्धपादेनाविद्धचार्यां संभ्रान्तमेकोत्तरशतम् । ततो भ्रमरकमष्टत्रिंशत् । वामसूच्यार्धसूची वामपादेन । ततोऽतिक्रान्तं षट्षष्टितमम् । भुजङ्गत्रासितादीनि त्रीणि च नवभिः परिच्छिन्नः ।

(१९) परिवृत्तकरेचितः ।

शिरसस्त्वति । शिरस उपरीति नितम्बं पञ्चाशीतितमम् ।

"भुजावूर्ध्वविनिष्क्रान्तौ हस्तौ चाभिमुखाङ्गुली" । (ना. शा. ४-१४६) इति

नितम्बम् । ततः स्वस्तिकरेचितं सप्तमम् (ना. शा. ४-६७) । गात्रस्यानमनेन विक्षिप्ताक्षिप्तकमेकविंशम् (ना. शा. ४-८१) । पुनः पुनरिति लताख्यावित्यनेनार्धेन लतावृश्चिकम् (ना. शा. ४-१०५)

---

१. K.S.S. M.G. वामं सूच्या G.O.S. N.S. वामसूच्या ।
२. K.S.S. doesnot read from verse No. 214 to verse No. 216 G.O.S. M.G. N.S. (Same as above).
३. K.S.S. पदम् G.O.S. N.S. M.G. पादम् ।
४. K.S.S. पराङ्मुखीविधिर्भूयात् M.G. पराङ्मुखो विधिर्भूय N.S. G.O.S. (Same as above).
५. N.S. एव एवं भवेदिह G.O.S. N.S. K.S.S. एवमेव भवेदिह ।

करिहस्तं कटिच्छिन्नं[1] परिवृत्तकरेचिते ।
रेचितौ सह गात्रेण ह्यपविद्धौ करौ यदा[2] ॥ २१८ ॥
पुनस्तेनैव देशेन गात्रमुन्नम्य रेचयेत् ।
कुर्यान्[3]नूपुरपादं च भुजङ्गत्रासितं तथा ॥ २१९ ॥
रेचितं मण्डलं चैव बाहुशीर्षे[4] निकुञ्चयेत् ।
ऊरूद्वृत्तं तथाक्षिप्तमुरोमण्डलमेव च ॥ २२० ॥
करिहस्तं कटिच्छिन्नं[5] कुर्याद्वैशाखरेचिते ।
आद्यं तु जनितं कृत्वा पादमेकं प्रसारयेत् ॥ २२१ ॥

"अञ्चितः पृष्ठतः पादः कुञ्चितोर्ध्वतलाङ्गुलिः ।]

लताख्यश्च करो वामः (ना. शा. ४-१०५) इति लतावृश्चिकम् । "एको वक्षःस्थितो हस्तः" इति (ना. शा. ४-१४८) ।

रेचितमित्युन्मत्तकरणम् । "अञ्चितेन तु पादेन रेचितौ" इति (ना. शा. ४-७४) । "एको वक्षःस्थितो हस्तः" इति करिहस्तकम् । "कुञ्चितं पादम्" इति (ना. शा. ४-८४) भुजङ्गत्रासितम् । "आक्षिप्तं हस्तपादम् । इत्याक्षिप्तकम् (ना. शा. ४-११६) । स्वस्तिकं पादमित्यस्यैव पादस्वस्तिकपर्यन्ततया बद्धां चारीं सूचयन्नितम्वकरणमाह—"भुजावूर्ध्वं विनिष्क्रान्तौ" (ना. शा. ४-११६) । पराङ्मुखेति । अङ्गहारेषु मध्ये परिभाषमाणो मुनिरेतदाह—सर्वेष्वेव चाङ्गहारेषु पाश्चात्यं करणद्वयं वर्जयित्वा वर्तनीयानि करणानि । तानि चतुर्दिङ्मुखेषु प्रयुज्य संमुखमन्त्ये करणद्वयेन पूरयेदिति ।

(२०) **वैशाखरेचितः ।**

रेचिताविति । अनेन श्लोकेन क्रमेण वैशाखरेचितमङ्गमङ्गद्वयेन प्रयोज्यमित्याह । "रेचितं हस्तपादं च" इत्यादि (ना. शा. ०-९८) वैशाखरेचितं करणम् ।

---

१. K.S.S. करिहस्तः कटिच्छेदः M.G. करिहस्तं कटिच्छेदं G.O.S. N.S. (Same as above) ।
२. K.S.S. M.G. यथा G.O.S. N.S. तदा ।
३. K.S.S. M.G. कार्यम् G.O.S. N.S. कुर्यात् ।
४. K.S.S. M.G. बाहुशीर्षं G.O.S. N.S. बाहुशीर्षे ।
५. K.S.S. M.G. कटिच्छेदं G.O.S. N.S. कटिच्छिन्नं ।

तथैवालातकं कुर्यात् त्रिकं तु परिवर्तयेत् ।
अञ्चितं वामहस्तं च गण्डदेशे निकुट्टयेत् ॥ २२२ ॥
कटिच्छिन्नं तथा चैव परावृत्तो[1] प्रयोजयेत् ।
स्वस्तिकं करणं कृत्वा व्यंसितौ च करौ पुनः[2] ॥ २२३ ॥

"त्रिकं सुवलितं कृत्वा लतारेचितकौ करौ ।
नूपुरं च तथा पादम् ।" (ना. शा. ४-९७)

इति नूपुरोर्ध्वपादम् । कुञ्चितं पादमुत्क्षिप्येति (ना. शा. ४-८४) भुजङ्गत्रासितम् । रेचितमित्युन्मत्तकरणम् । "अञ्चितेन तु पादेन रेचितौ" इति (ना. शा. ४-७४) मण्डलमिति मण्डलस्वस्तिकम्—

"स्वस्तिकौ तु करौ कृत्वा प्राङ्मुखोर्ध्वतलौ समौ ।
मण्डलस्थानकेन ।" इति (ना. शा. ४-६८)

बाहुशीर्ष इत्यनेन निकुट्टितं करणमाह "निकुट्टितौ यदा हस्तौ" इति (ना. शा. ४-६६) । ऊरूद्वृत्तादिकरणजातं क्रमेणोक्ताङ्गहारवत् ।

(२१) परावृत्तः ।

आद्यन्त्विति ।

"एको वक्षःस्थितो हस्तो द्वितीयश्च प्रलम्बितः ।
तलाग्रसंस्थितः पादो जनितम् ।" (ना. शा. ४-१५५) इति । आद्यशब्दो दक्षिणाङ्गप्रयोज्यत्वमस्याह । पादमेकं प्रसारयेदिति शकटास्यं करणमाह—

"निषण्णाङ्गस्तु चरणं प्रसार्य तलसञ्चरम् ।
उद्वाहितमुरःकृत्वा शकटास्यम् ।" (ना. शा. ४-१६८)
"अलातं चरणं कृत्वा व्यंसयेद्दक्षिणं करम् ।
ऊर्ध्वजानुक्रमं कुर्यादलातकम्" (ना. शा. ४-७८)

इत्यलातम् । त्रिकं तु परिवर्तयेदिति भ्रमरकम् ।

---

१. K.S.S. परावृत्तं M.G. G.O.S. N.S. परावृत्तो ।
२. K.S.S. M.G. ततः G.O.S. N.S. पुनः ।

अलातकं प्रयुञ्जीत ह्यूर्ध्वजानु[1] निकुञ्चितम् ।
[2]अर्धसूची च[3] विक्षिप्तमुद्वृत्ता[4]क्षिप्तके तथा ॥ २२४ ॥

करिहस्तं कटिच्छि[5]न्नमङ्गहारे ह्यलातके ।
निकुट्य वक्षसि करावूर्ध्वजानु प्रयोजयेत् ॥ २२५ ॥

आक्षिप्तः स्वस्तिकः पादः करौ चोद्वेष्टितौ तथा ।
'त्रिकस्य वलनाच्च'' इति (ना. शा. ४-६६)

अञ्चितं वामहस्तं चेत्यनेनार्धेन करिहस्तं करणं गण्डदेशे निकुट्टयेदिति विशेषयुक्तमाह ।

"वामो वक्षस्थितो हस्तः प्रोद्वेष्टिततलोऽपरः ।
अञ्चितं चरणं चैव प्रयोज्यः करिहस्तकः ॥ इति (ना.शा. ४-१४८)

'पर्यायश' इति कटिच्छिन्नम् (ना. शा. ४-७१)

(२२) अलातकः ।

स्वस्तिकमित्यादि । स्वस्तिकाविति (ना. शा. ४-६८) स्वस्तिकम् । व्यंसितौ चेति द्विवचनेन पुनश्शब्दे स्वस्तिकव्यवधानेन व्यंसितस्य द्विप्रयोगमाह ।

"आलीढस्थानकं यत्र करौ वक्षसि रेचितौ ।
ऊर्ध्वाधोविप्रकीर्णौ च व्यंसितम्'' (ना. शा. ४-१०६)

''अलातं चरणं कृत्वा व्यंसयेद्दक्षिणं करम् ।
ऊर्ध्वजानुक्रमं कुर्यात्' इत्यलातकम् । (ना. शा. ४-७८)

"कुञ्चितं पादमुत्क्षिप्य जानुस्तनसमं न्यसेत् ।
प्रयोगवशगौ हस्तावूर्ध्वजानु'' (ना. शा. ४-८६)

"वृश्चिकं चरणं कृत्वा करं पार्श्वे निकुञ्चयेत् ।
नासाग्रे दक्षिणं च'' इति निकुञ्चितम् । (ना. शा. ४-८७)

---

१. K.S.S. M.G. ऊर्ध्वजानु G.O.S. ह्यूर्ध्वजानु N.S. ऊर्ध्वं जानु ।
२. N.S. ऊर्ध्वसूची G.O.S. M.G. K.S.S. अर्धसूची ।
३. K.S.S. M.G. इव G.O.S. N.S च ।
४. K.S.S. उद्धृत M.G. N.S. G.O.S. उद्वृत्त ।
५. K.S.S. कटिच्छेदः M.G. कटिच्छेदं G.O.S. N.S. कटिच्छिन्नं ।

आक्षिप्तस्व[1]स्तिकं कृत्वा त्रिकं[7] तु परिवर्तयेत् ।
उरोमण्डलकौ हस्तौ नितम्बं करिहस्तकम्[2] ॥ २२६ ॥
कटिच्छिन्नं[3] तथा चैव पार्श्वच्छेदे विधीयते ।
सूची[4]वामपदं दद्याद्विद्युद्भ्रान्तं च दक्षिणम् ॥ २२७ ॥
दक्षिणेन पुनः सूची विद्युद्भ्रान्तं[5] च वामतः[6] ।
परिच्छिन्नं तथा चैव ह्यतिक्रान्तं च वामकम् ॥ २२८ ॥

"अलपद्मः शिरोदेशे सूचीपादश्च दक्षिणः" (ना. शा. ४-१३८) इत्यर्धसूची ।

"विक्षिप्तं हस्तपादं च पार्श्वतः पृष्ठतोऽपि वा ।
एकमार्गगतं यत्र तद्विक्षिप्तम् । (ना. शा. ४-११९)

आक्षिप्तहस्तमाक्षिप्तपादमुद्वृत्तं करणम् । (ना. शा. ४-१५२)

"आक्षिप्तं हस्तपादं च क्रियते यत्र वेगतः" (ना. शा. ४-११६) इत्याक्षिप्तम् ।

"वामो वक्षःस्थितो हस्तः प्रोद्वेष्टिततलोऽपरः ।
अञ्चितश्चरणश्चैव" (ना. शा. ४-१४८)

इति करिहस्तम् । "पर्यायशः कटिच्छिन्ने"ति (ना. शा. ४-७२) कटिच्छिन्नम् ।

(२३) पार्श्वच्छेदः ।

निकुट्येत्यादि । अनेन वृश्चिककुट्टितं द्विचत्वारिंशत्तमकरणमाह ।

---

१. K.S.S. M.G. आक्षिप्तं स्वस्तिकं G.O.S. N.S. आक्षिप्तस्वस्तिकं ।
२. K.S.S. M.G नितम्बः करिहस्तकः G.O.S N.S. नितम्बं करिहस्तकम् ।
३. M.G. कटिच्छेदं K.S.S. कटिच्छेदः G.O.S. N.S. कटिच्छिन्नं ।
४. K.S.S. M.G. सूचीं वामपदं G.O.S. N.S. सूचीवामपदं ।
५. K.S.S. M.G. विद्युद्भ्रान्तः G.O.S. N.S. विद्युद्भ्रान्तं ।
६. N.S. वामकम् G.O.S. M.G. K.S.S. वामतः ।
७. N.S. K.S.S. M.G. त्रिकं तु परिवर्तयेत् G.O.S. (Same as above) ।

लताख्यं सकटिच्छिन्नं[1] विद्युद्भ्रान्तश्च स स्मृतः ।
कृत्वा नूपुरपादं तु सव्यवामौ प्रलम्बितौ ॥ २२९ ॥
करौ पार्श्वे ततस्ताभ्यां विक्षिप्तं सम्प्रयोजयेत् ।
ताभ्यां सूची तथा चैव त्रिकं तु परिवर्तयेत् ॥ २३० ॥
लताख्यं सकटिच्छिन्नं[2] कुर्यादुद्वृत्तके[3] सदा ।
आलीढव्यंसितौ हस्तौ बाहुशीर्षे निकुट्टयेत् ॥ २३१ ॥

"वृश्चिकं चरणं कृत्वा द्वावप्यथ निकुट्टितौ ।
विधातव्यौ करौ ।" (ना. शा. ४-१०३)

कुञ्चितं पादमित्यूर्ध्वजानु (ना. शा. ४-८६), "आक्षिप्तं हस्तपादं च" इत्याक्षिप्तकम् (ना. शा. ४-११६) "हस्ताभ्यामथ पादाभ्याम्" (ना. शा. ४-७५) इति स्वस्तिकम् । हस्तद्वारेणोरोमण्डलकरणम्—

"स्वस्तिकापसृतौ पादावाविद्धक्रमणं यदा ।
उरोमण्डलकौ हस्तौ ।" (ना. शा. ४-११५)

नितम्बादित्रयं पूर्ववत् ।

(२४) **विद्युद्भ्रान्तः ।**

सूचीत्यादि वामाङ्गप्रयोज्यमर्धसूचीकरणमाह—"अलपद्मः **शिरोदेशे**" इति (ना. शा. ४-१३८), दक्षिणेन विद्युद्भ्रान्तं करणम्—

"पृष्ठतो वलितं पादं शिरोघृष्टं प्रसारयेत् ।
सर्वतो मण्डलाविद्धं विद्युद्भ्रान्तम् ।" (ना. शा. ४-१२६)

एतद्दक्षिणेन । पुनरेतदेव द्वयमङ्गविपर्ययेण । तदाह **दक्षिणेन पुनरिति** । **परिच्छिन्नमिति** छिन्नं करणम् ।

"पल्लवौ तु कटीदेशे छिन्ना पर्यायशः कटी ।
वैशाखस्थानकेन" इति (ना. शा. ४-१०६)

---

१. G.O.S. N.S. सकटिच्छिन्नं K.S.S. M.G. सकटिच्छेदं ।
२ G.O.S. N.S. सकटिच्छिन्नं K.S.S. M.G. सकटिच्छेदं ।
३. K.S.S. उद्धृतके M.G. G.O.S. N.S. उद्वृत्तके ।

नूपुरश्चरणो वामस्तथालातश्च दक्षिणः ।
तेनैवाक्षिप्तकं कुर्यादुरोमण्डलकौ करौ ॥ २३२ ॥

करिहस्तं कटिच्छिन्नमालीढे[1] सम्प्रयोजयेत् ।
हस्तं तु रेचितं कृत्वा पार्श्वमानम्य रेचयेत् ॥ २३३ ॥

पुनस्तेनैव योगेन गात्रमानम्य[2] रेचयेत्[3] ।
रेचितं करणं का[4]र्यमुरोमण्डलमेव च ॥ २३४ ॥

"अतिक्रान्तक्रमं कृत्वा पुरस्तात्संप्रसारयेत् ।
प्रयोगवशगौ हस्तावतिक्रान्तम् ।" (ना. शा. ४-१२७)

एतद्वामेनाङ्गेन लताख्यमिति लतावृश्चिकम् ।

"अञ्चितः पृष्ठतः पादः कुञ्चितोर्ध्वतलाङ्गुलिः ।
लताख्यश्च करो वामः" । (ना. शा. ४-१०५) इति

लतावृश्चिकम् । कटिच्छिन्नं प्राग्वत् ।

(२५) उद्वृत्तकः ।

कृत्वा **नूपुरपाद**मिति ।

"त्रिकं सुवलितं कृत्वा लतारेचितकौ करौ ।
नूपुरं च तथा पादं करणे नूपुरे न्यसेत् ॥" (ना. शा. ४-९७)

सव्यवामग्रहणेन पर्यायशः **करा**विति च द्विवचनेन यौगपद्यं सूचयन् भुजङ्गत्रासितं च द्वात्रिंशत्तमम् (भुजङ्गाञ्चितं चत्वारिंशत्तमम्) गृध्रावलीनकं चतुस्सप्ततितमं करणं दर्शयति ।

"भुजङ्गत्रासितः पादो रेचितो दक्षिणः करः ।
लताख्यश्च करो वामः ।" इति (ना. शा. ४-१०१)

---

१. K.S.S. आलीढं M.G. G.O.S. N.S. आलीढे ।

२ K.S.S. उन्नम्य M.G. N.S. G.O.S. आनम्य ।

३. N.S. M.G. K:S.S. Read in addition कार्यं नूपुरपादं च भुजङ्गत्रासित तदा G.O.S. Omits this.

४. K.S.S. M.G. कुर्यात् G.O.S. N.S. कार्यम् ।

कटिच्छिन्नं[1] तु कर्तव्यमङ्ग[2]हारे तु रेचिते[3] ।
नूपुरं चरणं[4] कृत्वा त्रिकं तु परिवर्तयेत् ॥ २३५ ॥

"पृष्ठप्रसारितः पादः किञ्चिदञ्चितजानुकः ।
यत्र प्रसारितौ बाहू तत्स्याद् गृध्रावलीनकम् ॥"
(ना. शा. ४-१३५)

अतएव करणद्वयमेवोपसंहरति ताभ्यामनन्तरं विक्षिप्तमिति "विक्षिप्तं हस्तपादं च" इति (ना. शा. ४-११६) तदपीच्छया अङ्ग पर्यायेणेत्युपसंहारेणाह—**ताभ्यामनन्तरं सूचीति** । तेनाङ्गपर्यायेण योगस्याक्षेपोपलब्धेः तेन सन्धानायोद्वृत्तं करणम् । [त्रिकपरिवर्तनेन बद्धया चार्या नितम्बं करणम् । ततो "अञ्चितः पृष्ठतः पाद" इत्यादिना लतावृश्चिकं चतुश्चत्वारिंशत्तमम् । ततः कटिच्छिन्नम् ।

(२६) आलीढः ।

आलीढेति ।

आलीढं स्थानकं यत्र करौ वक्षसि रेचितौ
ऊर्ध्वाधो विप्रकीर्णौ च व्यंसितम ॥" (ना. शा. ४-१०६)

इति व्यंसितं दर्शयति । बाहुशीर्ष इति निकुट्टकं नवमं करणम् । वामतो नूपुरं, षट्त्रिंशत्] "निकुट्टितौ यदा हस्तौ" (ना. शा. ४-६६) निकुट्टितकरणम् । ततः "अलातं चरणं कृत्वा व्यंसये" दित्यलातकम् (ना. शा. ४-७८) । तेनैवेति दक्षिणेन । "आक्षिप्तं हस्तपादं चे"त्याक्षिप्तम् (ना. शा. ४-११६) । उरोमण्डलकादिकरणत्रयं पूर्ववत् ।

(२७) रेचितः ।

हस्तौ तु रेचितमिति । अनेन श्लोकेन सर्वाणि हस्तरेचनवन्ति करणानि सङ्गृह्णीते । तथा चोपसंहरिष्यति रेचितं करणमिति । जातावेकवचनेन **हि**

१. K.S.S. कटिच्छेदः M.G. कटिच्छेदं G.O.S. N.S. कटिच्छिन्नं ।
२. G.O.S. N.S. अङ्गहारे K.S.S. M.G. ह्यङ्गहारे ।
३. N.S. च रेचयेत् G.O.S. M.G. K.S.S. तु रेचिते ।
४. K.S.S. M.G. करणं G.O.S. N.S. चरणं ।

किञ्चित्प्रतिपद्येत। रेचितं नाम करणमस्ति यदनेनोच्यते। कार्यमित्यनेन तावतां करणानां श्लिष्टाङ्गतया स्वबुध्या स्वकार्यवद्धि चित्रमेव योजनं कार्यमिति सूचयति। अत एवायं विचित्रभेदसङ्कीर्णोऽङ्गहार:। तथा चान्यत्र श्रूयते।

"पञ्चविंशतिविचित्र (मातृका) प्रक्रमेण विविधं व्यरीरिचत्।

रेचिताङ्गहरणं महेश्वरो गेयमार्गमिव सप्तभि: स्वरै:॥" इति।

'स्वस्तिकौ रेचिताविद्धौ' (ना. शा. ४-६७) इति स्वस्तिकरेचितम्।

'अपविद्ध: कर: सूच्या' (ना. शा. ४-७२) इत्यादीन्यर्धरेचितम्।

वक्ष: स्वस्तिकमुन्मत्तश्चेति द्वादशादीनि त्रीणि, "हस्तो हृदि भवेद्वाम:" इति (ना. शा. ४-८०) आक्षिप्तरेचितम्। "स्खलितापसृत: पाद:" इत्यर्धमत्तल्लि (ना. शा. ४-८९)। रेचकनिकुट्टकं च (ना. शा. ४-९०)

"भुजङ्गत्रासितं कृत्वा यत्रोभावपि रेचितौ"

इत्यादित्रयं भुजङ्गत्रस्तरेचितं (ना. शा. ४-९६) नूपुरं (ना. शा. ४-९७), वैशाखरेचितं च। (ना. शा. ४-९८)

"भुजङ्गत्रासित: पादो रेचितो दक्षिण: कर:" (ना. शा. ४-१०१) इत्यादिकरणद्वयं भुजङ्गाञ्चितकं दण्डरेचितकं च (ना. शा. ४-१०२) "वृश्चिकं चरणं कृत्वा स्वस्तिकौ च" इत्यादि (ना. शा. ४-१०७) वृश्चिकरेचितम्। "आलीढस्थानकं यत्र" इत्यादि (ना. शा. ४-१०९) व्यंसितम्। "आक्षिप्तं हस्तपादे" त्यादिद्वयम्। (ना. शा. ४-१२२) विवृत्तं विनिवृत्तं च (ना. शा. ४-१२३)

"आक्षिप्तं हस्तपादं च त्रिकं चैव विवर्तितम्" (ना. शा. ४-१२८) इति विवर्तितकम्। "पृष्ठप्रसारित: पाद" इत्यादि (ना. शा. ४-१३१) गरुडप्लुतकम्।

"वृश्चिकं चरणं कृत्वा रेचितौ च तथा करौ" (ना. शा. ५-१४१) इति मयूरललितम्। सर्पितकं च, (ना. शा. ४-१४२)। "दोलापादक्रम: कार्य:" (ना. शा. ४-१४७) इत्यादि स्खलितम्। "एकस्तु रेचित" इति (ना. शा. ४-१४९) प्रसर्पितकम्। दोलापादक्रम"मिति (ना. शा. ४-१५४) तलसङ्घट्टितम्। "प्रयुज्यालातक "मित्यादिद्वयं (ना. शा. ४-१६५) वृषभक्रीडितकं लोलितं च (ना. शा. ४-१६६)। एवं करणपञ्चविंशतिर्वैचित्र्येण प्रयोज्या:। चतुष्षडादिक्रमेण पुनरुक्ततया चतुर्दिङ्मुखेषु यावत्समाप्ता भवति। यत उक्तम्—

"द्वाभ्यां त्रिचतुराभिर्वाप्यङ्गहारस्तु मातृभि: "इति (ना. शा. ४-३१) "पुनस्तेनैव योगेन गात्रमानम्ये" त्येनेन मध्ये वैचित्र्याच्चक्रमण्डलेन (ना. शा. ४-११४) व्यवहितेयं करणपरम्परा प्रयोज्येत्याह।

व्यंसितेन तु हस्तेन त्रिकमेव[1] वि[2]वर्तयेत् ।
वामं[3] चालातकं कृत्वा सूचीमत्रैव[4] योजयेत् ॥ २३६ ॥

करिहस्तं कटिच्छिन्नं कुर्यादाच्छुरिते[5] सदा ।
रेचितौ स्वस्तिकौ[6] पादौ रेचितौ स्वस्तिकौ[7] करौ ॥ २३७ ॥

कृत्वा विश्लेषमेवं तु तेनैव विधिना पुनः ।
पुनरुत्क्षेपणं चैव रेचितैरेव कारयेत् ॥ २३८ ॥

"प्रलम्बिताभ्यां बाहुभ्यां यद्गात्रेण नतेन च ।
अभ्यन्तरापविद्धं स्यात्तज्ज्ञेयं चक्रमण्डलम् ॥" (ना. शा. ४-११४)

आनम्येत्यादिरन्तर्भावितण्यर्थः । प्रयोग एवं प्रयोज्यः । प्राग्वदुरोमण्डलं कटिच्छिन्नं च।

(२८) **आच्छुरितः** ।

नूपुरमित्यादि । त्रिकन्तु परिमितं नूपुरं परिवर्तयेदित्यनेन भ्रमरकम्— "आक्षिप्तः स्वस्तिकः पादः...त्रिकस्य वलनं चैव ।" (ना. शा. ४-९९) इति । व्यंसितेन त्विति व्यंसितम्—"आलीढं स्थानकं यत्र"ति (ना. शा. ४-१०९) । ततोऽलातकम्—"अलातं चरणं कृत्वा" इति (ना. शा. ४-७८) । त्रिकमेवेत्येवकारेण नितम्बं "भुजावूर्ध्वविनिष्क्रान्तौ" इति (ना. शा. ४-११६) सूचितम् । ततः करणद्वयं पूर्ववत् ।

(२९) **आक्षिप्तरेचितः** ।

रेचितौ स्वस्तिकावित्यादि । यत्र यत्र करणे करयोः पादयोर्वा रेचितस्वस्तिकसाहित्यं तत्तदिहाप्यनुजानाति पृथगभिधानेन । रेचितं स्वस्तिकं ह्येतेनैव ह्येतानि करणानि । स्वस्तिकरेचितं "स्वस्तिकौ रेचिताविद्धौ" इति पृष्ठस्वस्तिकं दिक्स्वस्तिकं च "विक्षिप्ताक्षिप्तबाहुभ्याम्" इत्यादि (ना. शा. ४-७६-७७) कटीसमं "स्वस्तिकापसृतः पाद" इत्यादि (ना. शा. ४-७९) । घूर्णितम्—

१. K.S.S. M.G. चैव G.O.S. N.S. एव ।
२. K.S.S. निवर्तयेत् M.G. N.S. G.O.S. विवर्तयेत् ।
३. N.S. M.G. पादं G.O.S. K.S.S. वामं ।
४. K.S.S. M.G. तत्र G.O.S. N.S. अत्र ।
५. K.S.S. आच्छुरितं G.O.S. N.S. M.G. आच्छुरिते ।
६. G.O.S. K.S.S. M.G. रेचितौ स्वस्तिकौ N.S. रेचितस्वस्तिकौ ।
G.O.S. K.S.S. M.G. रेचितौ स्वस्तिकौ N.S. रेचितस्वस्तिकौ ।

उद्वृत्ताक्षिप्तके[1] चैव ह्यु[2]रोमण्डलमेव च ।
नितम्बं करिहस्तं च कटिच्छिन्नं तथैव च ॥ २३९ ॥
आक्षिप्तरेचितो[3] ह्येष करणानां विधिः स्मृतः ।
विक्षिप्तं[4] करणं कृत्वा हस्तपादं मुखानुगम्[5] ॥ २४० ॥

"वर्तिताघूर्णितः सव्यो हस्तो वामश्च दोलितः ।
स्वस्तिकापसृतः पादः ।" (ना. शा. ४-९३) इति

भ्रमरकम् "आक्षिप्तः स्वस्तिकः पाद" इति (ना. शा. ४-९९) । वृश्चिकरेचितम् । "वृश्चिकं चरणं कृत्वा स्वस्तिकं च" इति (ना. शा. ४-१०७) । पार्श्वनिकुट्टकम् । "हस्तौ तु स्वस्तिकौ पार्श्वे" इति (ना. शा. ४-११०), उरोमण्डलकम् । "स्वस्तिकापसृतौ" इति (ना. शा. ४-११५) । सन्नतम् । "उत्प्लुत्य चरणौ कार्यावग्रतः स्वस्तिकौ स्थितौ" (ना. शा. ४-१३६) इति, सिंहाकर्षितकम् । "पृष्टप्रसारित" इति (ना. शा. ४-१५१) । नागापसर्पितम् । "स्वस्तिकापसृतौ पादौ" इति (ना. शा. ४-१६७) । वक्षःस्वस्तिकादौ तु रेचनं नास्तीति न सङ्गृहीतम् । परे त्वङ्गपरिवर्तनक्रमेण तत्रापि रेचितमिच्छन्तस्तदपि सङ्गृह्णते ।

एवं हस्तपादस्वस्तिकश्च (कञ्च) तद्रेचितश्च (तञ्च) वैचित्र्येण विधाय तेनैव विधिनेत्यत्रुटितेनाङ्गेनोत्क्षेपणं हस्तपादस्य कार्यम् । अनेन यत्र यत्रैतदस्ति तत्तत्करणं सूचयति । तद्यथा दण्डपक्षम् "ऊर्ध्वजानुं विधायाथ तस्योपरि लतां न्यसेत्" इति (ना. शा. ४-९५), ललाटतिलकं "वृश्चिकं चरणं कृत्वा" इति (ना. शा. ४-१११), तलविलासितम् "ऊर्ध्वाङ्गुलितलः पाद" इति (ना. शा. ४-११७), निशुम्भितं—

"पृष्ठतः कुञ्चितः पादो वक्षश्चैव समुन्नतम् ।
तिलके च करः स्थाप्यः ।" इति (ना. शा. ४-१२५)

---

१. K.S.S. M.G. उद्वृत्ताक्षिप्तकं G.O.S. N.S. उद्वृत्ताक्षिप्तके ।
२. K.S.S. M.G. उरोमण्डलम् G.O.S. N.S. ह्युरोमण्डलम् ।
३. M.G. आक्षिप्तरेचिते त्वेष K.S.S. आक्षिप्तरेचकेष्वेषः G.O.S N.S. (Same as above) ।
४. N.S. विक्षिप्तकरणं G.O.S. K.S.S. M.G. विक्षिप्तं करणं ।
५. K.S.S. N.S. हस्तपादमुखानुगम् M.G. G.O.S. (Same as above) ।

वामसूचीसहकृतं[1] विक्षिपेद्वामकं करम् ।
वक्षःस्थाने[2] भवेत्सव्यो वलितं त्रिकमेव च ॥ २४१ ॥

नूपुराक्षिप्तके चैव ह्य[3]र्धस्वस्तिकमेव च ।
नितम्बं करिहस्तं च ह्यु[4]रोमण्डलकं तथा ॥ २४२ ॥

कटिच्छिन्नं[5] च कर्तव्यं सम्भ्रान्ते नृत्तयोक्तृभिः ।
अपक्रान्तक्रमं कृत्वा व्यंसितं हस्तमेव च ॥ २४३ ॥

विद्युद्भ्रान्तं "पृष्ठतो वलितं पादम् । इति (ना. शा. ४-१२६), गजक्रीडितं कर्णेऽञ्चितः करो वामः" इति (ना. शा. ४-१२९), नितम्बं "भुजावूर्ध्वं-विनिष्क्रान्ता" विति (ना. शा. ४-१४६) विष्णुक्रान्तम् "ऊर्ध्वं प्रसारितः पादः" इति (ना. शा. ४-१६१) । तत उद्वृत्तमित्यूरूद्वृत्तम् । (ना. शा. ४-१५९); अत्र समाक्षिप्तकरणमध्ये तस्य दृष्टत्वात् करमावृत्य तत्करण-मिति । "आप्तिक्षं हस्तपादं च" इत्याक्षिप्तम् (ना. शा. ४-११६) । "स्वस्तिकापसृतौ पादौ" इत्युरोमण्डलम् (ना. शा. ४-११५) साहचकाराच्च (साहचर्याच्चकाराच्च) कटिच्छिन्नमप्यन्ते केचिदिच्छन्ति ॥

(३०) सम्भ्रान्तः ।

विक्षिप्तमित्यादि । "विक्षिप्तं हस्तपादं च" इति (ना. शा. ४-११९) विक्षिप्तम् । "हस्तपादं मुखानुगम्" इत्यञ्चितं गण्डसूची गङ्गावतरणं चेति दर्शयति ।

"व्यावृत्तपरिवृत्तस्तु स एव तु करो यदा ।
अञ्चितो नासिकाग्रे ।" इति (ना. शा. ४-८३)

"सूचीपादोन्नतं पार्श्वम्" इति (ना. शा. ४-१३२) गण्डसूची ।

"ऊर्ध्वाङ्गुलितलः पादस्त्रिपताकावधोमुखौ ।
हस्तौ च सन्नतौ" (ना. शा. ४-१६९) इति गङ्गावतरणम् ।

---

१. K.S.S. M.G. करं कृत्वा G.O.S. N.S. सहकृतं ।
२. K.S.S. M.G. वक्षःस्थं G.O.S. N.S. वक्षःस्थाने ।
३. G.O.S. N.S. हि K.S.S. M.G. Omit हि ।
४. K.S.S. M.G. स्यात् G.O.S. N.S. च हि ।
५. K.S.S. M.G. कटिच्छेदः G.O.S. N.S. कटिच्छिन्नं ।

कुर्यादुद्वेष्टितं चैव ह्यर्धसूचीं[1] तथैव च ।
विक्षिप्तं सकटिच्छिन्नमुद्वृत्ताक्षिप्तके तथा ॥ २४४ ॥

करिहस्तं कटिच्छिन्नं कर्तव्यमपसर्पिते ।
कृत्वा नूपुरपादं च द्रुतमाक्षिप्य च क्रमम् ॥ २४५ ॥

वामसूचीसहकृतमित्यनेनार्धसूचीं दण्डपादं च दर्शयति । "अलपद्मः शिरोदेशे" (ना. शा. ४-१३८) इत्यर्धसूची ।

"नूपुरं चरणं कृत्वा दण्डपादं प्रसारयेत ।
क्षिप्राविद्धकरम्" (ना. शा. ४-१४३) इति दण्डपादम् ।

एतच्च वामेनाङ्गेन । सव्य इति दक्षिणे वक्षसि । वामस्योपयोगित्वात् । अनेन चतुरं करणं सूचयति—

"अञ्चितः स्यात्करो वामः सव्यश्चतुर एव च ।
दक्षिणः कुट्टितः पादश्चतुरं तत्प्रकीर्तितम् ॥" इति
(ना. शा. ४-१००) ।

वलितं त्रिकमिति भ्रमरकम्—"आक्षिप्तः स्वस्तिक" इति (ना. शा. ४-९९), "त्रिकं सुवलितं कृत्वा" इति (ना. शा. ४-९७) नूपुरम् । "आक्षिप्तं हस्तपादं च" इत्याक्षिप्तम् । ना. शा. ४-११६) ।

स्वस्तिकं चरणं कृत्वा कटिहस्तं च दक्षिणम् ।
वक्षस्थाने तथा वाममर्धस्वस्तिकम् ॥" (ना. शा. ४-८२)

इत्यर्धस्वस्तिकम् । नितम्बादिचतुष्कं पूर्ववत् । (२०२)

(३१) अपसर्पितः ।

अपक्रान्तमित्यादि । अपक्रान्तं—

"कृत्वोरुवलितं पादमपक्रान्तक्रमं न्यसेत् ।
प्रयोगवशगौ हस्तावपक्रान्तम् ॥" (ना. शा. ४-१०४) इति ।

---

१. K.S.S. N.S. सूची G.O.S. सूचीं ।
२. K.S.S. M.G. सकटिच्छेदं G.O.S. N.S. सकटिच्छिन्नम् ।

पादस्य चानुगौ हस्तौ[1] त्रिकं च[2] परिवर्तयेत् ।
निकुट्य करपादं चाप्युरोमण्डलकं पुनः ॥ २४६ ॥
करिहस्तं कटिच्छिन्नं[3] कार्यमर्धनिकुट्टके ।
द्वात्रिंशदेते सम्प्रोक्ता ह्य[4]ङ्गहारा द्विजोत्तमाः ॥ २४७ ॥

व्यंसितमिति "आलीढं स्थानकं यत्र करौ वक्षसि" इति (ना. शा. ४-१०९) । अतो व्यंसितात्करणात्करक्रियामेव गृह्णीयादित्येवकारेणाह । एकवचनं जातौ । **उद्वेष्टितमिति** करिहस्तकरणं निर्दिशति—

"वामो वक्षःस्थितो हस्तः प्रोद्वेष्टिततलोऽपरः ।" इति (ना. शा. ४-१४८) । "अलपद्मः शिरोदेशे सूचीपादः" (ना. शा. ४-१३८) इत्यर्धसूची । "विक्षिप्तं हस्तपादं च" इति (ना. शा. ४-११९) विक्षिप्तम् । "पर्यायशः कटीच्छिन्ना" इति (ना. शा. ४-७१) कटिच्छिन्नम् । उरूद्वृत्तमिहोद्वृत्तशब्देनोक्तम् । (ना. शा. ४-१५९) । प्राग्वदन्ते (त्रीणि) करणानि । (२४४) ।

(३२) अर्धनिकुट्टकः ।

कृत्वा नूपुरपादमित्यादि । "त्रिकं सुवलितं कृत्वा" इति (ना. शा. ४-९७) नूपुरपादम् । **द्रुतमाक्षिप्ये**त्यादिना विवृत्तं करणमाह—

"आक्षिप्तं हस्तपादं च त्रिकं चैव विवर्तितम् :
रेचितौ च तथा हस्तौ विवृत्ते करणे द्विजाः ॥ इति
(ना. शा. ४-१२२)

निकुट्येत्यनेन करपादनिकुट्टितं यत्र तानि करणान्याह निकुट्टितार्धनिकुट्टकादीनि । उरोमडणलकादित्रयं पूर्वाङ्गहारवत् ।

ये येऽङ्गहारास्तेषां प्रतिकरणं गुरुपरिमाणं कलानिवर्तनकालस्तावता सम्यक्करणं वर्तनाक्रमेण शक्यम् । तत्र ये षड्द्वादशचतुर्विंश (ति) रित्यादिकरणात्मका एकेन द्वाभ्यां वाऽभ्यसितेन युक्तास्ते त्र्यश्रमानेन बोद्धव्याः ।

---

१. N.S. पादौ G.O.S. M.G. K.S.S. हस्तौ ।
२. K.S.S. M.G. N.S. तु G.O.S. च ।
३. K.S.S. M.G. करिहस्तः कटिच्छेदः M.G. G.O.S. N.S. (Same as above) ।
४. G.O.S. N.S. हि K.S.S. M.G. तु ।

चतुरो रेचकांश्चापि[1] गदतो मे निबोधत ।
पादरेचक एकः स्यात् द्वितीयः कटिरेचकः ॥ २४८ ॥

कररेचकस्तृतीयस्तु चतुर्थः कण्ठरेचकः ।
[रेचिताख्यः पृथग्भावे वलने चाभिधीयते ॥ ॥

उद्वाहनात्पृथग्भावाच्च[2]लनाच्चापि रेचकः ।
पार्श्वात्पार्श्वे तु गमनं स्खलितैश्चलितैः पदैः ॥

एकस्य द्वयोर्वा मध्ये तु प्रवेशयितुं तालकलाद्यभिसन्धानेन शक्यत्वात् । ते च षोडशात्र सन्ति । पूर्ववदेवाष्टषोडशादिकरणात्मका एकेन द्वाभ्यां वाऽभ्यसितेन किंचिदधिका वा ते चतुरश्रतालविषया द्रष्टव्याः । तेऽपि षोडशैव । एकस्य् क्वचिदूनत्वेऽपि कस्यचित्पुनः क्रियया तालहरणं शक्यमिति मन्तव्यम् ।

तत्रापविद्ध उद्धट्टितो विष्कम्भस्तदपसृतः स्वस्तिकरेचितो वृश्चिकापसृतो मत्तस्खलितो गतिमण्डलः परिवृत्तकरेचितः परावृत्तकोऽलातक उद्धृत्तको रेचित आक्षिप्तरेचितः सम्भ्रान्तोऽर्धनिकुट्टकश्चेति त्र्यश्रतालकाः षोडश । एषां चतुरश्राश्रयास्तावन्तः । तत्र द्विभेदैर्भिन्नेष्ववान्तरभेदेन षोडशसु पूर्वरङ्गाङ्गे-षूत्थापनादिप्ररोचनान्तेषु बहिर्यवनिकागतेषु प्रयोगात् द्वात्रिंशद्रूपतत्येवं केचित् ।

एके त्वाहुः—चतसृणां नर्तकीनां प्रतिप्रयोगं चत्वार इतिं पुनः पिण्डीरेचक-न्यासापन्यासश्चतुर्धेति द्वात्रिंशत् । एतच्च पूर्वरङ्ग (ना. शा. ५) व्याख्याने स्पष्टयिष्याम इत्यलम् ।

अन्ये तु गीतकानामाङ्गनिबन्धानां वस्तुनिबन्धानां च वस्तु त्रिविधम् । बद्ध (वर्ध) मानकरणानि (नव) । चत्वारि आसारितानि । पाणिकैकप्रकारा । इत्येवंभूतं च यतो ब्रह्मगीतिवैचित्र्यं द्वात्रिंशद्भासितं तस्मात्तत्प्रयोगानात्मनोऽङ्गहारेऽपि तावदेवेत्याहुः । अन्ये तु परमेश्वरभाषितत्वादि यथा (दियता ?) सफलसम्पत्तिहेतुत्वमित्याहुः । एतन्मनसि कृत्वोपसंहरति—**द्वात्रिंशदेत** इति । (२४७)

---

१. K.S.S. M.G. एव G.O.S. N.S. अपि ।

२. K.S.S. वलनात् G.O.S. N.S. M.G. चलनात् ।

विविधैश्चैव पादस्य पादरेचक उच्यते ।
त्रिकस्योद्वर्तनं चैव कटीवल[1]नमेव च ॥

तथाऽ[2]पसर्पणं चैव कटि[3]रेचक उच्यते ।
उद्वर्तनं[4] परिक्षेपो विक्षेपः परिवर्तनम्[5] ॥

विसर्पणं च हस्तस्य हस्तरेचक उच्यते ।
उद्वाहनं सन्नमनं तथा पार्श्वस्य[6] सन्नतिः ॥

भ्रमणं चापि विज्ञेयो ग्रीवाया रेचको बुधैः ।]
रेचकैरङ्गहारैश्च नृत्यन्तं वीक्ष्य शङ्करम् ॥ २४९ ॥

सुकुमारप्रयोगेण नृत्यन्तीं[7] चैव पार्वतीम् ।
मृदङ्गभेरीपटहैर्भाण्ड[8]डिण्डिमगोमुखैः ॥ २५० ॥

अथ रेचकानाह—**पादरेचक** इति । पादयोरेव चलनं न च पार्ष्णिभूतयोरन्तर्बहिश्च सन्नतं नमनोन्नमनह(व्यं ?)सितं गमनमङ्गुष्ठाग्रस्य च । हस्तयोरेव चलनं हंसपक्षयोः पर्यायेण द्रुतभ्रमणम् । ग्रीवायास्तु रेचितत्वं विधुतभ्रान्तता । सर्वतो भ्रमणाच्चापि विज्ञेयं तु रेचिताङ्गक इत्यादिसङ्ख्योपादानात्पृथगेते वैशाखमण्डलादिस्थानकस्थेन प्रयोज्या इति दर्शयन् वैशाखरेचितेन करणेन सङ्गृहीतत्वमेषां दर्शयति । पृथग्दृष्टार्थताख्यापनार्थं चैषां करणाङ्गहारान्तर्भूतानामप्युपादानम् । सुकुमारगीतवाद्यप्रधाने च प्रयोग एषां प्रयोगः ।

---

१. K.S.S. M.G. चलनम् G.O.S. N.S. वलनम् ।

२. N.S. तथापि सर्पणं G.O.S. K.S.S. M.G. तथाऽपसर्पणं ।

३. G.O.S. कटि K.S.S. M.G. N.S. कटी ।

४. G.O.S. K.S.S. उद्वर्तनं M.G N.S. उद्वर्तनः ।

५. K.S.S. M.G. विक्षेपपरिवर्तनम् G.O.S. N.S. विक्षेपः परिवर्तनम् ।

६. N.S. पार्श्वं च G.O.S. M.G. K.S.S. पार्श्वस्य ।

७. K.S.S. M.G. नृत्यति स्म च पार्वती G.O.S. नृत्यन्तीं चैव पार्वतीम् N.S. नृत्यन्ती चैव पार्वतीम् ।

८. M.G. N.S. झञ्झा K.S.S. G.O.S भाण्ड ।

पणवैर्दर्दुरैश्चैव[1] सर्वातोद्यैः[2] प्रवादितैः[3] ।
दक्षयज्ञे विनिहते सन्ध्याकाले महेश्वरः ॥२५१॥
नानाङ्गहारैः प्रानृत्यल्लयतालवशानुगैः[4] ।
पिण्डीबन्धांस्ततो[5] दृष्ट्वा नन्दिभद्रमुखा गणाः ॥ २५२ ॥
चक्रुस्ते नाम पिण्डीनां बन्धमासां सलक्षणम्[6] ।
ईश्वरस्येश्वरी पिण्डी नन्दिनश्चापि पट्टसी[7] ॥ २५३ ॥

तुम्बुरुणेदमुक्तम् —

"अङ्गहाराभिधानात्तु करणै रेचकान्विदुः ।" (इति) । इहाप्येतन्मुनेर्मतमिति लक्ष्यते । यत्सहशब्देन तत्र तत्र निर्दिशति "व्याख्यास्यामि सरेचकान्" (ना. शा. ४-१९) इति । नन्वेवं करणाङ्गहाररेचकाः किं पूर्वरङ्गानेव (ङ्ग एव) वैचित्र्यकारित्वमात्रे (णै) वोपयुज्यन्ते । नेह प्रस्तुमः (नेति ब्रूमः) ।

कथं तर्हि । देवतापरितोषकत्वेनापि । तदपि च वैचित्र्यमात्रात् । यावत्तत्तद्देवताध्वजप्रतिकृतिभूतपिण्डीबन्धनिष्पत्तिद्वारेणेत्यभिप्रायेण पिण्डीबन्धावतरणाय **भरतमुनिः** पुराकल्पमाह श्लोकचतुष्टयेन—**रेचकैरङ्गहारैश्चे**त्यादिना । इह चत्वारश्चकाराः (?) । तत्रैको हेतावन्ये समुच्चये । तत्रैवमभिसम्बन्धः । यस्मात्प्रहर्षपरवशप्रमथाभिहतैर्मृदङ्गादिभिरुपलक्षिते दक्षयज्ञे निहते प्रहर्षवशान्नर्तिनि । (नृत्यन्तीमिति) धातुसम्बन्धे प्रत्यया इत्यनेन । [प्रयोगः । अन्यथा नृत्तवन्तमित्यादि स्यात् ।] सन्ध्याकाले दिनात्यय इति प्रमोदविकासमये । तत एव पुण्यात्मके । सततमतिशयेन भृशं च नृत्यति तद्धेतोः । रेचकैरङ्गहारैश्चैव न तु सुकुमारं प्रणृत्यन्तं शङ्करं वीक्ष्य सुकुमार-

---

१. K.S.S. M.G. आद्यैश्च G.O.S. N.S. चैव ।
२. K.S.S. M.G. नाना G.O.S. N.S. सर्व ।
३. N.S. प्रमादितैः K.S.S. G.O.S. M.G. प्रवादितैः ।
४. N.S. वशानुगम् G.O.S. K.S.S. M.G. वशानुगैः ।
५. K.S.S. डिण्डिमभ्रान्ततो M.G. G.O.S. पिण्डीबन्धान् ततो N.S. पिण्डीबन्धाः ततो ।
६. K.S.S. M.G. चक्रुर्नामानि पिण्डीनां बन्धांश्चैव सलक्षणान् G.O.S. N.S. (Same as above).
७. M.G. पट्टिसी K.S.S. पादसी G.O.S. N.S. पट्टसी ।

प्रयोगमेव कृत्वा तु अर्थतत्त्वेन नृत्यन्तीं भगवतीं च वीक्ष्य। तत एवेति तावतामेव। अङ्गहारा रेचकाश्चेति। तद्धेतुकान्पिण्डीबन्धान्दृष्ट्वा नन्दी तथा भद्रमुखवीरभद्रप्रभृतयो नन्दिभद्रदेवतागणास्तत्प्रमुखाः पिण्डीबन्धनाम चक्रुः। आकारसादृश्येऽयं (न) च पिण्डीबन्धं प्रयोगं चक्रुः। **सलक्षणं** लक्षणपर्यन्तम्। अन्तवचनेऽव्ययीभावः। अङ्गहारप्रयोगनान्तरीयकतया आकारविशेषसम्पत्ति दृष्ट्वा सम्यक्प्रयुज्य लक्षणं विदधिर इति यावत्। द्वयोः प्रयोक्तृतया सुकुमारावृत्त—नृत्तयोः समकालप्रयोगेण पिण्डीबन्धनिष्पत्तिं सूचयति—**नन्दिभद्रमुखा गणा** इति। अनेन चतुष्प्रभृतिप्रयोज्यतामप्याह—नन्दिभद्रनामैव गण इति। नन्दिकेश्वरनियतस्थानं मृदङ्ग। मुरजः भेरी कांस्यशकलान्तःपूर्णा महर्षकाभङ्गमर्दलः। डिण्डिमः करटिका। गोमुखो भङ्गी (ण्डी)। अन्तरीयुक्तस्तन्त्रीयुक्तः पटहः पणवो दर्दुरो महाघटिकाधार इति सर्वे एते चर्मावनद्धभेदाः। लयो द्रुतमध्यविलम्बितात्मा। तस्य यस्तालः प्रतिष्ठा। अपि च तत्त्वं विशिष्टवर्धमानगीतकादिनियतवैणवस्वरविशेषात्मकधातुवाद्यशेषभूतशुष्कप्रयोगप्रकृतिकावनद्धवाद्यगीतिनियतप्रतिष्ठितलयात्मकत्वम्। नाट्ये च प्रयोज्यचित्तवृत्तिपरिवृत्तानुसारेणान्यथान्यथाभावेन। तस्य यो वशः सामर्थ्यं तस्यानुषङ्गं कृत्वा तदनुसारित्वेनानुगम्यमानः अनुसृतं कृत्वेत्युभयथा तन्त्रेण द्रष्टव्यम्। लयतालवशस्यास्य लयतालवशत्वानुगो यत्रेति।

ननु च नाट्य एवाङ्गानुसारित्वेन लयादि। न तु नृत्त एव। आङ्गिके नाट्यस्य भेदः। उच्यते—इहादृष्टविशेषसम्पत्तिहेतुत्वं वर्धमानादिप्रयोगस्य सोपकरणनृत्तप्रयोगस्य च। तत्र गुणप्रधावभावं प्रति कामचारः। यदा गीतकादेः प्राधान्यं तदा तदनुसार्यङ्गं भवति। तदभिप्रायेणैव यद्वक्ष्यति—

"गत्या वाद्यानुसारिण्या तस्याश्चारीं प्रयोजयेत्"। इति (ना. शा. ४-२८१)। यदा तु नृत्तस्यादृष्टसम्पादकत्वे प्राधान्यं क्रियते तदा तदनुसारेण गीतकादेराश्रयणम्। यदाश्रयेण वक्ष्यति—

"गीतानां मद्रकादीनां योज्यमेकं तु गीतकम्।
वर्धमानमथापीह ताण्डवं यत्र युज्यते॥" (ना. शा. ५-१३) इति।

अनेन हि चतुर्थेन पादेन ताण्डवस्य प्राधान्यं तदुपयोगित्वं च गीतकादेरुक्तम्। न च नाट्यात्तु भेदः। नाट्ये ह्यङ्गं गीतकं चेत्युभयमप्यप्रतिष्ठितम्। तथा च करचरणचारीमण्डलादि यत्तत्राङ्गोपयोगि तत्स्वरूपेण लयादिव्यवस्थया वा नियतमेव यथारसं प्रयुज्यमानत्वेन विपर्ययात्। एवं ध्रुवागानादावपि द्रष्टव्यम्। सैव हि ध्रुवा कदाचित् द्रुता प्रयुज्यते कदाचिद्विलम्बितेति द्वयमपि (कुत्रचित्)। तत्रापि गीतं च प्रयोज्यचित्तवृत्ति (परिवर्तत्वं तन्त्रम्)

चण्डिकाया भवेत्पिण्डी तथा वै सिंहवाहिनी ।
तार्क्ष्यपिण्डी भवेद्विष्णोः पद्मपिण्डी स्वयम्भुवः ॥ २५४ ॥
शक्रस्यैरावती पिण्डी झ[1]षपिण्डी तु मान्मथी ।
शिखिपिण्डी कुमारस्य रूप[2]पिण्डी भवेच्छ्रियः ॥ २५५ ॥
धारापिण्डी च जाह्नव्याः पाशपिण्डी यमस्य च[3] ।
वारुणी च नदीपिण्डी याक्षी स्याद्धनदस्य तु[4] ॥ २५६ ॥

(?) । इह तु गीतमङ्गं च द्वयमपि स्वप्रतिष्ठितम् । तथा हि यस्य यादृशं लययतिस्वरूपादिकं निरूपितं तन्न विपर्येति मन्त्रादिवत् । वेदवत् न वा (इह तु) योग्यतयाऽङ्गाङ्गिभावः । तथा हि—अपविद्धं द्रुतं चैव" (ना. शा. ४-२०७) इत्यङ्गहारे गीतकादावपि मध्ये स्रोतोगतलयादिरित्यादिकं नान्यथा क्रियते । तेन "प्रधानमनु भि द्य(बध्य)न्ते गुणाः" इत्येतदिह सङ्कोचयति । किन्तु स्वप्रतिष्ठितेऽपि द्वये येन यत्संमेलनयोग्यं तत्तत्र प्रयुज्यत इत्येतावानङ्गाङ्गिभावः । एवं शत्रुज्वलनप्रवृत्तामर्षा(त्तसा)भिमाननरपतिद्वितयवत् । अत एव प्रयुज्यत इत्युक्तम् । तेनैव तथाकरणं सूच्यते ।

तत्र दक्षयज्ञे निहते मृदङ्गादिवाद्यं प्रथमैः प्रवर्तितमिति तदनुगं नृत्तम् । सन्ध्याकालेषु हृदयभूतानन्दोल्लासात्मकेषु भगवन्नृत्तप्राधान्ये स्थिते वाद्यादिप्रवृत्तिः । एतदर्थमेवेत्थंभूतलक्षणतृतीयया साधारण्येनार्थोऽभिहितः । अवसरद्वयाभिधानं चैतदर्थमेव लक्षणमर्थत्वे तथैव दृश्यते ? । तथा हि—गीतमेव तदाऽन्यार्थं तदन्यगतत्वेन नृत्तादि यथा डोम्बिकादौ । तत्र हि परिष्कर(क्रम)णाद्यपि सुकुमारेणैवाङ्गेन । तत्रापि वर्णाङ्गप्राधान्यं क्वचित् । यथा प्रस्थानादौ । क्वचिद्गीयमानरूपकाभिधेयप्राधान्यं यथा त्रिपुरदाहडिमादौ [शिलपकादौ] क्वचिद्वाद्यप्राधान्यं भाणकादिषु भग्न(ण्ड)तालपरिक्रमणादौ । क्वचिन्नृत्तप्राधान्यं यथा डोम्बिकादिप्रयोगानन्तरं हुडुक्कावाद्यावसरे । अत एव तत्र लोकभाषया चिल्लिमार्ग इति प्रसिद्धिः । चारीमार्गो ह्यसावङ्गप्राधान्यात् । तत्रापि वैचित्र्येण

---

१. N.S. झषा स्यात्मन्मथस्य तु G.O.S. M.G. K.S.S. (Same as above) except M.G. reads झषा ।

२. M.G. ऊलु K.S.S. G.O.S. N.S. रूपपिण्डी ।

३. G.O.S. N.S. च K.S.S. M.G. तु ।

४. K.S.S. M.G. च G.O.S. N.S. तु ।

हलपिण्डी बलस्यापि[1] सर्पपिण्डी तु भोगिनाम् ।

गाणेश्वरी महापिण्डी दक्षयज्ञविमर्दिनी ॥ २५७ ॥

त्रिशूलाकृतिसंस्थाना रौद्री स्यादन्ध[2]कद्विषः ।

एवमन्यास्वपि तथा देवतासु यथाक्रमम् ॥ २५८ ॥

मध्ये मध्ये गीतवाद्यादेरपि प्राधान्यम् । वाद्यस्यापि कूप(क्वचित्)सुषिरावनद्ध-भेदेन प्राधान्यं यथायोगं विवेचनीयमित्यलं बहुना ।

तत्रैते पिण्डीबन्धा आधाराङ्गप्रयोगसाधकतभेदाद्बहुप्रकारं भिद्यन्ते । तत्र भूमिर्देश आकाशद्वयभेदात्सप्तसप्तभेद एकैक इत्याधारभेदाः सप्त(?) । हस्तौ पादौ (अक्षिणी) शिर इत्यङ्गभेदा अपि सप्तेत्येकान्नपञ्चाशत् । एकोऽनेको वा प्रयोक्ता । सोऽपि समप्रयोगो विषमप्रयोगो वेति चतुर्धाकरणेन सम्पाद्यते अङ्गहारेण वेत्यष्टाभिरेकान्नपञ्चाशतो गुणनात् द्विनवत्यधिकं त्रिशतं पारमेश्वराः (पिण्डीबन्धाः) ।

"कल्पापायनिशान्तसान्ध्यसमये सद्व्योमरङ्गं गणः (ङ्गाङ्गणं)

सम्प्राप्य प्रतताङ्गहारवलनावैचित्र्यचित्रस्थितिः ।

आकाशे स्ववपुष्यके(?)च विविधां सृष्टिं समासूत्रयन्

त्रैलोक्यस्थपतिस्त्वमेव भगवन्विश्वाकृतिर्जृम्भसि ॥" इति ।

अनया च (दिशा) पिण्डीबन्धानां तत्तद्देवताप्रकृतिमद्भागादिसूचनद्वारेण केवलमपि करणं प्रयुज्यमानमेव हर्षदायि भवति । एवं तत्र प्रधानदेवतोद्देशेन तावत्पिण्डीबन्धान्दर्शयति श्लोकपञ्चके नेश्वरस्येत्यादिना । भगवत एव प्राधान्यात् परितोषणीयत्वेति तस्याव्यक्तं यदीश्वरशब्दवाच्यं निर्विशेषं रूपं तस्य तादृश एव शिवलिङ्गाकृतिः पिण्डीबन्धः । पिण्डी आधाराङ्गादिसङ्घातः । तया बध्यते बुद्धौ प्रवेश्यते तनुभावेन सकलया वा व्योमादाविति पिण्डीवन्ध आकृतिविशेषः । तस्यैकदेशाभिधानं पिण्डीति । यदि वा पिण्डीविशिष्टान्येव तान्याहेति । आबध्यते पुनरनेनेति पिण्डीबन्धः करणाङ्गहारादिः । अन्ते च भगवत एव व्यक्तरूपस्य पिण्डीबन्धो भविष्यति ।

---

१. G.O.S. N.S. अपि K.S.S. M.G. अथ ।

२. K.S.S. अन्तक M.G. G.O.S. N.S. अन्धक ।

ध्व[1]जभूताः प्रयोक्तव्याः पिण्डीबन्धाः सुचि[2]ह्निताः ।
रेचका अङ्गहाराश्च पिण्डीबन्धास्तथैव च[3] ॥ २५९ ॥

परमेश्वरानन्तरं च प्रधानभूतस्य पिण्डीबन्धलक्षणविधायिनो नन्दिनः । पट्टसः उभयत्र त्रिशूलाकृतिरायुधविशेषः । तदनन्तरं भगवत्याः । सिंहश्चासौ वाहनञ्च तस्यैवमिति । आक्रान्ततया । भूमिर्वा लिङ्गस्य सिंहः । तदाकृतिकत्वं दर्शयति । तदनन्तरं विष्णोर्ब्रह्मणश्च । **ऐरावती**ति गजाकारा । **रूपपिण्डी** स्वा (पद्मा)कारा । धारापिण्डी पुनः पुनः प्रयुज्यमाना नदीपिण्डी भवति । याक्षी वैश्रवणायुधः मुद्गराकारा ।

एवं प्रतिपाद्यानभिधायान्यत्रापि दर्शयत्य**ेवमित्यादिना** । **अन्यास्विति** । तृतीयाध्याये पूज्यत्वेन निरूपितासु । तदभिप्रायेणैव **यथाक्रममित्युक्तम्** । ध्वजपूजाहुत्यायुधवाहनविशेषरूपाः । सचिह्नका इत्यनेनापि केनचित्कर्मादि(क्रमादि) सूचकेन रूपेणोपलक्षिताः ।

एतदुक्तं भवति—या काचिद्देवतेत्युच्यते तस्याः पश्चान्नृत्तेन परितोषणं कार्यम् । तन्मध्ये च तदीयायुधवाहनकर्मभावाभ्य(द्य)नुकारी अङ्गप्रयोगो विधेयः । अत एव "पादाग्रस्थितया" (रत्न। १-१) इत्यत्र तलपुष्पपुटकरणेन कर्मणा विशेषसूचकेन भगवत्याः परितोषणं सम्पाद्यते । "तिलके च करः स्थाप्य" (६४ करणम्) इत्यभिनयेन भगवतः परितोषः । "निकुट्टितौ यदा हस्तौ" (९ करणम्) इत्यनेन त्रिशूलाकृतिर्या कायसम्पत्तिः । गरुडप्लुतकेन ताक्ष्यकारगतिसूचनम् । गङ्गावतरणेन धारापिण्डी । नागापसर्पितेन भोगिपिण्डी । "प्रसार्योत्क्षिप्य च करौ" इत्यङ्गहारेण (ना. शा. ४-१७४) आका(धा)रीयभौमत्रिशूलशिवलिङ्गादिपिण्डीनिष्पत्तिः । रेचितेनाक्षिप्तरेचितेन च समस्तानामुक्तानां चारा(चाधारा)द्यनन्तभेदानां निष्पत्तिः । तथा च **नन्दिमत** उक्तम्—

"रेचिताख्योऽङ्गहारो यो द्विधा तेन ह्यशेषतः ।
तुष्यन्ति देवतास्तेन ताण्डवे तं नियोजयेत् ॥" इति ॥

एवमन्यदप्यूह्यमित्यनुपयोगात्समस्तं न लिखितम् । आगमभ्रंशरक्षणाय तु दिङ्निरूपिता ।

---

१. N.S. K.S.S. वज्रभूताः M.G. G.O.S. ध्वजभूताः ।

२. M.G. स्व G.O.S. K.S.S. N.S. सु ।

३. K.S.S. रेचिताश्चाङ्गहाराश्च पिण्डीवद्धास्तथैव च । M.G. रेचकाश्चाङ्गहाराश्च पिण्डीबन्धास्तथैव च G.O.S. N.S. (Same as above).

सृष्ट्वा भगवता दत्तास्त[1]ण्डवे मुनये तदा ।
तेनापि[2] हि ततः सम्यग्गानभाण्डसमन्वितः ॥ २६० ॥

एतदुपसंहरति—**रेचिका** इति । पिण्डीबन्धग्रहणेन शिखिपिण्डप्रभृत्युपाय-मयूरललितादिकरणसङ्ग्रहः । अतएवानयो केवलस्यापि करणस्य देवतापरितोषणेनादृष्टार्थं प्रयोगः । यथा विष्णुक्रान्तस्य चक्रमण्डलस्य च वैष्णवक्रीडासूचकस्य सः । एवकारेणाङ्गहारप्रयोगनान्तरीयकपिण्डीबन्धसम्बन्धः । अङ्गहारा एव पिण्डीबन्धाः तथान्येऽपि पिण्डीबन्धा इति केवलकरणसंग्रहः । चकारात्पिण्डीबन्धनिष्पत्त्युपायत्वं करणद्वयस्यापि यदा विद्यते अन्यस्य करणसमूहात्मनः कल्पितस्याङ्गहारस्य वा । तस्यापि प्रयोगे प्रत्यनुज्ञानमाह । एतदर्थमेव नृत्तमातृकाया लक्षणमङ्गहाराणां च सामान्यलक्षणं प्रणीतम् । (२४८-२५९)

सृष्ट्वेति । ननु स्मृतं नृत्तं सन्ध्याकालेष्वित्यनेनैतद्विरुद्धयते । न । स्थानकचारीनृत्तहस्तभ्रूताराकर्मादीनां वर्णानामिव प्रवाहानादित्वेऽपि विशिष्टपरमात्मना(नः) शोभाविशेषेण भगवता पुनः निर्माणं वेदानामिवेत्यविरोधः । वेदरचनापि हि वर्णानां नित्यत्वेऽपि प्रतिप्राणि-स्थानकरणाभिघातसम्पत्त्यभिव्यक्तपौर्वापर्यनिबन्धना कृतका । सा परं पूर्वपूर्वरचनासजातीयत्वप्रवाहेण नित्या । तथा नृत्तमपीति न किञ्चि(कश्चि)द्विरोधः

दत्ता इति । या तन्त्या(स्वातन्त्र्य)मनुजानानो निजबुद्धिकृतं यत्तेन तत्र वैचित्र्यमनुप्रवेशितं न तद्दृष्टप्रतिघातीति दर्शयति । तेन शोभाप्राधान्यमेवात्र ज्याय इत्यनद्यतन इति यावल्लक्ष्यं न विरूपमिति मन्तव्यम् । **मुनये** इत्यूहापोहादिकुशलाय ।

हि यस्मात् अर्था यतो दत्ताः अतो नृत्तात्मकः प्रयोगः सम्यग्वैचित्र्येण । **स्प-(सृ)ष्टः । सम्यगिति** समञ्चितताल साम्यातिका(त्मिका)(सङ्गे ति(अञ्चन्ति) गच्छन्तीति सम्यग्भूतं यद्गानं गीतम् । **भाण्डं भण**ति शब्दं करोतीति भडितव्याण्ण (?)इत्यनया वा पुष्कराध्यायोदितया व्युत्पत्त्या (तदादि)तदिति । इह तद्गीतं वाद्यं च सम्यगञ्चितं तदनुसारि । तत्प्रधानतया नृत्तप्रधानत्वेन गीतेन वाद्येन च समन्वितः । अत एव तण्डोरयं ताण्डव इति वैयाकरणैः स्मृतम् । (२६०)

अत्र भरतमुनिरेव परकीयामाशङ्कामुपनिबध्नाति । **अनभिज्ञानाच्च मुनी-**नामभिनयादीनामप्यविदुषां कथम् 'अभिनयः कृत' इति गीतकार्थेति गीतेष्वा-

---

१. K.S.S. ताण्डिने मुनये तथा G.O.S. M.G. N.S.(Same as above).
२. K.S.S. तण्डिनापि M.G. G.O.S. N.S. तेनापि हि ।

सारितेष्विति च वचनोपपत्तिस्स्यात् । (न) । तस्मान्मुनिरेवेदं स्वयमाशङ्कते । पूर्वपक्षत्वेन वा शङ्क्येयमिति प्रकटयितुं सुकुमारमिति (रमतिभिः) मध्ये 'ऋषय ऊचुः' इति प्रक्षिप्तम् :

तत्रेत्थमाशङ्का । नृत्तं नाट्याद्भिन्नमभिन्नं वा । भिन्नत्वेऽपि सप्रयोजनमप्रयोजनं वा । न तावद्भिन्नम् । अङ्गविक्षेपनृत्तगीतवत्त्वेनावैलक्षण्यात् । अभिनयप्रयोगस्य गीयमानपदार्थवाक्यार्थगतनाट्यविषयस्य भाव्यविकलस्य दर्शनमस्ति तावत् । अवान्तरवैलक्षण्यं च दशरूपके न विद्यते । एकपात्रहार्ये त्वसन्निहितेऽपि च प्रियतमसखीप्रभृतौ तद्विषयोक्तिप्रत्युक्त्यादिप्रयोगो नाट्येपि । आकाशभाषितादौ भाणरूपके च विद्यते । ते च यथाह **राहुलः**—

"परोक्षोऽपि हि वक्तव्यो नार्या प्रत्यक्षवत्प्रियः ।
सखी च नाट्यधर्मोऽयं भरतेनोदितं द्वयम् ।।" इति ।।

तथा

भाणे चैकाकी वा यो योज्योऽनेकाङ्गहारिणि । **मुनिना** हि वक्ष्यते "भाणकवच्चैकहार्यं स्यात्" इति । **वार्तिककृता**ऽप्युक्तम्—

"वाच्यानुगतेऽभिनये प्रतिपाद्येऽर्थे च गात्रविक्षेपैः ।
उभयोरपि हि समाने को भेदो नृत्तनाट्यगतः (योः) ।।"

अत्रोच्यते । (यदि) साक्षाद्बुद्ध्यभावान्न नाट्यं तदसत् । इयं प्रियतमगुणकीर्तनपरा नृत्यति । खण्डिता नृत्यति । कलहान्तरिता नृत्यति-इति बुद्धेः सम्भवात् । यदाह—

"या चैवंविधगुणकीर्तनवचनेषु प्रियतमस्य संरक्ता ।
सख्याः समक्षमुच्चैः प्रमदा सैवानुकार्यात्र ।।"

एतेनोत्साहगातव्यानामर्थेऽनुकार्यत्वं दर्शितम् ।

अथ गीयमानरूपकाभिनयदर्शनात् नाट्यतो वैलक्षण्यं न तत्तावत् । वैलक्षण्यमात्रप्रयोजकावान्तरभेदस्य सर्वत्र सम्भवादिति ह्युक्तम् । न चेदं वैलक्षण्यम् । नाट्येऽपि तस्य भावात् । वक्ष्यते चाङ्गोपाङ्गकशारीराभिनयलक्षणविधौ ।

"स्थाने ध्रुवास्वभिनयो यत् क्रियते हर्षशोकरोषाद्यैः ।
भावरससंप्रयुक्तं ज्ञेयं नाट्यायितं तच्च ।।" इति ।। (ना. शा. २२-४७)

उपरञ्जकमपि तत्र गीतं नाट्यायितं रूपकं वाद्याभिनययोश्च व्यक्त इति । तत्प्रयोगस्य (श्च) सर्वत्र । डोम्बिकाप्रस्थानषिद्गकभाणकभाणिकारागकाव्यादेर्द-

नृ[1]त्तप्रयोगः सृष्टो यः स ताण्डव इति स्मृतः ।
ऋषय ऊचुः—यदा प्राप्त्यर्थमर्थानां तज्ज्ञैरभिनयः कृतः ॥ २६१ ॥

शरूपकलक्षणेनासङ्ग्रहान्नाट्याद्भेद इति चेत् । तदैकान्तिकम् । तोटकप्रकरणिकारासकप्रभृतेस्तदसङ्गृहीतस्यापि नाट्यरूपत्वात् । "कोहलस्तु ब्रवीति" इति च परिहारस्य समानत्वात् । वाचिकोऽप्यभिनय आसीनपाठ्यादौ क्वचिदस्त्येव । "अहो गाणगाणबुल्लिभाण" इत्यादौ । आहार्यस्तु प्राधान्येनैकः कृतः भाणादावपि न क्षणे क्षणे परिवर्तते । सात्त्विकोऽप्यङ्गीकृत एव **कोहलाद्यैः** "सत्त्वातिरिक्तोऽभिनयः" इत्यादिवचनमालिखद्भिः । आङ्गिकस्तु स्फुट एव । अस्त्री (अन्यस्त्री) डोम्बिकाषिद्गकानामन्योन्यानन्वितत्वं वाक्यानामिव । समवकारेपि अङ्गानामस्त्रीप्रधानेऽर्थे तत्रान्वय इति चेदिहापि समानम् । देवतास्तुतेः स्त्रीपुंभावाश्रयस्य च शृङ्गारस्य सर्वत्रानुगमात्तस्यैव च प्राधान्याद्वक्ष्यति—"देवस्तुत्याश्रयकृतं स्त्रीपुंभावसमाश्रयम् ।" इति । अत एव च **चूडामणिडोम्बिकायां** प्रतिज्ञातं "बिंदुगुणं वमि सहि इह्रोदिवचो अमिदुणधं । महसारकः गेते उं (?) ।" अत एव सहृदयाः स्मरन्ति "वध(स)मचूडामणिआ" (इति ।) तस्मान्नृत्तं नाट्यादभिन्नं तल्लक्षणोपेतत्वात् ।

एतदाह—**यदा प्राप्त्यर्थमि**ति । यतो हेतोरर्थानां काव्यार्थानां प्राप्त्यर्थं साक्षात्कारबुद्ध्या स्वीकारार्थं तज्ज्ञैः प्रयोक्तृभिराङ्गिकाद्यभिनयः कृतः । तत्र त(क)स्मादेतन्नृत्तं कृतम् । नृत्तशब्देन व्यपदिष्टम् । न तु नाट्यशब्देनैवेत्यर्थः । भवतु वा भिन्नं तथापि कं स्वभावं लक्षणं च स्वात्मन्यङ्गीकरोति । लौकिकत्वं लोकोत्तरत्वं वा । लौकिकत्वे घटादिवस्तुतुल्यत्वं तदनुकारत्वं प्रतिबिम्बादिरूपता वा । तत्रापि नाट्यच्छायात्मकतैव । नाट्यस्यैव ह्यमी भागनिष्पन्दाश्चित्रपत्रिकापुस्तप्रभृतयो ग्रन्थकारकल्पिताः साक्षात्कारकल्पप्रत्ययसम्पदा कथापर्यन्तम् । तथा लोकोत्तरत्वे न तु नाट्यस्यैवावान्तरभेदमात्रं तत् ।

तथाविधमपि च तन्न निष्प्रयोजनम् । तद्भावाद्युपलक्षणीयं स्यात् । असिद्धमेतत्—चतुर्वर्गोपदेशस्य राघवविजयादिकरागकाव्येषु दृष्टत्वात् । डोम्बिकादौ तु कामस्यैव प्रच्छन्नरागपरमरहस्योपदेशात् । "यद्वामाभिनिवेशित्वम्" (ना. शा. २२-१९९) इत्यनेन सामान्याभिनये प्रच्छन्नरागस्यातीव देव(मन्मथ)सारसर्वस्वत्वेनाभिधानात् । सिंहसूकरमल्लूककासरादिवर्णनेनापि भाणप्रेरणभाणिकादावप्रस्तुतप्रशंसार्थान्तरन्यासदृष्टान्तादिनां पुरुषार्थस्यैवोपदेशदर्शनादिति प्रयोजनभेदादपि न भेदः । यदा यतोऽर्थानां प्राप्त्यर्थं तज्ज्ञैरनृता(नुवा)दिभिः (नृत्तानुरागिभिः) कविभिरभिनय इत्यभिनीयमानो रागकाव्यादिः कृतः ।

---

१. K.S.S. नृत्य M.G. G.O.S. N.S. नृत्त ।

तस्मात्कस्माद्धेतोरेतन्नृत्तं न नाट्यम् । नाट्यं च कस्मान्न नृत्तम् । गात्रविक्षेपात्मकं हि तदपि । तुल्ये च तथाऽर्थे कं भेदकं स्वभावमपेक्षते । नास्त्यसौ भिन्नस्वभाव इति यावत् । **यद्वार्तिकम्**—

एवमवान्तरवाक्यैरुपदेशो रागदर्शनीयेषु ।
सिंहादिवर्णनैर्वा क्वचिदप्यर्थान्तरन्यासात् ॥" इति ॥

तस्मात्स्वभावस्य प्रयोजनस्य चाभेदान्नृत्तं नाट्यादभिन्नमिति ।

अथोच्यते (राघवविजयादि) रागकाव्यादिप्रयोगो नाट्यमेव । अभिनययोगात् । यत्त्वभिनयादिशून्यं केवलं वलनावर्तनाभ्रूक्षेपताराचलनचरणधारणकम्पस्फुरितकटिच्छेदरेचकादि तदस्माकं नृत्तं भविष्यति । यत्र नाट्यशङ्कापि (नास्ति) ननु किं तेन मो(प्रे)क्षितेन प्रयोजनम् । ननूक्तं नाट्योपयोगित्वं—

"तस्य शाखा च नृत्तं च तथैवाङ्कुर एव च ।
वस्तून्यभिनयस्य" इति (ना. शा. ८-१५) ।

एतद्दूषयति—**यदा प्राप्त्यर्थमिति** । इह "योऽयं स्वभावो लोकस्य" इति (ना. शा. १-११९) लक्षणेन नाट्यं लक्षितम् । तत्राभिनयानामुपयोग उक्तार्थाभिमुख्यप्राप्तिः । नृत्तस्य तूक्तरूपस्य न किञ्चित्प्रयोजनम् । उपरञ्जकतया गीतवाद्यादिवदुपयोग इति चेत्—गीतस्य तावत्—

"यत्तु काव्येन नोक्तं स्यात्तद्गीतेन प्रसाधयेत् ॥" इति

'यानि वाक्यैस्तु न ब्रूयात्" इति "न तैरेव तु वाक्यार्थैः" इति न्यायेन प्रकृतिचित्तवृत्तिकथावस्थादि सूचयतोऽस्त्युपयोगः । वाद्यस्यापि गीतसाम्याक्षिप्ततालोद्दीपकत्वेन । एतन्मध्यात्तु नृत्तं कर्तृ कं स्वभावमपेक्षते । न युद्धनियुद्धगतिपरिक्रमादावस्योपयोग इत्युक्तम् । तत्रापि कं स्वभावं लौकिकमलौकिकं वाऽपेक्षते । लौकिकत्वे प्रयोज्यत्वेन लोकधर्म्यां सङ्ग्रहोऽस्य । चारीमण्डलादिक्रमेण च तस्याङ्ग एव निरूपणं भविष्यति । अथाप्यलौकिकस्तथापि सिद्धम् । 'ऊर्ध्वेन तु कुर्यात्' इत्यादिचतुरहस्तभिनेतव्यविषयविभागन्यायेनाभ्यधिकं सुन्दरोपरञ्जकभागानुप्रवेशेन नाट्यधर्म्यनुप्रवेशे पुनरपि नाट्यादभ्यधिकता ।

अथोच्यते—पूर्वरङ्गप्रयोगस्य वैचित्र्यसिद्ध्यर्थं तदेतदिति । तत्रापि पूर्वरङ्गप्रयोज्यया ब्रह्मगीतया साकम् । अस्या(था)ङ्गाङ्गिभावेन वा । तत्राद्ये पक्षे स्यादसामञ्जस्यम् । अन्त्ये तु पक्षे कथमाहित(ङ्गिक)हस्तचार्याद्यभावः ।

तदुक्तम्—

कस्मान्नृत्तं कृतं ह्येतत्कं स्वभावमपेक्षते ।[1]

न गीतकार्थसम्बद्धं न चाप्यर्थस्य भावकम्[2] ॥ २६२ ॥

कस्मान्नृत्तं कृतं ह्येतद्गीतेष्वासारितेषु च ।

[भरतः]—अत्रोच्यते न खल्वर्थं कञ्चिन्नृत्तमपेक्षते[3] ॥ २६३ ॥

"महागीतेषु चैवार्थान् सम्यगेवाभिनेष्यसि ।" इति (ना. शा. ४-१५) ।

अत्राह—**यदा प्राप्त्यर्थमिति** । अर्थानां गीतकपदाभिधेयानां प्राप्त्यर्थमभिमुखं नयनार्थम् । यद्ययं नृत्ताभिमतोऽभिनयो विहितस्तत्कस्मादभिनयत्वे तुल्ये नृत्तमेतन्न नाट्यम् । तथाहि—गीतकार्थाभिनये कर्तव्ये कमन्यमाङ्गिकहस्तका (चा)र्यद्यभिनयव्यतिरिक्तं स्वभावमपेक्षते । न कञ्चिदन्यमित्यर्थः ।

अथोच्यते—न गीतकादिपदार्थाभिनयतयाऽस्योपयोग इति । किन्तर्ह्यन्यथा गीतकादावस्योपयोग इति । तत्राह—**न गीतकार्थसम्बद्धं न चाप्यर्थस्य भावकमिति** । इह गीतकार्थास्तदारम्भकाः वस्त्वङ्गप्रभृतयः । तेषु न संबद्धं तन्मध्ये न परिगणितमित्यर्थः । यदि ह्यङ्गवस्त्वादित(व)न्मध्यपरिगणनमस्य भवेन्न तद्भवेदप्यन्तदुपयोगस्तदारम्भकत्वात् । नचैतदुपगतम् । न च युक्तम् । नृत्तस्य गीतद्वितीयजातीयत्वात् ।

ननु यथा तत्सुषिरादिवाद्यं तदङ्गसम्बद्धमपि तत्रोपयोगि तथेदं भविष्यतीत्याशङ्क्याह—**न चाप्यर्थस्येति** । अर्थ्यते प्रधानतया गीतकादौ निरूप्यत इत्यर्थः स्वरूपपदतालादिः । तस्याप्येतद्भावकं प्रापकं न भवति ।

एतदुक्तं भवति—स्वरात्मके भागे प्रतिबिम्बरूपतया लग्नस्वरत्वेन स्थानप्रदायितया स्वरपरमार्थप्रापकतया स्वरात्मगीतिभागे स्तुतः सुषिरोपयोगः । अवनद्धस्यापि तत्साम्योपायतालांशप्रापकत्वेन पदपातादभिधेयोपयोगित्वेऽप्यभिनयरूपया (पतया) नाट्यादभेद एव स्यादित्युक्तम् ।

अथोच्यते रेचकाङ्गहारनिबन्धात्मकं यन्नृत्तं न तेन कश्चिदर्थोऽभिनीयते । अपि तु यथा विशिष्टैर्मन्त्रैः भावनाविशेषैश्चाभ्युदयसिद्धिः तथा विशिष्टदेवता-

---

१. K.S.S. तस्मान्नृत्तं कृते ह्येतत् तत्स्वभावमपेक्षते । G.O.S. M.G. N.S. (Same as above) except N.S. reads तस्मात् in place of कस्मात् ।

२. K.S.S. न गीतकार्थसम्बन्धो न वाच्यार्थस्य भावकम् M.G. न गीतकार्थसम्बद्धं न वाच्यार्थस्य भावकम् G.O.S. N.S. (Same as above).

३. K.S.S. M.G. नृत्तं कञ्चिदपेक्षते G.O.S. N.S. (Same as above).

सूचकैर्णन्त्रैस्तथा तद्नीते चाभ्यधायि। भवाभ(ब्रह्म)गीताङ्गवस्तुषु सप्तविंशतिसङ्ख्ये ष्वासारितेषु वर्धमानारम्भकेषु चतुर्षु चकारात्पाणिकाथमित्येतेषु सम्बद्धमेतदङ्गहारात्मकं द्वात्रिंशत्प्रकारं नृत्तमिति तत्संबन्धश्चेदानीं न किञ्चित्। एवं पृथङ्निवृत्त(नृत्त)काव्यादौ नाट्यरूपतैव। नाट्योपयोगित्वेनापि नृत्ततालगीतकाद्युपयोगोऽपि दुर्घट इति त्रिधा पूर्वपक्षसंक्षेपः।

एतत्परिहर्तुमाह—**अत्रोच्यत** इत्यादिश्लोकत्रयेण। अस्मिन्पूर्वपक्षे तूच्यते प्रत्युत्तरमिति शेषः। तत्र यदुक्तमङ्गविक्षेपनृत्तगीतमयत्वान्नाट्यादेर्भेदो (दभेदो) रागकाव्यादिनृत्तस्येति तदनैकान्तिक(त्व)मस्य हेतोः लौकिकनृत्तेऽपि स्फुटम्। नाट्यादिलक्षणसहगोपने तु लौकिके गात्रविक्षेपणं(णे) पठ्यमानमभिनीयमानं वा यावत्पदजातमर्थोनाभिनीयते इति किं नानुसन्धीयते। किं वा न साक्षात्क्रियायोग्यतां नीयते। प्राप्यकल्पोऽसिद्धः। लोकेऽपि सौमनस्याभावादङ्गोपाङ्गपरिक्षेपानुयातस्य वाक्यादीरितस्य दृष्टत्वात्। गीयता (गायतां) पदार्थसंवादकृततन्मयीभावदग्धा(बद्धा)याश्च स्फुटमेव सात्त्विकाङ्गतावलोकनात्।

अथापरः पक्षस्तु नृत्तेऽपि समानम्(नः)। तथाहि—नृत्तकाव्ये डोम्बिकादौ वर्णच्युतादिव वर्णादिप्रयोगे तावदभिनयकथैव नास्तीति किं तत्र विचार्यते। केवलं नृत्तस्वभावमात्रमपि तत्केवलं भावितकाव्यार्थगतार्थतत्त्वसौकुमार्यकृतमङ्गस्य तथात्वमिति निर्णेष्यत इत्यास्तां तावदेतत्।

तदनन्तरं तु धारापरिक्रमपूर्वकलयप्रयोगावसरे "पाआलअलोससाहिणिहुजयजयळच्छिमच्चमलिआ" इत्यादि यद्गीयते तत्कस्योक्तिरूपम्। यदि तावन्नर्तितुमागताया लौकिक्या डोम्बिकाप्रवृत्तनर्तक्याः तदा सैवेदानीमेवंभूतं वस्तुरूपं लौकिकं वचनमभिधत्ते। गायनादिस्वक्रमिकस्ववाक्यत एकवाक्यतः साक्षात्कारकल्पार्थः। साक्षात्कारकल्पानुव्यवसायगोचरकार्यत्वं च नाट्यस्य लक्षणमित्यवोचाम।

तेन यथा कश्चित्कंचिदन्यापदेशगानादिक्रमेण वस्तूद्बोधनकरणद्वारेण वा छन्दानुप्रवेशितया वा कस्यचिन्मनसावर्जनातिशयं विधत्ते। नृत्यन्नपि गायन्नपि तद्वदेव डोम्बिकादौ द्रष्टव्यम्। विडम्बिडोम्बीत्यादावपि (?) वचसि सैवं डोम्बिका। नरपतिपरितोषकार्थाभिधायिवचननिष्ठेन गीतेन नृत्तेन वान्येन (वाद्येन)च राजानमनुरञ्जयितुं गृहीतो मन्त्रित्वेन पूर्वं स्थित्वा मध्य काचिदीदृशी चौर्यकामुककेलीवासमनासाद्य कापि पुनरेवंविधा कश्चिदेवम्भूतश्चौर्यकामुकः कोऽप्येवम्भूतस्तत्र काचिदेवम्भूता प्रौढदूतीत्येवमादि राजपुत्रहृदयानुप्रवेशयोग्यं तत्प्रसादेन धनार्जनोपायमभिदधती तमेव राजपुत्रं परत्वेन तथैव वा

धनमुद्दिश्यान्यदपि चेष्टितमभिधीयते। डोम्बिकाकृत्यमेवोपसंहरति **गुणमालायां** "जामि हराधीतुं गिअपुण्णं चिसमि" इत्यादौ। तत्र सा नृत्यती डोम्बिका च बहुतरोपरञ्जकगीतादिपटुचेटकपरिवृता त्वां प्रत्येवमहमुपश्लोकितवतीति तन्मध्यवर्तिगायनमुखसङ्क्रमितनिजवचना लौकिकेनैव रूपेण तद्गीयमानरूपक-गतलयतालसाम्येन तावन्नृत्यति। तद्गीयमानपदार्थस्य च सातिशयमावर्जनीये राजादौ हृदयानुप्रवेशितां दर्शयितुं लौकिकव्यवहारगतहस्तभ्रूकर्मरोमाञ्चा-क्षिविकारतुल्ययोगक्षेमतयैवाङ्गविकारादिसंभवमप्याक्षिपति।

एवं गीतेन रञ्जनं प्राधान्येन विधाय तदुपयोगिनं चाङ्गिनं चाङ्गव्यापारं प्रदर्श्य नृत्तेन पुनस्तच्चित्तग्रहणं कुर्वती नृत्तं प्रधानभावं गीतं च तदुपसर्जनभावं नयन्ती तत एव तदभिनयमनाद्रियमाणा तद्गीयमानाद्भावाद्विक्षिप्ततदुदित-भावमेवाङ्गविक्षेपं करोति लयपरिष्वक्तंकरणादौ। तत्रेयत्यंशे लौकिकमात्र-स्वभावरामनटादिव्यवहारवत् क्व प्रयोज्यप्रयोजकभावाशङ्का। कस्य वा सामाजिकस्य व्युत्पादनमाभिसंहितम्। तदनन्तरं च यथैव सा गीतनृत्तादि प्रायुङ्क्त तथैव सदृशं न नर्तकी प्रयुङ्क्ते। न तु डोम्बिका साक्षात्कारकल्पेन दर्शयति तदीयाहार्यादिना स्वात्मरूपप्रच्छादनाद्यभावात्। तत एव न डोम्बिकां साक्षात्कारकल्पेन सा दर्शयति। अपि तु तथैव नृत्तं साभिनयं केवलं च प्रदर्शयति तेन नाटचाङ्गतायां यत् दृष्टं पताकादि तद्दर्शनमात्रतया। अतो नाटच संस्कारकं नृत्तस्येत्यङ्गादिव्यपदेश इत्युपचारादुच्यते।

नाटचस्य प्रस्तावनाप्राणप्रतिबिम्बकल्प नृत्तमित्ययमपि व्यवहारस्ततस्त्य एव। नाटचस्यात्र नामाप्यस्ति पदमूर्ध्वादौ चातुरश्रचभङ्गाभावे (?) तद्भावाद्ययोगात् नाटचरूपत्वे हि साक्षात्कारकल्पानुव्यवसायसम्पत्त्युपयोगिनः पात्रं प्रति भाषानियमस्य छन्दोऽलङ्कारादिनियमोऽवश (श्य) रूपाद्योगयोगिन आहार्यविशेषस्य जात्यंशकादे (रि)ति परिक्रमादेश्च स नास्यैवोपयोगो भवेत्। न चैवमस्ति। मूलभूतस्य च पाठचस्य सम्भावनानुषक्तमाकाशभाषितमपि स्यात्। **पादताडितकादि** भाणरूपक इव। इह तु मूलत एव न केनचित्किञ्चि-दुच्यते। "अहो गाणे" त्यादि गायनं यचोक्तं "प्रमदा सैवानुकार्यात्र" इति तदप्यनेन प्रतिसमाहितं नर्तक्याः स्वरूपानाच्छादनात्। कलहान्तरितेयं खण्डितेयं नृत्यतीति व्यवहार औपचारिकः। तदर्थगेयमानरूपकगतगीत-वाद्यानुसारित्वात्तन्नृत्तस्य। न तु मुख्यः। लम्बालकत्ववेणीधारणमङ्गल-वलयापरिग्रहादितदुचितवेषादिपरिग्रहवैकल्यात्। यच्च नाटचायितत्वमाशङ्कितं तदस्थाने भ्रान्तम्। सहृदयैर्नाटचायितमिति हि तावन्त गीयमानमभिनीयते असाङ्गत्यापत्तेः। अपि तु यादृशा लयतालादिना यादृगर्थसूचनयोग्याभिनयः सात्त्विकादिप्रधानरसानुसारितया प्रयोगयोग्यस्तदुचितार्थपरिपूरणं ध्रुवागीतेन क्रियते। सूच्या (क्ष्मा) ह्यमी पल्लवप्रकारा अङ्कुरादयो निवृत्त्यङ्कुरान्ता ये विनायितवच्च नाटचायितम्। एतच्च स्वक्षेत्र एव वितनिष्यामः।

किं तु शोभां प्रज[1]नयेदिति नृत्तं प्रवर्तितम् ।
प्रायेण सर्वलोकस्य नृत्तमिष्टं स्वभावतः ॥ २६४ ॥

एवं नाटचायितशङ्काऽप्यत्र न काचित् । मूलभूतस्याभिनयस्यैवाभावात् । तद्भावे यथा—"मुंचइ वळवि अंअअ इरोअगुहंसणळिण अग्गि चिङज" इत्यादौ मूर्च्छादिसाक्षात्कारः शय्यागाश्चाङ्गनिपतनादिबाहुस्तथा नृत्तकाव्येऽपि स्यात् "होशं दणषक हमहुमाइषक" इत्यादौ । नचैवमस्तीत्युक्तमसकृत् । एतेन प्रयोजनभेदोऽपि प्रत्याप्तः (त्युक्तः) । नहि सामाजिकाः प्रीयन्तां व्युत्पद्यन्तां वेत्यभिसन्धिना नृत्तप्रयोगः । तत्संपत्तिस्तु नान्तरीयकत्वाद्भवतु । ज्योतिष्टोमादिप्रयोगसङ्गीतापनोदादिवददृष्टविशेषोद्देशेनैव हि तस्य प्रयोगः । डोम्बिकाभेदृष्टोद्देशेन राजपुत्रादिप्रीतये यद्यपि प्रवृत्तिर्लौकिकी सा । अद्यत्वे तु न द्वयम् । नर्तक्याः प्रवृत्तिः प्रवर्तना वा देवतापरितोषफलैव । यथोक्तं तत्र—

"यत्किञ्चिल्लास्यमेतेन देवस्तु(वी तु)ष्यति नित्यशः ।
यत्किञ्चित्ताण्डवं तेन सोमः सानुचरः शिवः ॥" इति ॥

मूले च सूदादेरिव वस्तुभूतरूपरसादिमध्यपातिविषयविशेषयोजनया कृता प्रीतिः साध्या । डोम्बिकावर्णनगतस्यैवालौकिकरूपान्तरप्रादुर्भावान्तरस्येति व्युत्पत्त्यभिसन्धानं चानुभवतीति केयं सम्भावना गेयेऽपि । नाटचे तु तदेव प्रधानं भरतमुनिप्रभृतीनां तथैव मूलतः प्रवृत्तेः । अन्यत्वे तु जीविता(का)पर्यवसितत्वमिति पुरुषमि(म)तिपुरुषदौरात्म्यमेतद्धर्मादिचतुष्टयोपदेशि पुराकल्पोपदेशनमिव पुस्तकवाचकानां मूलेन प्रवर्तनात्तत्र व्युत्पत्त्यभिसन्धेरेवेति फलभेदः ।

अन्योऽपि लक्षणभेदो नाटचरूपताशङ्कापराकरणहेतुग्रन्थव्याख्यानावसरे वक्ष्यते । तन्नाटचलक्षणप्रयोजनाभेदादित्यसिद्धो हेतुः । तदाह नृत्तं कर्तृ कंचिदर्थमर्थ्यमानं साक्षात्कारं प्राप्यमानं नाटचवेदमपेक्षते येन लक्षणभेदः स्यात् । तथा न कश्चिदर्थः सामाजिकान्प्रति व्युत्पादनीयधर्माद्युपायान्यतमं व्यपेक्षते येन प्रयोजनभेदोऽपि स्यादित्यतो हेतोरेतन्नृत्तं प्रवर्तितं नृत्तवाचोयुक्त्यैव व्यवहृतम् । ननु(तु)नाटचमिति ।

किञ्चिदपि शुद्धं नाटचाङ्गं पूर्वरङ्गादिकं वेति पाठो वा यदा प्राप्त्यर्थमित्यादि प्रतिसमाहितम् । ननु भवत्वेवंभूतं नृत्तं, नाटचे तु कथमस्योपयोग इत्युक्तं गीतकस्यापि कथमुपयोगः ।

१. N.S. K.S.S. M.G. जनयतीत्यतो G.O.S. प्रजनयेदिति ।

मङ्गल्यमिति कृत्वा च नृत्तमेतत्प्रकीर्तितम् ।
विवाहप्रसवावाहप्रमोदाभ्युदयादिषु ॥ २६५ ॥
विनोदकारणं चेति[1] नृत्तमेतत्प्रवर्तितम्[2] ।
अतश्चैव प्रतिक्षेपाद्भूत[3]सङ्घैः प्रवर्तिताः[4] ॥ २६६ ॥

उक्तं—"यानि वाक्यैस्तु न ब्रूयात्" इति "यत्तु काव्येन नोक्तं स्यात्" इति । ध्रुवायास्तु सम्पाठमात्रमेवास्तु । अलं वर्णालङ्कारयोजनात्मकगान-क्रियादिप्रसारायासेन ।

ननु रामरावणादिगत(ता)ग्राम्यत्याज्यरूपचरितार्थडम्बरस्य हृदयानुप्रवेशद्वारभूतं हृद्यं तत्सूचीकल्पं स्वयं हृदयानुप्रवेशित्वादित्युक्तं प्राक् । स एव तर्हि नृत्तस्य वलनावर्तनादेरन्तरङ्गोऽस्य नाट्य उपयोगः विशेषतो हि तद्विनाऽलातचक्रप्रतिमत्वे तैर्बुद्धिग्राह्यमेव नाट्यं न स्यात् तत एव विमलाभिनयमाणिक्यगुम्फविधायिसूत्रस्थानीयं वलनादिरूपनृत्तसजातीयत्वान्निकटत्वादन्तरङ्गगीतादिवद्यापि नाट्यम् ।

तदेतदाह—**किन्तु शोभां प्रजनयेदिति** । नृत्तं प्रवर्तितं प्रकृष्टमत्रुटितं वर्णनाविलासवलनादिदक्षिणं यद्वर्णितं कायावयवानां कायस्य च विलासचेष्टावस्थानात्मकं वर्तितं तदात्मकं यन्नृत्तं तच्छोभां रञ्जनायोग्यत्वं शोभानान्तरीयकचमत्कारं प्रकर्षेण गानादिना वैलक्षण्येन जनयेदिति नृत्तं प्रवर्तितमित्यन्तेनाभिसम्बन्धः । हेतौ लिङ् ।

ननु रञ्जकत्वं भोजनादीनामप्यस्ति । तत्तदनुप्रवेशनियमोऽत्रेत्याशङ्कां मध्येऽपाकरोति—**प्रायेणेति । विवाहप्रसवावाहादिषु** सर्वस्य लोकस्य स्वभावतः स्वभावेष्वात्माभिमतेषु स्वदेहेनात्मना नर्तनमिष्टं वल्लभम् । सर्वोऽपि जनो विवाहादौ नृत्यति योऽपि वादयन्नृत्यति तेनापि । दर्दुरूढेनापि(दरिद्रेणापि) **मङ्गल्यमिति । विवाहो** वध्वा आनयनम् । तत्पूर्वकः सर्व उत्सवः । पुत्रजन्म **प्रसवः** । ततो जामातुः सवधूकस्य सर्वत्र श्वशुरभवनगमन**मावाहः । प्रमोदा** राज्ञामर्थकरणादयः । **अभ्युदयो** मनोरथप्राप्तिरभिलषितस्योदय इति । आदिग्रहणेनानाकाङ्क्षितशुभप्राप्त्यादि । एतेन निनिमिति(विनोदनमिति) श्लोक-

---

१. K.S.S. M.G. एव G.O.S. N.S. चेति ।
२. K.S.S. M.G. प्रकीर्तितम् G.O.S. N.S. प्रवर्तितम् ।
३. N.S. भुजा G.O.S. K.S.S. M.G. भूत ।
४. N.S. G.O.S. प्रवर्तिताः K.S.S. M.G. प्रकीर्तिताः ।

ये गीतकादौ युज्यन्ते सम्यङ्नृत्तविभागकाः ।
देवेन चापि[1] सम्प्रोक्तस्तण्डुस्ताण्डवपूर्वकम्[2] ॥ २६७ ॥

त्रयस्य सम्बन्धः । एतच्च "कैशिकीमपि योजय" (ना. शा. १-४२) इत्यत्र दर्शितम् ।

कं स्वभावमपेक्षत इति प्रतिसमाधातुमाह—**अतश्चैवेति** । अतश्च कारणान्नृत्तं प्रवर्तितम् । प्रारम्भे पूर्वरङ्गे लक्षणवर्तितं योजितमिति संबन्धः । एवकारो हेतौ यस्मात्प्रतिक्षेपात् । झण्टुमाद्याः शुष्काक्षराः देवैः प्रतिक्षिप्तत्वात् भूतसङ्घैश्च दैत्यादिभिः प्रवर्तिताः । (२६६)

"निर्गीतं तु सवादित्रमिदं गृह्णीमहे वयम् ।" (ना. शा. ५-३५)

इति वक्ष्यते ।

अत एवम्भूता गीतानां मद्रकादीनामादौ सम्यङ्नृत्तस्याभिनेयपदार्थाभावेनाभिनयशून्यतया नाश(तयाश)ङ्किता नाट्याङ्गस्य शुद्धस्य विभागका विभागप्रापका आदौ प्रयुज्यन्ते । एतदुक्तं भवति—गीतकानां यान्युपोहनानि तत्र तावन्नृत्तं शुद्धमेवं कर्तव्यम् । यद्वक्ष्यति—

"तत्रावतरणं कार्यं नर्तक्याः सर्वभाण्डकम् ।
क्षेपप्रतिक्षेपकृतम् ।" इति (ना. शा. ४-३००)

तद्गत(त)श्च गीतकाङ्गमध्ये तु प्रवेशाभावोऽसि(भावस्सि)द्धः । विचारणीयस्य चावापनिष्क्रामादेरगीतकाङ्गत्वमस्त्येव । यद्यपि "महागीतेषु चैवार्थान्" (ना. शा. ४-१५) इत्युक्तं वक्ष्यते च "ततोऽभिनयमाचरेत्" (ना. शा. ४-२९०) इति प्रथमत्वेऽभिनयनेऽस्यापि तथापि तत्र न मुख्यो नाट्यप्रसिद्धोऽभिनयार्थ इत्युक्तम् ।

किञ्चाभिनेयत्वेन नाट्याङ्गत्वदशायामवलोकनात् तथा वाचोयुक्तिः । लौकिककथास्विवाङ्गव्यवहारादावभिमुखीभावमात्रनयनश्चापि स्वार्थो यथावाच्यमभिनीतः । नहि तत्र साक्षात्कारकल्पतापादनमभिनयार्थः । किन्तु तल्लयाद्याहारित्वमात्रम् । एवमत्रापि तदर्थानुसारित्वमात्रं परप्रतिपत्तिमात्रं स्यात् ।

...दस्थेनैवाङ्गभूतत्वेप्यनुगयिते(गमित)कालात्पृथग्भूत एवादौ प्रयुज्यमानो लोकप्रसिद्धप्रथमगीयमानाक्षिप्तडोम्बिकप्रायः प्रचुरस्तुतिपदयुक्तो गीतिविशेषप्रतिक्षेप इत्याह । इदं भरतमुनिना न क्वचिल्लक्षितम् ।

१. K.S.S. M.G. वापि G.O.S. N.S. चापि ।
२. K.S.S. ताण्डचस्ताण्डवपूर्वकः G.O.S. N S. M.G. (Same as above)

गीतप्रयोगमाश्रित्य नृत्तमेतत्प्रवर्त्यताम्[1] ।
प्रायेण ताण्डवविधिर्देवस्तुत्याश्रयो भवेत् ॥ २६८ ॥

अन्ये तु गीतान्ते प्रयोज्याश्छन्दकादय एवं नृत्तवैचित्र्याश्रया यथारुचि प्रतिक्षिप्यमाणाङ्गकाः प्रतिक्षेपाः । आदिशब्दश्च व्यवस्थायामासारितादिसङ्ग्रहार्थः प्रयुक्तः । सतीति चाध्याहार इति । मुनिमतं चाद्य तयोरनुग्राहकम् ।

एवं नाटचाङ्गानां......गीताङ्गाद्युपयोगश्च समर्थितः । अधुना नृत्तप्रधानरागकाव्यादिविषयः काव्यं च नाटचाङ्गमिति दर्शयन्पुराकल्पच्छायया प्रकारान्तरमपि नृत्तस्य समर्थयितुमाह—**देवे**नेत्यादि । चकार एवकारार्थे । देवेनैव महेश्वरेणैव । तण्डुः सन्तोषपूर्वकं प्रकर्षेणादरेणोक्तः । किमित्याह—गीयत इति **गीतं** काव्यम् । तस्य यः प्रकर्षेण योगस्तदर्थानुप्रवेशलक्षण(स्त) माश्रित्य न छायाम् । आसमन्ताच्छ्रित्वा । अङ्गविक्षेपिताङ्गत्वं सामरस्यलयसत्त्वादिना नृत्तं तच्छब्दस्वभावमपि यदभूत्ताण्डवप्रभृति नृत्तं तद्गीयमानरूपकगतवर्णालङ्कारल पदार्थवाक्यार्थसम्मिलितं यत्तत्प्रवर्त्यताम् तदुक्तं **कोहलेन**—

> "सन्ध्यायां नृत्यतः शम्भोर्भक्त्याऽऽद्रौ नारदः पुरा ।
> गीतवांस्त्रिपुरोन्माथं तच्चित्तस्त्वथ गीतके ॥
>
> चकाराभिनयं प्रीतस्ततस्तण्डुं च सोऽब्रवीत् ।
> नाटचोक्तयाभिनयेनेदं वत्स योजय ताण्डवम् ॥ इति ॥

अथशब्दान्न केवलमिदं शुद्धमेव । नापि गानक्रिया । भाण्डवाद्यमात्रसम्बन्धमेव यावद्गीत्याधारपदानुसार्यपि । तदर्थानुसरणाच्च तदनुसारणमिति ।

ननु किं तत्ताण्डवप्रवृत्तिनिमित्तमित्याशंक्याह—**प्रायेणे**ति । ताण्डवमिति सर्वं नृत्तमुच्यते । लास्यशब्देन सन्निधौ गोबलीवर्दन्यायेन प्रवर्तते । तत्र विधीयतेऽस्मिन्नृत्तमिति विधिः विधीयमानं काव्यं यदैव (यद्देव) स्तुतिं वर्णनीयत्वेन चाश्रयति । तेन धर्मवीरप्रधानं तत्र काव्यम् । (इत्युद्धतरूपतासूचनेनान्यरसपरिग्रहः ।) प्रयुज्यत इति **प्रयोगः** काव्यं **सुकुमारो** मसृणोऽनुसृतो यस्य तं दर्शयति । **शृङ्गाररसस्य सम्भवो** विद्यमानत्वमस्मिन् । शृङ्गाररसाच्च परिपूर्णात्सम्भवो यस्य कामावस्था मनसोऽस्मिन्नस्तीति । शृङ्गारेण पूर्णापूर्णरूपेण मसृणप्रयोगोपलक्षणम् । यद्यपि च नाटचान्नान्यत्र रस इति वक्ष्यते

---

१. K.S.S. प्रनृत्यताम् G.O.S. N.S. M.G. प्रवर्त्यताम् ।

तथापि काव्यान्नाट्यं निष्पद्यत एवेत्यस्ति रसानुप्रवेशः। अनेन च रसाङ्गान्नृ(ङ्ग नृ)त्तस्य नाट्यम्। प्रायेणेति वचनान्नरपतिचाटुकार्यपि सङ्गृहीतम्। चकारान्मसृणमप्युद्धतमिश्रमुद्धतं च मसृणमिश्रमित्यादिकमपि सङ्गृहीतं भविष्यतीति सर्वं लक्ष्यमनेन सूचितम्। तथा हि—डोम्बिकासु नरपतिचाटुकप्राधान्येन प्रवृत्तासु सुकुमारमेव शुद्धं रूपम्। भाणकेषु नृसिंहादिचरितवर्णनमुद्धतमेव। यत्पुनर्मसृणेऽप्युद्धतं प्रविशति तत्तदुचितमेव। ततोऽप्यल्पत्वबहुत्वकृतो भेदः (पूर्वः प्रस्थानप्रबन्धः। उत्तरः शिद्गकभेदः। उद्धते तु मसृणानुप्रवेशाद्भाणिकाभेदः।) अन्यदपि प्रेरणरामाक्रीडकरासकहल्लीसकादिकमल्पत्वबहुत्ववैचित्र्यकृतमिहैव प्रविष्टं वेदितव्यम्।

तदुक्तं **चिरन्तनैः**—

"छन्नानुरागगर्भाभिरुक्तिभिर्यत्र भूपतेः।
आवर्ज्यते मनः सा तु मसृणा **डोम्बिका** मता॥
नृसिंहसूकरादीनां वर्णनां जल्पयेद्यतः।
नर्तकी तेन **भाणः** स्यादुद्धताङ्गप्रवर्तितः॥
गजादीनां गतिं तुल्यां कृत्वा प्रवसनं तथा।
अल्पाविद्धं सुमसृणं **तत्प्रस्थानं** प्रचक्षते॥
सख्याः समक्षं भर्तुर्यदुद्धतं वृत्तमुच्यते।
मसृणं च क्वचिद्धूर्तचरितं **षिद्गकस्तु** सः॥
बालक्रीडानियुद्धादि तथा सूकरसिंहजा।
ध्वजादिना कृता क्रीडा यत्र सा **भाणिका** मता॥
हास्यप्रायं **प्रेरणं** तु स्यात्प्रहेलिकयाऽन्वितम्।
ऋतुवर्णनसंयुक्तं **रामाक्रीडं** तु भाष्यते॥
मण्डलेन तु यन्नृत्तं **हल्लीसकमिति** स्मृतम्।
एकस्तत्र तु नेता स्याद्गोपस्त्रीणां यथा हरिः॥
अनेकनर्तकीयोज्यं चित्रताललयान्वितम्।
आचतुष्षष्टियुगलाद्रासकं मसृणोद्धतम्॥" इत्यादि

(एते प्रबन्धा नृत्तात्मकाः न नाट्यात्मकनाटकादिविलक्षणाः। राघवविजयमारीचबधादिकं रागकाव्यम्।) एतच्च ग्रन्थविस्तारभीत्या बहुतरं यथासम्भवं न लिखितमनुपयोगाच्च। यत्तूपयोगि तद्यथावसरं वर्णयिष्यामः।

सुकुमारप्रयोग[1]श्च शृङ्गाररससम्भवः ।
तस्य तण्डु[2]प्रयुक्तस्य ताण्डवस्य विधिक्रियाम्[3] ॥ २६६ ।

एष तावत्पदगते चोद्यकप्रकारः । तत्र तु परस्परमसङ्गतिदोषोऽयं कैश्चिदुद्भाव्यते । स पूर्वादिनैव प्रतिसमाहितः । एक एव तु प्रकारः कलाविधिना निबध्यमानो **राघवविजयमारीचवधादिकं** रागकाव्यभेदमुद्भावयतीति । यथोक्त (**कोहलेन**)—

["लयान्तरप्रयोगेण रागैश्चापि विवेचितम् ।]
नानारसं सुनिर्वाह्य कथं **काव्यमिति** स्मृतम् ।।

लयनश्चास्य गीत्याधारत्वेनाप्राधान्ये गीतेरेव प्राधान्यमिति न काव्यार्थविपर्यासवशेन रागभाषादिविपर्यासो नाट्य इव ।

तथा हि **राघवविजयस्य** हि ठक्करागेणैव विचित्रवर्णनीयत्वेऽपि निर्वाहः । **मारीचवधस्य** ककुभग्रामरागेणैव । अतएव रागकाव्यानीत्युच्यन्त एतानि । रागो गीत्यात्मकत्वात्स्व(कः स्व)रस्य तदाधारभूतं काव्यमिति । एवमिदं च नृत्तं सप्तकृतिप्रकारैर्भगवत एव प्रसृतम् । तथाहि—शुद्धमेव नृत्तं रेचकाङ्गहारात्मकम् । ततो गीतकाद्यभिनयोन्मुखम् । ततोऽपि गानक्रियामात्रानुसारि वाद्यतालानुसारि च । (बाहु)प्रेङ्खणोरःकम्पपार्श्वनमनोन्नमनचरणसरणस्फुरितकम्पितभ्रूतारापरिस्पन्दकटिच्छेदाङ्गवलनमात्ररूपम् । यत्रो(च्चो)क्तं—

"तण्डुनापि ततः सम्यग्गानभाण्डसमन्वितः ।
नृत्तप्रयोगः ।" इत्यादि । (ना. शा. ४-२६०)

गीतिर्गानमिति ह्यत्र व्युत्पात्तरुक्ता । ततोऽप्युद्धतसुकुमारमिश्रात्मकभेदचतुष्टयभिन्नकाव्यार्थानुसारितया चतुर्विधम् । तत्र प्रथमो भेदो लौकिके स्वतन्त्रनृत्ते देवतातोषणादौ वा । द्वितीयः पूर्वरङ्गविधौ परिशिष्टनृत्तलक्ष्यतया वास्य ताण्डवादि विश्वं व्याप्तमितीह पूर्वमुक्तम्—

"प्रयोगमङ्गहाराणामाचक्ष्व भरताय वै ।" इति (ना.शा. ४-१८)

भगवता तत्र तण्डुनाऽङ्गहाराः सप्रयोगाः प्रोक्ताः । तत्रैवं भूतास्तावदङ्गहारा मह्यं प्रोक्ता इति रेचकैः पिण्डीबन्धेश्च सहितं मुनिना निरूपिताः । करणान्यपि तदुपयोगित्वेनाशङ्कितचोद्यनिराकरणप्रसक्तानुप्रसक्तं नृत्तस्वरूपं दर्शितम् ।

---

१. G.O.S. N.S. च K.S.S. M.G. तु ।
२. K.S.S. ताण्ड्य G.O.S. N.S. M.G. तण्डु ।
३. N.S. विधिक्रिया G.O.S. K.S.S. M.G. विधिक्रियाम् ।

वर्धमानकमासाद्य संप्रवक्ष्यामि लक्षणम् ।

कलानां वृद्धिमासाद्य ह्य[1]क्षराणां च वर्धनात् ॥ २७० ॥

अधुना तु प्रयोगः कीदृशोऽङ्गहाराणां प्रोक्त इति प्रकृतमेवानुसन्धातुमाह—**तस्य तण्डुप्रयुक्तस्येति** । तत्र पूर्वरङ्गोचितत्वायाङ्गहारप्रयोग इत्युक्तम् । तत्र च "ताण्डवं यत्र युज्यते ।" (ना. शा. ५-१३) इति वर्धमानकताल एव ताण्डव-योगयोग्य इति पूर्वं वर्धमानं गृह्णाति । तदनन्तरं तु गीतकादिविषयो विधि-र्वक्ष्यते । **तस्येति** व्यवहितानुसन्धानार्थः परामर्शः । **तण्डुप्रयुक्त**ग्रहणं समनन्त-रोक्तनृत्तकाव्यादिविषयताण्डवशङ्कां निरस्यति । विधीयतेऽननेति विधिः गात्रम् । तत् दृष्ट्वा येयं क्रिया प्रयोगः सैव लक्षणम् । अन्यतो व्यवच्छेदकत्वात् । तत्र क्रियात्मकं लक्षणं वक्ष्यामीति सम्बन्धः । (२६९)

ननु सा क्रियोक्ता करणाङ्गहारविषया । सत्यम् । गीततालसंमिश्रा तु नोक्ता । इह तु वर्धमानाख्यं तालमासाद्य साम्यापादनायोपायतां नीत्वा तत्प्र-मितिगीत्याधारत्वाच्च वर्धमानशब्दवाच्यं "देवं देवैः संस्तुतमीशम् ।" (ना.शा. ३१-९८) इत्यादिवाक्यसमूहमासाद्याभिनेयतयाश्रित्य तदाक्षिप्तच्च गीतविशेष-मासाद्याङ्गस्य वलनावर्तनादिगतद्रुततारादिनियमकारित्वेनावलम्ब्य वक्ष्यामीति सम्बन्धः । वर्धमानकगीततालाभिनयसम्बन्धतयोदितं ताण्डवं वक्ष्यतीति यावत् ।

तत्र वर्धमानस्य भविष्यल्लक्षणानुवादेन (ना. शा. अ-३१) ताण्डवयोगा-भिधानायाद्यरूपमाह—**कलानामित्यादि** । सप्तदशकलः कनिष्ठासारितकः । स एव द्विगुणलयो लयान्तरः । त्रयस्त्रिंशत्कलो मध्यमः । पञ्चषष्टिकलो ज्येष्ठः । तेन कलानां लयद्वारेण सङ्ख्याद्वारेण च वृद्धिः । तद्वृद्ध्यै च हीय-मानपदवृत्ति(द्धि)राक्षिप्ता । यद्वक्ष्यते—"चत्वारस्तु गणा युग्मे ओजे" इत्यादि (ना. शा. ३१-९७) । इह त्वक्षराणि तेषां वृद्धिः कलानुसारेणैव नर्तकीनां च वृद्धिः । एका हि प्रथमासारिते नृत्तप्रयोक्त्री । द्वितीये द्वे इत्यादिक्रमेण । अतो वृद्धियोगाद्वर्धमानकम् ततः संज्ञायां कन् । कण्डिकानां च दशपरिवर्तक्रमो भविष्यति । प्रयोगे यथा यथाक्षरं विनिवृत्तमित्यपि यो भेदो भविष्यति तेनापि क्रमेण कलादीनां वृद्धिः । अतोऽत्राङ्गहारप्रयोगस्य परिपूर्णस्य च पिण्डीबन्धविधेः सम्यङ्निष्पत्तिर्भवतीति तात्पर्यम् । (२७०)

एवं लक्षणानुवादेन ताण्डवोपयोगमभिधाय विधिदृष्टां क्रियां प्रतिज्ञान-पूर्वमाह—**कृत्वेत्यादि** । पूर्वरङ्गविधौ वक्ष्यते—

---

१. K.S.S. M.G. तु G.O.S. N.S. हि ।

लयस्य वर्धनाच्चापि वर्धमानकमुच्यते[1] ।

कृत्वा कुतपविन्यासं यथावद्द्विजसत्तमाः ॥ २७१ ॥

'कलापातविभागार्थं भवेदासारितक्रिया ।

कीर्तनाद्देवतानां च ज्ञेयो गीतविधिस्तथा ॥'' इति(ना.शा.५-२१) ।

तत्र प्रथमार्धेन शुष्काक्षरैरासारितप्रयोगमाह । तथा च वक्ष्यति—

''एतानि तु बहिर्गीते त्वन्तर्यवनिकागतैः ॥'' इति (ना.शा. ५-११) ।

बहिर्गीतशब्देन द्वितीयार्धेन सार्थकपदयुक्तमासारितप्रयोगमाह । तत्रैव चोच्यते—

''ततः सर्वैस्तु कुतपैः संयुक्तानीह कारयेत् ।

विघाटच वै यवनिकां नृत्तपाठचकृतानि तु ॥''

गीतानां मद्रकादीनाम् । (ना. शा. ५-१२) इत्यादि ।

तस्मिन्नवसरेऽयं नृत्तप्रयोग इति तमेवावसरं दर्शयति—**कृत्वे**त्यर्धेन । कुतं शब्दं पातीति चतुर्विधमातोद्यं कुतपं तत्प्रयोक्तृजातञ्च । तत्र **विशेषेण** व्यवस्थापनम् । तत्र विशेषेण न्यासो यथायोगं स्वरताललयकलादिनिवेशनम् । स एव प्रत्याहारादिरासारितक्रियान्तः परिपूर्णो विन्यासः । आसारितक्रिययाभिघातातोद्ये तत्प्रयोक्तरि च प्रयोक्ष्यमाणासारितगतकलापातप्रस्ताव एवं क्रियत इत्युक्तम् । स च परिपूर्णो विन्यासो **यथाव**च्छब्देन दर्शितः । **अनुपूर्वश** इति पाठे प्रत्याहारावतरणाद्यङ्गजातं सूचयति । तेन(ए)तदुक्तं भवति—अन्तर्यवनिकागते शुष्काक्षरप्रयोगप्राणभविष्यदातोद्यप्रयोगप्रस्तावनात्मके दृष्टफलदैत्यादिपरितोषणका तद्विघ्नशमनशास्त्रीयफले च प्रयुक्तेऽङ्गकलापेऽयं प्रयोगविधिः । **आसारितप्रयोग** इति सार्थकपदं य इत्यर्थः । **प्रयोक्तृभि**रित्यातोद्यान्तरसाहित्यं बहुवचनेनाह ।

प्रयोगक्रमं दर्शयति—**तत्र** त्वित्यादिना । उपोहनं शुष्काक्षरं कनिष्टासारिते पञ्चकलम् । उपोह्यन्ते समासव्यासतः पदकालतालमभिहिताः स्वरा यस्मिन्नङ्गे तत्तथोक्तम् । **गानं** सुषिरातोद्यं गीयते यतः स्थानस्वरादिति गानम् । तेन घनावनद्धातोद्यद्वयस्यात्र निरासः । उपोहनसमाप्तौ नर्तक्याः प्रवेशः । तत्र **भाण्डवाद्यं** पुष्करवाद्यं तत्र विशुद्धकरणजातौ । सा च मध्यस्त्रीणां लक्ष्यते । तत एवात्रानुकारसाक्षात्कारशङ्कानिराकरणम् ।

---

१. N.S. वर्धनान्नर्तकीनां च वर्धमानकमुच्यते K.S.S. लक्ष्यस्य बन्धनाच्चापि वर्धमानकमुच्यते G.O.S. M.G. (Same as above).

आसारितप्रयोग[1]स्तु ततः कार्यः प्रयोक्तृभिः ।
तत्र तू[2]पोहनं कृत्वा तन्त्रीगान[3]समन्वितम् ॥ २७२ ॥

कार्यः प्रवेशो नर्तक्या भाण्डवाद्यसमन्वितः ।
विशुद्धकरणायां तु जात्यां वाद्यं प्रयोजयेत् ॥ २७३ ॥

गत्या[4] वाद्यानुसारि[5]ण्या तस्या[6]श्चारीं प्रयोजयेत् ।
वैशाखस्था[7]नकेनेह सर्वरेचकचारिणी ॥ २७४ ॥

पुष्पाञ्जलिधरा भूत्वा प्रविशेद्रङ्गमण्डपम् ।
पुष्पाञ्जलिं विसृज्याथ रङ्गपीठं परीत्य च ॥ २७५ ॥

तथा हि—सति परमेश्वरस्य रामादिवत्प्रयोज्यत्वे प्रथमप्रकृत्यादिचित्त-जातिप्रसङ्ग । तत्र —

"एकाक्षरं विशुद्धायां वाद्यं स्यात्सर्वमार्गकम् ।"
"द्ध द्धं खो खो णा णादि या विहितवाक्या ।
सा शुद्धा विज्ञेया मध्यस्त्रीणां समा जातिः ॥" इति ।
(ना. शा. ३४-१३६-१३८)

आद्यत्वे अयमेव वर्णस्तत्तत् "रुन्दहि रुन्दहि" इत्यादि । तथाविधवाद्यानुसारिणी या गतिः तदुपलक्षणचारीति सम्बन्धः । 'करणाङ्गहारान्प्रयुञ्जीत' इति भाण्ड-वाद्यस्यानुप्रयोज्यता प्राधान्येनोक्ता । यथोक्तं भवति **भट्टतोतेन**—"पर्यादिशस्त्र-स्यास्य प्रयोगः" इति । तदनन्तरं प्रयोगमाह—**वैशाखस्थानकेने**त्यादि । वैशाख-रेचितकरणमनेन लक्षयति—

"रेचितं हस्तपादं च कटिग्रीवं च रेचितम् ।" इति (ना. शा. ४-९७)
(२७४) **पुष्पाञ्जलिधरेति** । तलपुष्पपुटकरणमनेन लक्ष्यते—**विसृज्येति** । पुष्पाक्षेपमङ्गप्रक्रमेण प्रदर्श्येत्यर्थः ।

---

१. K.S.S. आसारित. प्रयोगस्तु G.O.S. N.S. M.G. (Same as above)
२. K.S.S. M.G. च G.O.S. N.S. तु ।
३. K.S.S. M.G. भाण्ड G.O.S. N.S. गान ।
४. K.S.S. गीत्या M.G. G.O.S. N.S. गत्या ।
५. M.G. K.S.S. अनुसर्पिण्या G.O.S. N.S. अनुसारिण्या ।
६. K.S.S. M.G. ततः G.O.S. N.S. तस्याः ।
७. K.S.S. स्तालकेन M.G. G.O.S. N.S. स्थानकेन ।

प्रणम्य देवताभ्य[1]**श्च ततोऽभिनयमाचरेत् ।**

यत्राभिनेयं गीतं स्यात्तत्र वाद्ये न योजयेत् ॥ २७६ ॥

अङ्गहारप्रयोगे तु भाण्डवाद्यं विधीय[2]**ते ।**

समं रक्तं विभक्तं च स्फुटं शुद्धप्रहारजम् ॥ २७७ ॥

अन्ये तु सद्य एव पुष्पाञ्जलिं तन्मोक्षं चाहुः—रङ्गपीठे यः परिगमः परिध्वङ्गकरणं मध्य एव देवतानां पूर्वपूजितानां प्रणामाभिनय इत्येककालत्वं चशब्देनोक्तत्वात् द्वयं चाचरेदित्येतदुपेक्ष्यम् । पौर्वकाल्यमाश्रित्य **ततोऽभिनयमिति ।** भक्त्यतिशयेन तदर्थभावनया विशिष्टतां प्रदर्शयितुम् । आसारितवाक्यस्य पदार्थवाक्यार्थविषयोऽभिनयः स्वात्मन्याभिमुख्यनयनात् । न तु सामाजिकान्प्रति ।

यत्रेति निपातो यतो हेतोरित्यर्थे । तेन यतो गीतमिति गीयमानं वाक्यमभिनेयं स्वात्माभिमुख्यं नेयम् । तच्च गानं स्वरवर्णालङ्कारलक्षणमाभिमुख्यमङ्गसाम्यं नेयम् । ततो हेतोस्तस्यैव प्राधान्यात्तस्मिन्कालेऽवनद्धवाद्यं तदाच्छादनकारि भवतीति स्वातन्त्र्येण **न योजये**दतिशयेन नयनं स्यात् । यत्रेति च वीप्सया परिभाषां सार्वत्रिकीमाह । (२७६)

अनुवादमुखेन परिशिष्टं प्रयोगमाह—**अङ्गहारप्रयोगे**ष्विति । तुशब्द एवकारार्थे । अङ्गहारस्य शुद्धस्यैवाभिनयशून्यस्य प्रयोगे नृत्तप्राधान्ये तदनुसारि वाद्यम् । विशेषेणान्तरयोगानन्तरयोगापेक्षया स विधेयो विधीयते धार्यते । अत एव चानुपादानात्—

"तदेव हि पुनर्वस्तु भूयो नृत्तेन योजयेत् ।" (ना. शा. ४-२८४)

इति वक्ष्यमाणस्य नर्तक्या समाकर्षणे पुनरासारितगाने शुद्धनृत्तमिति वाद्यस्य गीयमानसहितस्य गानस्य नृत्तस्य च क्रमेण प्राधान्येन प्रयोगो दर्शितः ।

भाण्डवाद्यं विधीयत इत्युक्तम् । तदीदृशमिति दर्शयति **सममिति ।** अक्षराङ्गतालल‍ययतिपाणिग्रहन्यासविकृतमष्टविधकालदेशसमतात्मकं साम्यं पुष्कराध्याये च वक्ष्यते । तत्र षोढा तालकृतम् । द्विधा स्वरोच्चारणस्थानदेशकृतम् । तद्योगात् समरक्तभावः शब्दस्य हृद्यस्वरूपता । सा च मायूर्यादिमति (मर्-त्र)विधमार्जनायोगात् । तेन सम्यङ्मार्जनायोगात् **रक्तं विभक्तम् ।** आह-

१. M.G. K.S.S. तु G.O.S. N.S. च ।

२. K.S.S. M.G. प्रयोजयेत् G.O.S. N.S. विधीयते ।

नृत्ताङ्गग्राहि वाद्यज्ञैर्वाद्यं योज्यं तु ताण्डवे ।
प्रयुज्य गीतवाद्ये[1] तु निष्क्रामेन्नर्तकी ततः ॥ २७८ ॥
अनेनैव विधानेन प्रविशन्त्यपराः पृथक्[2] ।
अन्याश्चानुक्रमेणाथ पिण्डीं बध्नन्ति याः[3] स्त्रियः ॥ २७९ ॥

त्यानन्तरं च पीडितयोगेन विच्छेदप्रतिभा समानाक्षरम् । **स्फुटमिति** कादिवर्णानामनुहारो यत्र स्पष्टो भवति । प्रहारजा वर्णान्ते शुद्धविशुद्धका(क) रणान्ते-स्थिताः । यदि वा आलिप्तिकादिमार्गादन्यतम एव मार्गे स्थिताः । यत्र नृत्तमङ्गहारात्मकं तदङ्गानीव करणानि । यदि वा गीताङ्गानि मुखादीनि गृह्णाति समया (तया) स्वीकुरुते एतच्च सममिति गतार्थम् । तेनायमर्थः—नृत्तकर्मभूतमङ्गकर्तृभूतं यद्वाद्यं ग्राहयति नृत्तं तन्नृत्यतेति यदङ्गानि प्रयुङ्क्त इव स्वयं वैचित्र्यप्रयोगात्सविलासमिव श्रूयमाणमेव यद्बलादङ्गानि नर्तयतीति तत्तथोक्तम् । तद्यथा कर्तृ ककतकणककुन्दन्तरकरहततततर्हीकटिच्छिदशतहीत इति चञ्चत्पुटे । यदेवंविधं वाद्यं पुष्कराध्याये वक्ष्यते तत्ताण्डवे इहावसरे योज्यम् । पुष्कराध्याये त्वीदृशी एव श्लोकौ भविष्यति (ना. शा. ३४-१७२) । तत्र विध्यनुवादाविह द्वौ विपर्यसनीयौ । ताण्डवमुक्तं प्राक् । तत्रैवंविधं वाद्यं कार्यमिति ।

एवं प्रथमासारितस्य प्रयोगमुपसंहरत्यर्धेन—**प्रयुज्येत्यनेन** । एषां च प्रयोगे प्रथमं परिभाषां करोति श्लोकत्रयेण—**अनेनैवेत्यादिना-करणान्वितमित्यन्तेन** । गानमिति गीयते च गीतम् । **गीतवाद्ये** प्रधानतयावस्थिते नर्तकी नृत्तेन प्रयुज्य तथा स्वरागतो नृत्तप्राधान्यं तदौचित्याय गीतवाद्यं प्रयुज्य स्वानुसारिणीकृत्य । **नर्तकी** न तु नाटच इव साक्षाद्रामादिरूपताप्रच्छन्नात्मिका । सा निष्क्रामेदपसरेत् । न तु सर्वथैव निर्गच्छेत् । द्वे द्वितीयमिति (ना. शा. ४-२८६) वक्ष्यमाणत्वात् । अपराः किं युगपत्प्रविशन्ति नेत्याह । **पृथक्** एकैकक्रमेण प्रविशेदित्यर्थः ।

ननु कियत्यस्ता अपरा या अनेनैव विधिना प्रविशन्तीत्याशङ्क्याह-**अन्याश्चेति** । **अनुक्रमेण** कनिष्ठादिषु चतुर्ष्वासारितेषु यथासङ्ख्यं वक्ष्यमाणाश्चतुरः पिण्डीबन्धप्रकारान् या अन्याः बध्नन्ति ताः अपराः । तेन चतस्र एवेत्युक्तं भवति । पिण्डीमिति जातावेकवचनम् । (२७९)

१. K.S.S M.G. गीतमेवं तु G.O.S. N.S. गीतवाद्ये ।
२. K.S.S. M.G. पुनः G.O.S. N.S. पृथक् ।
३. K.S.S. M.G. ताः G.O.S. N.S. याः ।

तावत्पर्यस्तकः[1] कार्यो यावत्पिण्डी न ब[2]ध्यते ।
पिण्डीं बध्वा ततः सर्वा निष्क्रामेयुः स्त्रियस्तु ताः ॥ २८० ॥

पिण्डीबन्धेषु[3] वाद्य तु[4] कर्तव्यमिह वादकैः ।
पर्यस्तकप्रमाणेन चित्रौघकरणान्वितम् ॥ २८१ ॥

एवं प्रवेशपृथक्त्वं परिभाषान्तरमाह—**तावत्पर्यस्तक** इति । तावद्यावदिति भिन्नक्रमः । यावत्पर्यस्तकः केवलासारिताभी (भिर्हि) तलक्षणः प्रयोगः कार्यः तावन्न पिण्डी बध्यते । तावत्पिण्डीबन्धो न कार्यः । तदनन्तरं तु कर्तव्य इत्यर्थः । पूर्वप्रविष्टया परा परिवर्ज्यते । महावाक्यानुसारादेकघन एव वाहिन्यात्मकोऽङ्गविक्षेपो यत्र प्रयोगे स पर्यस्तको नृत्ताचार्यभाषया पर्यस्तक इति प्रसिद्धः । अभिनयशून्यमा (आ) ङ्गिकविधिः पर्यस्तकः । स च पिण्डीबन्धे न कार्यः । तदनन्तरं तु कर्तव्य इत्यर्थः । पूर्वप्रविष्टया नर्तक्याः शिक्षार्थमित्याद्यसङ्गतमेव कैश्चिदुक्तं तदुपेक्ष्यमेव । यावच्च पिण्डीबन्धोपयोगि नृत्तं न प्रवर्तते तावत्प्रविष्टनर्तकीनिवर्तनेनैकाकिन्यैवासारिताभिनयः प्रयोक्तव्य इति परिभाष्यते ।

परिभाषान्तरमाह—**पिण्डीं बध्वेति** । तस्यासारितस्य नृत्तप्रयोगं कृत्वा सर्वास्ता निष्क्रामेयुरपसरेयुः । अत एवैतत्स्थानोपजीविभिरेव **श्रीराणकादिक**-विभिर्डोम्बिकादौ चतुरपसारकः प्रयोगः । (२८०)

परिभाषान्तरमाह—**पिण्डीबन्धेष्विति** । यावदेव पर्यस्तक आसारिताभिनयप्रयोगे वाद्यं तावदेव तदन्तरतापि (पाति) नि पिण्डीबन्धोपयोगिन्यङ्गहारप्रयोगे । किन्तु चित्रं विचित्रं नानाप्रकारं प्रयोजितमोघे च वाद्यविधौ (ना. शा. अ-३४) वक्ष्यमाणानि यानि करणानि क्रिया याभिवेध्या भगवत्यारूपास्ताभिरन्वितम् (?) । द्विमात्रा यत्र कला स चित्रमार्ग ओघशब्दादेव लब्धः । तत्रैव ह्योघो लक्ष्यते । (२८१)

एवं पृथक्प्रवेश एकाकिन्या अभिनयप्रयोगः सम्भूयाङ्गहारप्रयोगः तदनन्तरमपसारस्तावत्कालता नृत्तस्य वाद्यस्य वैचित्र्यमिति परिभाषाषट्कं कृत्वा द्वितीयस्य लयान्तरस्यासारितप्रयोगमाह—**तत्रोपवहन**मिति । तत्रैवं परिभाष-

---

१. K.S.S. पर्यस्ततः M.G. G.O.S. N.S: पर्यस्तकः ।
२. K.S.S. प्रयुज्यते G.O.S. M.G. N.S. न बध्यते ।
३. K.S.S. पिण्डीषट्केषु M.G. पिण्डीबन्धे तु N.S. G.O.S. पिण्डीबन्धेषु
४. K.S.S. M.G. हि G.O.S. N.S. तु ।

तत्रो[1]पवहनं भूय: कार्यं पूर्ववदेव हि ।
ततश्चासारितं भूयो गायनं[2] तु प्रयोजयेत् ॥ २८२ ॥
पूर्वेणैव विधानेन प्रविशेच्चापि नर्तकी ।
गीतकार्थं त्वभिनयेद्[3] द्वितीयासारितस्य तु ॥ २८३ ॥
तदेव च[4] पुनर्वस्तु नृत्तेनापि प्रदर्शयेत्[5] ।
आसारिते समाप्ते तु निष्क्रामेन्नर्तकी तत: ॥ २८४ ॥
पूर्ववत्प्रविशन्त्यन्या:[6] प्रयोग: स्यात्स एव हि[7] ।
एवं पदे पदे कार्यो विधिरासारितस्य तु ॥ २८५ ॥

यति तावत् । यत्रेति पूर्वं कनिष्ठासारितं प्रयुक्तम् । **भूय** इति बहुतरं षट्कलमित्यर्थ: । **भूय** इति लयाधिकत्वात्कथं तस्याधिक्यमित्यर्थ: । **पूर्वेणैवेति** । तत्र तूपोहनमित्यादिना । **अपिशब्दात्** "गत्या वाद्यानुसारिण्या" इत्यादि "प्रणम्य देवतां च" इत्यनन्तरमुद्दिष्टम् । तत: सा द्वितीया नर्तक्यासारितस्य तालविशेषसंबन्धि यद्गीतकं गीयमानं च वाक्यं तस्यार्थमभिनयेत् । पुनस्तदेव लयान्तरासारितलक्षणं वस्तु । सा द्वितीया । चकारात्पूर्वप्रविष्टा च । नृत्तेन च केवलाङ्गहारात्मनाऽभिनयस्तत्साम्येन प्रदर्शयेत् । आसारितप्रयोगानन्तरं तया सह साऽप्यपसरेत् । (२८४)

अथ तृतीयचतुर्थयोरासारितयोरतिदेशेन प्रयोगमाह—**पूर्वव**दिति । पृथक्त्वेनेत्यर्थ: । **स एवेति** । तत्र तूपोहनं कृत्वेति य उक्तो यश्च[ौ] परिभाषाषट्केनोक्त इत्यर्थ: ।

अथ यदैकमेवापसारितं प्रयुज्यते तदायं प्रयोगवैचित्र्यक्रम इत्यतिदेशेन दर्शयति—**एवमि**त्यादिना । एकवचनमतन्त्रम् । एकमप्यासारितं यदा प्रयुज्यते

---

१. N.S. तत्रैवोपोहनं K.S.S. M.G. अथोपवहनं G.O.S. तत्रोपवहनं ।
२. N.S. गायन: G.O.S K.S.S. M.G. गायनं ।
३. K.S.S. गीतकार्थप्रयोगश्च M.G. गीतकार्थं प्रयोजयेत् G.O.S. N.S. (Same as above) ।
४. K.S.S. M.G. तु G.O.S. N.S. च ।
५. N.S. भूयो नृत्तेन दर्शयेत् K.S.S. M.G. नृत्तेनापि प्रयोजयेत् G.O.S (Same as above).
६. K.S.S. M.G. प्रविशेच्चान्या G.O.S. N.S. (Same as above).
७. K.S.S. M.G. तु N.S. G.O.S. हि ।

भाण्डवाद्यकृते[1] चैव तथा गानकृतेऽपि[2] च ।
एका तु प्रथमं योज्या[3] द्वे द्वितीये तथैव[4] च ॥ २८६ ॥
तिस्रो वस्तु तृतीयं तु चतस्रस्तु चतुर्थकम् ।
पिण्डीनां विधयश्चैव चत्वारः सम्प्रकीर्तिताः ॥ २८७ ॥

तदास्य यानि पदानि छेदाश्चत्वारो मुखप्रतिमुखशरीरसंहरण(ना. शा. ३१-८०) लक्षणास्तदाश्रयेणायं वर्धमानवच्चतुरपसारप्रयोगो भाण्डवाद्यक्रियायां गीतिक्रियायां च कार्यः । यद्वक्ष्यति "इत्येवं चतुरङ्गानि" इति(ना. शा. ३१-८२) । एतदेव स्पष्टयत्येकं त्वित्यादिना (एका त्वित्यादिना) । **वस्त्वित्यङ्गम्** । **युञ्ज्यादि** (योज्या इ)ति नृत्तेनेति शेषः । त्रिमात्रादिकं यदत्र वस्तु केचित् द्विः कुर्वते तदसदेव । अन्ये त्वेवं पदे पद इत्यादि सार्धश्लोकमुपसंहारवाक्यं वर्धमानप्रयोगस्येति वर्णयाञ्चक्रुः । अपरे पुनराहुः—आसारितस्य पदमभिव्यक्तिस्थानं कण्डिकानां दशपरिवर्तितेन प्रयोगः । तथा हि—विशाला सङ्गता सुनन्दा सुमुखीति चतस्रः कण्डिका वक्ष्यन्ते (ना. शा.—अ. ३१-१२०) क्रमेण नवाष्टौ षोडश द्वात्रिंशत्कलाः । तस्य विशालामनु सङ्गता अनुविशालं सुनन्दा सङ्गता विशालामनु सुमुखी सुनन्दा सङ्गता विशालेति दश परिवर्ताः । तत्र विशालादिपरिवर्तत्रये सङ्गताः परिवर्ताः काकक्षिवदुभयत्र संबन्ध इति सप्तदशकलस्य द्विः प्रयोगे कनिष्टलयान्तरितयोः स्थानं भवति । ततः सुनन्दादिपरिवर्तत्रये त्रयस्त्रिंशत्कलस्य मध्यमासारितस्य स्थानं भवति । ततः सुमुख्यादिचतुष्टये पञ्चषष्टिकलस्य ज्येष्ठासारितस्य । एवमासारितस्य पदेषु स्थानेषु कण्डिकादिपरिवर्तेषु चतुरपसारको नर्तकीप्रयोगः । तदाहैकापीति (एका त्विति) । वस्त्वासारितस्थानमित्येवं कण्डिकावर्धमानस्यायं प्रयोगोऽतिदेश इति तृतीयव्याख्यानतात्पर्यम् । द्वितीये तु व्याख्याने न किञ्चिदधिकमुक्तमिति तदुपेक्ष्यमेव ।

पिण्डीबन्धप्रकारा अनुक्रमेणासारितेषु प्रयोज्या इत्युक्तम् । के त इत्याह—**पिण्डीनामित्यादि** । **विधयः** प्रकाराः । तत्र विशेषान्तरहृद्यमेकप्रयोज्यं पिण्डीबन्धरूपमित्येकः प्रकारो विशेषनामधेयविरहात्सामान्यशब्देनोक्तः ।

---

१. K.S.S. M.G. भाण्डवाद्यकृतश्चैव N.S. भाण्डवाद्ये कृते G.O.S. (Same as above).
२. K.S.S. M.G. गानकृतः G.O.S. N.S. (Same as above).
३. N.S. एकं तु प्रथमं युञ्ज्यात् K.S.S. M.G. एकां तु प्रथमां कुर्यात् except M.G. reads एकं in place of एकां G.O.S. (Same as above).
४. K.S.S. M.G. तु वस्तुकम् G.O.S. N.S. तथैव च ।

पिण्डी शृङ्खलिका[1] चैव लताबन्धोऽथ भेद्यकः ।
पिण्डीबन्धस्तु पिण्डत्वाद्गुल्मः शृ[2]ङ्खलिका भवेत् ॥ २८८ ॥
जालोपनद्धा च लता सनृत्तो भेद्यकः स्मृतः[3] ।
पिण्डीबन्धः कनिष्ठे तु शृङ्खला तु लयान्तरे ॥ २८६ ॥
मध्यमे च लताबन्धो ज्येष्ठे चैवाथ भेद्यकः ।
पिण्डीनां विविधा[4] योनिर्यन्त्रं[5] भद्रासनं तथा ॥ २६० ॥

तदाह—**पिण्डीबन्धः पिण्डत्वादिति** । नर्तकीयोज्यः परस्परसंबन्ध एव पिण्डीबन्धद्वयप्रकारः सजातीयो वा एकता(ना) लावबद्धकमलयुगलवत् विजातीयो वा हंसवदनपरिगृहीतनालनलिनवत् गुल्मः शृंखलिकाशब्दवाच्यः । नर्तकीत्रयप्रयोज्यस्तु ततोऽपि वैचित्र्यसहिष्णुत्वाज्जालवद्विचित्रतां गच्छत्पूर्ववत्सजातीयविजातीयात्मा लताबन्धः । चतुष्टयप्रयोज्यस्तु गतो(ते)ऽत्र रूपत्रयो(य) महावाक्ये तावद्भिः प्रकारैर्भेदनीय इति तेभ्य एकसत्वयोजनाच्चाज्ञातो भेद्यकः । महावाक्यार्थ इति वैकस्यां योजनायां प्रविष्ट इत्यर्थः । स तूक्तविधैस्त्रिभिः नृत्तैः सह वर्तते । (२८८)

एकादिप्रयोज्यत्वं स्पष्टयति—**पिण्डीबन्धः कनिष्ठे**त्वित्यादिना । ननु कथमेते पिण्डीबन्धान्निष्पद्यन्त इत्याशंक्याधा रादिभेदकृतां निष्पत्तिं दर्शयति-**पिण्डीनां विविधा योनि**रित्यादिना । तत्र यत्र पुत्रकादीनां यथा पृथग्भूताङ्गानामनुसन्धिस्तथैव भूमिदेहाकाशाद्याधारखण्डलकानुसन्धानं यन्त्रम् । तस्य भूतसा सम्भवात्पूर्वमभिधानम् । अनेन मिश्रा भेदाः सङ्गृहीताः । भद्रं स्फुटमेवेत्यस्यासनं स्थानं भूम्यादौ स्फुटमेव दर्शनादित्येकभेदसङ्ग्रहः । अनेनाधाराङ्गभेदो दर्शितः । प्रयोक्तृप्रयोगभेदस्तु पूर्वमेव दर्शितः इहापि चोक्तः **शिक्षायोग** इति । करणाङ्गहारविशेषेष्वङ्गविक्षे पवैचित्र्याभ्यास इति साधकतमभेदो दर्शितः । इत एवोवजीव्यास्मभिर्भावितत्योक्तं "रेचकैरङ्गहारैश्च "रेचकैरङ्गहारैश्च" (ना. शा.४-२४६) इत्यादिव्याख्यानावसरे । **विविध**ग्रहणेन तद्धामिश्रणया भेदानन्त्यं सूचयति । तच्चास्माभिः पूर्वमेव दर्शितम् । (२६०)

---

१. K.S.S. पिण्डीशृङ्खलिता N.S. G.O.S. M.G. (Same as above) ।
२. K.S.S. N.S. गुल्मशृङ्खलिका G.O.S. M.G. (Same as above) ।
३. K.S.S. तालोपनद्धाश्च लताः सनृत्तो भेदकः स्मृतः G.O.S. N.S. M.G. (Same as above).
४. K.S.S. द्विविधो M.G. द्विविधा G.O.S. N.S. विविधा ।
५. K.S.S. यज्ञम M.G. N.S. G.O.S. यन्त्रम ।

शिक्षायोग[1]स्तथा चैव प्रयोक्तव्यः प्रयोक्तृभिः ।

एवं प्रयोगः कर्तव्यो वर्धमाने तपोधनाः[2] ॥ २९१ ॥

ननु सर्वोऽयं पिण्डीबन्धप्रकार इहोपयोगी वा न वेत्याशङ्क्याह—**तथा चैव प्रयोक्तव्य** इति । तैः सर्वैरेव प्रकारैः पिण्डीशृङ्खलकादिबन्धो योज्यत इति यावत् । यत्रच्छेद्यकर्म चर्मयन्त्रं काष्ठमयी प्रकृतिर्भद्रासनमिति केचिदत्र व्याख्यां कुर्वन्ति । युक्तायुक्ततां तु सहृदया एव विदुः ।

एवं गीतकाङ्गवाद्यनर्तकीपिण्डीबन्धादिदर्शनादपि नाट्यान्नृत्यमभिन्नमित्यपि सूचितम् । न चाय पिण्डीबन्धप्रकारो लक्ष्ये विच्छिन्नः । केवलमृत्तक (मृत्तिका)पक्षयोः पतितमहौषधिवदनवस्थि तैरभ्युद्धर्तु न शक्यते सावधानतया तु शक्यत एवेति नात्रालस्यं श्रयितव्यम् । अन्यथा प्रगोगमाहुः तथा हि—एकं तु प्रथममित्यत्र प्रथमासारितमभिनयति । ततो द्वितीया द्वितीयासारितम् । तत्समकालं तु प्रथमा केवलमङ्गहारं करोतीति । एवं तृतीया तृतीयासारितार्थमभिनयति । तदा द्वेऽङ्गहारं प्रयुञ्जाते । चतुर्थी चतुर्थाभिनयं यदा करोति तिस्रोऽङ्गहारं रञ्जयन्ति । अन्ये त्वभिनयप्रयोगेऽपि सहिततामाहुः । जालशृङ्खलिकादिपिण्डीबन्धजातं चान्योन्यं बाहुबन्धवैचित्र्यरचितमिच्छन्ति ।

अथ वर्धमानकमासाद्येति प्रतिज्ञातमुपसंहरति **एवमित्यादिना** । एवं प्राधान्याद्वर्धमानप्रयोगमभिधाय "गीतानां मद्रकादीनाम्" (ना. शा. ५-१३) इति यद्वक्ष्यते तन्निर्णयाय प्रतिजानीते—**गीतानामित्यादि** । चकारः सर्वशेषतां द्योतयति अन्वाचयं च । आसारितादिपर्यन्तप्रयोज्यानां छन्दकादीनां तच्छेषतयैव लक्षणं वक्ष्यते । तथाहि तालाध्याये (ना. शा. अ-३१) वर्धमानासारितकगीतकपाणिकान्ते च्छन्दकप्रयोगश्चतुष्पदाप्रयोगश्चाभिधास्यते ।

"सर्वेषामेव गीतानामन्ते छन्दक इष्यते ।

चतुरङ्गस्ततः त्र्यङ्गो नवाङ्गो युग्म एव च ॥ (ना. शा. ३१-२९३)

चतुष्पदा तथैकाङ्गा" इत्यादौ । तेन प्रधानतया तावद्गीतकादिविशेषाणां विधिस्तत्प्रयोगे न तु स्वतन्त्राणाम् । गीतकगतवस्त्वङ्गादि यत्र स्वेच्छया समाश्रित्यैकद्वित्र्याद्यनियमेन प्रयुज्यते तानि च्छन्दकानि । यान्यद्यत्वे नृत्ततालात्मना डोम्बिकानर्तकीलयचरणादिरूपेण प्रसिद्धानि । **भूय** (इति) । उक्तो हि वर्धमानविधिस्तत्राप्यधिकं वस्तु वक्ष्यते ।

१. K.S.S. कार्याः M.G. कार्या G.O.S. N.S. योगः ।

२. K.S.S. M.G. प्रयोक्तभिः G.O.S. N.S. तपोधनाः ।

गीतानां छन्दकानां च भूयो वक्ष्याम्यहं विधिम् ।
यानि वस्तुनिबद्धानि यानि चाङ्गकृतानि तु[1] ॥ २९२ ॥
गीतानि तेषां वक्ष्यामि प्रयोगं नृत्तवाद्ययोः ।
तत्रा[2]वतरणं कार्यं नर्तक्याः सा[3]र्वभाण्डिकम् ॥ २९३ ॥
क्षेप[4]प्रतिक्षेपकृतं भाण्डोपोहनसंस्कृतम्[5] ।
प्रथमं त्वभिनेयं स्याद्गीतके सर्ववस्तुकम्[6] ॥ २९४ ॥

तत्र गीतकतालाश्रितनृत्तविधानं तावद्दर्शयितुमुपक्रमते—**यानीति** । भूयांसि खण्डलकादिवस्तूनि । स्वल्पानि त्वङ्गानि । तत्र वस्तुनिबन्धनानि त्रीणि गीतकादि—मद्रक परान्तकं प्रकरी च । अन्यानि चत्वार्यन्ङ्गयुल्लोप्यकं रोविन्दकमोवेणकमुत्तरं च । तेषां क्रमेणाह—**तेषामिति** । तेषामपि नृत्ते वाद्ये च यो विधिस्तं वक्ष्यामि । तत्र गीतकेषु ये क्षेपाः प्रथमवस्त्वादावुपोहनानि ये च प्रतिक्षेपाः द्वितीयवस्त्वादिषु प्रत्युपोहनानि, मतान्तरे त्वनन्तर्भूतपृथक्कालात्मकगीतशेषरूपाणि तानि तन्त्रीगतानि (गा)नयुक्तानि प्रयुज्य नर्तक्या अवतरणं भाण्डवाद्यसहितं पुष्कराध्यायभाविना प्रविरलचलदङ्गुलि—(ना. शा. ६-२०) दलाभिहन्यमानाङ्किकप्राधान्येन कार्यम् ।

एतदुक्तं भवति—प्रथमे वस्तुन्याक्षिप्तिकामुपोहनं च प्रयुज्य नर्तकीप्रवेशः । द्वितीयादौ प्रत्युपोहनम् । पदयोजना तु-तन्त्रीगानान्वितं कृत्वा क्षेपप्रतिक्षेपयोः कृतं परिसमाप्तता यत्र । तादृगवतरणात्का(णं का)र्यं सर्वभाण्डवाद्याविर्भावम् । **प्रथममित्यादावित्यर्थः** वस्त्वेव **वस्तुकम्** । तत्सर्वमादावभिनेयं पुनर्नृत्तेन योज्यम् । (२९४)

---

१. N.S. यानि वस्तूनि मुनयः सन्ति चाङ्गकृतानि तु K.S.S. M.G. G.O.S. (Same as above) except K.S.S. M,G. read वस्तूनि बद्धानि in place of वस्तुनिबद्धानि and च in place of तु ।

२. N.S. सर्वं G.O.S. M.G. तत्र K.S.S. यत्र ।

३. N.S. सर्व K.S.S. G.O.S. M.G. सार्व ।

४. K.S.S छेद G.O.S. N.S. M.G. क्षेप ।

५. G.O.S. K.S.S. (Same as above) M.G. N.S. तन्त्रीगानसमन्वितम् ।

६. G.O.S. N:S. (Same as above) K.S.S. M.G. प्रथमं त्वभिनेयं तु गीतके सर्ववस्तु तत् ।

तदेव च पुनर्वस्तु नृत्तेनापि प्रदर्शयेत् ।
यो विधिः पूर्वमुक्तस्तु नृत्ता[1]भिनयवादिते ॥ २९५ ॥

आसारितविधौ स स्याद्गीतानां वस्तुकेष्व[2]पि ।
एवं[3] वस्तुनिबन्धानां गीतका[4]नां विधिः स्मृतः ॥ २९६ ॥

शृणुताङ्गनिबद्धानां गीतानामपि लक्षणम् ।
य एव वस्तुक[5]विधिर्नृत्ताभिनयवादिते ॥ २९७ ॥

तमेवाङ्गनिबद्धेषु च्छन्दकेष्वपि योजयेत्[6] ।
वाद्यं गुर्वक्षरकृतं तथाल्पाक्षरमेव च ॥ २९८ ॥

मुखे सोपोहने[7] कुर्याद्वर्णानां विप्रकर्षतः ।
यदा गीति[8]वशादङ्गं भूयो भूयो निवर्तते ॥ २९९ ॥

कथमित्याह—**यो विधिरिति** । आसारितविधौ यः प्रकारः स एवात्र प्रकारः । यथाऽऽसारितेष्व(षु)सङ्ख्यानियमो नर्तकीवृद्धया नृत्तप्रयोगः । पूर्वं चैकाकिन्याऽभिनयः । नृत्ते च भाण्डवाद्यादिप्रयोगः । तथात्रापि । तेन वस्तु-सङ्ख्यां (सङ्ख्यया) नर्तक्य इहेति मन्तव्यम् ।

एतदुपसंहरन्नन्यदुपक्रमते—**एवं वस्तुनिबन्धानामित्यादि** । **वादिते च** विशुद्धकरणायामित्यादि योजयेत् । तदेवाङ्गनिबन्धेषु योजयेत् । तथा सर्वशेष-भूतेषु स्वतन्त्रेषु छन्दकेष्वपि । (२९७)

विशेषं तु दर्शयति—**वाद्यमिति** । घिंघि ढन् त्रन् इत्यादीनि रूपाणि गुरूण्यपि कदाचित्प्रयत्नशीघ्रतया ताले प्रयुक्तानि बहूनि भवन्ति । यथो-त्साहच्छटादौ त्थीत्थीत्थीत्थन् धृत् दत्थकुदहिं—एषैका कला । अत आह—

---

१. K.S.S. वृत्त G.O.S. N.S. M.G. नृत्त ।
२. K.S.S. वस्तु तेष्वपि G.O.S. N.S. M.G. वस्तुकेष्वपि ।
३. K.S.S. M.G. एष G.O.S. N.S. एवम् ।
४. N.S. गीतानां च G.O.S. K.S.S. M.G. गीतकानां ।
५. G.O.S. K.S.S. वस्तुकविधिः M.G. N.S. वस्तुषु विधिः ।
६. K.S.S. M.G. स सर्व एव कर्तव्यः छन्दकेषु प्रयोक्तृभिः N.S. G.O.S. (Same as above) ।
७. K.S.S. सापोहने G.O.S. N.S. M.G. सोपोहने ।
८. K.S.S. M.G. N.S. गीत G.O.S. गीति ।

तत्राद्यमभिनेयं स्याच्छेषं नृत्तेन योजयेत् ।

यदा गीति[1]वशादङ्गं भूयो भूयो निवर्तते[2] ॥ ३०० ॥

अल्पाक्षरमयेऽपि च भवत्यर्धादौ वाद्ययोजनात्क**लार्धादेश्च** शून्यत्वात् । तथा चञ्चत्पुटे प्रथमकलायां द्विविटा ? एव । तत्परिहारार्थमाह—**वर्णानां गुरुणां** विशेषेणाणुपर्यन्तं त्रिमात्रचतुर्मात्रतया प्रकृष्टं तद्वाद्यं **कर्तव्यम् । मुखनाम्न्युपवहसंज्ञके** वाङ्गे **वस्तुनिबन्धेषूपोहनेऽङ्गेऽयं वाद्यविधिः ।** अङ्गाल्पत्वात्तु तत्र नाङ्गनिबन्धव्यपदेशः ।

अथ वक्तव्यं सर्वशेषत्वेनाह—**यदा गीतिवशादङ्गमित्यादि** । मुख्याङ्गानि यदा पुनः पुनरावर्तन्ते । कथम् । गीतेश्चतुर्विधाया मागध्यादिकाया वशात्सामर्थ्यात् । वक्ष्यते हि ध्रुवाध्यायान्ते—

"अ(त्रिः)निवृत्त्या पदानां तु मागधी समुदाहृता ।" (ना. शा. ३२-४३८) । इत्यादि । गीतवशादित्यपि पाठ एवमर्थः । गीतिं **वा गेयमानं वा** । तत्र विधिमिति । तालाध्याये वक्ष्यते—

"यथाक्षरं द्विसंख्यातं त्रिसंख्यातमथापि च । " (ना. शा. ३१-१०३) इति । **तत्रेति** । निवर्तने । **आद्यमिति** । आद्य आवर्तः । **शेषमित्यादि** । आवर्तान्तराणि शुद्धनृत्तप्रयोज्यानि । तेन न केवलं वस्त्वङ्गादिसमाप्तौ नृत्तम् । यावन्मध्येऽपि कदाचित्परिवर्तेषु भवतीति दर्शनम् । यत्तु **राहुलकेनोक्तमपौ**नरुक्त्येनाभिनयनं तदेवंविधमेव मन्तव्यम् ।

यत्तु अहं "जळणिहिचुळुइ माइमा" इत्यत्र, जलनिधिचुलुके मानितेन चोन्मीयत इत्यादि कैश्चिदुत्प्रेक्षितं तन्न सर्वत्र निर्वहतीत्यास्तां तावत् । (३००)

तत्र वाद्यविधिमाह । आवर्तमानगीतवशादङ्गं शाखाचारीप्रयोगात्मकं यदाऽऽवर्तते वाद्यप्राधान्येन नृत्तमिव वाद्यस्य यथासम्भवं वैचित्र्यं प्रदर्शनीयम् । पूर्वं हि तद्वैचित्र्यं काव्यार्थेन नियन्त्रिम् । अधुना तु सङ्कोचोऽस्य नास्ति । तथा च लक्ष्ये प्रावेशिक्यां पात्रकृतसङ्कोचाद्यभावं मन्यमाना गीताचार्याः त्रितयप्रयोगमाहुः । एतच्च विचारयिष्यत इत्यास्तां तावत् ।

समपाणिरुपरिपाणिर्ध(रव)पाणिश्चेति (ना. शा. ३१-३२९) त्रिधापाणिः तालः । तदभिव्यङ्ग्यत्वात् । सङ्गीतनृत्ताभ्यां । सह या(वा)पूर्वं वेति त्रिधा ।

१. K.S.S. M.G. N.S. गीत G.O.S. गीति ।

२ K.S.S. M.G. निवर्तयेत् G.O.S. N.S. निवर्तते ।

त्रिपाणिलयसंयुक्तं तत्र वाद्यं प्रयोजयेत् ।
यथा लयस्तथा वाद्यं कर्तव्यमिह वादकैः[१] ॥ ३०१ ॥
[ततं[२] चानुगतं चापि ओघं च करणान्वितम् ।
स्थिरे[३] तत्त्वं (तं) प्रयोक्तव्यं मध्ये चानुगतं भवेत् ॥
भूय[४]श्चौघः प्रयोक्तव्यस्त्वेष वाद्यगतो विधिः ।
छन्दोगीतकमासाद्य त्वङ्गानि परिवर्तयेत् ॥
एष कार्यो विधिर्नित्यं[५] नृत्ताभिनयवादिते ।
यानि वस्तुनि[६]बद्धानि तेषामन्ते ग्रहो भवेत् ॥
अङ्गानां तु परावृत्तावादावेव[७] ग्रहो मतः ॥]

छन्दोऽक्षरपदानां साम्यं लयः । कलाकालान्तरकृतो द्रुतादिभेदस्त्रिविधः (ना. शा. ३१-३२६) । एतच्च त्रैविध्यं यतिमार्गादिभेदस्याप्युपलक्षणम् ।

ननु प्रथम आवर्ते कीदृशं वाद्यमित्याशंक्याह—**यथा लय इति** । प्रथमे ह्यावर्ते काव्यार्थाभिनयवशादङ्गस्य य उचितो द्रुतादिस्तदनुसार्यत्र वाद्य कार्यम् । अन्ये तु यथातथाशब्दावविचार्यास्य पूर्वशेषत्वेनैव श्लोकार्थं गमयन्ति यथा वाद्यं त्रिपाणिलयवैचित्र्ययुक्तं तथाङ्गस्य गीतस्य च लयः कार्य इति । (३०१)

न चैवं तद्यतिक्रमणीयमिति सहेतुकं दर्शयति पादोनेन श्लोकेन—**एवमेष** इति । हि यस्माद्देवस्य भगवतो महादेवस्य स्तुतिनिमित्तं परितोषणप्रयोजनमेतन्नृत्तमतो हेतोर्नियमादृष्टसम्पत्त्यै । एष एव गीतकासारितेषु तच्चैषु (तच्छेषेषु) च छन्दकेषु विधिः । पाणिका तु परिमितशरीरत्वात्स्वयं ताण्डवभाजनं न भवति । सा हि सुकुमारे पूर्वरङ्गे लास्यप्रधाने तत्सत्तावैदग्ध्यायो-

---

१. K.S.S. M.G. कर्तव्यं त्वङ्गसंश्रयम् G.O.S. N.S. कर्तव्यमिह वादकैः ।
२. K.S.S. M.G. तत्त्वं G.O.S. ततं N.S. omits verses in bracket above.
३. K.S.S. G.O.S. स्थिरे M.G. स्थिते ।
४. M.G. द्रुते K.S.S. G.O.S. भूयः ।
५. K.S.S. नृत्य G.O.S. M.G. नित्यं ।
६. K.S.S. M.G. वस्तूनि वद्धानि G.O.S. वस्तुनिवद्धानि ।
७. K.S.S. परावृत्तापदावत्र M.G. परावृत्तावादावेवं G.G.S. Same except एव in place of एव ।

एवमेष विधिः कार्यो गीतेष्वासारितेष्वपि[1] ।
देवस्तुत्याश्रयं ह्येतत्सुकुमारं निबोधत ॥ ३०२ ॥
स्त्रीपुंसयोस्तु संलापो यस्तु कामसमुद्भवः ।
तज्ज्ञेयं सुकुमारं[2] हि शृङ्गाररससम्भवम् ॥ ३०३ ॥

क्ताल्लास्यस्वरूपादेव निश्चीयते । अन्यथा पूर्वरङ्गोपयोगे प्रक्रान्ते तत्राध्याये लास्यस्य कोऽवसरः । वाद्याङ्गमात्रे तदनुपयोगीति चेत् तत्र दशाङ्गस्य चेत्प्रयोज्यता तद(दा)तिप्रसङ्गः । स च निषेत्स्यते । तदप्रयोगे कृतानि गेयपदानीति न नियमः । तालाध्याये चैतद्भविष्यति । गीतकादिशेषत्वे तु छन्दकसङ्गृहीतैर्वेति नात्रोक्ता । गीतकं च स्वतन्त्रेऽप्यासारिते भवति । ताण्डवप्रयोगस्तु यदा त्वेष पिण्डीबन्धैर्विकल्प्यते प्रत्येकमङ्गविन्यासस्तदा तेषां पृथक्पृथग्गति(त...दोताति)देशेनासारितेष्वप्येवमेव । मुख्यान्यङ्गचतुष्टयविभागेननर्तकीक्रमप्रवेशादिप्रयोगः । एतदर्थमेव वर्धमानेऽप्युक्ते पुनरासारितसङ्कीर्तनम् । परपूर्वरङ्गे चापिशब्दात्तत्सङग्रहो व्याख्येयः ।

"सर्वेषामेव गीतानामन्ते" इत्युपक्रम्य

"चतुष्पदा तथैकाङ्गा...युग्मौ यौ वा प्रमाणतः ।"

"तथा शृङ्गारभूयिष्ठा" "त्रिलया वा" (ना. शा. ३१-२९३)

इति निरूप्य दशाङ्गं लास्यं तालाध्याये (ना. शा. ३१) निरूपयिष्यते । मुनेश्चतुष्पदान्तर्भूतं लास्यगानमित्यादि भूयो भविष्यत ए(त्ये)त्र । **विशाखिलादिप्रणीतं** लास्यगानान्तरं मुनिनाऽभिहितचतुष्पद एव सङ्गृहीतत्वात् । सा चतुष्पदा गीतकानामन्ते पाणिकान्ते वा प्रयोज्येति दर्शितम् । तदभिप्रायेणोपक्रममाह—**सुकुमारं निबोधतेति** । तु शब्द उत्तरतोऽपेक्षणीयः सुकुमारं त्विति । एवो(वमु)क्तरञ्जकतांविधिं निजओहापोहधिया कल्पयति । तत्रापि ह्यङ्गवृद्ध्या नर्तकीवृद्धिरित्यादि सर्वमुन्नेयमित्यर्थः । (३०२)

ननु किं तत्सुकुमारमित्याह—**स्त्रीपुंसयोस्त्विति** । एकस्तुशब्दः पूर्वत्र नीतः । द्वितीयः सुकुमारकं विशेषयति । तदेव हि सुकुमारं न तु करुणहास्यादिमयम् । किं तदित्याह । स्त्रीपुंसयोर्यः कामः । स्त्रियाः पुरुषस्य कामना । पुंसो वा स्त्रियाः । तस्य कविहृदयस्थितात्विवक्षाक्रमेण समुद्भवो यस्य लापस्य काव्यव्यु(त्पादकवा)क्यस्य तत्सुकुमारम् । तत एव परस्परहेतुकत्वं भवति ।

---

१. K.S.S. M.G. च G.O.S. N.S. अपि ।
२. K.S.S. स्वक्तारम्भि M.G. N.S. G.O.S. सुकुमारं हि ।

यस्यां यस्यामवस्थायां नृत्तं योज्यं प्रयोक्तृभिः ।
तत्सर्वं सम्प्रवक्ष्यामि तच्च मे शृणुत द्विजाः[1] ॥ ३०४ ॥

अङ्गवस्तुनिवृत्तौ तु[2] तथा वर्णनिवृत्तिषु ।
तथा चाभ्युदयस्थाने नृत्तं तज्ज्ञः प्रयोजयेत् ॥ ३०५ ॥

यत्तु[3] संदृश्यते किञ्चिद्दम्पत्योर्मदनाश्रयम् ।
नृत्तं तत्र प्रयोक्तव्यं प्रहर्षार्थगुणोद्भवम् ॥ ३०६ ॥

अत एवाह—**शृङ्गाररसस्य** परस्परहेतुकत्वे **संभवमात्र**मयोगव्यवच्छेदनं यत्र । तेन तदवस्थामात्रोपनिबन्धोऽपि डोम्बिकादिकविरुद्धेष्टितादौ चावगन्तव्यो- त्साहादौ शृङ्गाररसस्याव्यापत्तिबन्धः । परमेश्वरे हि तपस्यति(न्ती) भगवती तदेकहृदया बभूवेति तावति परस्परार्था(नु)बन्धात्मकरत्यभावे कामा- वस्थामात्रकम् । परतस्त्वर्धशरीराक्रमणादौ शृङ्गार इत्येवं परमेश्वरचरिते सुकुमारस्य वि (द्वि) शाखत्वेनाप्रसरात्तस्यैवाद्यापि पक्षे स्थितिः । करुणादि- भंगवति न सम्भवति । नापि तत्तत्र समुचितमिति न तत्सुकुमारम् ।

यत्तु **राघवविजयादौ** भी (सी) तामूर्च्छादिव्यावर्णनान्तं ताण्डवम् । न च तत्र तारचि(तादृशे)तत्सुकुमाराङ्गहारात्मकनृत्तयोजना । अपि तु गीतकार्थ- भावनान्यायेन 'रौद्रस्य चैव यत्कर्म स करुण' इति प्रसक्त्या तत्र तथाविधा- भिनययोग इत्यलं बहुना । (३०३)

वक्तव्यशेषमाह—**यस्यां यस्या**मित्यादि । सुकुमारं यत्काव्यं तदाश्रितं गानमपि तथा । अन्तर्लग्नं नृत्तमपि । तत्र यदुक्तं—

'तदेव हि पुनर्वस्तु' (ना. शा. ४.२९५) इति तथा "यदा गीतिवशादङ्गम्" (ना. शा. ४.२९६) इति नृत्तायोजनं तु तदनुवादपूर्वकं नियम इति । (३०४)

अङ्गवस्तुनिवृत्तौ त्विति । तुर्भिन्नक्रमोऽवधारणे । वर्णानां स्थाय्यादीनां गीतक्रियाविस्ताररूपाणां निवृत्तिर्यथा परान्तकादौ । प्रतिशाखायां यद्वक्ष्यते— "प्रतिशाखाद्यपि **च**" इति तेनाङ्गवस्तुवर्णापरावर्तेषु यत्तथाभूतेनैव वाद्यादिवै- चित्र्यप्रकारेण नृत्तमुक्तं तदध्यायाभ्युदयस्थानभेदभावज्ञो नृत्ताचार्यः प्रयोजयेत् । (३०५)

---

१. K.S.S. M.G. सर्वगीतकसम्बन्धं तच्च मे शृणुत द्विजाः G.O.S. N.S. (Same as above).
२. K.S.S. M.G. च N.S. G.O.S. तु ।
३. K.S.S. M.G. यत्र G.O.S. N.S. यत्तु ।

यत्र सन्निहिते कान्ते ऋतुकालादिदर्शनम् ।
गीतकार्थाभिसम्बद्धं नृत्तं तत्रापि चेष्यते ॥ ३०७ ॥
खण्डिता विप्रलब्धा वा कलहान्तरितापि वा ।
यस्मिन्नङ्गे तु युवतिर्न नृत्तं तत्र योजयेत्[1] ॥ ३०८ ॥
सखीप्रवृत्ते संलापे तथाऽसन्निहिते प्रिये[2] ।
नहि नृत्तं प्रयोक्तव्यं यस्या वा प्रोषितः प्रियः ॥ ३०९ ॥

तदनु (तदु) दाहरति—**यत्तु संदृश्यत** इति । यत्काव्यमखण्डं **दम्पत्योः** स्त्रीपुंसयोः कामकृतं वाच्यत्वेन, श्रूयते, अन्यच्च **प्रहर्षप्रयोजनो** यो **गुणः** आस्थाबन्धो वचनं दूतीवचनावर्णनादिरशस्तदुद्भवं तदारम्भं तत्र नृत्तं योज्यमिति कामावस्थासु मन्तव्यम् । श्रृङ्गारेऽप्यनेन वासकसज्जाभिसारिकाविषयनृत्तमुक्तम् । (३०६)

स्वाधीनभर्तृकाविषयमाह—**यत्र सन्निहित** इति । यस्मिन्नङ्गे गीतकस्य गीयमानस्य काव्यस्यार्थत्वेन वाच्यत्वेन संबन्धः । कान्तसन्निधामे ऋतोर्वसन्तादेः कालस्य चन्द्रोदयादेरवलोकं (कनं) भवति तत्र नृत्तम् । (३०७)

नियमफलं दर्शयितुमाह—**खण्डिते**त्यादि ।

"व्यासङ्गादुचिते यस्या वासके नागतः प्रियः ।
सा खण्डिता" (ना. शा. २२-२०९)
"यस्या दूतीं प्रियः प्रेष्य दत्वा सङ्केतमेव च ।
नागतः कारणेनेह विप्रलब्धा तु सा ॥" (ना. शा. २२-२१०)
"ईर्ष्याकलहनिष्क्रान्तो यस्या नागच्छति प्रियः ।
साऽनुतापवशप्राप्ता कलहान्तरिता ।" (ना. शा. २२-२०८)

अङ्ग इति । तदाधारभूते काव्यखण्डे । किमियत्येव न नृत्तमित्याशङ्कयाह—**सखी प्रवृत्त** इति । तथा असन्निहिते प्रिये यद्विषयकसल्लापतत्समागमोपायपर्यालोचनाविरूपवृत्त (त्तान्त) स्तत्रापि न नृत्तं योज्यम् । अनेन विरहोत्कण्टिता लक्षिता । वासकसज्जा प्रियानागमने तथोक्ता । खण्डिता ज्ञाततदीयव्यलीकेति विशेषः । **यस्या वा प्रोषितः प्रिय** इति । प्रोषितकर्तृकावस्थास्वपि यदा

---

१. K.S.S. नृत्तं तत्र प्रयोजयेत् G.O.S. N.S. M.G. न नृत्तं तत्र योजयेत् ।
२. K.S.S. संप्रवृत्तेऽथ संलापे तथा सन्निहिते प्रिये G.O.S. M.G. N.S. (Same as above).

[दूत्याश्रयं यदा तु स्यादृतुकालादिदर्शनम् ।
औत्सुक्यचिन्तासंबद्धं[1] न नृत्तं तत्र योजयेत् ॥]
यस्मिन्नङ्गे प्रसादं तु गृह्णीयान्नायिका क्रमात् ।
ततःप्रभृति नृत्तं तु शेषेष्वङ्गेषु योजयेत् ॥ ३१० ॥

प्रियोऽसन् दुर्लभः खि(ख)लो वेति हृदये(य)निहतो वेति तदा(न)नृत्तम् । तत्र हि कारणानन्तरमेव परिसमाप्तिः । तथा विधेय(यं) यथा क्षरत्वात्तत्र तदेवाश्रयणीयम् । न तु द्विसङ्ख्यातं त्रिसङ्ख्यातं वेत्युक्तं भवति । व्यतिरेकलब्धेऽप्युदाहरणे प्रदर्शितोऽयमर्थो नृत्तस्येह प्राधान्येनाभीष्टत्वान्न स्वेन कण्ठेनोच्यते । (३०९)

यस्मिन्नङ्ग इति । प्रसादमिति । प्रसन्नहृदयत्वं येन प्रकारेण युवतिर्लभेतेति । तेन (न) खण्डितादिविषयमेवैतदपि तु सर्वविषयं मन्तव्यम् । ततःप्रभृति शेषेष्वङ्गेष्वित्यस्यायं भावः । लब्धास्थाबन्धा यदि (दा) भवति तद्वति (यदि) प्रियोऽसन्निहितो भवति तदा नृत्तं योज्यमेव । एतस्मिन्प्रकरणे नाट्यगतानि नाटकोदाहरणानि कैश्चिद्दत्तानि तान्ययुक्तानीति मन्तव्यम् ।

खण्डितादयो नायिका यत्र साक्षात्क्रियन्ते तत्र वलनावर्तनादिरूपनृत्तं न योज्यमिति यदुच्यते तदनवकाशमेव । तथाहि—

"चिन्तानिश्वासखेदेन हृद्दाहाभिनयेन च ।
सखीभिः सह संलापैरात्मावस्थावलोकनैः ॥
ग्लानिदैन्याश्रुपातैश्च रोषस्याभिनयेन च ।
निर्भूषणामृजात्वेन दुःखेन रुदितेन च ॥
खण्डिता विप्रलब्धा च कलहान्तरितापि च ।
तथा प्रोषितनाथा च भावानेतान्प्रयोजयेत् ॥"
(ना. शा. २२-२१४-२१६)

इति सामान्याभिनये वक्ष्यते ।

"विषण्णे मूर्च्छिते भीते जुगुप्साशोकपीडिते ।
ग्लाने सुप्ते विहस्ते च निश्चेष्टे तन्द्रिते तथा ॥
मत्ते प्रमत्ते चोन्मत्ते चिन्तायां तपसि स्थिते ।

---

१. K.S.S. नृत्तं तत्र प्रयोजयेत् G.O.S. M.G. N.S. न नृत्तं तत्र योजयेत् ।

देवस्तुत्याश्रयकृतं[1] यदङ्गं तु भवेदथ[2] ।
माहेश्वरैरङ्गहारैरुद्धतैस्तत्प्रयोजयेत् ॥ ३११ ॥
यत्तु शृङ्गारसंबद्धं[3] गानं स्त्रीपुरुषाश्रयम् ।
देवीकृ[4]तैरङ्गहारैर्ललितैस्तत्प्रयोजयेत् ॥ ३१२ ॥
चतुष्पदा नर्कुटके[5] खञ्जके परिगीतके[6] ।
विधानं सम्प्रवक्ष्यामि भाण्डवा[7]द्यविधिं प्रति ॥ ३१३ ॥
खञ्जनर्कुटसंयुक्ता[8] भवेद्या तु चतुष्पदा ।
पादान्ते सन्निपाते तु तस्या[9] भाण्डग्रहो भवेत् ॥ ३१४ ॥

व्याधिते रुग्ज्वरार्ते च भयार्ते शीतविप्लुते ॥
न हस्ताभिनयः कार्यः कार्यः सत्त्वसमाश्रयः"
(ना. शा. ९-१७६-१७८)

इत्याङ्गिकाभिनये वक्ष्यति ।

तदेवं स्थिते हस्ताभिनयस्यैवात्रावकाशो नास्तीति कस्तत्र तत्संमेलनात्मनो वलनावर्तनादेराशङ्कावकाशो यन्निषेधोऽत्र वचनीयः स्यात् । न चेह नाट्यप्रकृतमित्यास्ताम् । एकं(वं) गीतकादेरन्ते च्छन्दकं पाणिकायास्तु लास्यगान-स्वीकारिणी चतुष्पदा प्रयोज्या । इयता गीतकादि पूर्णं प्रयुक्तम् । एतदर्थमेव "वीक्ष्य शङ्करम् । सुकुमारप्रयोगे नृत्यन्तीं चैव पार्वतीम् ।" (ना. शा. ४-२४९) इत्युपक्रमात्प्रभृति वि(द्वि)शाखत्वेनैव नृत्तस्वरूपमुपदर्शितम् । (३१०)

तदत्र द्विविधे नृत्तविभागमाह श्लोकत्रयेण । **देवस्तुत्याश्रयमिति** । **यदङ्ग-मिति** । छन्दकसम्बन्धि । **उद्धतैरिति** । विद्युद्भ्रान्तगरुडप्लुतकादिप्रधानैः । अत्र हेतुर्यतस्ते महेश्वरप्रयुक्ताः । **यत्** द्वितीयचतुष्पदासंबन्धि । **ललितैरिति** । तलपुष्पपुटलीननितम्बाद्यारब्धैः । अत्र हेतुः यतस्ते देवीकृताः । (३१२)

---

१. K.S.S. M.G. गतं G.O.S. N.S. कृतं ।
२. M.G. K.S.S. इह G.O.S. N.S. अथ ।
३. K.S.S. सम्बन्धं G.O.S. N,S. M.G. सम्बद्धं ।
४. K.S.S. देवैः कृतैः G.O.S. N.S. M.G. देवीकृतैः ।
५. K.S.S. नकुटके G.O.S. N.S. M.G. नर्कुटके ।
६. K.S.S. परिधानके G.O.S. N.S. M.G. परिगीतके ।
७. K.S.S. N.S. नृत्त G.O.S. M.G. वाद्य ।
८. K.S.S. खञ्जनं कुटसंयुक्ता G.O.S. N.S. M·G. खञ्जनर्कुटसंयुक्ता ।
९. M.G. तस्यां K.S.S. G.O.S. N.S. तस्याः ।

या ध्रुवा छन्दसा युक्ता समपादा समाक्षरा ।

तस्याः पादावसाने तु प्रदेशिन्या ग्रहो भवेत् ॥ ३१५ ॥

कृत्वैकं परिवर्तं तु गानस्याभिनय[1]स्य च ।

पुनः पादनिवृत्ति[2] तु भाण्डवाद्येन योजयेत्[3] ॥ ३१६ ॥

एवं नृत्तविधिश्चतुष्पदायां सलास्यगानस्वीकारिण्यामुक्तः । अधुना भाण्डविधिर्वक्तव्यः । तत्र चतुर्भिः पादैर्ध्रुवा क्रियते । ते च पादाः शुष्काक्षरैर्झे (ल्ला) ण्टुमादिभिः (दिग्ल इत्यादिभिर्वा) । यत्र वक्ष्यते—

"आसनेषूपविष्टैर्यत्तान्त्रीगानसमन्वितम् ।
गायनैर्गीयते शुष्कं तद्गेयपदमुच्यते ॥"

(का. मा. ना. शा. १८-१८५)

इति सार्थकपदैर्वा । तत्रापि वर्णवृत्ताकृता वा पादा मात्रावृत्ताकृता वा । समा अर्धसमा विषमा वा । ते च प्राधान्येन खञ्जनर्कुटकवृत्तैर्योज्यन्ते । यद्वक्ष्यते । ध्रुवाध्याये—

"अष्टौ नर्कुटकानां तु । तिस्रः खञ्जकजातयः ।"

(का मा. ना. शा. ३२-२८०; ३०१)

इत्युपक्रम्य "आभ्यो विनिस्सृताश्चान्या युग्मौजा विषमास्तथा ।" इति (ना.शा. ३२-३०८) एतद्विषयं भाण्डवाद्योपक्रमं करोति । चतुष्पदा नर्कुटक इति । चतुष्पदापि सन्निधानच्चतुष्पदायां परिगीतमपि ध्रुवाध्याये त्रिवृत्तकं यदि वा शुष्कगीतं तत्रैव । तदेतेषु त्रिषु प्रकारेषु भाण्डवाद्यस्य पुष्करवाद्यस्य विधिं वक्ष्यामि ।

खञ्जकजात्या नर्कुटकजात्या वा या चतुष्पदा ध्रुवा क्रियतेऽस्यां प्रथम-पादस्य यावदुपा (न्त्य) (कला) तावच्च श्रीवंशान्वितं गानम् । अन्ये (न्या) तु या सन्निपाताख्या हस्तद्वयसमायोगशब्दपरिच्छेद्या कला तद्गानसमये भाण्डवाद्यमारम्भणीयम् । येषामर्ध (एषोऽर्ध) समविषमो (म) वृत्तात्मकं (को) नर्कुटकखञ्जकजात्यारब्धायां चतुष्पदायां विधिः । (३१४)

---

१. K.S.S. M.G. अभिनये पुनः G.O.S. N.S. अभिनयस्य च ।

२. K.S.S. M.G. निवृत्तौ G.O.S. N.S. निवृत्ति ।

३. K.S.S. M.G. भाण्डवाद्यं नियोजयेत् G.O.S. भाण्डवाद्येन योजयेत् N.S. भाण्डवाद्यैर्नियोजयेत ।

अङ्गवस्तुनिवृत्तौ[1] तु वर्णान्तरनिवृत्तिषु ।
तथोपस्थाने[2] चैव भाण्डवाद्यं प्रयोजयेत् ॥३१७॥
येऽपि चान्तरमार्गास्स्युः[3] तन्त्रीवाक्करणैः[4] कृताः ।
तेषु सूची प्रयोक्तव्या भाण्डेन सह ताण्डवे ॥ ३१८ ॥

वर्णवृत्तसमवृत्तात्मकतज्जात्यारब्धायां तु विधिमाह—**या ध्रुवेति** । **समपादा** चतुष्पादा । तदयमर्थः—या चतुष्पदा । **छन्दसा युक्तेति** । युक्ता जातिगतवर्णवृत्तयोजिता । **समाक्षरेति**। तज्जातिकसमवृत्तमयी । तस्याः प्रथमे पादे परिसमाप्ते द्वितीयपादे या प्रदेशिनी तर्जनी तदुपलक्षिता या चातीतकलमप्र(चात्र त्रिकलप्र)भृति भाण्डवाद्यं योज्यम् । तत्र युग्मेन मानेन यदा चतुष्पदा भवति—यद्वक्ष्यते "युग्मौजा वा प्रमाणता ।" (ना. शा. ३१-२९३) इति त्रि (द्वि) कलश्च मार्गः तदा द्वितीयपादे सप्तमी । या निष्क्रामकला सा तर्जनीप्रयोज्यत्वात्तर्जनी । चतुष्कलमाने तु त्रयोदशी । आवापकालतर्जनी । यदा तु त्र्यश्रेण मानेन तदा द्विकले पञ्चमी । कनिष्ठा निष्क्रामकला तर्जनी । चतुष्कले तु नवमी । आवापकला तर्जनी ।

एतच्च तालाध्याये वक्ष्यते—"कनिष्ठाङ्गुलिनिष्क्रामः" तर्जनीकृतो निष्क्रामः" (ना. शा. ३१-४१, ४२ इत्यादिना । **दत्तिलाचार्येण** न संक्षिप्योक्तमेतत्—

"आद्यद्वितीयमध्यान्तात्पादभागाद्विदुः क्रमात् ।
कनिष्ठानामिकायुक्तो मध्यमादेशिनीकृतात् ॥
अयुग्ममध्यहीनः स्यात्" इति ।

एवं तर्जनीप्रयोज्यो योऽसौ द्वितीयपादे कलापातः त(तस्त)त्र भाण्डग्रहस्तदुपलक्षितश्च नर्तकीप्रवेश इत्युक्तं भवति । अन्ये त्वाकाशग्रहासु निश्शब्दकलातो ग्रहं मन्यमानाः सन्निपातप्रकरणात्सशब्दात्पातादेव ग्रह इहेति वदन्तः प्रदेशिनीशब्देन तदुपलक्षितपादभागगमनं सशब्दमेव पादग्रहावधिके नाचक्षते । पञ्चपाणिप्रपाता ये पुष्कराध्याये वक्ष्यन्ते तन्मध्यात्प्रदेशिनीपातेन भाण्डग्रह

---

१. K.S.S M.G. निवृत्तेन G.O.S. N.S. निवृत्तौ ।

२. K.S.S. ततोऽवस्थापने G.O.S. N.S. M.G. तथोपस्थापने ।

३. N.S. तु G.O.S. K.S.S. M.G. स्युः ।

४. K.S.S. तन्त्र्या वा करणैः कृताः M.G. तन्त्र्या वाक्करणैः कृताः G.O.S. N.S (Same as above) ।

महेश्वरस्य चरितं य इदं सम्प्रयोजयेत् ।

सर्वपापविशुद्धात्मा शिवलोकं स गच्छति ।। ३१९ ।।

इति व्याख्यानं "सन्निपातोऽनुग्रहः" इति प्रकरणेन तथा ध्रुवाध्याये वक्ष्यमाणेन "चतुर्ग्रहा ध्रुवा" इत्युपक्रम्य,

"सन्निपातग्रहाः काश्चित्तथाकाशग्रहाः पराः ।

प्रदेशिनीग्रहास्त्वन्यास्तथैवान्याः समग्रहाः ।। " (नाः शा. ३२-४२३)

इति त्रिधिना विरुद्धमित्युपेक्षितं लक्ष्यवेदिभिः । (३१५)

नन्वेवं नर्तकी प्रविष्टा ततः प्रभृत्यभिनयं तावत्करोति । यस्त्वसावाद्यः पादस्ततोऽधिकोऽपि वा भागस्तत्र नर्तकी नैव प्रविष्टेति वा (का) तत्र वार्तेत्याशङ्क्याह—कृत्वैकमिति । योऽसौ शुद्धविभागः पूर्वं गीतः स परावर्तनीयो भाण्डवाद्येन सहाभिनेतव्य इति पश्चादसौ प्रयोज्य इत्युक्तं भवति । पादग्रहण-मुपलक्षणम् । तेन यावान्भागो भाण्डवाद्येन प्राङ् नियोजितोऽत एव नाभिनी-तस्तावतो निवृत्तिः परावर्तनं कार्यमित्युक्तं भवति । (३१६)

अथात्र चतुष्पदायां भाण्डवाद्यविशेषाभिधानव्याजेन नृत्तस्थानं दर्शयति—**अङ्गवस्तुनिवृत्तौ त्विति** । तुभिन्नक्रमोऽवधारणे । अङ्गस्यैवस्य वा वस्तुनो वा सर्वस्य ध्रुवाशरीरस्य स्थाय्यादिविशेषस्य वा प्रतिशाखान्यायेन तत्परावर्तनं यच्चोपस्थानमोहना (पस्थापना) त्मकं तेषु प्रकर्षेण भाण्डवाद्यं वैचित्र्ययुक्तं योजयेत् । तद्वशाच्च तत्र नृत्ताङ्गहारयोजनां कुर्यादित्यर्थः । (३१७)

अथ शुष्काक्षरायाश्चतुष्पदाया विधिर्वक्तव्यः । सा च पूर्वमेव प्रयुज्यते "आसनेषूपविष्टेषु" इत्युक्तत्वात् । अत एव गेये गातव्ये काव्ये पदमवगमयन्त इति तत्पीठबन्धरूपत्वं तस्याः । तथा चान्यत्वे षिद्गकेषु गातव्यात्पूर्वं भावतीति नान्यावसरे । अत एव गेये ध्रुवागीते गेयं गातव्यमिति ह्येकोऽर्थः । तं विधिमाह—**येऽपि चान्तरमार्गा** इति । अन्तरं परस्परवैलक्षण्यं मान्यते (मृग्यते) येनोपायेन सोऽन्तरमार्गः । संवाद्यनुवादिन्या स स्वर उपलक्षणात्मकोऽर्थप्राधान्या-भावाच्च तेनैव व्यपदेशः । अत एवाह तन्त्रीक्रियया वाक्क्रियया । तदे (ए) व निरर्थकतया योजितास्तेषु समग्रहत्वेनैव भाव (ण्ड) प्रयोगः । नर्तक्या रचहाद्वि (रचनाद्वि) लास्याङ्गगतकाव्यार्थानुसारिहस्ताभिनयशून्यः सात्त्विकाङ्गवलना-दिमात्रेण सूच्याभिनयः । यद्वक्ष्यति—

"वाक्यार्थो वाक्यवस्त्वङ्गैर्योज्यते यदा पूर्वम् ।' पश्चाद्वाचाऽभिनय इत्ययं त्वङ्ग इहोपलक्ष्यः । एतच्च गातव्यप्रयोगे त्रिप्रकारकृततावन्मात्रतालगान-सूच्याऽभिनयमद्यापि दृश्यते ।

एवमेष विधिः सृ(दृ)ष्टस्ताण्डवस्य प्रयोगतः[1] ।
भूयः किं कथ्यतामन्यन्नाटचवेदविधिं प्रति[2] ॥ ३२० ॥

इति भारतीये नाटचशास्त्रे ताण्डवलक्षणं नाम चतुर्थोऽध्यायः ॥

एवं वर्धमानकप्रयोगो गीतकप्रयोगो वा छन्दकप्रयोगेन चतुष्पदाप्रयोगेन च सहेतुकः परिपूर्णो भवति । अत एव तालाध्याय इत्यु(एतदु)पक्रमानुसारेणैव वर्धमानासारितकगीतकच्छन्दकचतुष्पदा तदन्तर्भूतलास्यगानस्य विधेः क्रमेण निरूपणं भविष्यतीयता "गीतानां मद्रकादीनाम्" (ना. शा. ५-१३) इति पूर्वरङ्गाध्याये श्लोको भविष्यति । तस्यार्थः पुरस्तादेव निर्णीतः । तेन तदपसारेणैतत्पर्यालोच्योदीरितोऽयमर्थोऽनुष्ठेयः । (३१८)

नन्वत्र पूर्वरङ्गगतप्रधानफलेनैव किं फलवत्ता उत फलान्तरमप्यस्तीत्याशङ्क्याह—(महेश्वरस्येति) । पृथक्फलवत्त्वं च दर्शयन् स्वातन्त्र्येण प्रयोज्यमिदमिति दर्शयति—**महेश्वरस्येति । चरितमिति** चेष्टितम् । प्रयोजयेदिति स्वार्थे हेतुमति च तन्त्रेण णिचि । तेन प्रयोक्तु(क्तुः) प्रेक्षाप्रवर्तयितुश्चार्थपतेः सामाजिकवर्गस्य च पापविशुद्धिः शिवलोकगतमनन्तफलं नृत्तस्येति नान्य(टच) दृष्टैकप्रयोजनाद्भिन्नप्रयोजनत्वमुक्तम् । स्वातन्त्र्येण प्रयोगे च छन्दकानां चतुष्पदायाश्च केवलत्वेनापि प्रयोगो ह्यनुज्ञातो भवति । तदङ्गानां च पुनः "पुष्पाञ्जलिधरा भूत्वा" इत्याद्यनुसारेण वर्णानां लोके प्रयोगः । "तस्याः पादावसाने तु" इत्याद्यनुसारेण धारापरिक्रमादेः 'यदा गीतवशात्" (ना. शा. ४-३००) इत्यनुसारेण द्विगुणाद्यर्थं गुणावयवारणकगुञ्जिथकादेश्चतुरपसारकादिविधा च डोम्बिकादिषु क्रमेण नर्तकीवृद्धिराचार्यैराधेया(?) । तालानुसारेण च 'त्रिपाणिलयसंयुक्तम्' इत्याद्यनुसारेण धारापरिक्रमादेः लयपरिष्वङ्कितलयतालपरिक्रमादेः । (३१९)

तदेतत्सर्वमीश्वरपरितोषकार्यवेति तथैतदुपसंहारपूर्वकमध्यायान्तरावकाश करोति—**एवमेष** इत्यादिना । **एवं** पूर्वोक्तेन प्रकारेण । **प्रयोगत** इति । प्रयोगं नाटचात्मकमपेक्ष्य ततोऽन्यस्तद्विलक्षणो विधि प्रकारो **दृष्टः** । तथा नाटकादिसा (दौ सा) माजिकवत्प्रयोक्तृतन्मयीभाववशेन नाटच संस्कारमपेक्ष्यादिविधिर्दृष्टो न तु साक्षात्कारकल्प्यनाटचरूपताऽत्रास्ति । चतुर्विधाभिनययोगाभावाद्रसभावा-

१. N.S. प्रयोक्तृभिः G.O.S. N.S. K.S.S. प्रयोगतः ।
२. K.S.S. M.G. विप्रा नाटचयोगविधिं प्रति G.O.S. N.S. (Same as above) ।

प्राधान्याद्गीतवाद्यनृत्तानां यथेष्टं प्राधान्यं नर्तकीवृद्धेः । काव्ये वस्त्वपेक्षत्वान्नाटयप्रस्तावनाप्राणप्रतिबिम्बात्मकता त्रिविधत्वान्मदमूर्च्छादौ तत्त्वापत्त्ययोगाद्गीतकादेश्च नियमादृष्टप्रयुक्तत्वाद्गीतादिप्राधान्येनैव प्रयोगात्कुलकाच्छेद्यात्मनः काव्यस्य गीत्याधारतानान्तरीयकत्वमात्रेण गमनापि(त्पि)ण्डीबन्धप्रकारे वैचित्र्यान्ते नृत्तमात्रविश्रान्तः प्रयोक्तृप्रवर्तयितृगा(मा)त्रदृष्टफलप्राधान्याच्च तद्विलक्षणं नाटयं तद्वृत्तिर्भिद्यत इति एवं शब्दस्यार्थ **इत्युपाध्यायमतम्** ।

"रसभावदृष्टिहस्तशिर आद्यं यद्यङ्गं पूर्णं वाऽपूर्णं वा कृ(कु)त एव नाटयनृत्तयोर्भेदस्तुल्यानुकारत्वे" इति **हर्षवार्तिकम्** । "शिक्षार्हरवेच्छान्यनृत्ताकतिपयनाटयाङ्गकृतं नृत्तमभ्यासफलम् ।" इति **भट्टयन्त्रः** । "समयमात्रमित्यदिमङ्गलवद्विवाहादौ" इति **भट्टलोल्लटः** । दशरूपकभेदवल्लास्यताण्डवप्रयोगो नाटयभेद एव । तत्र पूर्णानुकाररूपत्वात् ।

तथाहि—प्रवेशेऽश्वत्थाम्नः सूचीविद्धोर्ध्वजान्वादि । पुरूरवसोऽलपल्लवसूची । गरुडप्लुतकम् । रावणस्य पुष्करो वैशाखरेचितकः । वत्सराजस्याग्नि सम्भ्रमोऽ(तिका)न्तः । जटायुषो गृध्रावलीनकमेलकाक्रीडितं चेति "चित्राभिनयेन बाल्ये(वान्ये)न करणप्रयोग एव । अभिनेयपदादीनां च नाटयेऽपि सक्तो(क्तते)" ति नाटयमेवेदमिति **कीर्तिधराचार्यः** ।

एतच्च(वच्च)स्वमतानुसारेण **एवं** शब्दार्थमाहुः । युक्तायुक्तां तत्र परीक्षका एव विदुरित्यलं बहुना ।

प्रसङ्गाङ्ग(ग)तया नृत्ततया(वार्तया)प्रसक्तानुसक्तत्वेन नृत्तागतमेवान्यत्किञ्चित्प्रसिद्धिः(द्ध)प्रकृता(त)नाटयगतानां(गतता(मा)विच्छेदीत्यभिप्रायेणाह—**नाटये**ति । नाटयमेव वेदस्तस्य यो विधिः प्रयोगस्तं प्रतीति शिवम् । (३२०)

रविशशिहुतभुक्कल्पितनयनत्रयकिरणदलिततिमिरततिः ।

अभिनवगुप्तस्ताण्डवविधिमेनं व्यवृणुत स्पष्टम् ॥

इति माहेश्वराचार्याभिनवगुप्तविरचितायामभिनवभारत्यां नाटयशास्त्रविवृतौ ताण्डवविधानाध्यायश्चतुर्थः ॥

पञ्चमोऽध्यायः ।

भरतस्य वचः श्रुत्वा नाटचसन्तानकारणम् ।
पुनरेवाब्रुवन्वाक्यमृषयो हृष्टमानसाः ॥ १ ॥

यथा नाटचस्य जन्मेदं[1] जर्जरस्य च सम्भवः ।
विघ्नानां शमनं चैव देवतानां च पूजनम् ॥ २ ॥

त[2]दस्माभिः श्रुतं सर्वं गृहीत्वा चावधारितम् ।
निखिलेन यथातत्त्वमिच्छामो वेदितुं पुनः ॥ ३ ॥

पूर्वरङ्गं महातेजः सर्वलक्षणसंयुतम् ।
यथा बुद्धयामहे ब्रह्मंस्तथा व्याख्यातुमर्हसि ॥ ४ ॥

संसारनाटचनिर्माणे याऽवकाशविधानतः ।
पूर्वरङ्गायते व्योममूर्ति तां शाङ्करीं नुमः ॥

अध्यायसङ्गतिं कर्तुं पुराकल्पेनोपक्रमते—**भरतस्येति । नाटचसन्तानम् । नाटचस्य** सन्तानं नृत्तक(थ)या विच्छेदाशङ्कानिरासेनाविच्छेदः । नाटचे पृष्टे दैववशात् महाफलं नृत्तमिति तद्विवेकेन ज्ञातम् । तज्ज्ञानाच्च तद्विविक्तं नाटचमपि सुष्ठु ज्ञातम् । तदनुरक्तं च नाटचं हृदयावर्जकमिति हृष्टमानसत्वम् । स्वगत(त)त्त्वग्रहणधारणादिसामर्थ्यात्मकशिष्यसम्पद्दर्शनायां(नात्) गुरुप्रोत्साहनमित्यभिप्रायेणाहुः । **त(य)थेति ।** पूजामध्य एव नृत्तं प्रविष्टमित्यध्यायचतुष्टयतात्पर्यं प्रत्यनुभाषितम् । ऊहापोहविज्ञानादिकमपि दर्शयन्ति—**गृहीत्वेति ।** चकारात् धारयित्वाऽवधारितं निश्चितम् । **निखिलेन** साकल्येनेति । **यथातत्त्व**मिति तत्त्वादिनिवेशम् । आहुः **पूर्वरङ्गं वेदितुमिच्छाम**

---

१. K.S.S. M.G. वै जन्म G.O.S. N.S. जन्मेदं ।

२. K.S.S. M.G. त्वत्तः श्रुतं गृहीतं च G.O.S. N.S. (Same as above).

तेषां तु वचनं श्रुत्वा मुनीनां भरतो मुनिः ।
प्रत्युवाच पुनर्वाक्यं पूर्वरङ्गविधिं प्रति ॥ ५ ॥

पूर्वरङ्गं महाभागा गदतो मे निबोधत ।
पादभागाः कलाश्चैव परिवर्तास्तथैव च ॥ ६ ॥

इति जिज्ञासा दर्शिता। यथा सर्वलक्षणसंयुक्त बुध्यामहे तथा व्याचक्ष्वेति व्याख्याप्रकारविषयेऽप्याचार्यान्वेषणम् । महत्तेजो ज्ञानात्मकमस्य तत् । आमन्त्रणं गुरुप्रोत्साहनार्थम् ।

"पूर्वरङ्गे कृते पूर्वं तत्रायं द्विजसत्तमाः ॥" (ना. शा. ४-१०)

इति जिज्ञासादर्शनपूर्वप्रयोज्यतया तथैव जिज्ञासा जाता ।

"पूर्वरङ्गविधावस्मिंस्त्वया सम्यक्प्रयुज्यताम् ॥" (ना. शा. ४-१४) इति ।

"यस्त्वयं पूर्वरङ्गस्तु त्वया शुद्धः ।" (४-१५) इति परमेश्वरादरवचनेन सुष्ठुतरां द्रढीकृता । तथैव तावदवश्योपासनीयेति तात्पर्यम् (१-५) । **गदत** इति शब्दमात्रेण तावन्निरूपयत इत्यर्थः । आश्रावणादिस्वरूपं हि गेयाधिकारे (ना. शा. २९) सम्यक् निर्णेष्यते । अनादरे षष्ठी । निगदन्तमनादृत्य स्वबुद्धया बुद्धयध्वम् । यद्यपि मयाऽत्र क्रमेण नैतदुक्तं गेयाधिकारस्यापि सुदूरत्वात् । तथापि 'यस्य येनार्थसम्बन्ध' इत्यर्थक्रम आदर्तव्यो न शाब्द इति गदनक्रमानादरणं गदितरि सङ्क्रमय्योक्तम् ।

तत्र पूर्वरङ्गशब्दं निरुक्त्या तावद्व्याचष्टे—**पादभागा** इत्यादिना । इह बहिर्यवनिकाङ्गान्येव पूर्वरङ्गः । तानि च गीतकानीत्युत्थापनानि ध्रुवारूपाणि । तत् द्विकलचञ्चत्पुट चाचपुटतालेन विशिष्टगतिगतेनेति तदेव पूर्वरङ्ग इति तावत्तात्पर्यम् । तत्र मात्रायाः यः षोडशो भागः तदारब्धा मात्रा । तदारब्धं वस्तु । एवं वस्तुनिबन्धेषु गीयमानं तावत्स्वीकृतम् । भागश्च द्विकलचतुष्कलयोर्मार्गस्य चञ्चत्पुटादीनां सञ्ज्ञाद्भवति । यथाऽक्षरेषु तु चञ्चत्पुटादिषु कलादिभागलग्ना इति यथाऽक्षरमार्गः कलाग्रहणेन सङ्गृहीतः । यथाक्षरद्विकलचतुष्कलतया सर्वमेव गीतकवर्धमानादि गानं गीयमानं मे(गे)यं रूपं सङ्गृहीतम् । कलाशब्देन च सप्तविधा तालकला निष्कामादिरुच्यते । तया समस्तो मानात्मकस्तालमार्गो गृहीतः । भिन्नार्थानामपि च सरूपाणामेकशेषः ।

---

१. K.S.S. G.O.S. N.S. परिवर्ताः M.G. परिवर्तः ।

यस्माद्रङ्गे प्र[1]योगोऽयं पूर्वमेव प्रयुज्यते[2] ।

तस्मादयं पूर्वरङ्गो विज्ञेयो[3] द्विजसत्तमाः ॥ ७ ॥

पादा इत्यादि । एवं परिवर्तन्त इति **परिवर्ताः** । द्विसङ्ख्यातत्रिसङ्ख्याता दिषु परिचितैः (वर्तैः) सकलेतिकर्तव्यता परिगृहीता । चकारात्केवलं तन्त्र्यादि । **एवकारेण** केवलप्रयोगः । **तथाशब्देनाङ्गाङ्गिभावप्रयोगो** यथायोगं दर्शितः । द्वितीयेनैवकारेण नाटचाङ्गता सूचिता । द्वितीयेन चकारेण च पाठ्यादि नृत्तं च । तेन गीततालवाद्यनृत्तपाठ्यं व्यस्तसमस्ततया प्रयुज्यमानं यन्नाटचाङ्गभूतं स पूर्वरङ्ग इत्युक्तं भवति । यः स्याद्रङ्गे मण्डपे आधारे नाट्ये वा रङ्गे बुद्धिस्थे भविष्यति । युज्यत एव च पूर्वम् प्रत्याहारादिकेन ह्यङ्गेन विना गायनादिसामग्र्यसम्पत्तेः कथं नाटचप्रयोगः । न ह्यहो (ह्येव) किल तन्तुतुरीवेमादेः (विना) शक्यः पटः कर्तुम् । केवलं प्राङ्मुखान्नभोजनवन्नि (यमप्र) योजनत्वेऽपी (त्वमपी) ति वक्ष्यते । तेन पूर्वो रङ्गे पूर्वरङ्गः । सुप्सुपेति समासः राजदन्तादित्वाद्वा परनिपातः ।

श्रीहर्षस्तु रङ्गशब्देन तौर्यत्रिकं ब्रुवन् नाटचाङ्गप्रयोगस्य तस्यैव पूर्वरङ्गतां मन्यमानः पूर्वश्चासौ रङ्ग इति समासममंस्त । यदाह—

"दृष्टा येऽवस्थार्थे (वस्त्वर्थे) नाटचे रङ्गाय पादभागाः स्युः ।
पूर्वं त एव तु यस्मिन् शुद्धाः स्युः पूर्वरङ्गोऽसौ ॥" इत्यादि ।

रङ्गस्य पूर्वो भाग इति त्वसत् । न ह्ययं मण्डपस्यैकदेशः । नापि नाटचस्य । नह्ययं भावानुकीर्तनात्मकव्याख्यानानुकारस्वभावः । अपि तु शिक्षाद्विवत्पारमार्थिक एव प्रयोगसम्पत्त्युपकरणभूतो भोजनादितुल्यः प्रत्याहारादिरर्थः । नृत्तमप्यत्र वैचित्र्यकारित्वेन प्रविशत् "नाटचरूपगतं नृत्तम्" इत्यङ्कुरसूचितनृत्तन्यायेनानुकारधुरारोहि । अपि तु देवतापरितोषणफलं सू (धू) पविलेपनादिदानवत् सत्यमेवेति पूर्वो रङ्ग इत्येष एव संन्या (समा) सः । (५-७)

ननु प्रत्याहाराद्यङ्गसमूहः पूर्वरङ्गः । तत्कथमुक्तं गीतादिः पूर्वरङ्ग इत्याशङ्कयाह—**अस्याङ्गानि त्वित्यादि पूर्वरङ्गे भवन्ति** हीत्यन्तेन श्लोकसप्तकेन सार्धेन महाकाव्यं (वाक्यम्) । तुर्हेतौ । लक्षिष्यमाणानि प्रत्याहारादीन्यासारि-

---

१. M.G. N.S. K.S.S. रङ्गप्रयोगः G.O.S. रङ्गे प्रयोगः ।

२. K.S.S. प्रयोज्यते M.G. G.O.S. N.S. प्रयुज्यते ।

३. K.S.S. M.G. विज्ञेयोऽत्र द्विजोत्तमाः G.O.S. N.S. विज्ञेयो द्विजसत्तमा

अस्याङ्गानि तु कार्याणि यथावदनुपूर्वशः ।
तन्त्रीभाण्डसमायोगैः पाठ्ययोगकृतैस्तथा ॥ ८ ॥

प्रत्याहारोऽवतरणं तथा ह्यारम्भ एव च ।
आश्रावणा वक्त्रपाणिस्तथा च परिघट्टना ॥ ९ ॥

सङ्घोटना ततः कार्या मार्गासारि[1]तमेव च ।
[2]ज्येष्ठमध्यकनिष्ठानि तथैवासारितानि च ॥ १० ॥

एतानि तु[3] बहिर्गीतान्यन्तर्यवनिकागतैः ।
प्रयोक्तृभिः प्रयोज्यानि तन्त्रीभाण्डकृतानि च[4] ॥ ११ ॥

तान्तानि अन्तर्यवनिकाङ्गानि नव प्रयोज्यानि । यानि च यवनिकाया बहिर्गीतकप्रयोगादीनि प्ररोचनान्तानि दश तानि सर्वाण्य(ण्यपि)पादभागाद्युपलक्षितादिरूपस्योक्तस्य सम्बन्धित्वेन यस्मात्कार्याणि तस्मात् पादभागादिरेव पूर्वरङ्ग इति पूर्वेण सम्बन्धः । अङ्गानां न्यूनाधिकभावे हि भूयांसः पूर्वरङ्गभेदाः । ते च गेयाधिकारे (अ-२९) दर्शयिष्यन्ते ।

इह तु दृ (तूद्दि) श्यमानास्तन्त्रभावानभिज्ञानामसम्प्रमोहफला एव ।

उक्तं च **वार्तिके**—"बुद्धयाय षट्कचेदिज (?) रङ्गभेदः । न तु प्रत्याहारावतरणे । आद्यो (द्ये) रङ्गद्वारादीनि । पाश्चात्यानि न पादभागाद्यारब्धानि" इति । सत्यम् । किन्तु समुदितत्वे नात्र रङ्गता रमणीयभावः सम्वन्धः । अपि तु सद्भावमात्रम् । तच्च सर्वत्रैव विद्यत इति वक्ष्यते । तदाह—यस्मादेतानि पूर्वरङ्गे संभवन्ति तस्मादस्य संबन्धित्वेन कार्याणि ।

तत्र यवनिका रङ्गपीठतच्छिरसोर्मध्ये । तस्या अन्तरागतैः प्रयोक्तृभिर्नटैः प्राधान्यात् यदि वा वैणिकादिभिरेव प्रयोक्तृभिः प्रयोज्यानि प्रत्याहारादीनि । गीतकपिण्ड्या(पाठ्या)दीनि तु यवनिकायामपसारितायां गीतानामित्यादिना श्लोकेन गीतकवर्धमानान्यतरप्रयोग उक्तः । अन्ये तु **अथापि** स्थाने (ना. शा.

१. K.S.S. मार्गोत्सारितम् G.O.S. N.S. M.G. मार्गासारितम् ।

२. K.S.S. M.G. ज्येष्ठमध्यकनिष्ठा च तथैवासारितक्रिया (Same as above).

३. G.O.S. N.S. च K.S.S. M.G. तु ।

४. K.S.S. M.G. तु G.O.S. N.S. च ।

ततः[1] सर्वैस्तु कुतपैः संयुक्तानीह कारयेत् ।
विघटय्य[2] वै यवनिकां नृ[3]त्तपाठ्यकृतानि तु[4] ॥ १२ ॥
गीतानां मद्रका[5]दीनां यो[6]ज्यमेकं तु गीतकम् ।
वर्धमानमथापीह ताण्डवं यत्र युज्यते ॥ १३ ॥
ततश्चोत्थापनं कार्यं परिवर्तन[7]मेव च ।
नान्दी शुष्कावकृष्टा[8] च रङ्गद्वारं तथैव च ॥ १४ ॥

५-१३) **अतोऽपी**ति पठन्त उभयप्रधानमनुजानते । तच्चान्त्यपदार्थेन विरुद्धम् । निर्देशविधौ चैकमेवाङ्गं भविष्यति । न तु द्वे ।

"कीर्तनाद्देवतानां च ज्ञेयो गीतविधिस्तथा ।" (ना. शा. ५-२१) इति ।

उभयात्मकं तावदेवैकमङ्गमस्तीति केचित् । अपिशब्दाद्यानि कानि । उद्देशावसर एव '**ताण्डवं यत्र**' इत्यभिधानमस्याङ्गस्य नृत्ते विनियोगं दर्शयति । तेन नाट्याद्यङ्गानि नृत्तशून्यान्यपि भवन्तीति दर्शयतीति तदेव च शुद्धत्वव्यवहारः । यद्वक्ष्यति—"शुद्धं चित्रमथापि च ।" इति । (८-१५)

एवं पूर्वरङ्गसामान्यलक्षणसमाना(सा)र्थे विहाचित्येप्रसङ्गानि (विभावितानि । एतत्प्रसङ्गात्) तेषामयमेवोद्देशो भवतीति दर्शयति—**एतानीति** । क्रमकथनेनैतत्सङ्ख्यान्येव चेत्यर्थः ।

यथोद्देशं लक्षणं कर्तुमुपक्रमते—**एतेषामिति** । तत्क्रममाह—**कुतपस्य त्विति** । नेपथ्यगृहद्वारयोर्मध्ये पूर्वाभिमुखो मार्दङ्गिकः । तस्य पाणिकौ वामतः । रङ्गपीठस्य दक्षिणतः उत्तराभिमुखो गायनः । अस्याग्रे उत्तरतो दक्षिणाभिमुखस्थिता गायिकाः । अस्य वामे वैणिकः । अन्यत्र वंशद्वार(धार)कावित्येवं कुतं पाति कुं तपतीति शब्दविशेषपालकस्य नाट्यभूमिकोज्ज्वलताधायिनश्च वर्गस्य यो विचित्रो न्यासः स विप्रकीर्णानामेकत्र ढौकनात्मा प्रत्याहारः

१. K.S.S. M.G. ततश्च सर्वकुतपैर्युक्तान्यानि कारयेत् G.O.S. N.S. (Same as above).
२. K.S.S. M.G. विघाट्य G.O.S. N.S. विघट्य ।
३. N.S. वृत्त K.S.S. नृत्य G.O.S. M.G. नृत्त ।
४. K.S.S. M.G. च G.O.S. N.S. तु ।
५. K.S.S. मुद्रक M.G. N.S. G.O.S. मद्रक ।
६. K.S.S. M.G. एकं योज्यं तु गीतकम् G.O.S. N.S. (Same as above)
७. K.S.S. परिवर्तकम् G.O.S. N.S. M.G. परिवर्तनम् ।
८. K.S.S. M.G. अपकृष्टा G.O.S. N.S. अवकृष्टा ।

चारी चैव ततः कार्या महाचारी तथैव च ।
त्रिकं प्ररोचना चापि पूर्वरङ्गे भवन्ति हि ॥ १५ ॥

एतान्यङ्गानि कार्याणि पूर्वरङ्गविधौ द्वि[1]जाः ।
एतेषां लक्षणमहं व्याख्यास्याम्यनुपूर्वशः ॥ १६ ॥

यद्यपि कुतपस्य विन्यासमध्य एव च गायकस्याभिमुख्यो रङ्गपीठस्योत्तरतो गायिन्य इति गाय(यि)कानां विन्यासः तथापि त्ववतरणं नाम पृथगुक्तमङ्गानां गीत(मङ्गनागीत)स्यावश्यंभावित्वं रञ्जकवर्गं ख्यापयितुम् । यद्वक्ष्यते—

"यद्यपि पुरुषो गायति गीतविधानं तु लक्षणोपेतम् ।
स्त्रीविरहितः प्रयोगस्तथापि न सुखावहो भवति ॥"
(ना. शा. ३३-५-७) इति ।

यस्त्वाह—"नारदाद्यैस्तु गन्धर्वैः" (ना. शा. ५-३२) इति भाविश्लोके केवलपुरुषाणां गातृत्वं वक्ष्यनाणमिहशङ्केति (हाशङ्क्यचे तेति) पृथगवतरण-मुक्तम् (मिति) । तस्यैतदनवकाशम् । गन्धर्व्यश्च गन्धर्वाश्चेत्येकशेषेण स्त्री-गीतस्याप्यत्र संभावनात् । एवमवतरणान्तं वस्तुत एकमेवाङ्गम् । अत एव प्रयोग एक उभयत्र कृतो भवति । यद्वक्ष्यति पुष्कराध्याये (ना. शा ३४-१६८) "अनुपविष्टेषु मार्दङ्गिकादिषु" इत्युपक्रम्य प्रथमं त्रिसाम ।

"त्रिप्रकारं त्रिगुणितं तथैवात्राड्डिताश्रयम् ।
त्रिकलं षट्कलं चैव त्रिसामत्वात्त्रिसामसु ॥
(काशी. मु. ना. शा. ३३-२०९)

त्रिसामान्वितः ।

त्रिसामाक्षरविद्धस्तु गुरुलध्वक्षरान्वितः ।
यकारश्च मकारश्च त्रिकैस्त्रिगुणितो भवेत् ॥ (ना. शा. ३४-१५९)
(काशी-३३-२१०)

यस्त्रिसामा स प्रत्याहारो यावदवतीर्णकोटीनि । अवतरणकोटौ छन्दसोऽक्षरसमं वामबहिर्गीतानुवर्ति वाद्यं स्त्रीबालमूर्खादिकुतूहलादिजननं प्रयोज्यम् ।

अन्ये मन्यन्ते निवेशनं स्थानस्वरादौ । न तूपवेशनमत्र । तथा च सप्तस्वर-परिग्रहोऽवतरणादाशुगत्या (णमिति जात्या) दिरूपाङ्गसप्तकेन शुद्धसप्तकेन

---

१ K.S.S. M.G. नृ. न. G.O.S. N.S. द्विजाः ।

कुतपस्य तु विन्यासः प्रत्याहार इति स्मृतः।
तथावतरणं प्रोक्तं गायिका[1]नां निवेशनम् ॥ १७ ॥
परिगीतक्रियारम्भ आरम्भ इति कीर्तितः।
आतोद्यरञ्जनार्थं तु भवेदाश्रावणाविधिः ॥ १८ ॥
वाद्यावृत्तिविभागार्थं वक्त्रपाणिर्विधीयते ।
तन्त्र्योजःकरणा[2]र्थं तु भवेच्च परिघट्टनां ॥ १९ ॥

शुद्धसप्तकगीतिज्ञप्रयोज्यमिति । एतद्घनतालविधौ (ना. शा. ३१) **वितत्य** विचारयिष्यते । (१६-१७)

ननु च (यावत्) परिगीतक्रियाद्यारम्भो न कृतस्तावत् त्रिसामप्रयोगोऽपि कथम्। सत्यम्। किञ्चिद (किम) र्थमयं प्रयोगक्रम इत्यवधार्यताम् । **इह** दृष्टार्थान्येव तावदेतान्यङ्गानि । तथा हि—पूर्वं रञ्जकवर्गढौकनं **ततोमेव** (तत एव) तद्गीतस्योपरञ्जकस्य प्राधान्यम् । तस्य च बिम्बभूतं शारीरं शारीरस्वराणां मूलत्वात् । तदनुसन्धानायालापाख्य **आरम्भः** । ततोऽपि मानरूपतालप्रधानसर्वातोद्यगर्भमनुसन्धानमासमन्ताच्छ्रावयतीत्या**श्रवणा**। ततोऽपि प्रतिबिम्बभूतवैणवस्वरस्वरूपानुसन्धानाय दक्षिणादिवृत्तिविभागानुसन्धानात्मना **वक्त्रपाणिः**,। वक्त्रे प्रारम्भे हस्ताङ्गुलिव्यापारः। ततस्तु वृत्तिविभागगतशुष्कप्रयोगानुसन्धानात् ज्या**परिघट्टना**। घट्ट चलन इति पाठात् । पश्चाद्वीणावाद्योपजीवकत्वादवनद्धस्यानुसन्धानसंवाद्यादिना प्रहारपञ्चकयोगेन क्रियत इति **सङ्घटना**। घुट परिवर्तने । यतः **पुष्कराध्याये**ऽभिवक्ष्यते—

पूर्वं शरीरादुद्भूता ततो गच्छति दारवीम् ।
ततः पुष्करजं च।' (ना. शा. ३४-३१) इति। (१८-१९)

ततोऽपि प्रकृतिमेव यन्मानानुहार्यानुहर्तृरूपस्य वैणवपौष्करशब्दस्य परस्परसंमेलनं कार्यमिति **मार्गासारितम्**। मार्गे प्रकृत्यादिलक्षणादि गोचरे विकाररूपस्य (?) पुष्करवाद्यस्यासमन्तात्सारणं गमनं यत्रेति । पश्चान्मेयमानस्वरूपे तु संहिते गेयवस्तुहततालस्वरूपोपक्षेपः। कलानामा(वा)पाद्यानां शम्यादीनां चानुसन्धितेत्यासारितविधिः। एवं तावदन्तर्यवनिकाङ्गानां दृष्टार्थ एव प्रयोगः। तान्यन्तरेण प्रयोगस्यैवासम्पत्तेः । तथा च भेज्जलनाम्ना कविना निजपद्ये उक्तम्—

---

१. G.O.S गायिकानां M.G. N.S. K.S.S. गायकानाम्।

२. K.S.S. तन्त्र्येजस्तरणार्थं G.O.S. N.S. M.G. तन्त्र्य... [illegible]र्थं।

तथा पाणिविभागार्थं भवेत्संघोटनाविधिः ।

तन्त्रीभाण्डसमायोगान्मा[1]र्गासारितमिष्यते ॥ २० ॥

कला[2]पातविभागार्थं भवेदासारितक्रिया ।

कीर्तनाद्दैवतानां च ज्ञेयो गीतविधिस्तथा ॥ २१ ॥

"मेघाशङ्किशिखण्डिताण्डवविधौ" इत्यादि ।

एवं दृष्टार्थे प्रयोगे पूर्वं कृते पश्चात् दृष्टार्थाज्ञानुसारेणैव बहिर्गीतविधिः। तदनुसारेण च तानि त्रिशेषधातुवाद्ये(तन्निवेशगीतवाद्य)विधिः । तत्र प्रत्याहारावतरणयोस्त्रिसाम्ना प्रयोगः । रङ्गपीठस्य तिसृषु दिक्षु कुतपविन्यासात् ।

तालस्त्रिकलस्त्वादौ शम्यैककला कलाद्वये तालाः ।

वि(द्वि)कला च पुनः शम्या तालो द्विकलस्तु कर्तव्यः ॥ (ना. शा. २९-१४)

द्विकलश्च सन्निपातः पुनः पिता पुत्रकश्च षट्पूर्वः । (ना.शा.२९-१००)

चञ्चत्पुटस्तथा चेदारम्भे तालयोगस्तु ।

त्रिशम्योपरिपाणौ तालावित्येवमेककलः ।

समपाणौ द्वे शम्ये तालावप्येवमेवाथ ॥ (ना. शा. २९-८९)

भूयश्शम्या तालाववपाणावुत्तरस्तथा चैव ।

चञ्चत्पुटस्तथा स्यादेवं ह्याश्रावणातालः ॥ (ना. शा. २९-९०)

शङ्कुकस्तु पठति "उत्तरस्तथा चैव" इति स्थाने "उत्तरस्तथा द्विकलः" इति, "एककल" इत्यत्र च स्थाने "निर्दिष्ट" इति

केचिच्चाष्टाविंशेऽध्याये (२९-८६) आश्रावणायाः पूर्वमभिधानादिह चारम्भस्य पूर्वपाठाद् ज्ञापकाद्विकल्पमिच्छन्ति । अतः सर्वातोद्यस्वरूपानुसन्धिनिर्गीतालापक्रिया चेति (निर्गीततालप्रक्रियाचेति ?) ।

"द्विकले मद्रके यत्तु शम्यातालादियोजनम् ।

तत्सर्वं वक्त्रपाणौ तु कार्यमष्टकले मुखे ॥

तस्याधस्तात्पुनः कार्यं पञ्चपाणिचतुष्टयम् ।

वक्त्रपाणेरयं तालो मुखप्रतिमुखाश्रयः ॥" (ना. शा. २९-९७)

---

१. N.S. K.S.S. मार्गोन्सारितम् G.O.S. M.G. मार्गासारितम् ।

२. K.S.S. कालपात G.O.S. N.S. M.G. कलापात ।

[अतः परं प्रवक्ष्यामि ह्यु[१]त्थापनविधिक्रियाम् ।]

यस्मादुत्थापयन्त्य[२]त्र प्रयोगं नान्दिपाठकाः ।

पूर्वमेव तु रङ्गेऽस्मिस्तस्मादुत्थापनं स्मृतम् ॥ २२ ॥

केचित्तु वक्त्रवार्ध (पाण्यर्ध) गतमिच्छन्ति तैर्वस्तुक्रमो वृत्तिशब्दश्च न चर्चितः । संपिष्टकवच्चास्यास्ताल (ना. शा. २९-११२) इति परिघट्टनातालः ।

तत्र—'सप्ताङ्गे द्वादशकलं द्वादशाङ्गे दशैव तु ।

निष्क्राममादितः कृत्वा शम्यास्तिस्रः प्रयोजयेत् ॥ (ना.शा. ३१-२७८)

द्वालत्रयं ततश्चैव शम्यातालौ ततः परम् ।

शम्यातालौ ततः कार्यौ सन्निपातोऽन्त्य एत्र च ॥ (ना.शा. ३१-२७९)

ओवेणके तु सप्ताङ्गे सम्पिष्टकमिदं मतम् ।

द्विशम्यातालयोगेन द्वादशाङ्गे कला दश ॥'' (ना. शा. ३१-२८०)

शङ्कुकस्तु ''सम्पक्वेष्ट कवदस्यास्ताल'' (ना. शा. २९-११२) इति पठति ।

''तालादिस्त्र्यश्रभेदोऽन्यो ज्ञेयः पक्केष्टको बुधैः ।

गुरुपञ्चाक्षराभ्यान्तु (द्यन्त) प्लुतमात्रासमन्वितः ॥'' (ना.शा. ३१-२१)

इति, अन्ये तु पठन्ति—

''गुरुपञ्चाक्षरेऽन्ते च प्लुतमात्राद्वयान्वितः । '' इति ॥

तथा द्वौ सम्पिष्टशब्देतु व(त्करणवाचकं शीर्षकवदितिवत् । न हि तस्य च तदानीमङ्गता । केवलप्रयोगात्प्रकरणं चात्र साक्षी । शीर्षकवद्वालासारितवदिति चानयोर्मध्ये पठितमेतत् ।

पक्केष्टकस्य तथैव तालाद्य(प्लुत द्वयेत्यर्थो ? न सङ्गतः ।

सङ्गोटनायां तालस्तु शीर्षवत्पञ्चपाणिना । (ना. शा. काशी. २९-१४२) अनयोरप्यङ्गयोः पूर्ववत्केचित्क्रमविकल्पमिच्छन्ति ।

''वालासारितवच्चैव तालोऽस्य परिकीर्तितः ।'' (ना. शा. २९-११६) इति मार्गासारितस्य तालः । अभिसृतपरिसृतान्यप्यत्र मार्गासारितमध्य एव

---

१. K.S.S. M.G. च G.O.S. N.S. हि ।

२. N.S. K.S.S. M.G. आदौ G.O.S. अत्र ।

यस्माच्च लोकपालानां परिवृत्य चतुर्दिशम् ।
वन्दनानि प्रकुर्वन्ति तस्माच्च[1] परिवर्तनम् ॥ २३ ॥

तत्स्थाने वा विकल्पेन प्रयोक्तव्यानि । लीलाकृतं नाम यत्तता(दा)तोद्यविधौ (ना. शा. २९-११७) वक्ष्यते तदिह न सङ्गृहीतम् । आसारितानां च त्रयाणां स्वत एकस्तालाध्याये (ना. शा. ३१-१४६-१७३) वितत्य वक्ष्यत इत्येवं प्रयोगक्रमः । अत एव पूर्वरङ्गे सद्भावमात्रेण सप्रत्याहारका(रादा)वपि सामान्यलक्षणमनुगतमेव । अत्र च शुष्काक्षरधातुवाद्यविधिरष्टाविंशेऽध्याये ततातोद्यविधौ भविष्यति 'त्रिसाम्नि' पुष्कराध्याये (ना. शा. ३४) तत एवावधार्यमिति । विस्तरभयात्तु न लिखितम् ।

अत्र च वैचित्र्यार्थं समुचितमात्र मित्यादिप्रवृत्तिमपि भाविरूपकोचितं काव्यमपि पठ्यमानं केचिदिच्छन्ति । तथा हि सति "पाठ्ययोगकृतस्तथा" (ना. शा. ५-८) इति न सङ्कोचितं भविष्यति । युक्तं चैतत् । यथा हि रमणीयात्यु(द्यु)पकरणभूतशयनविरचनादौ प्रतिपादुकस्तम्भधूपवस्त्रादिष्वपि तदुचितनायकयुगलादिप्रायविचित्राकृतियोगो युद्धोचितसन्नाहक(स)ङ्कटादौ च कातरजनभयभावनं नृसिंहगरुडादिरचनाकृतियोगस्तथैव ह्यतिरमणीये नाटचे भविष्यन्ति(ति) यदुपरञ्जकवर्गढौकनादौ—एतदपि सुकुमारतदुक्तगीतपाठ्याभिनययोगेनैव कार्यम् । तच्चापसारितायामेव यवनिकायामुत्थापनाङ्गमध्ये ह्यस्यैककलः पाठ्यसहितः प्रयोगः । तथा हि वक्ष्यति "यस्मादुत्थापयन्ति" इत्यादि । रङ्गे यः पूर्वं प्रयोगः कृतः प्रत्याहारादिस्तं यस्मादुत्थापयन्ति फलस्वरूपनिरूपकपाठ्यतदभिनयादिना स्फुटीकुर्वन्ति तस्मादित्यर्थः । पाठ्यावकाशदानार्थमेव चात्रेदं देवतास्तुतिगीतिफलविशेषाभिधानम् । अन्यथा देवतापरितोषायैतत्प्रयोज्यमिति सामान्येन वक्तव्यं स्यात् । विशेषोपदेशस्य प्रयोगे विफलत्वात् ।

अन्ये तु प्रत्यङ्गं पश्चात्तत्प्रयोगमाहुः तैस्तु प्रयोक्ता **कस्तदेति निरूप्यम्** । **अत्र** त्विदमित्यर्थः । **कृतमित्युक्तिभङ्ग्या** पाठ्यं तद्गीतप्रयोगः **पदयुक्तो**ऽपि **केवलमन्तर्यवनिका**गतप्रत्याहारादिविषयत्वात्पाठ्ययोगादीनामप्यन्त**र्यवनिकार्थ**मुच्यते । एवं नवाङ्गान्युक्तानि ।

अथ "विघाटच वै यवनिकाम्" (ना. शा. ५-१२) इत्यादिना यद्गीतकविध्याद्यङ्गदशकं दर्शितं तत्क्रमेण लक्षयति—**कीर्तनादित्यादि** । कीर्तनं स्तुतिः । तस्मात्पाठ्याद्धेतोः । ततः परं शुष्काक्षरनिर्वृत्तशब्देन निर्गीतकानामन्यतमं वर्धमानं वा । तत्र च तालस्तालाध्याये(एक)त्रिंशे वक्ष्यते । (२१)

---

१. K.S.S. M.G. तु G.C.S. N.S. च ।

आशीर्वचनसंयुक्ता नित्यं यस्मात्प्रयुज्यते[1] ।
देवद्विजनृपादीनां तस्मान्नान्दीति संज्ञिता ॥ २४ ॥

यस्मादिति । तत्र प्रत्याहारादीनि चेत् अत्र प्रयोज्यानि तत्पूर्वरङ्ग इत्यनुवादोऽयं स्यात् । क्रमस्य सिद्धत्वात् । **नान्दिपाठका** इति । तदुपलक्षित-पूर्वक्रमद्वारेणैव पुराणकवयो लिखन्ति स्म "नान्द्यन्ते सूत्रधारः" इति । अहरहश्चैषा प्रयोगे प्रयोज्या । एवं च नित्यमेवंरूपमेव । अन्यपाठ्यानामुत्था-पनादीनां प्रयोगवशादन्यथात्वोपपत्तिर्दृश्यते । न तु नान्दीपाठस्येति **नित्य**शब्द-स्याभिप्रायः । **आदि**ग्रहणात्प्रेक्षापतिप्रभृतयः । एषैव च नान्दी भारत्यङ्गनिरूपणे प्ररोचनेति निर्देक्ष्यते—"जयाभ्युदयिनी चैव मङ्गल्या" (ना. शा. २०-२७) इत्यादिना । इह तु सा(या)प्ररोचना सा तत्र भविष्यति । अत्र नान्दीपदा नामन्तरेषु चित्रे पूर्वरङ्गे वर्धमानं यत्प्रयोज्यं तत्पञ्चममङ्गं गणयति ।

नन्वेवं गीतकविधिः प्रथमाङ्गानन्तरमन्याङ्गमध्येऽपि च वर्धमानप्रयोगस्य चित्रेऽपि भावात्सङ्ख्याया अनवस्थानं न पदेऽपतदिति न पुनर्गणनार्हमिति न दोषः (इति) केचिदाहुः । (२४)

(शुष्कावकृष्टैवादिष्टा । असावेव च लक्षिता । अवकृष्टायास्त्वनुवादद्वारेण लक्षणं मन्तव्यम् । अन्यथा वक्ष्यमाणं)

"युक्तायामपकृष्टायां प्रीता नागा भवन्ति हि ।
तथा शुष्कावकृष्टायां प्रीतः पितृगणो भवेत् ॥" (ना. शा. ५-५०)

इति तन्निर्विषयं स्यात् । तत्रावकृष्टाया लक्षणं—

"मुखप्रतिमुखोपेता ह्यवकृष्टा विधीयते ॥" (ना. शा. ३२-१२)
इति तालविधिः ।

अन्यभावेषु कृष्टश्च (द्रव्यहेतुषु पठ्यते ।)
यस्मात्कारुण्यसंयुक्ता ह्य(वकृष्टा भवेत्ततः ।)"
(ना. शा. ३२-३४१)

इति वाक्यार्थगानेतिकर्तव्यताविधिवृत्तस्वरूपं शम्यादेर्योजनं चाग्रेऽस्या वक्ष्यते । तदेतस्यां प्रयुक्तायां तदनन्तरं नाट्यम् । ईदृश्येव शुष्काक्षरैः प्रयोज्या । तत्रावकृष्टात्वसामान्यात् पृथकृकगवात(थगवगते) (क्रमपातै ?)**जर्जरश्लोक-**

---

१. K.S.S. M.G. प्रवर्तते G.O.S. N.S. प्रयुज्यते ।

अत्र[1] शुष्काक्षरैरेव ह्यव[2]कृष्टा ध्रुवा यतः ।
तस्माच्छुष्कावकृष्टेयं[3] जर्जरश्लोकर्दाशका[4] ॥ २५ ॥

यस्मादभिनयस्त्व[5]त्र प्रथमं ह्यवतार्यते ।
रङ्गद्वारमतो ज्ञेयं वागङ्गाभिनयात्मकम् ॥ २६ ॥

र्दाशका यत्त(तस्त)दनन्तरम् । **शुष्कावकृष्टेयमिति** । असावकृष्टे(ष्टा) ध्रुवा । सा तस्माच्छुष्कावकृष्टा । आह । हि यस्मात् । **अत्रेति** अस्याङ्गतायाम् । अवकृष्टस्य (ष्टा) समस्ततल्लक्षणोपेता केवलं शुष्कैरक्षरैरर्थकैः झण्टुमाद्यैः ।

अन्ये त्वेकस्यामेव ध्रुवायां शुष्कावकृष्टत्वधर्मद्वयविषयोऽयं "युक्तायामपकृष्टायाम्" इति श्लोको भविष्यतीति मन्यन्ते । **उपाध्यायास्तु** शुष्कायामवकृष्टायामेवान्तर्भूतं फलं वक्ष्यते । अत्र तु शुष्कैव लक्ष्यते । अनेन च लक्षणेनावकृष्टापि सूचिताऽत्रेति **इयमिति** च पदाभ्याम् । (२५)

अभिनीयत इत्य**भिनयो** रूपकविशेषः । सोऽ**वतार्यते** संक्षेपेण तस्यार्थप्रयोजनादिनिरूपणपाठचद्वारेण तथैव चाभिनयः क्रियते यत्र तद्रङ्गस्य भाविनो रूपकस्य द्वारमिव **रङ्गद्वाराद्**(**रम्**)त्थापनाङ्गं सामान्येन नाटचमुत्थापितम् । इह तु रूपकविशेषेण भेदः । (२६) **शृङ्गारस्येति** शृङ्गारप्रधानं भगवतो महादेव्या सह यत्र चरितं वर्ण्यते काव्ये च तत्स्तुतिप्रधानं तदेव यत्राङ्गहारचार्यादिना प्रदर्श्यते सा **चारी** । (भगवतस्त्रिपुरमर्दनादीव गीतं रौद्ररसभूयिष्ठं यत्र काव्ये वर्ण्यते स्तुतिरूपेण तद्यत्र) तदुचितैरेवोद्धतैर्मण्डलाङ्गहारैः प्रयुज्यते सा **महाचारी** ।

विदूषक इति । पारिपार्श्विकयोरन्यतरो विदूषकवेषभाषाचारो विदूषकः । सञ्जल्पो भविष्यन्नाटकादिविशेषो (षयः) । यद्यप्युक्तः तथापि तद्विशेषो **नागानन्दादिभिः** विवक्षित इत्यपौनरुक्त्यम् । स एव काव्योपक्षेपस्त्रियु समायत्तत्वात्त्रिगतशब्देनोक्तः ।

१. K.S.S. यत्र G.O.S. N.S. M.G. अत्र ।
२. K.S.S. M.G. अपकृष्टा G.O.S. N.S. अवकृष्टा ।
३. K.S.S. अवकृष्टेव M.G. अपकृष्टेव G.O.S. N.S. अवकृष्टेय ।
४. K.S.S. M.G. र्दाशता G.O.S. N.S. र्दाशका ।
५ K.S.S. M.G. तत्र G.O.S. N.S. त्वत्र ।

शृङ्गारस्य प्रचरणाच्चारी सम्परिकीर्तिता ।
रौद्रप्रचर[1]णाच्चापि महाचारीति कीर्तिता ॥ २७ ॥

विदूषकः सूत्रधारस्तथा वै पारिपार्श्वकः ।
यत्र कुर्वन्ति सञ्जल्पं [2]तच्चापि त्रिगतं मतम्[3] ॥ २८ ॥

उपक्षेपेण काव्यस्य हेतुयुक्तिसमाश्रया ।
सिद्धेनामन्त्रणा या तु विज्ञेया सा प्ररोचना ॥ २९ ॥

तेन काव्योपक्षेपेण हेतुभूतेन तद्विषये सामाजिकानां या **आमन्त्रणा** निमन्त्रणं **सिद्धेन** सिद्धचोपलक्षितमित्यर्थः । यस्मात्खल्वतः प्रीत्युत्पत्तिर्भविष्यति तस्मादवलोक्यतामेतदिति सा प्ररोचना प्रकृष्टरुचिहेतुभूतत्वात् । न च तद्वचनात्प्रवृत्तिर्भवतीत्याह—**हेतुयुक्तीति** । हेतोर्या युक्तिर्योजना संक्षेपेणाभिधानं तन्निमित्त मस्या इति ।

एवमेतानि बहिर्यवनिकाङ्गान्यपि दश दृष्टफलान्येव । तथा हि गीतकवर्धमानान्युपजीव्य ध्रुवागानं नाटचम (मि) ति प्रकृतेरुपजीव्यत्वादवश्यं प्रथमं बुद्धौ कृति (कर्तव्यम् ?—ततोऽपि यदारभ्यते तदा बुद्धौ निवेश्यं तावत् सामान्ये । ततः सदाचारपालनाय देवतावन्दनम् । ततः परमाशीर्वादनमभिमुखीकरणार्थम् । ततोऽपि शङ्क्यमानविघ्नशान्त्युपकरणीभूतस्योत्तेजनम् । ततोऽपि विशेषेण प्रयोक्तव्यानुसन्धानम् । ततोऽपि शृङ्गारवीरयोः सर्वत्र रञ्जकपरमपुमर्थताप्रकर्षादुपक्षेपः । तदपि नाटचविनेयसुकुमारजने स्वच्छन्दता (कर) सर्वरञ्जकहास्यप्राधान्येन काव्यविशेषे भवदभिधेयानुसन्धानम् । तस्यापि प्रयोजननिरूपणम् !

एवं यथा शास्त्रं कुर्वतामादिवाक्यपरिग्रहो लौकिकस्य वा कर्तव्यविषयमनुसन्धानं तथैव नाटचारम्भे गीतकपिण्डचादिप्ररोचनान्तं लौकिकानुसार्येव । नात्र कस्यचिदङ्गस्य सामर्थ्यलक्ष्यत्वादि चोदनीयम् । सुकुमारजनविषयत्वादस्य प्रयोगस्य । तस्मान्नालौकिकं किञ्चिदेतत् । केवलं नाटचस्य रचनाप्राधान्याद्वैचित्र्येण योजनीयमदृष्टसम्पत्तये चेति मन्तव्यमित्यलं बहुना । (२७-२९)

---

१. N.S. प्रचारणात् K.S.S. M.G. G.O.S. प्रचरणात् ।

२. M.G. K.S.S. तत्र G.O.S. N.S. तच्च ।

३. K.S.S. M.G. स्मृतम् G.O.S. N.S. मतम् ।

अतः परं प्रवक्ष्यामि ह्याश्रावणविधिक्रियाम् ।
बहिर्गीतविधौ सम्यगुत्पत्तिं कारणं तथा ॥ ३० ॥
चि[1]त्रदक्षिणवृत्तौ[2] तु सप्तरूपे प्रवर्तिते[3] ।
सोपोहने सनिर्गीते देवस्तुत्यभिनन्दिते ॥ ३१ ॥

ननु भवत्ये(त्वे)वम् । किञ्चारम्भाश्रावणादौ वेगगी(बहिर्गी)तशब्द-स्वरूपम् । [पदार्थः] (तदर्थः) कोऽत्र पदार्थः । तदयमर्थः—तेषामाश्रावणादीनां विधौ क्रियां प्रयोगरक्षात्मिकां बहिर्गीतशब्दस्य च वाचकत्वेन विधाने **उत्पत्तिं** बहिर्गीतस्य च विधौ प्रयोगे प्रयोजनरूपं **कारणं** वक्ष्यमि । (३०)

तत्पुराकल्पद्वारेणाह—**चित्रे**त्यादिना श्लोकैकादशकेन "**बहिर्गीतमिति स्मृतम् ।**" इत्यन्तेन (गीतवाद्यगीतोभयप्रधानाः क्रमेण चित्रादयो वृत्तिमार्गाः । चित्रदक्षिणसहिता वृत्तिरिति मध्यमपदलोपी समासः । तद्विषयं यद्गीतकं सहोपोहनप्रत्युपोहनैः वर्धमाननिर्गीतेन च "आश्रावणा तथारम्भः" इत्यादिना अष्टाविंशे(ना. शा. २९-८२) (एकोनत्रिंशे)ऽध्याये वक्ष्यमाणेन सहितं देवस्तुत्या च वाच्यभूतयाऽभितो नन्दितं समृद्धं युद्धम् । तस्मिन्प्रवर्तिते प्रयुक्ते सति तद्गानं गीयमानं सुखजनकमपि श्रुत्वा दैत्याः क्षुभिताः । कुतः । (मात्सर्यात् । तदपि कुतः ।)आह—देवैरहो रम्यं साधु साध्वित्यादिभिः स्तुतिभिरभिनन्द्यमानं यतः । **तु**रप्यर्थः । केन वा प्रवर्तितं तदित्याह—**नारदाद्यै**रिति तदधिष्ठितैरित्यर्थः । **तदि**ति सप्तरूपम् (ना. शा. ३१. का. मा. पु. ५२१) । **लयो** द्रुतादिः । **तालाः** शम्यादिविशिष्टाः त्र्यश्रश्चतुरश्रो मिश्रश्च । **सम्प्रधार्ये**त्यनेन परितोष्टव्यमन्यैस्त्वत्रेति । स्थितिं कृत्वा**वस्थिताः** । इति शब्दसूचितमुच्यमानं निर्दिशति—**त्वमिति** । (निर्गीतमिति) वादित्रं तद्गतं शुष्काख्यं वीणावाद्यम् । ननु किं तस्य ग्रहणे निमित्तमित्याह—**तुष्याम** इति । स्तुतिकीर्तनाभावेऽप्यामिभानिकेन परितोषेणेत्यर्थः । दृष्टोह्यभिमानकृतः प्रीतौ विशेषो यथा राजाकर्णनेऽपि । **तत्रे**ति निर्गीते । **साधयन्ति** । साधनं सिद्धं ब्रुवते । (**धातुवाद्याश्रयकृतमिति**) धातवस्तन्त्रीविशेषाङ्गुलिविशेषसंयोगजा वैणवस्वराः । रञ्जनया अदृ(दृ)ष्टविशेषस्य क्रमेण चतुष्टयपृथक्कृता विस्तारव्यञ्जनाविद्धकरणसंज्ञा । धातुवाद्यं सप्तभेदलक्षणम् । तस्य यदाश्रयणं तेन हेतुना कृतमिति चित्रम् ।

---

१. K.S.S. चित्त G.O.S. N.S. M.G. चित्र ।

२. N.S. वृत्ते K.S.S. M.G. G.O.S. वृत्तौ ।

३. N.S. प्रकीर्तिता G.O.S. N.S. M.G. प्रवर्तिते ।

नारदाद्यैस्तु[1] गन्धर्वैः सभायां देवदानवाः ।
निर्गीतं[2] श्राविताः सम्यग्लयतालसमन्वितम् ॥ ३२ ॥

तच्छ्रुत्वा तु सुखं[3] गानं देवस्तुत्यभिनन्दितम् ।
अभवन्क्षुभिताः सर्वे मात्सर्याद्दैत्यराक्षसाः ॥ ३३ ॥

सम्प्रधार्य च तेऽन्योन्यमित्यवोचन्नवस्थिताः ।
निर्गीतं तु सवादित्रमिदं गृह्णीमहे वयम् ॥ ३४ ॥

सत्तरूपेण सन्तुष्टा देवाः कर्मानुकीर्तनात् ।
वयं[4] गृह्णीम निर्गीतं तुष्यामोऽत्रैव सर्वदा[5] ॥ ३५ ॥

ते तत्र तुष्टा दैत्यास्तु साधयन्ति पुनः पुनः ।
हृष्टाश्चापि ततो देवाः प्रत्यभाषन्त नारदम् ॥ ३६ ॥

तत्तादृशेनादृष्ट(ष्टेन)को गुणो न त्वन(दृ)ष्टे स्तुतिनिरूपणेषु यद्विधानं तेन हि पूर्वमध्यान्तेषु प्रयुज्यमानेन वीणाद्याद्यवैचित्र्यावकाशदायिना । हृद्यतागतिकादि-कन्यायादिगुणान्तरमप्याह—**निर्गीतेनेति** । अपदावखेलने अयत्नेन वालहेवाक-पोषणेन्यायेन **बद्धाः** । स्वीकृता इत्यर्थः ।

एवमविनाशकारणं प्रतिपाद्य संज्ञानिर्वचनं रूपयति—**एवमिति** तावदाद्यं **निर्गीतमिति** तावदाद्यं नाम । निरर्थकं गीतमिति । तत्तु गन्धर्वै**र्बहिर्गीतमिति स्मृतम्** । कुतो **दैत्यानां स्पर्धयेति** । तत्कृतोऽयं स्वीकारः । ततो हेतोः ।

ननु यदि स्वीकृतं ततः किमित्येषा संज्ञा कृता । अत आह—**देवानामिति** । देवकर्मकं यद्वहुतयोत्कृष्टतया मननं तेन प्रयोजनभूतेन । वयं देवान्दानवेभ्यो बहुत्वेन मन्यामहे । तथा चेदं नाभ्यन्तरं वाह्यं गीतमस्माभिर्गीयत इति तैरेव वेदितव्यमित्यर्थः । (३१-४१)

---

१. K.S.S. M.G. च G.O.S. N.S. तु ।
२. N.S. निगीतं G.O.S. M.G. K.S.S. निर्गीतं ।
३. K.S.S. समं M.G. शुभं N.S. G.O.S. सुखं ।
४. K.S.S. M.G. एवं G.O.S. N.S. वयं ।
५. K.S.S. M.G. वै वयम् G.O.S. N.S. सर्वदा ।

एते तुष्यन्ति निर्गीते दानवाः सह राक्षसैः ।
प्रणश्यतु प्रयोगोऽयं कथं वा[1] मन्यते भवान् ॥ ३७ ॥

देवानां वचनं श्रुत्वा नारदो वाक्यमब्रवीत् ।
धातुवाद्याश्रयकृतं निर्गीतं[2] मा प्रणश्यतु ॥ ३८ ॥
किन्तूपोहनसंयुक्तं धातुवाद्य[3]विभूषितम् ।
भविष्यतीदं निर्गीतं सप्तरूप[4]विधानतः ॥ ३९ ॥

निर्गीतेनावबद्धा[5]श्च दैत्यदानवराक्षसाः ।
न क्षोभं न विघातं च करिष्यन्तीह तोषिताः ॥ ४० ॥

एवं[6] निर्गीतमेतत्तु दैत्यानां स्पर्धया द्विजाः ।
देवानां बहुमानेन बहिर्गीतमिति[7] स्मृतम् ॥ ४१ ॥

धातुभिश्चित्रवीणायां गुरुलघ्वक्षरान्वितम् ।
वर्णालङ्कारसंयुक्तं प्रयोक्तव्यं बुधैरथ ॥ ४२ ॥

ननु सप्तरूप एव किमिदं प्रयोज्यम् । नेत्याह—**धातुभिरिति** । चित्रा नाट्योपरञ्जनार्था या वीणा तस्यामप्येतद्धातुभिरुक्तस्वरूपैः (करतलनिष्कोटितादिभिः) उपलक्षितं प्रयोज्यम् । कथम् । भाण्डवाद्ये गत्यर्थे यानि **गुरूणि** "घृत् दृङ" इत्यादिकानि **लघूनि** "मट कट" इत्यादिकानि । तत्रान्वितं कृत्वा । अनेन भाण्डवाद्योपरञ्जकत्वमुक्तम् । तथा ध्रुवागाने ये स्थाय्यादयो **वर्णा** ये च प्रसन्नादिप्रभृतयोऽलङ्कारास्तत्र सम्यग्युक्तं संबद्धं कृत्वा । अनेन गीतोपरञ्जकत्वं दर्शितम् । अथ शब्दोऽप्यर्थे । योजितः पूर्वैरिति (**बुधैरिति**) योजनाकुशलैः ।

---

१. K.S.S. M.G. वै G.O.S. N.S. वा ।
२. N.S. निगीतं G.O.S M.G K.S.S. निर्गीतं ।
३. K.S.S. वाक्य G.O.S. M.G. N.S. वाद्य ।
४. N.S. सप्तरूपे विधानतः G.O.S. K.S.S. M.G. (Same as above)
५. N.S. निगीतेनावनद्धाश्च G.O.S. निर्गीतेनावबद्धाश्च K.S.S. M.G. निर्गीतेनावबद्धास्तु ।
६. K.S.S. M.G. एतन्निर्गीतमेवं तु G.O.S. N.S. (Same as above) ।
७. K.S.S. बहु गीतमिदं M.G. बहिर्गीतमिदं G.O.S. N.S. बहिर्गीतमिति ।

निर्गीतं गीयते यस्मादपदं वर्णयोजनात् ।
असूयया च देवानां बहिर्गीतमिदं स्मृतम् ॥ ४३ ॥

निर्गीतं ग्रन्थया प्रोक्तं सप्तरूपसमन्वितम् ।
उत्थापनादिकं यच्च तस्य कारणमुच्यते ॥ ४४ ॥

आश्रावणायां युक्तायां दैत्यास्तुष्यन्ति नित्यशः ।
वक्त्रपाणौ कृते चैव नित्यं तुष्यन्ति दानवाः ॥ ४५ ॥

ननु निर्गीतसंज्ञाऽस्य या पुराणी तत्र किन्निमित्तमित्याशङ्क्याह—**निर्गीत-मिति** । **पद**मित्यर्थप्रत्यायकमित्यर्थः वर्णा झटुमादयः स्थाय्यादयश्च । ननु लक्षणाभ्यन्तर एव तदिति कथं बाह्यमित्याशङ्क्याह—**असूयया चेति** । तैर्यतोऽसूयिन बलादेवाविष्कृतबहुमानैः अतस्तदीयहृदयग्रहणायैव व्याहृतम् । न च सर्वथा निर्निबन्धनमेवेदमिति दर्शयितुं **च**कारेणान्वर्थताप्यस्तीति सूचयति । गीयमानेभ्यः पदेभ्यः सार्थकेभ्यः पदेभ्यो बहिर्गीतमिति । एवमत्रिनाशकारणं संज्ञानियोजननिमित्तं च तेनैव क्रमेणाभिधाय प्रतिजानीते—**निर्गीतमि**त्यादिना । आश्रावणादि निर्गीतं **सप्तरूपसमन्वितम्** । इति गीतकविधिः । **उत्थापनादि**कमिन्यवशिष्टं बहिर्यवनिकाङ्गम् । तस्य **कारणं** प्रयोजनम् । (४२-४४) ।

तद्दर्शयति—**आश्रावणाया**मित्यादिना **भूतगणो भवेदि**त्यन्तेन श्लोकाष्टकेन । प्रत्याहाराद्याश्रावणायामेवान्तर्भूतम् । अवधित्वादस्याः । (कस्मिश्चित्पुस्तके—

"प्रत्याहारे यातुधानाः प्रीयन्ते सह पन्नगैः ।
तुष्यन्त्यप्सरसस्तत्र कृतेऽवतरणे द्विजाः ॥
तुष्यन्त्यपि च गन्धर्वा आरम्भे सम्प्रयोजिते ।"

इति सार्धश्लोको दृश्यते) यादृच्छिकसम्प्रधारितपरिग्रहबहुमानकृतः परितोषो विशिष्टविषयो मन्तव्यः । **मार्गासारित**शब्देनैकदेशेन सर्वमङ्गं लक्षितम् । आसारितशब्देनासारितविधिरिति समाहारद्वन्द्वेन द्वयोरङ्गयोः फलमेतन्निरूपितम् । **देवाः** । **रुद्र** इति । तदियकर्मस्तुतेः । एतच्च गीतकवर्धमानयोरन्यतरप्रयोगे वैकल्पिकं फलद्वयम् । **ब्रह्मेति** । प्रथमसृष्टिव्यापारः तत्र नाट्यविषयः । स चात्र पुष्पाञ्जलिना पूज्यते (सूच्यते) । **चन्द्रमा** इति । "जित सोमेन" इति (ना. शा. ५-११०) नान्द्यां पाठात् । **नागा** इत्यवकृष्टगतिः ।

---

१. K.S.S. M.G. सर्वशः G.O.S. N.S. नित्यशः ।

परिघट्टनया तुष्टा युक्तायां रक्षसां गणाः[1] ।
सङ्घोटना[2] क्रियायां च[3] तुष्यन्त्यपि च गुह्यकाः ॥ ४६ ॥

मार्गासारितमासाद्य तुष्टा[4] यक्षा भवन्ति हि ।
गीतकेषु प्रयुक्तेषु देवास्तुष्यन्ति नित्यशः ॥ ४७ ॥

वर्धमाने प्रयुक्ते तु रुद्रस्तुष्यति सानुगः ।
तथा चोत्थापने युक्ते ब्रह्मा तुष्टो भवेदिह ॥ ४८ ॥

तुष्यन्ति लोकपालाश्च प्रयुक्ते परिवर्तने ।
नान्दीप्रयोगेऽथ कृते प्रीतो भवति चन्द्रमाः ॥ ४९ ॥

युक्तायामव[5] कृष्टायां प्रीता नागा भवन्ति हि ।
तथा शुष्कावकृष्टायां[6] प्रीतः पितृगणो भवेत् ॥ ५० ॥

रङ्गद्वारे प्रयुक्ते तु विष्णुः प्रीतो भवेदिह ।
जर्जरस्य प्रयोगे तु तुष्टा विघ्नविनायकाः ॥ ५१ ॥

जर्जरस्येति । शुष्कावकृष्टालक्षणस्यैवाङ्गस्य शेषभूतो जर्जरस्तुतिप्रदर्शकः श्लोको वक्ष्यते "ततः श्लोकं पठेदेकम्" (ना. शा. ५-११८) इति । तस्येदं प्रयोजनं—विघ्नानां यो विनायको निवारयिता स तुष्टो भवति । तन्निवारणोपकरण-समुत्तेजनाद्विघ्नविनायका विरूपाक्षादयः । ते विघातं न कुर्वन्तीति । सैव फल-साम्यात्तुष्टिरेषामिति केचित् । उमेति । तस्या एव स्वरूपकीर्तनात् । (४५-५२)

एतत्सर्वमुपसंहर्तुमाह—आश्रावणादीत्यादि कृतानि त्वित्यन्तं श्लोकचतुष्टयम् । प्रत्याहारादीनामाश्रावणायामन्तर्भावः । चारीशब्देनेह महाचारी ।

---

१. K.S.S. N.S. परिघट्टनायां तुष्टाः स्युर्युक्तायां रक्षसां गणाः M.G. परिघट्टनायां तुष्टा युक्तायां रक्षसां गणाः । G.O.S. (Same as above) ।
२. K.S.S. M.G. N.S. सङ्घोटन G.O.S. सङ्घोटना ।
३. G.O.S. K.S.S. च N.S. M.G. तु ।
४. N.S. प्रीताः K.S.S. M.G. G.O.S. तुष्टाः ।
५. K.S.S. M.G. अपकृष्टायां G.O.S. N.S. अवकृष्टायां ।
६. M.G. अपकृष्टायां G.O.S. K.S.S. N.S. अवकृष्टायां ।

तथा चार्यां प्रयुक्तायामुमा तुष्टा भवेदिह ।
महाचार्यां प्रयुक्तायां तुष्टो भूतगणो भवेत्[1] ॥ ५२ ॥

आश्रावणादि[2] चार्यन्तमेतद्दैवतपूजनम् ।
पूर्वरङ्गे मया ख्यातं तथा चाङ्गविकल्पनम् ॥ ५३ ॥

देवस्तुष्यति यो येन यस्य यन्मनसः प्रियम्[3] ।
तत्तथा पूर्वरङ्गे तु मया प्रोक्तं द्विजोत्तमाः ॥ ५४ ॥

त्रिगतप्ररोचनयोर्दृष्टैकं प्रयोजनमिति तात्पर्यम् । **पूर्वरङ्ग** इति । तदुपश्लिष्टमित्यर्थः । **ख्यातमित्युद्दे**शेन । अङ्गानां चैषां विकल्पनं **लक्षण**मित्यर्थः । देवस्तुष्यतीत्यादिना प्रयोजनोपसंहारः । **मनसः** प्रियमित्यभिमानपरिग्रहबलादित्यर्थः ।

प्रशंसामस्य दर्शयति—सर्वैर्दैवतैः पूजार्हं प्रशंसनीयम् । अत्र हेतुः—यतो दैवतान्यनेन पूज्यन्ते । अत एव प्रेक्षापतिप्रयोक्तृप्रभृतीनामेव तत् । धनेषु यशस्यायुषि तत्साधु । तत्कारित्वात् । नह्यत्र कश्चिदपि (कस्यचिदपि) विरक्तिरिति । **दैत्येति**—निर्गीतं दैत्यादिकस्य तुष्टिकृत् । गीतकादि च देवानाम् । (५३-५६)

नन्वस्य लक्षणं कुतो ज्ञेयम् । यत इह तावन्नोक्तम् । चाङ्गप्रसङ्गतः लक्षणमस्य पश्यामो वयम् । इत्याशङ्क्य प्रसङ्गादत्र (दन्यत्र) लक्षणं वक्ष्यामीति प्रसङ्गावकाशं दर्शयितुमाह—**निर्गीतानामिति** । तेषां लक्षणं "तथा रुद्रे" ति (यथा ऋदुम् इति) लक्ष्यमुदाहरणं वक्ष्यामि । ध्रुवाणां विधाने (ना. शा. ३१-१२२) कर्तव्ये सतीत्यर्थः । न तु ध्रुवाध्याये ।

---

१. K.S.S. रङ्गप्रयोगमाचार्यं (चर्यं) तुष्टो भूतगणं (णो) भवेत् । G.O.S. N.S. M.G. (Same as above) ।

२ K.S.S. M.G. प्रत्याहारादि G.O.S. N.S. आश्रावणादि ।

३. N.S. येनतुष्यति यो देवो यस्य यन्मनसः प्रियम् G.O.S. M.G. K.S.S. (Same as above) ।

सर्वदैवतपूजार्हं सर्वदैवतपूजनम् ।
धन्यं[1] यशस्यमायुष्यं पूर्वरङ्गप्रवर्तनम् ॥ ५५ ॥

दैत्यदानवतुष्टचर्थं सर्वेषां च दिवौकसाम् ।
निर्गीतानि सगीतानि पूर्वरङ्गकृतानि तु ॥ ५६ ॥

[या विद्या यानि शिल्पानि या गतिर्यच्च चेष्टितम् ।
लोकालोकस्य[2] जगतस्तदस्मिन्नाटकाश्रये ॥]

निर्गीतानां सगीतानां वर्धमानस्य चैव हि ।
ध्रुवाविधाने वक्ष्यामि लक्षणं कर्म चैव हि ॥ ५७ ॥

प्रयुज्य गीतकविधिं वर्धमानमथापि[3] च ।
गीतकान्ते ततश्चापि कार्या ह्युत्थापनी ध्रुवा ॥ ५८ ॥

एतदुक्तं भवति—ध्रुवागानस्येहोपरञ्जकज्येष्ठतया तस्य वक्तव्यप्रकृतिभूतं गान्धर्वं ज्ञातुं यत्तल्लक्षणं वक्ष्यते तत्रैतत्ततातोद्यविधाने तालाध्याये च वक्ष्यामि (इति) । एतदविदितत्व (दविदित्वा य)द्ध्रुवाशब्दोऽत्र छन्दोनिबद्धनिमित्ता(त्त ?)निर्गीतत्वे वर्तत इत्याहुः तदसत् । अनुक्तसमत्वादस्य । तद्विधाने तल्लक्षणं वक्ष्यामीति न किञ्चित् । अनार्षोऽयं श्लोक इति तु महत्साहसम् । (५७)

अथोत्थापनादीनां लक्षणशेषः पूरयितव्यः । तत्रोत्थापनस्यानुवादपूर्वकं ध्रुवालक्षणं तत्प्रयोगद्वारेण पूर्णं कर्तुमाह—**प्रयुज्येत्यादि योजयेदित्यन्तं** श्लोकचतुष्टयम् । तत्र प्रथमः श्लोकोऽनुवादकः । गीतकवर्धमानयोरन्यतरत्प्रयुज्यते । **गीतकान्ते । ततो** वा । वर्धमानादनन्तरम् । **उत्थापनी** ध्रुवा कार्येत्यनुवादः । चो भिन्नक्रमो वार्थे । अन्ये तु समुच्चये । निपातसमुदायं युगपद्गीतकवर्धमानप्रयोगाशयेनाहुः ।

---

१. K.S.S. N.S. M.G. धर्म्यं G.O.S. धन्यं ।

२. K.S.S. लोका लोकस्य G.O.S. N.S. लोकालोकस्य M.G. omits the verse या विद्या...नाटकाश्रये ।

३. K.S.S. M.G. तथैव च G.O.S. N.S. अथापि च ।

आदौ द्वे च चतुर्थं चाप्यष्टमैकादशे तथा ।
गुर्वक्षराणि जानीयात्पादे ह्येकादशाक्षरे ॥ ५९ ॥

चतुष्पदा भवेत्सा तु चतुरश्रा[1] तथैव च ।
चतुर्भिस्सन्निपातैश्च त्रिलया त्रियतिस्तथा ॥ ६० ॥

परिवर्ताश्च[2] चत्वारः पाणयस्त्रय एव च ।
जात्या[3] चैव हि वि[4]श्लोका तां च तालेन योजयेत् ॥ ६१ ॥

शम्या तु द्विकला कार्या तालो द्विकल एव च ।
पुनश्चैकला शम्या सन्निपातः कलात्रयम् ॥ ६२ ॥

एवमष्टकलः कार्यः सन्निपातो विचक्षणैः ।
चत्वारः सन्निपाताश्च[5] परिवर्तः[6] स उच्यते ॥ ६३ ॥

ध्रुवाया लक्षणम्—आदौ द्वे चेति । शेषाणि तु लघूनि । एवम्भूताश्चत्वारोऽस्याः पादाः । तालश्चास्याश्चञ्चपुटः द्विकलः । भावविधिना तल्लाभेऽपि चतुरश्रग्रहणाद् द्विकलचञ्चत्पुटपादभागविषयो वक्ष्यमाणाङ्गुलिनियमोपजीवनार्थः । सर्वपादान्ते यतोऽस्याः सन्निपातस्तेन चतुस्सन्निपाता । द्रुतादयो लयाः । स्रोतोगतादयो यतयः । परिवर्ता गानक्रियाभ्यावृत्तयः । ते चत्वारः । समपाणिरपरपा(रवपा)णिरुपरिपाणिश्चेति त्रयः पाणयोऽस्यां कार्या इति शेषः । किमियं ध्रुवा वृत्तजातिमध्ये न गणितेत्याशङ्क्याह—विश्लोकाऽऽख्यवृत्तजातिरियम्—

"आद्यां (द्ये) चतुर्थमपि चाष्टमकं सैकादशं यदि भवेच्च गुरु ।
सा त्रैष्टुभे भवति पादविधौ विश्लोकजातिरवकृष्टकृता ॥
(ना. शा. ३२-१४९) (५८-६१)

१. K.S.S. चतुरश्रे G.O.S. N.S. M.G. चतुरश्रा ।
२. K.S.S. M.G. तु G.O.S. N.S. च ।
३. K.S.S. जात्यां G.O.S. N.S. M.G. जात्या ।
४. K.S.S. N.S. M.G. विश्लोकास्तांश्च G.O.S. विश्लोका तां च ।
५. K.S.S. M.G. तु G.O.S. N.S. च ।
६. K.S.S. M.G. परिवर्तस्य G.O.S. N.S. परिवर्तः स ।

पूर्वं स्थितलयः[1] कार्यः परिवर्तो विचक्षणैः ।

तृतीये सन्निपाते तु तस्य भाण्डग्रहो भवेत् ॥ ६४ ॥

एकस्मिन्परिवर्ते तु गते प्राप्ते द्वितीयके ।

कार्यं मध्यलये[2] तज्ज्ञैः सूत्रधारप्रवेशनम् ॥ ६५ ॥

पुष्पाञ्जलिं[3] समादाय रक्षामङ्गलसंस्कृताः[4] ।

शुद्धवस्त्राः[5] सुमनसस्तथा चाद्भुतदृष्टयः ॥ ६६ ॥

चतुरश्रेति तालेन योजयेदिति च यदुक्तं तत्स्पष्टयति—**शम्या त्वित्यादि** । द्विकलचञ्चत्पुटस्य शम्यादेः स्वरूपमनेन दर्शितम् । सापि सशब्दपातगतहस्तनिर्वर्त्यैव । पूर्वादिशब्दात् द्विकलेति दर्शयति—**द्विकलेत्यादिना** । तेन निष्क्रामशम्ये दक्षिणेन । पुनः निष्क्रामतालौ वामेन । ततो दक्षिणेन शम्या । ततो द्वाभ्यां प्रवेशनिष्क्रामसन्निपाताः । तत्र—

'आवापसंज्ञकं ज्ञेयमुत्तानाङ्गुलिकुञ्चनम् ।
अधस्तलेन हस्तेन निष्क्रामोऽन्त्य(ल्प ?)प्रसारणम् ॥
भूयश्चाकुञ्चनं ज्ञेयं प्रवेशाख्यमधस्तलम् । (ना. शा. ३१-३३-३४)
शम्या दक्षिणपातस्तु तालो वामेन कीर्तितः ।
उभयोः सन्निपातः स सन्निपात इति स्मृतः ॥

चत्वारः सन्निपाता इति पादचतुष्टयस्यापि परिवर्तनमाह । **स्थितलयो** विलम्बितलय उक्तः । **तृतीय** इत्यन्त्यकलावर्जितपादत्रयं तन्त्रीगानसमन्वितं प्रयुज्य तृतीयपादान्त्यकला । ततः प्रभृति पुष्करवाद्यप्रयोगो यावत्तुर्यपादसमाप्तिः । पुनर्मध्यलयेन गानम् । तत्समये सूत्रधारप्रवेशः । **तस्येति**—प्रथमपरिवर्तस्य । प्रथममपि च गानमन्यद्वितीयादिसाहचर्यात्परिवर्तशब्देनोच्यते । अन्यत् द्विः पचतीति त्रयः पाकाः स्युः । सकृत्पचतीति द्वौ स्याताम् । **सूत्रधारशब्देन** तत्साहचर्यात्पारिपार्श्विकावपि । (६२-६५) तेषां प्रवेशे इतिकर्तव्यतामाह—

१. K.S.S. पूर्वस्थितिलयः M.G. पूर्वः स्थितलयः G.O.S. N.S. पूर्वं स्थितलयः ।
२. K.S.S. मध्यलयं G.O.S. N.S. M.G. मध्यलये ।
३. K.S.S. पुष्पाञ्जली G.O.S. N.S. M.G. पुष्पाञ्जलिं ।
४. N.S. सत्कृताः G.OS. K.S.S. M.G. संस्कृताः ।
५. M.G. K.S.S. शुद्धवर्णाः N.S. G.O.S. शुद्धवस्त्राः

स्थानन्तु वैष्णवं कृत्वा सौष्ठवाङ्गपुरस्कृतम् ।
दीक्षिताः शुचयश्चैव प्रविशेयुः समं त्रयः ॥ ६७ ॥
भृङ्गारजर्जरधरौ भवेतां पारिपार्श्विकौ[1] ।
मध्ये तु सूत्रभृत्[2]ताभ्यां वृतः[3] पञ्चपदीं व्रजेत् ॥ ६८ ॥
पदानि पञ्च गच्छेयुर्ब्रह्मणो यजनेच्छया ।
पदा[4]नाञ्चापि विक्षेपं व्याख्यास्याम्यनुपूर्वशः[5] ॥ ६९ ॥

पुष्पाञ्जलिमित्यादिना । पूर्वं पुष्पाञ्जलिः सूत्रधारस्यैव । इतरयोर्भृङ्गारजर्जरधरत्वेन वक्ष्यमाणत्वात् । शुद्धं शुक्लम् । गोहनं (शोभनं) सविस्मयं मनः येषाम् । विस्मयश्च ये श्रुत्यादिभिः दुर्विनेयास्तेऽस्माभिः सुखेन विनीयन्त इति ।

"या चाकुञ्चितपक्ष्माग्रा साश्चर्योद्वृत्ततारका ।
सौम्या विकसितान्ता च साद्भुता दृष्टिरद्भुते ॥ " (ना.शा. ८-५१)

सौष्ठवेत्यादिना लक्षणैकदेशेन वैष्णवमेव स्फुटयति । अन्यथा विष्णुत्वादावपि कस्यचित्सम्भावना भवेदन्वर्थतया ।

"द्वौ तालावर्धतालश्च पादयोरन्तरं भवेत् ।
तयोः समस्थितस्त्वेकः त्र्यश्रः पक्षगतोऽपरः ॥ (ना. शा. १०-५२)
किञ्चिदञ्चितजङ्घं च सौष्ठवाङ्गपुरस्कृतम् ।
वैष्णवं स्थानमेतद्धि । " (ना. शा. १०-५३)

दीक्षिता इति कृतोपवासाः ॥ (६६-६७)

भृङ्गारः शौचाय । जर्जरो विघ्नशान्त्यै । परिपार्श्वं भवौ पारिपार्श्विकौ । अत एव सूत्रधारो मध्ये द्वाभ्यां वृतस्सन्निति त्रयोऽपि पञ्चपदीं व्रजेयुरित्यर्थः । तत्प्रयोजनमाह—पदानीति । त्रयस्ताला अन्तरं मानं यस्य तादृशो विष्कम्भः ऊर्ध्वंगमने परिमाणं यस्य चरणस्य तं पार्श्वोत्थानेन न तु स्पष्टतरोर्ध्वतयोत्थितं चरणं मध्ये द्वयोः पातयेत् । गमनस्य प्रक्रान्तत्वात् । किञ्चित्पुरत इत्यमेवान्यानि चत्वारि पदानि । (६८-७०)

---

१. K.S.S. N.S. M.G. पारिपार्श्वकौ G.O.S. पारिपार्श्विकौ ।
२. K.S.S. M.G. सूत्रधृक् G.O.S. N.S.सूत्रभृत् ।
३. N.S. M.G. K.S.S. वृतः G.O.S. वृत्तः ।
४. K.S.S. M.G. पादानां G.O.S. पदानां N.S. Omits पदानाञ्चापि अनुपूर्वशः ।
५. K.S.S. M . यथाक्रमम् G.O.S. अनुपूर्वशः N.S. omits this verse,

त्रिताला[1]न्तरविष्कम्भमुत्क्षिपेच्चरणं शनैः ।
पार्श्वोत्थानोत्थितं[2] चैव तन्मध्ये पातयेत्पुनः ॥ ७० ॥

एवं पञ्चपदीं[3] गत्वा सूत्रधारः सहेतर[4]ः ।
सूचीं वामपदे[5] दद्याद्विक्षेपं दक्षिणेन च[6] ॥ ७१ ॥

पुष्पाञ्जल्यपवर्गश्च कार्यो ब्राह्मेऽथ मण्डले ।
रङ्गपीठस्य मध्ये तु स्वयं ब्रह्मा प्रतिष्ठितः ॥ ७२ ॥

ततः सललितैर्हस्तैरभिवन्द्य पितामहम्[7] ।
अभिवादानि[8] कार्याणि त्रीणि हस्तेन भूतले ॥ ७३ ॥

कालप्रकर्षहेतोश्च पादानां प्रविभागतः ।
सूत्रधारप्रवेशाद्यो वन्दनाभिनयान्तकः[9] ॥ ७४ ॥

द्वितीयः परिवर्तस्तु कार्यो मध्यलयाश्रितः[10] ।
ततः परं तृतीये तु[11] मण्डलस्य[12] प्रदक्षिणम् ॥ ७५ ॥

अथ यदर्थं पञ्चपदविक्षेपः कृतस्तं पुष्पाञ्जलिविमोक्षं सेतिकर्तव्यताकमाह—**सूचीमित्यादि** ।

"कुञ्चितं पादमुत्क्षिप्य जानूर्ध्वं सम्प्रसारयेत् ।
पातयेच्चाग्रयोगेन सा सूची परिकीर्तिता ॥ " (ना. शा. १०-३४)

---

१. K.S.S. काल G.O.S. N.S. M.G. ताल ।
२. K.S.S. M.G. उत्थितः G.O.S. N.S. उत्थितं ।
३. N.S. विष्णुपदीं G.O.S. K.S.S. M.G. पञ्चपदीं ।
४. K.S.S. M.G इतरैः G.O.S. N.S. इतरः ।
५. K.S.S. M.G. सूचीं वामपदं G.O.S. सूचीं वामपदे N.S. सूचीवामपदं ।
६. K.S.S. M.G. तु G.O.S. N.S. च ।
७. N.S. M.G. अभिवन्द्यः पितामहः G.O.S. K.S.S. अभिवन्द्य पितामहं ।
८. N.S. वन्दनान्यथ G.O.S. K.S.S M.G. अभिवादनानि ।
९. K.S.S. N.S. अनुगः G.O.S. M.G. अन्तकः ।
१०. K.S.S. M.G आश्रयः G.O.S. N.S. आश्रितः ।
११. K.S.S. अतः परं तृतीयस्तु M.G. अतः परं तृतीये तु G.O.S. N.S. ततः परं तृतीये तु ।
१२. K.S.S. मण्डपस्य G.O.S. N.S. M.G. मण्डलस्य ।

भवेदाचमनं चैव जर्जरग्रहणं तथा ।
उत्थाय मण्डलात्तूर्णं दक्षिणं पा[1]दमुद्धरेत् ।। ७६ ।।
वेधं तेनैव कुर्वीत[2] विक्षेपं वामकेन च ।
पुनश्च दक्षिणं पादं पार्श्वसंस्थं समुद्धरेत् ।। ७७ ।।
ततश्च वामवेधस्तु विक्षेपो दक्षिणस्य च[3] ।
इत्यनेन विधानेन[4] सम्यक्कृत्वा प्रदक्षिणम् ।। ७८ ।।
भृङ्गारभृत[5]माहूय शौचं चापि समाचरेत् ।
यथान्यायं तु कर्तव्या तेन ह्याचमनक्रिया ।। ७९ ।।
आत्मप्रोक्षणमेवाद्भिः कर्तव्यं तु यथाक्रमम् ।
प्रयत्नकृतशौचेन सूत्रधारेण यत्नतः ।। ८० ।।

पृष्ठदेश इति शेषः । तस्य पादस्य बहिःक्षेपः मण्डलं स्थानम् । किन्तत् । ब्राह्ममित्याह । **रङ्गपीठस्येति** । अभिवादनानीत्यर्थः । **त्रीणीति** । प्रत्येकं कथं वन्दनं कार्यमित्याह । कालस्य यः प्रकर्षो बहुतरत्वं तत्र । चो हेतौ । नृत्तहस्तकरणप्रयोगात्मकमवलम्ब्य । ननु किला(कियान्)सौ कालप्रकर्षः । आह—**पादानामिति** । तदुपलक्षितानां कलानां यः प्रविभागः कालपरिमाणान्तरमाश्रित्य । ननु तासामपि को विधिरित्याशङ्क्याह—**सूत्रधारप्रवेशाद्य इति** ।

एतदुक्तं भवति—द्वात्रिंशत्कलानां मध्ये प्रवेशः पञ्चपदीगमनं पुष्पत्यागोऽभिवादनत्रयं चेति निर्वर्तनीयम् । तत्र यावतीषु कलासु पञ्चपदीगमनान्तं कर्म सम्पन्नं ततो या अवशिष्यन्ते कलास्तदभिवादनयोग्यं व्यावर्तितपरिवर्तितादिकरणमुद्वृत्तनलिनीपद्मकोशादिनृत्तहस्तजातं वाऽवलम्ब्य सललितमभिवादनत्रयं कार्यम् ।

एवं द्वितीये परिवर्ते कर्मत्रयं प्रदर्श्य तृतीयपरिवर्ते द्रुतलये कर्मकलापमुपदिशति—**ततःपरमिति** । **मण्डलस्येति** । ब्रह्मस्थानस्य । तत्कर्मत्रयं लक्षयन्प्रथमस्य

---

१. N.S. पदम् G.O.S. K.S.S. M.G. पादम् ।
२. K.S.S. M.G. तेनैव वेधं कुर्वीत N.S. G.O.S. वेधं तेनैव कुर्वीत ।
३. K.S.S. M.G. तु G.O.S. N.S. च ।
४. N.S. प्रकारेण G.O.S. K.S.S. M.G. विधानन ।
५. K.S.S. M.G. भृङ्गारधारम् G.O.S. N.S. भृङ्गारभृतम् ।

सन्निपातसमं[1] ग्राह्यो जर्जरो विघ्नजर्जरः।
प्रदक्षिणाद्यो विज्ञेयो जर्जरग्रहणान्तकः ॥ ८१ ॥
तृतीयः परिवर्तस्तु विज्ञेयो वै द्रुते लये।
गृहीत्वा जर्जरं त्व[2]ष्टौ कला जप्यं[3] प्रयोजयेत् ॥ ८२ ॥
वा[4]मवेधं ततः कुर्याद्विक्षेपं दक्षिणस्य च।
ततः पञ्चपदीं चैव गच्छेत्तु कुतपोन्मुखः ॥ ८३ ॥
वाम[5]वेधस्तु तत्रापि विक्षेपो दक्षिणस्य तु।
जर्जरग्रहणाद्योऽयं कुतपाभिमुखान्तक[6]: ॥ ८४ ॥
चतुर्थः परिवर्तस्तु कार्यो द्रुतलये पुनः[7]।
करपाद[8]निपातास्तु भवन्त्यत्र तु षोडश ॥ ८५ ॥

लक्षणमाह—उत्थायेति। अभिवादने हि जानुशिरोविनमितभूश्लेषपर्यन्तं कृतम्। उद्धरेदिति। "कुञ्चितं पादम्" (ना. शा. १०-३४) इत्यादिसूचीं सूचयति। वेधमिति द्वितीयपादपार्ष्णिपृष्ठे पातनम्। पार्श्वसंस्थमिति पार्श्वक्रान्तां (ना. शा. १०-३२) चारीमाह।

एतत्कर्मोपसंहरन्द्वितीयं शौचाख्यं लक्षयति—इत्यनेनेति। आहूयेति वचनाद्भृङ्गारधारिणः प्रदक्षिणभ्रमणे तूष्णींभावेन स्थितिरिति लक्ष्यते। शौचप्रयोजनं वक्ष्यते। यतोऽभिवादने श्लिष्टं शिर इत्यादिन्यायस्मृत्यादिः प्राङ्मुख उपविश्याबहिर्जानुरित्यादिक्रमः। (७१-७९)

---

१. K.S.S. सन्निपातसमग्राह्यः N.S. सन्निपाते समं ग्राह्यः G.O.S. M.G. सन्निपातसमं ग्राह्यः।
२. K.S.S. M.G. च G.O.S. N.S. तु।
३. N.S. K.S.S. जाप्यं M.G. G.O.S. जप्यम्।
४. K.S.S. M.G. वामवेधस्ततः कार्यो विक्षेपो दक्षिणेन तु G.O.S. N.S (Same as above)।
५. K.S.S. N.S. do not read 84 a G.O.S. M.G. Read it.
६. K.S.S. M.G. कुतपाभिमुखान्तगः N.S. कुतपो निगमान्तकः G.O.S कुतपाभिमुखान्तकः।
७. K.S.S. M.G. विज्ञेयो वै द्रुते लये G.O.S. N.S. कार्यो द्रुतलये पुनः।
८. K.S.S. N.S. पात G.O.S. M.G. पाद।

'त्र्यश्रे द्वादश पातास्तु भवन्ति करपादयोः ।
वन्दनान्यथ कार्याणि त्रीणि हस्तेन भूतले[2] ॥ ८६ ॥

आत्मप्रोक्षणमद्भिश्च त्र्यश्रे[3] नैव त्रिधीयते ।
एवमुत्थापनं कार्यं ततस्तु[4] परिवर्तनम् ॥ ८७ ॥

चतुरश्रं[5] लये मध्ये सन्निपातै[6]स्तथा[7]ष्टभिः ।
यस्या[8] लघूनि सर्वाणि केवलं नैधनं[9] गुरु ॥ ८८ ॥

भवेदतिजगत्यान्तु सा ध्रुवा परिवर्त[10]नी ।
वार्तिकेन[11] तु मार्गेण वाद्ये नानुगतेन च ॥ ८९ ॥

ललितैः पाद[12]विन्यासैर्वन्द्या[13] देवा यथादिशम् ।
द्विकलं पादपतनं पादचार्यो[14] गतं भवेत् ॥ ९० ॥

---

१. G.O.S. त्र्यश्रे द्वादश पातास्तु भवन्ति करपादयोः K.S.S. त्र्यस्रे तु द्वादशपदा भवन्ति करपादजाः M.G. त्र्यस्रे पाता हि द्वादश भवन्ति करपादजाः N.S. त्र्यस्रे तु द्वादशपदा भवन्ति कर पादयोः ।

२. N.S. भूतके G.O.S. K.S.S. M.G. भूतले ।

३. K.S.S. N.S. त्र्यस्रे नैव G.O.S. M.G. त्र्यस्रे नैव ।

४. K.S.S. N.S. M.G. च G.O.S. तु ।

५. K.S.S. M.G. चतुरस्रे G.O.S. N.S. चतुश्रं ।

६. K.S.S. सन्निपात G.O.S. N.S. M.G. सन्निपातैः ।

७. K.S.S. M.G. तथा N.S. M.G. अथ ।

८. K.S.S. N.S. M.G. यस्यां G.O.S. यस्याः ।

९. K.S.S. M.G. निधनं G.O.S. N.S. नैधनं ।

१०. K.S.S. N.S. परिवर्तिनी G.O.S M.G. परिवर्तनी ।

११. K.S.S. M.G. वामकेन G.O.S. N.S. वार्तिकेन ।

१२. N.S. पद K.S.S. M.G. G.O.S. पाद ।

१३. N.S. M.G. वन्द्याद् देवान् G.O.S. K.S.S. वन्द्या देवा ।

१४. K.S.S. M.G. पादचर्या विधीयते N.S. G.O.S. पादचार्यो गतं भवेत् ।

१५. K.S.S. M.G. Read in additon after 90 एकैकस्यां दिशि तथा सन्निपातद्वयं भवेत् ।

वामपादेन वेधस्तु कर्तव्यो नृत्तयोक्तृभिः ।
द्वितालान्तरविष्कम्भो[1] विक्षेपो दक्षिणस्य च[2] ॥ ६१ ॥

ततः पञ्चपदीं गच्छेदतिक्रान्तैः पदैरथ ।
ततोऽभिवादनं कुर्याद्दैवतानां यथादिशम् ॥ ६२ ॥

वन्देत प्रथमं पूर्वां दिशं शक्राधिदैवताम् ।
द्वितीयां दक्षिणामाशां वन्देत यमदैवताम् ॥ ६३ ॥

वन्देत पश्चिमामाशां ततो वरुणदैवताम् ।
चतुर्थीमुत्तरामाशां वन्देत धनदाश्रयाम् ॥ ६४ ॥

तृतीयं कर्म दर्शयति—**प्रयत्नेति**। कस्मिन् सन्निपाते तद्ग्रहणमित्याशङ्कामपाकर्तुमाह—**प्रदक्षिणाद्य** इति। तेन तुर्यपदः(परिवर्ता ?)न्त्यसन्निपातकाले तद्ग्रहणमित्युक्तं भवति।

अथ द्रुतलय एव चतुर्थे परिवर्ते कर्मद्वयं—**गृहीत्वेति**। **ग्रहणं धारणम्**। **इहाष्टौ कला** इति। प्रथमपादगतपर्यन्तमित्यर्थः। **जप्यं** जपनीयं तृतीयाध्यायोक्तम्। "अत्र विघ्नविनाशार्थम्। (ना. शा. ३-७८) इत्यादिश्लोकचतुष्टयं प्रतिकलमर्धश्लोक इत्यनेनावसानप्रकर्षेण **योजयेदुच्चारयेदिति** यावत्। (८०-८२)

ननु पञ्चपद्यां कियान् कालविक्षेप इत्याशङ्क्याह—**जर्जरग्रहणाद्य** इति। ग्रहणं धारणम्। चतुर्विंशत्या कलानां कृतपगमानं कुर्यादिति तात्पर्यम्। **षोडशेति**। कलाद्वयेनैकं पतनमिति यावत्। (८३-८४)

व्यश्र इति। प्रसङ्गादेतदुक्तम्। न चैतावत्प्रयोगात्मकमेतदङ्गमिति दर्शयितुमाह—**एवमित्यादि**। एवम्भूतायामिहेतिकर्तव्यतायां कृतायाम्।

"यस्मादुत्थापयन्त्यत्र प्रयोगं नान्दिपाठकाः। पूर्वमेव तु रङ्गेऽस्मिन्" इति (ना. शा. ५-२२) श्लोकलक्षितं प्रत्याहारादीनां गीतकविध्यन्तानां प्रयोगस्य च नाट्यस्योत्थापनं व्याख्यातरूपं कार्यम्। **चशब्दस्तुशब्दस्यार्थे**। **ततस्तु परिवर्तनम्**। न तु ध्रुवाप्रयोगानन्तरमेव।

---

१. K.S.S. विष्टम्भः G.O.S. N.S. M.G. विष्कम्भः।

२. K.S.S. M.G. तु G.O.S. N.S. च।

३. G.O.S. N.S. read दैवत K.S.S. M.G. Read देवत।

विशां तु वन्दनं कृत्वा वामवेधं प्रयोजयेत् ।
दक्षिणेन च[1] कर्तव्यं विक्षेपपरिवर्तनम् ॥ ९५ ॥
प्राङ्मुखस्तु ततः कुर्यात्पुरुषस्त्रीनपुंसकैः ।
त्रिपद्या[2] सूत्रभृद्रुद्रब्रह्मोपेन्द्राभिवादनम्[3] ॥ ९६ ॥
दक्षिणं तु पदं पुंसो[4] वामं स्त्रीणां[5] प्रकीर्तितम् ।
पुन[6]र्दक्षिणमेव स्यान्नात्युत्क्षिप्तं नपुंसकम् ॥ ९७ ॥
वन्देत पौरुषेणेशं स्त्रीपदेन जनार्दनम् ।
नपुंसकपदेनापि तथैवाम्बुजसम्भवम् ॥ ९८ ॥
परिवर्तनमेवं स्यात्तस्यान्ते प्रविशेत्ततः ।
चतुर्थकारः[7] पुष्पाणि प्रगृह्य विधिपूर्वकम् ॥ ९९ ॥

ये तूपसंहारग्रन्थत्वेनैतद्व्याचक्षते "तस्मादुत्थापयन्ति' इति न (तैः) किञ्चिदनुस्मृ(सृ)तं स्यात् । न हि ब्रह्माभिवाद जर्जराभिमन्त्रणमात्रेण किञ्चिदप्युत्थापितं भवति । विघ्नशमनोपयोगित्वे त्थापकत्वं परिवर्तनादावपि स्यात् । उत्थापनीत्यन्वर्थत्वात् । नाटचायितेन प्रयोगोत्थापनान्तस्य च ध्रुवाभिनयरूपतयोचितार्थाक्षेपात् ।

"यत्तु काव्येन नोक्तं स्या तेन" इति ।
तथा "गीतं प्राणाः प्रयोगस्य इति,

१. K.S.S. M.G. तु G.O.S. N.S च ।
२. N.S. त्रिपदीं सूत्रभृत् M.G. त्रिपदैः सूत्रधृक् K.S.S. त्रिपाद्या सूत्रधृक् G.O.S. त्रिपद्या सूत्रभृत् ।
३. K.S.S. M.G. अभिवन्दनम् G.O.S. N.S. अभिवादनम् ।
४. K.S.S. M.G. नृणाम् G.O.S. N.S. पुंसः ।
५. N.S. वामं स्त्रीपदमुच्यते G.O.S. K.S.S. M.G. वामं स्त्रीणां प्रकीर्तितम् ।
६. K.S.S. M.G. दक्षिणं तु पदं ज्ञेयं नाभ्युत्क्षिप्तं नपुंसकम् N.S. पुनर्दक्षिणमेव स्यान्नाभ्युत्क्षिप्तं नपुंसकम् G.O.S. Same except नात्युक्षिप्तं ।
७. K.S.S. चतुष्प्रकारपुष्पाणि G.O.S. M.G. K.S.S. चतुर्थकारः पुष्पाणि ।

यथावत्तेन कर्तव्यं पूजनं जर्जरस्य तु ।
कुतपस्य[1] च सर्वस्य सूत्रधारस्य चैव हि ॥ १०० ॥

तस्य भाण्डसम[2]: कार्यस्तज्ज्ञैर्गति[3]परिक्रमः ।
न तत्र गानं कर्तव्यं तत्र स्तोभक्रिया भवेत् ॥ १०१ ॥

चतुर्थकार:[4] पूजां तु स कृत्वान्तर्हितो भवेत् ।
ततो गेया[5]वकृष्टा तु चतुरश्रा स्थिता[6] ध्रुवा ॥ १०२ ॥

गुरुप्राया तु सा कार्या तथा चैवावपाणि[7]का ।
स्थायिवर्णाश्रयोपेता[8] कलाष्टकविनिर्मिता[9] ॥ १०३ ॥

[चतुर्थं पञ्चमं चैव सप्तमं चाष्टमं तथा ।
लघूनि पादे पङ्क्त्यान्तु सावकृष्टा ध्रुवा स्मृता[10] ॥]

सूत्रधार: पठेत्तत्र[11] मध्यमं स्वरमाश्रित: ।
नान्दीं[12] पदैर्द्वादशभिरष्टभिर्वाऽप्यलङ्कृताम् ॥ १०४ ॥

नमोऽस्तु सर्वदेवेभ्यो द्विजातिभ्य: शुभं तथा ।
जितं सोमेन वै राज्ञा शिवं[13] गोब्राह्मणाय च ॥ १०४ ॥

---

१. K.S.S. भाण्डस्य G.O.S. N.S. M.G. कुतुपस्य ।
२. K.S.S. M.G. गत: G.O.S. N.S. सम: ।
३. K.S.S. गीति G.O.S. N.S. M.G. गति ।
४. K.S.S. चतुष्प्रकारपूजां तु निष्क्रामेत् सम्प्रयुज्य हि M.G. चतुर्थकार: पूजां तु निष्क्रामेत् सम्प्रयुज्य हि N.S. चतुर्थकारपूजां तु स कृत्वान्तर्हितो भवेत् । G.O.S. Same except चतुर्थकार: पूजां तु ।
५. K.S.S. G.O.S. गेयावकृष्टा N.S. गेहावकृष्टा M.G. गेयापकृष्टा ।
६. K.S.S. N.S. स्थिरा G.O.S. M.G. स्थिता ।
७. N.S. अर्धपाणिका G.O.S. M.G. K.S.S. अवपाणिका ।
८. K.S.S. M.G. उपेतां G.O.S. N.S. उपेता ।
९. K.S.S. M.G. विनिर्मितां G.O.S. N.S. विनिर्मिता ।
१०. K.S.S. does not read this verse.
११. K.S.S. M.G. नान्दीं G.O.S N.S. तत्र ।
१२. K.S.S. M.G. तत: G.O.S. N.S. नान्दीं ।
१३. K.S.S. आरोग्यं भोग एव च M.G. आरोग्यं गोष्ठ एव च G.O.S N.S. शिवं गोब्राह्मणाय च ।

"परिक्रमेण रङ्गस्य तथैवार्थवशेन च ।
परिवर्तास्तु"

इति वचनेन गान्धर्व इव ध्रुवागाने परिवर्तानामदृष्टार्थेतिकर्तव्यतारूपा(पत्वा)-भावात् । स्फुटश्चैषामुपाये निर्दिष्टेनोचितेनार्थचतुष्टयेन युक्तेयं सुकविना ध्रुवा कार्येति वृद्धाः ।

ततश्चेति चतुरश्रतालयुक्तध्रुवायोगात्परिवर्तनं चतुरश्रम् । पादैर्गीयत इति सन्निपाताञ्च(श्च) पादचतुष्टययोगात् । सन्निपाताष्टकमत्र लक्षयति—**यस्या** इति । अतिजगती त्रयोदशाक्षरा । तेन परिवर्तनचतुष्टयम् । गुरुः **वार्तिकमार्गो** यत्र चतुर्मात्रा कला । गीतं यदनुगच्छत्यनुगतमेतद्ध्रुवेद्वाद्यम् । **पादचार्यां** भौम्यामाकाशिक्यां वा कर्तव्यायां पादपतनं द्वे कले व्याप्नोति । एकस्यामुत्क्षेपोऽन्यस्यां पतनमिति यावत् । अन्ये तु शोभार्थं कलायां द्वौ पादपातौ वार्तिकमार्गे वर्णयन्त इत्थं व्याचक्षते—द्वित्वं वर्तयत्येको योऽ(न्यो)-भिवर्तते । न विद्यते कले यस्य पादपतनस्य तद्विकलमिति । एवं च वदन्तः पूर्वोक्त उक्तेत्यर्थः (उक्त इत्यर्थः) (पूर्वोत्तरविरुद्धतानभिज्ञाः ?) । (८६-९२)

शक्रोऽधिष्ठात्री देवता अस्या इति तां **पूर्वां यजेतेति (वन्देतेति)** । विशेष्येण वा विशेषेण वेदं बध्नातीति (विशेषतेन वा संबध्नातीति) सविशेषं वन्द्यमानत्वं शक्रस्य गम्यते ।

विक्षेपपूर्वकं परिवर्तनम् । येनोत्तराभिमुखं स्थितः परिवृत्य पूर्वाभिमुखो भवति । तत्र किं कुर्यादित्याह—**प्राङ्मुखस्त्विवति** । त्रिपदीं दर्शयति —**दक्षिण-न्त्विवति** (त्ये)तया त्रिपद्या । अभिवादनं दर्शयति—**वन्देतेति** ।

एवं दिग्देवतावन्दनं परिवर्तिन्या ध्रुवया विद्यु(ध्यु)द्गीयमानपदया कार्यम् । **तस्यान्त** इत्यादि । तस्येति परिवर्तस्य । सूत्रधारस्य पारिपार्श्विकयोश्च तिस्रः क्रियाः । तद्व्यतिरिक्तञ्चतुर्थं कर्म करोतीति **चतुर्थकारः** । **विधिः** "स्थानन्तु वैष्णवम्" इत्यादि (ना. शा. ५·६७) सूत्रधारोक्तः । **पुष्पाणां** प्रयोजनमाह—**यथावदिति** । तृतीयेऽध्याये पुष्कराध्याये (३४) च निरूपितदेवता-पूजाक्रमेण (९३-१००)

भाण्डेनैव सम इति । पुष्करवाद्यमेवास्य गत्यर्थे परितः क्रमेण कार्यम् । गीयत इति **गानमर्थवद्वाक्यम्** । **स्तोभानां** शुष्काक्षराणाम् । **क्रिया** गानमित्यर्थः । **स्थितेति** । विलम्बितलया । **गुरुप्रायेति** । "नव गुर्वक्षराण्यादौ" इति (ना. शा. ५-१११) यच्छुष्कावकृष्टाया लक्षणं भविष्यति तदेवास्यामिति यावत् । "स्थिताः स्वराः समा यत्र **स्थायी वर्णः** सः" (ना. शा. २९-१९) तमाश्रिता येऽलङ्कारा वक्ष्यन्ते तैरुपेताः । **कलाष्टकं** द्विकलचञ्चत्पुट उक्तपूर्वः (५-६२) (१०१-१०३)

ब्रह्मोत्तरं तथैवास्तु हता ब्रह्मद्विषस्तथा ।
प्रशास्त्वि[1]मां महाराजः पृथिवीं च ससागराम् ॥ १०६ ॥
राष्ट्रं[2] प्रवर्धतां चैव रङ्गस्या[3]शा समृद्धयतु ।
प्रेक्षकर्तुर्महान्धर्मो भवतु ब्रह्मभाषितः[4] ॥ १०७ ॥
काव्यकर्तुर्यशश्चास्तु धर्मश्चापि प्रवर्धताम् ।
इज्यया चानया नित्यं प्रीयन्तां देवता इति ॥ १०८ ॥
नान्दीपदान्तरेष्वेषु ह्ये[5]वमार्येति नित्यशः ।
वदेतां[6] सम्यगुक्ताभिर्वाग्भि[7]स्तौ पारिपार्श्विकौ[8] ॥ १०९ ॥

एवं पूर्वामितिकर्तव्यतामभिधाय नान्दीमाह—**सूत्रधार** इति । **तत्रे**त्यवकृष्टायां गीतायामित्यर्थः । तद्ध्रुवागानगतेन **मध्यमस्वरेण** पाठ इत्यतस्तस्या ध्रुवाया मध्यमांशको जात्यंशको गृहीत इत्युक्तं भवति । एतदुपजीवनेनोक्तं **कश्यपाचार्येण** "पूर्वरङ्गे तु षाडवः" इति ।

नान्दीं पठति—**नमोऽस्त्वित्यादि देवता** इत्यन्तम् । **पदमत्रावान्तरवाक्यम्** । तदन्तेष्वेव**मार्ये**ति । अन्तरशब्दो विशेषे । नान्दीपदविशेष उक्त इत्यर्थः । मध्यवाचिनीत्य(चिन्त्य)न्त रशब्दो(ब्दे)ऽन्त्यं पदं न स्व(स्वी)कृतम् । **वाग्रहणा**दपिशब्दाच्चतुष्षोडशपदत्वं चतुरश्रे पूर्वरङ्गे । त्र्यश्रे तु षट्पञ्च(त्रिषट्पद)त्वमपि लभ्यते । एतच्च प्रथमाध्याय एवास्माभिरुक्तम् (२५-२६) । **रङ्गस्ये**ति । नटकुशीलववर्गस्य । **धर्म** इति । "य इमं पूर्वरङ्गम्" इति (ना. शा. ५-१७०) वक्ष्यमाणः । (१०४-१०९)

एवमिति चतुर्थकारप्रवेशादितिकर्तव्यतेयमित्यर्थः ।

---

१. N.S. प्रशास्त्वेमां G.O.S. K.S.S. M.G. प्रशास्त्विमां ।
२. K.S.S. M.G. राज्यं G.O.S. N.S. राष्ट्रं ।
३. K.S.S. M.G. रङ्गश्चायं समृध्यताम् G.O.S. N.S. रङ्गस्याशा समृध्यतु ।
४. N.S. K.S.S. M.G. भावितः G.O.S. भाषितः ।
५. K.S.S. N.S. M.G. ह्येवमस्त्विति G.O.S. ह्येवमार्येति ।
६. K.S.S. N.S. M.G. वन्देतां G.O.S वदेतां ।
७. N.S. वाग्मिनौ K.S.S M.G. गीर्भिस्तौ G.O.S. वाग्भिस्तौ ।
८. K.S.S. M.G. N.S. पारिपार्श्वकौ G.O.S. पारिपार्श्विकौ ।

एवं नान्दी विधातव्या यथा[1]वल्लक्षणान्विता
ततश्शुष्कावकृष्टा[2] स्याज्जर्जरश्लोकदर्शिका[3] ॥ ११० ॥

नवगुर्वक्षराण्यादौ षड्लघूनि गुरुत्रयम् ।
शुष्कावकृष्टा तु भवेत्कला ह्यष्टौ प्रमाणतः[4] ॥ १११ ॥

यथा—

दिग्ले दिग्ले दिग्ले दिग्ले जम्बुकपलितकते तेचाम्[5] ।
कृत्वा शुष्कावकृष्टां[6] तु यथावद्द्विजसत्तमाः ॥ ११२ ॥

ततः श्लोकं पठेदेकं गम्भीरस्वरसंयुतम् ।
देवस्तोत्रं पुरस्कृत्य यस्य पूजा प्रवर्तते ॥ ११३ ॥

राज्ञो वा यत्र भक्तिः स्यादथ वा ब्रह्मणस्स्तवम्[7] ।
गदित्वा जर्जरश्लोकं रङ्गद्वारे च यत्स्मृतम्[8] ॥ ११४ ॥

एवं नान्दीं लक्षणतः पूरयित्वा शुष्कावकृष्टाख्यमङ्गं पूरयति—ततश्शुष्कावकृष्टेत्यादिना । (ततः) एतत्प्रयोगानन्तरम् । जर्जरस्तुतिश्लोको यतः सूत्रधारेण पठ्यतेऽतो जयतेर्दर्शिका तत्पुरस्सरीत्यर्थः । शुष्कावकृष्टामात्राः (नव गुर्वक्षराणीति) । उदाहरणं पठतीदं देव इत्यादि (?) । यथावदित्यनेन

१. K.S.S. M.G. यथोक्ता लक्षणैर्मया G.O.S. N.S. यथावल्लक्षणान्विता ।
२. K.S.S. M.G. अपकृष्टा G.O.S. N.S. अवकृष्टा ।
३. K.S.S. दर्शिता G.O.S. N.S. M.G. दर्शिका ।
४. K.S.S. M.G. कलाश्चाष्टौ प्रमाणेन पादैह्यष्टादशाक्षरैः G.O.S. N.S. (Same as above).
५. K.S.S. झण्डे झण्डे दिल्लग दिग्ले । जाम्बुक वलितक ते तेन्नाम् M.G. Same except निग्ले in place of दिल्लग् N.S. दिग्ले दिग्ले झण्डु झण्डु जम्बुकवलितक ते तेन्नाम् G.O.S. Same except दिग्ले दिग्ले in place of झण्डु झण्डु and तेचाम् in place of तेन्नाम् ।
६. M.G. अपकृष्टां G.O.S. N.S. K.S.S. अवकृष्टां ।
७. K.S.S. M.G. राज्ञो भक्तिश्च यत्र स्यादथवा ब्रह्मणः स्तवः G.O.S. राज्ञो वा यत्र भक्तिः स्यादथवा ब्रह्मणः स्तवम् N.S. Same except ब्राह्मणस्तवं in place of ब्रह्मणः स्तवम् ।
८. N.S. K.S.S. यः स्मृतः G.O.S. M.G. यत् स्मृतम् ।

पठेदन्यं पुनः श्लोकं जर्जरस्य विनाशनम्[1] ।
जर्जरं नमयित्वा[2] **तु ततश्चारीं प्रयोजयेत् ॥ ११५ ॥**
पारिपार्श्विकयोश्च स्यात्पश्चिमेनापसर्पणम् ।
अड्डिता चात्र[3] **कर्तव्या ध्रुवा मध्यलयान्विता ॥ ११६ ॥**
चतुर्भिः सन्निपातैश्च[4] **चतुरश्रा**[5] **प्रमाणतः ।**
आद्यमन्त्यं चतुर्थं च पञ्चमं च तथा गुरु ॥ ११७ ॥

तदनन्तरं जर्जरश्लोकपाठं सूचयति । तद्दर्शनेन तस्या उक्तत्वात् । **ततः श्लोकमित्यनेन** रङ्गद्वारमङ्ग निरूपयति । देवस्य विष्णोः स्तोत्रं पूर्वं कृत्वा यां देवतामुद्दिश्योत्सवादौ नाट्यं कृतं सा तत्र स्तोतव्या । **अयंवमेव** (येन) नाट्यं प्रवर्तितं तत्प्रेक्षापतेराराध्यदेवता । स चेदुदासीनस्तर्हि ब्रह्मणः अयमनौ । रङ्गद्वारमुपसंहरंश्चार्याङ्गमङ्ग पूरयितुं तत्र पूर्वेतिकर्तव्यतामाह—**गदित्वेति** । जर्जरश्लोकं गदित्वा यो रङ्गद्वारे श्लोकस्त च गदित्वा जर्जरोऽपि नाम्यते । वक्ष्यमाणतुलाधृतरूपतया येन श्लोकेन सपाद्यते तादृशमन्यं श्लोकं पठेत् । "अत्र विघ्नविनाशार्थम्" (ना. शा. ३-७८) इत्युक्तश्लोकाव्यतिरिक्तनाम्नाऽर्थाभिधायिनं श्लोकं चार्यङ्गभूतं पठेदिति यावत् ।

अन्ये तु शुष्कावकृष्टानन्तरं देवतास्तोत्रमिति श्लोकः । ततो जर्जरश्लोकः । ततो विष्णुस्तुतिकृद्रङ्गद्वारश्लोकः । ततो जर्जरश्लोक इत्याहुः (११०-११५) ।

पश्चिमेनेति । प्राङ्मुखावेव पृष्ठनिवृत्तिभिः पदैः पारिपार्श्विकावपसर्पेतामित्यनेन केवलसूत्रधारप्रयोज्यमानाश्चारीमहाचार्यैः सूचिताः । ध्रुवामाह-**अड्डिता चात्रेति** । रङ्गद्वारे चार्यां चेति केचित् । अन्ये तु सन्निधानाद्रङ्गद्वारेऽवकृष्टैवेत्याहुः । अध्रुवमेव रङ्गद्वारमित्येके । **चतुरश्रा इति** । प्रस्ताराञ्चित एव चञ्चत्पुटे स्यात् (ना. शा. ३१-पु. ५२२. का. मा.) इह छन्दो विशेषाभिधानेऽपि नियमो वक्ष्यते 'उष्णिगनुष्टुब्बृहती पङ्क्तिश्चेति ।' (ना. शा.) ३२-३६) अड्डिता जातिरिति ।

---

१. K.S.S. प्रकाशनम् M.G. विनामनम् G.O.S. N.S. विनाशनम् ।
२. K.S.S. मानयित्वा G.O.S. M.G. N.S. नमयित्वा ।
३. K.S.S. चानुकर्तव्या G.O.S. N.S. M.G. चात्र कर्तव्या ।
४. K.S.S. M.G. तु G.O.S. N.S. च ।
५. K.S.S. चतुरस्र G.O.S. N.S. M.G. चतुरश्रा ।

यस्यां ह्रस्वानि शेषाणि सा ज्ञेया त्वड्डिता बुधैः[1] ।

अस्याः प्रयोगं वक्ष्यामि यथा पूर्वं महेश्वरः ॥ ११८ ॥

सहोमया क्रीडितवान्नानाभावविचेष्टितैः ।

कृत्वाऽवहित्थं स्थानं तु वामं चाधोमुखं भुजम् ॥ ११९ ॥

चतुरश्रमुरः कार्यमञ्चितश्चापि मस्तकः[2] ।

नाभिप्रदेशे विन्यस्य जर्जरं च तु[3]लाधृतम् ॥ १२० ॥

अन्ये तु पठन्ति—

"आद्यं चतुर्थं दशममष्टमैकादशे तथा ।

गुरूणि दोधके या स्यादड्डिता नाम सा स्मृता ॥" इति ।

"आद्यमन्त्यं चतुर्थं च पञ्चमं च तथा गुरु । " इत्यन्ये ॥

अस्या इति । चार्याः । **सहोमयेति** । 'शृङ्गारस्य प्रचरणात् ।' (ना. शा. ५-२७) 'उमा तुष्टा' (ना. शा. ५-५२) इति चोक्तत्वादिति भावः । **क्रीडितवानिति** । स्त्रीचेष्टितेनेति भावः । **कृत्वावहित्थं स्थानन्त्विति** । अवहित्थं स्त्रीणां स्थानकम्—

"पूर्वो विरचितस्त्र्यश्रस्तदन्योऽपसृतः समः ।

पादस्तालान्तरन्यस्तस्त्रिकमीषत्समुन्नतम् ॥ (ना. शा. १२-१६८)

पाणिर्लताख्यो यत्रैकस्तदन्यस्तु नितम्बगः ।

अवहित्थं समाख्यातम्" (ना. शा. १२-१६९)

जर्जरमिति । खटकामुखमध्ये स्त्रीगतौ हि वक्ष्यते—

"नाभिप्रदेशे विन्यस्य सव्यं च खटकामुखम् । " इति (ना. शा. १२-१७९) ।

---

१. K.S.S. यस्यां तु जायते पादे सा भवेदड्डिता ध्रुवा M.G. Same except जागते in place of जायते G.O.S. N.S. (Same as above).

२. K.S.S. N.S. M.G. donot read 120 a. G.O.S. Reads it.

३. M.G. (त) लाधृतम् G.O.S. N.S. K.S.S. तुलाधृतम ।

वामपल्लवहस्तेन पादैस्तालान्तरोत्थितैः[१] ।
गच्छेत्पञ्चपदीं चैव सविलासाङ्गचेष्टितैः ॥ १२१ ॥
वामवेधस्तु कर्तव्यो विक्षेपो दक्षिणस्य च[२] ।
शृङ्गाररससंयुक्तां पठेदार्यां विचक्षणः[३] ॥ १२२ ॥
चारीश्लोकं गदित्वा[४] तु कृत्वा च परिवर्तनम् ।
तैरेव च पदैः कार्यं पश्चिमेना[५]पसर्पणम् ॥ १२३ ॥
पारिपार्श्विक[६]हस्ते तु न्यस्य जर्जरमुत्तमम् ।
महाचारीं ततश्चैव प्रयुञ्जीत यथाविधि ॥ १२४ ॥
चतुरश्रा ध्रुवा तत्र[७] तथा द्रुतलयान्विता[८] ।
चतुर्भिस्सन्निपातैश्च कला ह्यष्टौ[९] प्रमाणतः ॥ १२५ ॥
आद्यं चतुर्थमन्त्यं च सप्तमं दशमं गुरु ।
लघु शेषं ध्रुवापादे[१०] चतुर्विंशतिके भवेत्[११] ॥ १२६ ॥
(यथा-)

वामपल्लवः—"मणिबन्धनमुक्तौ तु पताकौ पल्लवौ" इति (ना. शा. ९-१९६) । **पञ्चपदीं** पूर्वोक्तामेव स्मारयति । **वामवेध**स्त्विति । **आर्या**मिति । यत्र देव्या सह भगवतः पार्वतीप्रियस्य प्रणयकोपादि वर्ण्यतेऽनेनेति । श्लोक आर्यैवात्र (११६-१२२)

---

१. K.S.S. N.S. M.G. स्थितैः G.O.S. उत्थितैः ।
२. K.S.S. M.G. दक्षिणेन तु G.O.S. N.S. दक्षिणस्य च ।
३. K.S.S. M.G. ततः शृङ्गारसंयुक्तं पठेच्छ्लोकं विचक्षणः G.O.S. N.S. (Same as above).
४. K.S.S. विदित्वा G.O.S. N.S. M.G. गदित्वा ।
५. K.S.S. M.G. प्राङ्मुखेन G.O.S. N.S. पश्चिमेन ।
६. K.S.S. M.G. पारिपार्श्वकयोर्हस्ते G.O.S. N,S. पारिपार्श्विकहस्ते ।
७. K.S.S. M.G. यत्र G.O.S. N.S. तत्र ।
८. K.S.S. M.G. आश्रया G.O.S. N.S. अन्विता ।
९. K.S.S. M.G. N.S. तु G.O.S. हि ।
१०. K.S.S. M.G. योगे G.O.S. N.S. पादे ।
११. K.S.S. त्रैष्टुभं चरणे यथा M·G. त्रैष्टुभे चरणे यथा G.O.S. N.S. चतुर्विंशतिके भवेत् ।

पादतलाहति[1]पातितशैलं
क्षोभितभूतसमग्रसमुद्रम् ।
ताण्डवनृत्तमिदं प्रलयान्ते
पातु जगत्सुखदायि हरस्य[2] ॥ १२७ ॥

भाण्डोन्मुखेन कर्तव्यं पादविक्षेपणं ततः ।
सूचीं कृत्वा[3] पुनः कुर्याद्विक्षेपपरिवर्तनम् ॥ १२८ ॥
अतिक्रान्तैः सललितैः पा[4]दैर्द्रुतलयान्वितैः ।
त्रितालान्तरमुत्क्षेपै[5]र्गच्छेत्पञ्चपदीं ततः ॥ १२९ ॥
तत्रापि वामवेधस्तु विक्षेपो दक्षिणस्य च ।
तै[6]रेव च पदैः कार्यं प्राङ्मुखेनापसर्पणम् ॥ १३० ॥

अथ महाचारीप्रयोगमवतारयति—**पारिपार्श्विकहस्ते त्विति** । तत्र ध्रुवामाह—**चतुरश्रेति** । द्विकलेनोक्तेन चञ्चत्पुटेन । **आद्यं चतुर्थमिति** ध्रुवालक्षणम् । अस्याः प्रयोगमाह—**भाण्डोन्मुखेनेति** । पश्चिमाभिमुखेन । महेश्वरत्वं यस्य न्यस्यात्मनि तस्यात्मनीच्छता ऊनचतुस्तालता तच्चेष्टितानुसरणाच्च मध्यत्वेऽपि तद्द्वितालतेत्यौचित्यात्तालान्तरत्वमुक्तम् । (१२४-१३१)

अथ महाचारीं सूचयति—**ततो रौद्ररसमिति** । रुद्रस्यायं रौद्रप्रायः स रसः । यत्र पादानां च संहरणं समासयोजनयैक्यं यत्रेत्योजःप्रधानत्वं दर्शितम् । **तस्येति** । पाठस्यान्ते । **त्रिपद्येति** । **पारिपार्श्विकावामुखरूपया** । अत्र च ध्रुवाया अनुक्तत्वात्पूर्वोक्तैवाड्डिता संश्रयणीया ।

---

१. K.S.S. N.S. M.G. आहत G.O.S. आहति ।

२. K.S.S. M.G. पातु हरस्य सदा सुखदायि G.O.S. N.S. (Same as above).

३. K.S.S. दत्त्वा G.O.S. N.S. M.G. कृत्वा ।

४. K.S.S. पदैः द्रुतलयाश्रितैः M.G. पदैः द्रुतलयान्वितैः G.O.S. N.S. पादैः द्रुतलयान्वितैः ।

५. K.S.S. उत्क्षिप्तैः G.O.S. N.S. M.G. उत्क्षेपैः ।

६. N.S. तत्रैव च G.O.S. K.S.S. M.G. तैरेव च ।

पुनः पदानि त्रीण्येव गच्छेत्प्राङ्मुख एव तु[१] ।
ततश्च वामवेधः स्याद्विक्षेपो दक्षिणस्य च ॥ १३१ ॥

ततो रौद्ररसं[२] श्लोकं पादसंहरणं पठेत् ।
तस्यान्ते तु त्रिपद्याथ व्याहरेत्पारिपार्श्विकौ[३] ॥ १३२ ॥

तयोरागमने[४] कार्यं ...नं नर्कुटकं[५] बुधैः ।
तथा च भारतीभेदं ...गतं सम्प्रयोजयेत्[६] ॥ १३३ ॥

विदूषकस्त्वेकप[७]दां सूत्रधारस्मितावहाम् ।
असम्बद्धकथाप्रायां कुर्यात्कथनिकां ततः[८] ॥ १३४ ॥

(वितण्डां गण्डसंयुक्तां तालिकां[९]ञ्च प्रयोजयेत् ।
कस्तिष्ठति जितं केनेत्यादिकाव्यप्ररूपिणीम् ॥
पारिपार्श्विकसञ्जल्पो विदूषकविरूपि[१०]तः ।
स्थापितः सूत्रधारेण त्रिगतं सम्प्रयुज्यते[११] ॥)

अथ त्रिगतमङ्ग दर्शयति—तयोरित्यादिना । तयोः पारिपार्श्विकयोः । नर्कुटकध्रुवा वक्ष्यते ।

"अष्टौ नर्कुटकानां तु विज्ञेया मूलजातयः ।
रथोद्धता बुद्बुदकम्" इत्यादि (ना. शा. ३२-२८०)

---

१. K.S.S. M.G. च G.O.S. N.S. तु ।
२. N.S. K.S.S. M.G. रौद्ररसश्लोकं G.O.S. रौद्ररसं श्लोकं ।
३. K.S.S. पारिपार्श्वकः M.G. N.S. G.O.S. पारिपार्श्विकौ ।
४. K.S.S. N.S. आगमनं G.O.S. M.G. आगमने ।
५. K.S.S. नकुटके M.G. G.O.S. N.S. नर्कुटकं ।
६. K.S.S. M.G. read in addition after 133 a तत्रापि वामवेधस्तु विक्षेपो दक्षिणस्य च ।
७. M.G. एकपदे G.O.S. K.S.S. N.S. एकपदाम् ।
८ K.S.S. M.G. तथा G.O.S. N.S. ततः ।
९. N.S. नालीकं K.S.S. नामिकां M.G. नालिकां G.O.S. तालिकां ।
१०. M.G. N.S. विदूषितः G.O.S. विरूपितः ।
११. K.S.S. does not read the verse पारिपार्श्विक ...

प्ररोचना च[1] कर्तव्या सिद्धेनोपनिमन्त्रणम्[2] ।
रङ्गसिद्धौ पुनः कार्यं [3]काव्यवस्तुनिरूपणम् ॥ १३५ ॥

सर्वमे[4]व विधिं कृत्वा सूचीवेधकृतै[5]रथ ।
पादैरनाविद्धगतैर्निष्क्रामेयु: समं त्रय: ॥ १३६ ॥

एवमेष[6] प्रयोक्तव्य: पूर्वरङ्गो यथाविधि ।
चतुरश्रो द्विजश्रेष्ठास्त्र्यश्रं[7] च[8]ापि निबोधत ॥ १३७ ॥

अयमेव प्रयोग: स्यादङ्गान्येतानि चैव हि ।
तालप्रमाणं सङ्क्षि[9]प्तं केवलं तु विशेषकृत् ॥ १३८ ॥

शम्या[10] तु द्विकला कार्या तालो ह्येककलस्तथा ।
पुनश्चैककला शम्या सन्निपात: कलाद्वयम् ॥ १३९ ॥

तदन्यतमध्रुवोपलक्षितं गानं नर्कुटकम् ।
(भारतीभेद इति । भारतीवृत्त्यङ्गमुपसंहरत्येवमेष इति । चतुरश्रस्त्र्यश्रश-शुद्धश्चित्र इति चतुर्धा पूर्वरङ्ग: । यद्वक्ष्यति—

"त्र्यश्रं वा चतुरश्रं वा शुद्धं चित्रमथापि वा ।" इति चित्र एव विशेषान्वितो भवति ।) तदा गमनकाले । ततोऽनन्तरम् । निष्क्रान्तासु नर्तकीषु तत: परं शुष्कावकृष्टादि यदङ्गजातं प्ररोचनान्तं तैरेव सूत्रधारादिभिस्तद(त:) परं कृत्वा तत: शुद्धादुत्कृष्टं चित्रं कृत्वाऽङ्गहारव्यामिश्रेण प्रयोक्तव्यम् ।

१. K.S.S. M.G. अथ G.O.S. N.S. च ।
२. K.S.S. M.G. उपनिमन्त्रणा G.O.S. N.S. उपनिमन्त्रणम् ।
३. N.S. काव्यं G.O.S. K.S.S. M.G. कार्यम् ।
४. K.S.S. M.G. एवं G.G.S. N.S. एव ।
५. N.S. कृते G.O.S. K.S.S. M.G. कृतै: ।
६. K.S.S M.G. एव G.O.S. N.S. एष ।
७. K.S.S. M.G. त्र्यस्र G.O.S. N.S. त्र्यश्रं ।
८. N.S. वा G.O.S. K.S.S. M.G. च ।
९. N.S. तालप्रमाणं विक्षिप्तं K.S.S. तालप्रमाणसंक्षिप्तं G.O.S. M.G. (Same as above).
१०. K.S.S. शम्याकृद् द्विकल: कार्यस्ताल एककलस्तथा M.G. Same except शम्या तु द्विकला कार्या G.O.S. N.S. (Same as above)

अनेन हि प्रमाणेन कलाताललयान्वितः ।
कर्तव्यः पूर्वरङ्गस्तु त्र्यश्रोऽप्यु[1]त्थापनादिकः ॥ १४० ॥

आद्यं चतुर्थं दशममष्टमं नैधनं गुरु ।
यस्यास्तु जागते[2] पादे सा त्र्यश्रोत्थापिनी ध्रुवा ॥ १४१ ॥

वाद्यं गतिप्रचारश्च ध्रुवा तालस्तथैव च ।
संक्षिप्तान्येव[3] कार्याणि त्र्यश्रे नृत्तप्रवेदिभिः ॥ १४२ ॥

वाद्यगीतप्रमाणेन कुर्यादङ्ग[5]विचेष्टितम् ।
विस्तीर्णमथ सङ्क्षिप्तं द्विप्रमा[6]णविनिर्मितम् ॥ १४३ ॥

हस्तपादप्रचारस्तु द्विकलः परिकीर्तितः ।
चतुरश्रे परिक्रान्ते[7] पाताः[8] स्युः षोडशैव तु[9] ॥ १४४ ॥

त्र्यश्रे द्वादश पातास्तु भवन्ति करपादयोः[10] ।
एतत्प्रमाणं विज्ञेय[11]मुभयोः पूर्वरङ्गयोः ॥ १४५ ॥

केवलं परिवर्ते तु गमने[12] त्रिपदी भवेत् ।
दिग्वन्दने पञ्चपदी चतुरश्रे विधीयते ॥ १४६ ॥

---

१. K.S.S. N.S. त्र्यस्रोऽभ्युत्थापनादिकः M.G. त्र्यस्रेऽप्युत्थापनादिकः G.O.S. त्र्यश्रोऽप्युत्थापनादिकः ।

२. K.S.S. जागते G.O.S. N.S. M.G. जायते ।

३. N.S. अत्र K.S.S. G.O.S. M.G. एव ।

४. N.S. त्र्यस्रनृत्तप्रवेदिभिः G.O.S. K.S.S. त्र्यस्रे नृत्तप्रवेदिभिः ।

५. K.S.S. कृति M.G. गति G.O.S. N.S. अङ्ग ।

६. K.S.S. प्रमाणं च विनिर्मितम् N.S. M.G. G.O.S. द्विप्रमाणविनिर्मितम् ।

७. N.S. परावर्ते G.O.S. K.S.S. M.G. परिक्रान्ते ।

८. K.S.S. पादाः G.O.S. M.G. N.S. पाताः ।

९. K.S.S. M.G. हि N.S. G.O.S. तु ।

१०. K.S.S. त्र्यस्रे तु द्वादशपदा भवन्ति करपादजाः M.G. Same except पाता in place of पदा G.O.S. N.S. (Same as above).

११. K.S.S. M.G. निर्दिष्टम् G.O.S. N.S. विज्ञेयम् ।

१२. K.S.S. गगने G.O.S. M.G. N.S. गमने ।

आचार्यबुद्ध्या कर्तव्यस्त्र्यश्रस्ताल[1]प्रमाणतः ।
तस्मान्न लक्षणं प्रोक्तं पुनरुक्तं भवेद्यतः ॥ १४७ ॥

एवमेष प्रयोक्तव्यः पूर्वरङ्गो द्विजोत्तमाः ।
त्र्यश्रश्च चतुरश्रश्च शुद्धो भारत्युपाश्रयः ॥ १४८ ॥

एवं तावदयं शुद्धः पूर्वरङ्गो मयोदितः ।
चित्रत्वमस्य वक्ष्यामि यथाकार्यं प्रयोक्तृभिः ॥ १४९ ॥

वृत्ते ह्युत्थापने विप्राः कृते च परिवर्तने ।
चतुर्थका[2]रदत्ताभिः सुमनोभिरलङ्कृते ॥ १५० ॥

उदात्तगानैर्गन्धर्वैः परिगीते[3] प्रमाणतः ।
देवदुन्दुभयश्चैव निनदेयुर्भृशं ततः ॥ १५१ ॥

सिद्धा[4] कुसुममालाभिर्विकिरेयुः समन्ततः ।
अङ्गहारैश्च देव्यस्ता उपनृत्येयुरग्रतः[5] ॥ १५२ ॥

यस्ताण्डवविधिः प्रोक्तो नृत्ते पिण्डी[6]समन्वितः ।
रेचकैरङ्गहारैश्च न्यासोपन्याससंयुतः ॥ १५३ ॥

नान्य (अन्ये) च "नास्ति पुरुषस्य नृत्तम्" इत्याशयेन **सर्वास्वि**त्यत्र नान्दीपदवैचित्र्याय याः प्रविष्टास्तासामेव निष्क्रामणमत्र पूर्वासां चतसृणाम् । तेन तत्कृतमेव गानं तेषु चित्रत्वमिति भन्यते । (१३२-१५७)

---

१. N.S. तज्ज्ञैः K.S.S. M.G. G.O.S. तालः ।

२. K.S.S. चतुष्प्रकार M.G. N.S. G.O.S. चतुर्थकार ।

३. K.S.S. परिगीतैः M.G. परिगतैः G.O.S. N.S. परिगीते ।

४. N.S. K.S.S. M.G. शुद्धाः G.O.S. सिद्धाः ।

५. K.S.S. अङ्गहारैश्च दैत्यश्च व्यासापन्याससंयुताः M.G. N.S. G.O.S. (Same as above) except M.G. Reads च in place of ताः ।

६. M.G. नृत्तं पिण्डी समन्वितः N.S. नृत्ते पिण्डी समन्ततः G.O.S. नृत्ते पिण्डी समन्वितः K.S.S. does not read 153.

नान्दीपदानां मध्ये तु एकैकस्मिन्पृथक्पृथक् ।
प्रयोक्तव्यो बुधैः सम्यक्चित्रभावमभीप्सुभिः[1] ॥ १५४ ॥

एवं कृत्वा यथान्यायं शुद्धं चित्रं प्रयत्नतः ।
ततःपरं प्रयुञ्जीत नाटकं लक्षणान्वितम्[2] ॥ १५५ ॥

ततस्त्वन्तर्हिताः सर्वा भवेयुर्दिव्ययोषितः ।
निष्क्रान्तासु च सर्वासु नर्तकीषु ततः परम् ॥ १५६ ॥

पूर्वरङ्गे प्रयोक्तव्यमङ्गजातमतःपरम्[3] ।
एवं शुद्धो भवेच्चित्रः[4] पूर्वरङ्गो विधानतः[5] ॥ १५७ ॥

कार्यो नातिप्रसङ्गोऽत्र नृत्तगीतवि[6]धिं प्रति ।
गीते [7]वाद्ये च नृत्ते च प्रवृत्तेऽतिप्रसङ्गतः ॥ १५८ ॥

खेदो भवेत्प्रयोक्तॄणां प्रेक्षकाणां तथैव च ।
खिन्नानां रसभावेषु स्पष्टता नोपजायते ॥ १५९ ॥

नातिप्रसङ्ग इति । तत्रैकाङ्गहारप्रयोग एव कार्य इत्यर्थः । अत एवा(ङ्गा)न्तरगणनया षोडशैवाङ्गहाराः । तथा चोत्थापनं परिवर्तनमवकृष्टागानं नान्दीपाठः शुष्कावकृष्टजर्जरश्लोकाः ध्रुवा रङ्गद्वारमड्डिता आर्यापाठो ध्रुवा रौद्रश्लोकपाठो नर्कुटकं त्रिगतं प्ररोचना चेत्येते । अङ्गहारषोडशकमेव त्र्यश्रेऽपीति । नान्दीपादान्तरेषु बहुतरं नृत्तम् ।

अन्ये तु तत्रैव नृत्तमिच्छन्ति मार्गान्तरेषु(नाङ्गान्तरेषु) । तच्चासङ्गतम् । एवं च सति 'वृत्ते ह्युत्थापन' इत्यादि तथा 'निष्क्रान्तासु च सर्वासु' इत्यादि

---

१. K.S.S. प्रयोक्तव्यो विधिः सम्यक् चित्रो लक्षणसंयुतः । G.O.S. N.S. M.G. (Same as above) except N.S. M.G. विधि read in place of बुधैः ।

२. K.S.S. M.G. do no not read 155B.

३. N.S. reads in addition प्रस्तावनां कृतः कुर्यात् काव्यप्रख्यापनाश्रयाम् after 157a.

४. K.S.S. चित्रं M.G. G.O.S. N.S. चित्रः ।

५. K.S.S. M.G. पूर्वरङ्गविधानतः N.S. G.O.S. पूर्वरङ्गो विधानतः ।

६. K.S.S. गीतनृत्यविधि M.G. गीतनृत्तविधि G.O.S. N.S. नृत्तगीतविधि ।

७. N.S. गीतवाद्ये G.O.S. N.S. M.G. गीते वाद्ये च ।

ततः शेषप्रयोगस्तु न रागजनको भवेत् ।
(लक्षणेन विना बाह्यलक्ष्याद्विस्तृतं भवेत्[1] ।
लोकशास्त्रानुसारेण तस्मान्नाट्यं प्रवर्तते ॥)
त्र्यश्रं वा चतुरश्रं वा शुद्धं चित्रमथापि वा ॥ १६० ॥

प्रयुज्य रङ्गान्निष्क्रामेत्सूत्रधारः सहानुगः ।
(वै[2]वर्णाथवरङ्गानामाशीर्वचनसंयुताम् ॥
कवेर्नामगुणोपेतां वस्तूपक्षेपरूपिकाम् ।
लघुवर्णपदोपेतां वृत्तैश्चित्रैरलङ्कृताम् ॥
अन्तर्यवनिकासंस्थः कुर्यादाश्रावणां ततः ।
आश्रावणावसाने च नान्दीं कृत्वा स सूत्रभृत्[3] ॥
पुनः प्रविश्य रङ्गं तु कुर्यात्प्रस्तावनां ततः ।)[4]
प्रयुज्य विधिनैवं तु पूर्वरङ्गं प्रयोगतः ॥ १६१ ॥

चानुपातसममेव स्यात् । न चैकाङ्ग्ग(ङ्गहार)विचित्रत्वाद्विमिश्रचित्रव्यपदेशे दृष्टातं(न्तो) ह्येकस्य तन्तोर्वर्णस्य वैचित्र्यं(त्र्ये) पटेऽपि वा तथा व्यपदेशः । 'एतद्विमिश्र' इति चोक्तं प्राक् । । (ना. शा. ४-१६) तदलमनेन ।

प्रेक्षकाणामित्यनेन सामाजिकानां पूर्वरङ्गे स्फुटैव नटवृत्तिर्भवतीति दर्शयति । तत्संस्कारसंस्कृतत्वात्तन्तु(रव)धीः । भ्रान्त्यादिबुद्धिश्च नाट्यधीर्भवतीति सूचयति । यदि हि तेषु नाट्यबुद्धिरेवोत्पादनीया स्यात्प्रत्युत प्रयत्नेन नटबुद्धिसम्पादकं पूर्वरङ्गप्रस्तावनादि तान्प्रति गोपनीयं स्यात् । दर्शितं चैतदस्माभिः प्रथमाध्याये । प्रयोक्तारः करणादेः प्रयोगे यत्र खिन्नाः प्रेक्षकाश्चादौ ततः शेषः प्रयोगः प्रीतिं न कुर्यात् । तत्प्रधानं चेदं नाट्यं व्युत्पत्तिप्रदमित्युक्तम् ।

---

१. K.S.S. M.G. do not read the verse लक्षणेन प्रवर्तते after 160A.

२. K.S.S. M.G. do not read the verses in brackets above G.O.S. N.S. read then.

३. N.S. ससूत्रधृत् G.O.S. स सूत्रधृत् ।
N.S. does not read पुनः प्रविश्य...ततः

स्थापकः प्रविशेत्तत्र सूत्रधारगुणाकृतिः ।
स्थानं तु वैष्णवं कृत्वा सौष्ठवाङ्गपुरस्कृतम् ॥ १६२ ॥

प्रविश्य रङ्गं तैरेव सूत्रधारपदै[1]र्व्रजेत् ।
स्थापकस्य प्रवेशे तु कर्तव्याऽर्थानुगा ध्रुवा ॥ १६३ ॥

त्र्यश्रा वा चतुरश्रा वा तज्ज्ञैर्मध्यलयान्विता[2] ।
कुर्यादनन्तरं[3] चारीं देवब्राह्मणशंसिनीम् ॥ १६४ ॥

शुद्धमिति । यत्र गीतकवर्धमानविधावेव नृत्तं न तु सर्वथा शुद्धमधुना प्रयोगार्हम् । (१५८-१६०)

एवं प्ररोचनान्तमङ्गजातमुक्त्वा यत्पूर्वमुक्तं—

"रङ्गसिद्धौ पुनः कार्यं काव्यवस्तुनिरूपणम् ।" इति (ना. शा. ५-१३५)

तद्वितत्य निरूपयति—**प्रयुज्येति** । प्रयोगेण **प्रयोगतः** स्थापयति समस्तं रूपकवृत्तिमिति **स्थापकः** । **सूत्रधारस्य गुणः** सौमनस्यविस्मययोगाद्भुतदृष्टित्वरक्षादिभिरा(दिरा)**कृतिश्च** वैष्णवादिरित्येतत्स्थापकभूयिष्ठं गतस्यापि भवति । तदेव स्पष्टयति—**स्थानन्त्वि**त्यादिना । सूत्रधार एव स्थापक इति सूत्रधारः पूर्वरङ्गं प्रयुज्य स्थापकः सन् प्रविशेदिति न भिन्नकर्तृकता । **अर्थानुगेति** । सारसचक्राह्वाद्युपमानक्रमेण तत्र प्रावेशिकी । तदर्थमप्येवमुत्थापन्यादिवत्कार्या । **मध्यलयान्विता** इत्यद्यतनानामिष्टत्वात् । शोकाद्याविष्टे हि विलम्बितलया । रोषाद्याविष्टे च द्रुतचक्रलया प्रावेशिकी । ततः प्रभृति हि सामाजिकानां हृदयं समुचितास्वादनयोग्यतां (योग्यम् । यैः संस्क(स्तु क)र्तव्यमिति त्रिभिर्लयैर्न्याय्यम् । अन्यत्वे सर्वप्रावेशिकीगानं स्वातन्त्र्याभिप्रायेण(इति) तदविचारितबाण(भाण)प्रसिद्धिमात्रमिति मन्तव्यम् । **कुर्यादनन्तरं चारीमिति** । महाचारीगतौ श्लोकौ वक्ष्येते । तेन शृंगाररसप्रधानं वीरादिरसप्रधानं देवद्विजस्तोत्रोद्देशश्लोकं पठेदित्यर्थः ।

अन्तरचारीमित्यन्ये पठन्ति । व्याचक्षते—स्वस्थानादन्यचारी, अनन्तरप्रतिहारासनिकादिवत् । तत्र पुनः प्ररोचनया जयाशीर्वादादिक्रमेण रङ्गस्थ-

---

१. K.S.S. पदं G.O.S. N.S. M.G. पदैः ।

२. K.S.S. M.G चतुरस्राथवा त्र्यस्रा तत्र मध्यलयाश्रिता G.O.S. N.S. (Same as above).

३. K.S.S. M.G. अन्तरचारी G.O.S, N.S. अनन्तरं चारीं ।

सुवाक्यमधुरैः श्लोकैर्नानाभाव[1]रसान्वितैः ।
प्रसाद्य रङ्गं विधिवत्कवेर्नाम च कीर्तयेत्[2] ॥ १६५ ॥

प्रस्तावनां ततः[3] कुर्यात्काव्यप्रख्यापनाश्रयाम् ।
उद्धात्यकादि[4] कर्तव्यं काव्योपक्षेपणाश्रयम् ॥ १३६ ॥

दिव्ये दिव्याश्रयो भूत्वा मानुषे मानुषाश्रयः[5] ।
दिव्यमानुषसंयोगे[6] दिव्यो वा मानुषोऽपि वा ॥ १६७ ॥

मुखबीजानुसदृशं[7] नानामार्गसमाश्रयम् ।
नानाविधैरुपक्षेपैः काव्योपक्षेपणं भवेत् ॥ १६८ ॥

प्रस्ताव्यैवं तु निष्क्रामेत्काव्यप्रस्तावकस्ततः[8] ।
एवमेष प्रयोक्तव्यः पूर्वरङ्गो यथाविधि ॥ १६९ ॥

सामाजिकवर्गप्रसादनं देवद्विजस्तोत्रोद्देशेन श्लोकं पठेत् (इति) । हृदयनिर्मलीकरणं रसास्वादोचितसंस्कारात् ग्रहणयोग्यताधानार्थं कुर्यात् । ततः **कविनाम** कीर्तयेत् । चशब्दात्तद्गुणादिकम् । येन प्रसिद्धादरणीयत्वं भवति । (१६१-१६५)

ततो रूपकविशेषप्रख्यापनमाश्रित्येति । तत्प्रख्यापनव्याजेन भाविरूपकार्थस्य **प्रस्तावना**मुपक्रमोपक्षेपपर्यायां कुर्यात् । येन प्रथमत एतत्प्रभृति सामाजिकाः सक्षेपेण संस्कारवन्तो भवन्ति । साधारणलोकवृत्ताभिमानसंस्कारवन्तश्च । तथा हि दिव्ये काव्यार्थे डिमादौ तत्सदृशवस्तूपक्षेपः । दिव्यमानुषो रामादिः । **वा**ग्रहणं समुच्चये ।

---

१. N.S. ताललय G.O.S. K.S.S. M.G. भावरस ।
२. K.S.S. M.G. अनुकीर्तयेत् G.O.S. N.S. च कीर्तयेत् ।
३. N.S. कृतः G.O.S. K.S.S. M.G. ततः ।
४. N.S. उद्धातकादि G.O.S. उद्धात्यकादि K.S.S. M.G. do not read 166b.
५. K.S.S. M.G. दिव्यो दिव्याश्रयैर्भूत्वा मानुषो मानुषाश्रयैः N.S. G.O.S. (Same as above).
६. K.S.S. M.G. संयोगः N.o. G.O.S. संयोगे ।
७. K.S.S. मुखं बीजानुसदृशं M.G. N.S. G.O.S. मुखबीजानुसदृशं ।
८. K.S.S. द्विजः M.G. N.S. G.O.S. ततः ।

य इमं पूर्वरङ्गं तु विधिनैव प्रयोजयेत्[1] ।
नाशुभं प्राप्नुयात्किञ्चित्स्वर्गलोकं च गच्छति ॥ १७० ॥

यश्चापि[2] विधिमुत्सृज्य यथेष्टं संप्रयोजयेत् ।
प्राप्नोत्यपचयं घोरं तिर्यग्योनिं च गच्छति ॥ १७१ ॥

न तथाऽग्निः प्रदहति प्रभञ्जनसमीरितः ।
यथा ह्यपप्रयोगस्तु प्रयुक्तो दहति क्षणात् ॥ १७२ ॥

इत्येवावन्तिपाञ्चालदाक्षिणात्यौढ्[4]मागधैः ।
कर्तव्यः पूर्वरङ्गस्तु द्विप्रमाणविनिर्मितः ॥ १७३ ॥

ननूपक्षेपात्मा प्रस्तावना मुखसन्ध्यङ्गादुपक्षेपाद्वीजलक्षणाया अर्थप्रकृतेश्च कथं भिद्यत इत्याशङ्क्याह—**मुखवीजानुसदृश**मिति । मुखाङ्गे ह्युपक्षेपे तदेवोपक्षिप्यते । बीजे च तदेव स्वल्पमात्रम् । इह तु तत्समम् । तथा हि—नटीविदूषकपारिपार्श्विकैः समन्तादिति विचित्रभेदेन स्वकार्यनिरूपणव्याजेन ये नानाविधा उपक्षेपाः उपांशु छन्नत्वेन रूपकार्थबीजस्य सामाजिकहृदयभूमौ क्षेपास्तैः काव्यं प्रस्ताव्य प्रस्तावकस्थापकौ निष्क्रामेताम् ।

नन्विह पूर्वरङ्गशेषभूता चेत्प्रस्तावना तर्हि भारत्यङ्गभूतत्वेन पुनः किमित्यामुखं प्ररोचना चाभिधास्यते (ना. शा. २०-२७) । उच्यते । द्विविधा प्रस्तावना भवति—पूर्वरङ्गस्याङ्गभूताऽन्यस्य वा । तत्र पूर्वरङ्गाङ्गेऽस्याः कविरुदासीनः । स्थापक एव स्वतन्त्रो निर्माता त्वन्यो वा कविध्रुवागानादावपि (पदम्) । यदाह **श्रीहर्षः**—अत एव हा(भा ?)सा नामा (कविः) कस्मिंश्चिन्नाटके ? "दिवं यातश्चित्तज्वरेणोत्कलित एवाभिवर्तते । अशक्यमस्य पुरतोऽवस्थातुम्" इत्यादि । सा द्वितीया सा(या) वृत्तिभेदमध्ये पठिता । एवं प्ररोचनादावपि मन्तव्यम् । यदाह—"तत्र काचित्काव्याभिमुखं नीयते पूर्वरङ्गविधिः तदभिमुखं वा काव्यारम्भस्तद्भवति सा द्विविधा" इत्यादिः । एतच्च वृत्त्यध्याये व्याख्यास्यते "नटी विदूषको वापि" (ना. शा. २०-३०) इत्यादौ । शास्त्रत्यागे मनागपि न वर्तितव्यमिति दर्शयितु**मेवमेष** इति । (१६६-१६९)

---

१. K.S.S. प्रपूजयेत् G.O.S. N.S. M.G. प्रयोजयेत् ।
२. K.S.S. M.G. इमम् G.O.S. N.S. अपि ।
३. N.S. एष G.O.S. K.S.S. M.G. एव ।
४. N.S. आन्ध्र K.S.S. उड्र M.G. औड्र G.O.S. औढ्र ।

एष वः कथितो विप्राः पूर्वरङ्गाश्रितो विधिः ।
भूयः किं कथ्यतां सम्यङ्नाटयवेदविधिं प्रति[1] ।। १७४ ।।

इति भारतीये नाटयशास्त्रे पूर्वरङ्गप्रयोगो नाम पञ्चमोऽध्यायः ।।

***[पुनश्चित्रे तथा मिश्रे शुद्धे चैव ब्रवीम्यहम् ।**
यथा योज्या ध्रुवाः पञ्च तथा वक्ष्यामि तत्त्वतः ।।

आदावुत्थापनी कार्या परिवर्तस्तथा भवेत् ।
अवकृष्टाड्डिता चैव विक्षिप्ता चैव पञ्चमी ।।

एवं पञ्च ध्रुवा ज्ञेया उपोहनसमन्विताः ।
कर्तव्यास्तु प्रयत्नेन पूर्वरङ्गे प्रयोक्तृभिः ।।

यथाविधि प्रयोगेऽभ्युदयः स्यादित्याह—**य इममिति** । अन्यथापि प्रयोगे प्रत्यवायमाह—**यश्चापीति** । **नाशुभमि**त्यादिना । **शुभमिति** दृष्टेऽभ्युदयः । **स्वर्गमिति** अदृष्टे । **अपचयमिति** । दृष्टे प्रत्यवाय इति । **तिर्यग्योनिं चे**त्यदृष्टे । दृष्टप्रत्यवायभीरुर्बाहुल्येन लोक इति । तमेवाधिकमवश्यंभावित्वेन दर्शयति—**न तथाग्निरिति** ।

ननु पाठ्यादियोजना च वेषाचारयोजना चात्र पूर्वरङ्गे नोक्तेत्याशङ्क्य तामनुवादद्वारेणाभिधातुं शुद्धश्चान्यत्वेन योज्य इत्याख्यातुं समुचितमुपसंहारं करोति—**इत्येवावन्तिपाञ्चालेत्यादि** । यादृक्प्रवृत्तिविशेषे नियतो रूपकनाय-(म)को भविष्यति तादृक्प्रवृत्तिसमुचितवेषभाषाचाराभिनयादिकमनुवर्तमानैः सूत्रधारादिभिः स्थापकान्तैः । पूर्वरङ्गो द्विविधस्त्र्यश्रश्चतुरश्रश्च । **एष** इत्यनन्तरोक्तस्वभाव एव कर्तव्यो न शुद्धः । अन्ये मन्यन्ते आवन्तीसारिवकीकैशिकीमिश्रेति । सा सूत्रधारस्य पाञ्चालदक्षिणयोर्मध्यमाभूमिः । (१७०-१७४)

इति महामाहेश्वराचार्याभिनवगुप्तविरचितायां नाटयवेदविवृतौ पूर्वरङ्गविधानं नाम पञ्चमोऽध्यायः ।।

---

१. K.S.S. does not read 174b. G.O.S. M.G. N.S. read it except that N.o. reads नाट्यवेदप्रयोक्तृभिः in place of नाट्यवेदविधिं प्रति ।

*एते श्लोकाः नाट्यशास्त्रस्य केषुचित् संस्करणेषु समुपलभ्यन्ते परन्तु श्रीमदभिनवगुप्तपादाचार्यैः एतद्व्याख्या न प्रस्तुता अतएव एतेषां प्रक्षिप्तत्वं परवर्तित्वं च सम्भाव्यते ।

अतः परं प्रवक्ष्यामि ह्युपोहनविधिक्रियाम् ।
उत्थापनस्याष्टकलं परिवर्तस्य षट्कलम् ॥

अवकृष्टं पुनः कार्यं कलाभिः पञ्चभिर्युतम् ।
ध्रुवायामड्डितायां च चतुष्कलमथापि च ॥

क्षिप्तायां चैव विज्ञेयं कलात्रयसमन्वितम् ।
एवं ह्युपोहनानां तु प्रमाणं समुदाहृतम् ॥

गुरुलाघवसंयुक्तं कलातालसमन्वितम् ।
पूर्वरङ्गं सदा ज्ञेयं चित्रमार्गे ह्युपोहनम् ॥

चित्रे चैत्राः कला ज्ञेया मिश्रे वार्तिकमाश्रिताः ।
शुद्धे दक्षिणमार्गेण प्रयोक्तव्याः प्रयोक्तृभिः ॥

चतस्त्रो गीतयः कार्या मागधी ह्यर्धमागधी ।
संभाविता तथा चैव पृथुला च प्रकीर्तिता ॥

मागधी त्वथ कर्तव्या त्वथवा त्वर्धमागधी ।
पूर्वरङ्गे भवेच्चित्रे चित्रमार्गसमाश्रिता ॥

यथा मिश्रस्तु योक्तव्यः पूर्वरङ्गे भवेदिह ।
मिश्रे सम्भाविता कार्या तदा वार्तिकमाश्रिता ॥

शुद्धे च पृथुला कार्या दक्षिणं मार्गमाश्रिता ।
अतः परं प्रवक्ष्यामि गुरुलाघवतः क्रियाम् ॥

उपोहनक्रियायां तु यथायोज्यं प्रयोक्तृभिः ।
दिग्ले दिग्ले पुनः कार्यमन्ते झण्टुं सदा बुधैः ॥

मध्ये लघ्वक्षराणि स्युः षोडशैव तु नित्यशः ।
एवं ह्युपोहनं कृत्वा तथा वस्तु समाचरेत् ॥
उत्थापन्यां प्रयोगेऽस्मिन्कलाकालसमन्वितम् ।
अक्षराणां कलायास्तु गुरुलाघवमेव च ॥
पूर्वं तु कथितं यस्मात्तस्मान्नाभिहितं भवेत्[1] ।

यथा —

देवं विभुं त्रिभुवनाधिपतिं कैलासपर्वतगुहाभिरतम् ।
शैलेन्द्रराजतनयादयितं मूर्ध्ना नतोऽस्मि पुरनाशकरम् ॥

एवमुत्थापनी कार्या पूर्वरङ्गप्रयोक्तृभिः ।
अतोऽन्यत्परिवर्ताया लक्षणं संविधीयते ॥

अस्यास्तूपोहनं कार्यं षट्कलं परिसङ्ख्यया ।
आदौ दिग्ले द्विरुक्तस्तु अन्ते झण्टुं सदा भवेत् ॥

मध्ये लघ्वक्षराण्येव द्वादशैव प्रयोजयेत् ।
वस्तुनोऽत्र प्रवक्ष्यामि गुरुलघ्वक्षरक्रमम् ॥

द्वे चादौ च चतुर्थं च अष्टमं दशमं तथा ।
चतुर्दशं पञ्चदशं पादे गुर्वक्षराणि तु ॥

सा ध्रुवा परिवर्ताख्या त्रिलया त्रियतिस्तथा ।
परिवर्तास्तु चत्वारः पाणयस्त्रय एव च ॥

चतुर्भिस्सन्निपातैस्तु द्वात्रिंशत्कलिकान्विता ।
पूर्वरङ्गे प्रयोक्तव्यः परिवर्तः प्रयोक्तृभिः ॥

यथा—

चन्द्रार्धभूषणजटं वरं वृषभकेतुं
कैलासपर्वतनिवासिनं सुरवरिष्ठम् ।
शैलाधिराजतनयाप्रियं प्रमथनाथं
मूर्ध्ना नतोऽस्मि त्रिपुरान्तकं परमयोगिनम् ॥

अवकृष्टामिदानीं तु कथ्यमानां निबोधत ।
अस्यास्तूपोहनं कार्यं कलाभिः पञ्चभिर्युतम् ॥

दिग्ले दिग्ले पुनश्चान्ते झण्टुमस्य प्रयोजयेत् ।
अष्टावेव तु कार्याणि मध्ये लघ्वक्षराणि तु ॥

तृतीयं चैव षष्ठं तु नवमैकादशे तथा ।
पादे पञ्चदशं चैव षोडशं च भवेद्गुरु ॥

अष्टषष्टिगणैः पादैरवकृष्टविधिर्बुधाः ।
चतुर्भिः सन्निपातैश्च पाणिभिस्त्रिभिरेव च ॥

यथा—

वरदं सगणं त्रिपुरान्तकं वृषभकेतुम् ।
गजचर्मपटं विषमेक्षणं भुवननाथम् ।
भुजगाभरणं जगतां हितं भुवनयोनिम् ।
प्रणतोऽस्मि भवन्तमुमापतिं त्वसितकण्ठम् ॥

तृतीयं चैव षष्ठं च गुरुपादे त्रयोदशम् ।
चतुर्गुणसमायुक्ता सा कार्या त्वड्डिता ध्रुवा ॥

तत्राप्युपोहनं कार्यं चतुष्कलसमन्वितम् ।
अड्डितायाः प्रयोगज्ञैरन्ते झण्टुविभूषितम् ॥

दिग्ले दिग्ले ततश्चैव कार्यमन्ते सदा बुधैः ।
चत्वार्येव तु कार्याणि मध्ये लघ्वक्षराणि तु ॥

यथा—

प्रवरं वरदं प्रणमत सततम् ।
गजचर्मपटं मुनिजनसहितम् ।
उमया सहितं भुजगवलयिनम् ।
प्रणतोऽस्मि शिवं त्रिभुवनसहितम् ॥

प्रयोज्या त्वड्डिता ह्येवं पूर्वरङ्गे यथार्थतः ।
अतःपरं प्रवक्ष्यामि विक्षिप्तायास्तु लक्षणम् ॥

तृतीयं चैव षष्ठं च नवमं दशमं तथा ।
गुर्वक्षराणि पादे तु यस्यां विक्षिप्तका तु सा ॥

द्विग्ले त्रिभिर्गुणैर्युक्ताः पातास्तस्य भवन्ति हि ।
त्रिकलं चापि निर्दिष्टमुपोहनमतः परम् ॥

द्विग्ले द्विग्ले पुनः कार्यमन्ते झण्टुं प्रयोक्तृभिः ।
लघ्वक्षरैर्विहीनं तु विक्षिप्तोपोहनं भवेत् ॥

यथा—

त्रिपुरान्तकरं वहुलीलमुभया सहितं बहुरूपम् ।
भुजगाभरणं त्रिपुरान्तकं प्रणमामि सदा परमीशम् ॥

एवं सर्वा ध्रुवाः कार्या युग्मौजकृतगीतकाः ।
आचार्यबुद्धया कर्तव्याः पूर्वरङ्गे यथाविधि ॥

एवं वः कथितं सम्यक्पूर्वरङ्गं त्रिधा मया ।
किमन्यत्सम्प्रवक्ष्यामि भूयोऽभीष्टं द्विजोत्तमाः ॥

इति भारतीये नाटचशास्त्रे पूर्वरङ्गविधानं नाम पञ्चमाध्यायस्य प्रक्षिप्तभागः समाप्तः ।

षष्ठोऽध्यायः ।

पूर्वरङ्गविधिं श्रुत्वा पुनराहुर्महत्तमाः ।

भरतं मुनयः सर्वे प्रश्नान्पञ्चाभिधत्स्व नः[1] ॥ १ ॥

... ... **पूर्वरङ्गविधिं श्रुत्वेति । पञ्च प्रश्नानिति ।** रसानां केन रसत्वमित्येकः प्रश्नः ।

... ... तथापि नाट्यतत्त्वे सम्यङ्निर्ज्ञाते निर्णीतं भवति । न वचनमात्रात् । अनेनैवाभिप्रायेण दशरूपकनिरूपणे प्रथमप्रश्नार्थो निगमयिष्यते—

"भविष्यति युगे प्रायो भविष्यन्त्यबुधा नराः । "

(ना. शा. १९-१५०) इत्यादि ।

तथा—

"बुद्धयः कर्मशिल्पानि वैचक्षण्यं कलासु च ॥ "

(ना. शा. १९-१५१) इत्यादि ।

सिद्ध्यध्याये च द्वितीयप्रश्नार्थविषयो निर्णेष्यते । "तुष्यन्ति तरुणाः कामे" (ना. शा. २७-५८) इत्यादिना । एवमन्यत्रापि तत्र तत्रेति । एतच्च तद्व्याख्यानप्रसङ्ग एव दर्शयिष्यामः । तेन पूर्वप्रश्नितवस्तुतत्त्वनिर्णय एव तात्पर्यम् । **प्रश्नान् पञ्चेति। ये रसा** इत्यादि तु यत्प्रश्नत्रयं तत्रायं भावः— इहाङ्गगणनायां "जग्राह पाठ्यम् (ना. शा. १-१७) इत्यादौ पाठ्यगीतयोस्तावत्सुप्रसिद्धं रूपम् । अभिनयानामपि " महागीतेषु चैवार्थान्सम्यगेवाभिनेष्यसि" इति (ना. शा. ४-१५)

१. K.S.S. M.G. मुनयो भरतं सर्वे पञ्च प्रश्नान् ब्रवीहि नः except M.G reads प्रश्नान् पञ्च in place of पञ्च प्रश्नान् G.O.S. N.S (Same as above).

ये रसा इति पठ्यन्ते नाट्ये नाट्यविचक्षणैः ।
रसत्वं केन वै[1] तेषामेतदाख्यातुमर्हसि ॥ २ ॥

भावाश्चैव कथं[2] प्रोक्ताः किं वा ते भावयन्त्यपि[3] ।
संग्रहं कारिकां चैव निरुक्तं चैव तत्त्वतः ॥ ३ ॥

तेषां तु वचनं श्रुत्वा मुनीनां भरतो मुनिः ।
प्रत्युवाच पुनर्वाक्यं रसभावविकल्पनम् ॥ ४ ॥

"यदा प्राप्त्यर्थमर्थानां तज्ज्ञैरभिनयः" (ना. शा. ४-२६१) इत्यादिवचनबलाच्च सु(स्व)रूपं तावन्नातीव हृदयङ्गमम् ।

ये तु "रसानाथर्वणात्" (ना. शा. १-१७) इति रसा उक्तास्ते तावत्प्रसिद्धाः षाडबादयः । न प्रकृतौ युक्ताः । ये त्वन्ये शृङ्गारादयः केचन रसशब्देन सह प्रयुक्ताः "शृङ्गाररससम्भवः" (ना. शा. ४-२६६) इति "ततो रौद्ररसं श्लोकम्" (ना. शा. ५-१३२) इति तत्रापि शृङ्गारादिषु कथं रसशब्दवाच्यत्वम् । **वैण**शब्दोऽक्षर(क्षमायाम्) । रसनेन्द्रियग्राह्ये हि रसशब्दः प्रसिद्धः । न चायमनादरस्थानभूतोऽर्थो येनाविचारित एवोपेक्ष्यते "खिन्नां रसभावेषु" (ना. शा. ५-१५६) इत्यादावादराशियप्रतीतेः । अत एव शब्दप्रादुर्भाव इति शब्दो **रसा इति पठ**यन्त इति । तेन प्राधान्यादङ्गाभिनयप्रश्नान्तर्भूतमप्येतत्पुनः प्रश्नितमित्यर्थः । पुनः प्रश्नाभिप्रायेणैवा**ख्यातुमर्हसी**त्युपपन्नम् । पूर्वाख्यानेषु तु पुनरुक्तमभित्स्वेत्युक्तत्वात् ।

भावाश्चेति चशब्दस्तुशब्दार्थे । भावास्त्वपठिता अपि कथं प्रोक्ताः । अथ पाठ्यादय एव भावाः । तत्किमेषां रूपम् । तेनादरविषयत्वाद्रसे प्रश्नान्तरम् (र)भूतावृत्त्या विस्मयस्थानत्वाद्भावेषु प्रश्नचतुष्कम् । तथा हि—रससहभावेन भावाः केचन प्रोक्ताः "खिन्नानाम्" इत्यत्र । ते च केन प्रकारेणोक्ताः । "जग्राह" इत्यादौ हि तेषां नामापि न श्रुतम् । अथैतेष्वेव भावशब्दः प्रवर्तितः । तत्रापि भवन्तीति व्युत्पत्तिः । भावयन्तीति किमेतत् । किमुत्पादयन्ति । अथ व्याप्नुवन्ति । द्वयोः कर्म किं स्यादिति **वा**शब्देन **च**शब्देना**पि**शब्देन च चत्वारो भावेषु प्रश्नाः । एवं प्राधान्यात्प्रश्नपञ्चकान्तरम् । वस्तुतः पुनः पञ्चप्रश्नी।

---

१. K.S.S. M.G. वा G.O.S. N.S. वै ।

२. K.S.S. हि ये M.G. G.O.S. N.S. कथं ।

३. K.S.S. M.G. हि G.O.S. N.S. अपि ।

अहं वः[1] कथयिष्यामि निखिलेन तपोधनाः ।
संग्रहं कारिकां चैव निरुक्तं च यथाक्रमम् ॥ ५ ॥
न शक्यमस्य[2] नाट्यस्य गन्तुमन्तं कथञ्चन ।
कस्माद्बहुत्वाज्ज्ञानानां[3] शिल्पानां वा[4]ऽप्यनन्तत: ॥ ६ ॥

पूर्वोक्तैवेयं विष्फार्यते । सङ्ग्रहादिति चा(दि चा) भिधत्स्व । ननु तैरिह किं प्रयोजनम् । आह—**तत्त्वत** इति । (१-३)

तुशब्दो हेतौ । तदित्याख्यानं परामृष्टम् । यतस्तदाख्यानमत एवा(वै)भ्यः सङ्ग्रहादिभ्य उद्देशलक्षणपरीक्षादिषु प्राधान्यात्तदुपक्रममेव सर्वमभिधेयम् । तदाह् । **निखिलेन** सङ्ग्राह्यलक्षणीयनिर्वचनीयात्मनोपलक्षितं सङ्ग्रहादित्रयमेव वक्ष्यामीति त्रय(त्रि) प्रकाररूपेभ्यः सदुपायेभ्यः । तस्मान्नोऽभिधत्स्वेति । पुनश्शब्दो भिन्नक्रमः । भरतमुनिः पुनः रसभावा विकल्प्यन्ते निश्चीयन्तेऽनेन (येन वचनेन) तादृग्वाक्यमुवाच न तु तदीयं वचनमुक्तमुत्तरदानेन समादृतमिति पुनश्शब्दार्थः । मुनेश्चायं भावो रसादिषु समुच्चयार्थश्च: । तदभिधानेऽन्यन्न किंचिदभिधेयमवशिष्यत इत्येवशब्दः । **यथाक्रममिति** । पूर्वं (प्राप्त) सङ्ग्रहः । उद्देशप्रकारत्वादित्यादिक्रमेण स(स्व)बुद्धिविषयं बहुमानं गृह्णतामभीषामित्यभिप्रायेण भवद्भिर्युक्तमेतदुक्तम् ।

सङ्ग्रहमित्यादि । तान्निदर्शयन्मुनिराह—**न शक्यमस्येति** । शक्यमिति सामान्योपक्रमात् माध्यस्थ्यविवक्षा । **गन्तुमिति** प्राप्तुम् । **अन्तो** निश्चयः । **कथञ्चनेति** । अमुं सङ्ग्रहादिप्रकारं वर्जयित्वाऽन्येन प्रतिपदनिरूपणादिनेत्यर्थः । यत्किल प्रतिपदं निरूपयितुं न शक्यं तल्लक्षणद्वारेणोच्यते । लक्षणस्यैवाङ्गमुद्देशपरीक्षे । तस्य विषयप्रदर्शने परिशुद्धौ च तयोर्व्यापारात् । न चात्र प्रतिपदं निरूपणं युक्तमिति ।

अत्र हेतुमाह—**बहुत्वादिति** । **ज्ञानाख्यानि** व्याकरणादीनि शास्त्राणि । **शिल्पानि** चित्रपुस्तादिकर्माणि । तेषामनन्ता(न्तत्वा)दन्ताभावात् । (४-६)

---

१. K.S.S. च G.O.S. N.S. M.G. वः ।
२. K.S.S. M.G. इह G.O.S. N.S. अस्य ।
३. N.S. भावानां G.O.S. K.S.S. M.G. ज्ञानानां ।
४. K.S.S. M.G. च G.O.S. N.S. वा ।

एकस्यापि न वै शक्यस्त्वन्तो ज्ञानार्णवस्य हि[1] ।
गन्तुं किं पुनरन्येषां[2] ज्ञाना[3]नामर्थतत्त्वतः ॥ ७ ॥
किन्त्वल्पसूत्रग्रन्था[4]र्थमनुमानप्रसाधकम् ।
नाटयस्यास्य प्रवक्ष्यामि रसभावादिसङ्ग्रहम् ॥ ८ ॥
विस्तरेणोपदिष्टानामर्थानां सूत्रभाष्ययोः ।
निबन्धो यः समासेन सङ्ग्रहं तं विदुर्बुधाः ॥ ९ ॥
रसा भावा ह्यभिनयाः धर्मी वृत्तिप्रवृत्तयः ।
सिद्धिः स्वरास्तथातोद्यं गानं रङ्गश्च सङ्ग्रहः[5] ॥ १० ॥

एतदेवोपोद्बलयत्**येकस्ये**ति । नाटयाङ्गभूतस्य कस्यचिदिति शेषः । **अर्थस्याभिधेयस्य तत्त्वतः** । तननं विस्तारः । तेन । **अन्येषा**मिति । अङ्गभूतस्यापि यान्यङ्गत्वेनायान्तीत्यर्थः ।

सङ्ग्रहादयस्त्वत्र सदुपाया इति दर्शयति—**किन्त्विति। नाटयस्य** नाटयविषयस्यार्थस्य **सङ्ग्रहं** संक्षिप्य गृह्यतेऽनेनेति तमुद्देशं **वक्ष्यामी**ति । कथम् । रसभावादि कृत्वा प्राधान्यात्तदुपक्रममित्यर्थः । किं तेनेत्या**हानुमानं** लक्षणं तद्धि केवलव्यतिरेकिहेतुरूपम् । तस्य चोद्देशधर्मिणं प्रकल्पयन् प्रकृष्टः साधकः आश्रयासिद्धत्वशङ्काशमनेन पक्षधर्मत्वमूलाङ्गपोषकत्वात् । तस्य सङ्ग्रहस्य स्वरूपमाह—सूत्रग्रन्थयोर्लक्षणपरीक्षयोर्योऽर्थो लक्ष्यपरीक्षितव्यलक्षणः सोऽल्पः सङ्कुचितो नाममात्रेणोद्देश्यतया यत्र । अन्येऽप्येवमेव मन्यन्त इति दर्शयति—**विस्तरेणेति** । सूत्रं लक्षणम् । भाष्यं तद्व्यक्तीकरणरूपा परीक्षा । अल्पौ सूत्रग्रन्थौ यत्रार्थे सोऽर्थो यत्रेति तु व्याख्यानमनेन श्लोकेन न संवदते । (७-९)

सङ्ग्रहं दर्शयति—**रसा भावा** इत्यादिना । **च**शब्द इतिशब्दर्थे । अभिनयत्रयं गीतातोद्ये चेति पञ्चाङ्गं नाटयम् । नटस्य हि रसभावयोगे मरणादौ

---

१. K.S.S. तु G.O.S. N.S. M.G. हि ।
२. K.S.S. M.G. सर्वेषां G.O.S. N.S. अन्येषां ।
३. K.S.S. भावानां G.O.S. N.S. M.G. ज्ञानानाम् ।
४. K.S.S. M.G. गूढ G.O.S. N.S. ग्रन्थ ।
५. N.S. reads in addition after verse 10 उपचारस्तथा विप्रा मण्डपश्चेति सर्वशः । त्रयोदशविधो ह्येष ह्यादिष्टो नाटयसंग्रहः G.O.S. K.S.S. M.G. omit it.

अल्पाभिधानेनार्थो यः समासेनोच्यते बुधैः ।

सूत्रतः साऽनु[1]मन्तव्या (नु पठिता) कारिकार्थप्रदर्शि[2]नी ॥ ११ ॥

तत्त्वावेशो लयादिभङ्गश्च स्यात् । दृष्टस्तु तत्प्रत्ययो नटे भ्रमः । अनेन तु श्लोकेन **कोहलमतेनैकादशाङ्गत्वमुच्यते** । न तु **भरते** । तत्सङ्गृहीतस्यापि पुनरत्रोद्देशः । निर्देशे **चैतत्क्रमव्यत्यासनादित्यौद्भटाः** । नैतदिति **भट्टलोल्लटः** । रसभावानामपि वासनावेशवशेन नटे सम्भवादनुबन्धिबलाच्च लयाद्यनुसरणादन्तर्भूतस्यापि प्रयोजनवशेन पुनरुद्देशदर्शनात् क्रमस्य चाविवक्षितत्वादिति । वयन्त्वत्र तत्त्वमग्रे वितनिष्याम इत्यास्तां तावत् ।

अथ कारिकां लक्षयति—**अल्पाभिधानेने**ति । अनेनार्थस्य कारिकात्वं लक्षणरूपस्य दर्शयति । तद्वाचकस्य सूत्रस्य तत्संक्षिप्तार्थविवरणात्मकस्य च श्लोकस्य । अनेन लक्षणवाक्यं द्विधेति तात्पर्यम् । योऽर्थोऽल्पैः शब्दैः समासेन बहुतरलक्ष्यसङ्ग्रहेण सूत्रं वाचकमाश्रित्योच्यते सोऽर्थः कारिका । ज्ञप्तिसाधकत्वात्तदर्थिनी कारिका । **सूत्रतः**सूत्रेन । एतेन सूत्रमपि कारिका । तत्सूत्रमपेक्ष्य या **अनु पश्चात्पठिता** श्लोकरूपा सापि कारिका । तथा हि—सूचनात्मकत्वात्सूत्राल्लब्धो योऽर्थो लक्षणात्मकः स एव सम्यगिति श्रय्य (सम्यगतिश्रव्य) तया पर्णान्यिनेनेति (वर्णनात्मनेति) वृत्तबन्धेनोच्यमानोऽल्पैश्च शब्दैर्निरूप्यमाणोऽर्थस्य लक्षणीयस्य प्रकर्षं धर्म्यन्तराद्यवच्छेदं दर्शयन् धर्मः कारिका । क्रियतेऽनेन ज्ञप्तिरिति कारिका । लक्षणमिति यावत् । तदर्थप्रकाशकत्वात् श्लोकोऽप्युपचारात्कारिका ।

एतदुक्तं भवति—उद्दिष्टस्य धर्म्यन्तरव्यवच्छेदकं लक्षणं वक्तव्यम् । तच्च पूर्वं सूत्रेण । ततोऽप्यकृताक्षेपोत्तरप्रपञ्चेन तद्विवरणमात्ररूपेण सुखग्राह्येण श्लोकेन । उभयोरपि हि लक्षणमेव प्रतिपाद्यम् । तदेव कारिकोच्यते । सूत्रश्लोकावुपचारादिति । (१०-११)

अथ परीक्षात्मकं निरुक्तं लक्षयति श्लोकद्वयेन—**नानानामेत्यादिना** । समासेन संक्षेपेणानकव्यक्तिभेदभिन्नस्यार्थस्य लक्षणीयस्य यः सूचकोऽर्थो लक्षणात्मकः स यत्राक्षेपप्रतिसमाधानलक्षणे वस्तुनि सति स्थापितो भवति तत्परीक्षारूपनिरुक्तम् । नचैवं परिभाषा । किन्त्वर्थमेतं निर्भज्याक्षेपप्रतिसमाधानाभ्यां लक्षणस्य वचनमिति । एतदाह—**धात्वर्थवचनेनेति** ।

---

१. N.S. K.S.S. M.G. तु विज्ञेया G.O.S. अनुमन्तव्या ।

२ K.S.S. प्रयोगिनी G.O.S. N.S. M.G. प्रदर्शिनी ।

नानानामाश्रयोत्पन्नं निघण्टु[1]निगमान्वितम् ।
धात्वर्थहेतुसंयुक्तं नानासिद्धान्तसाधितम् ॥ १२ ॥

कथं तल्लक्षणं स्थाप्यत इत्याशङ्क्य क्रियाविशेषणाभिधानद्वारेणाक्षेपप्रतिसमाधानप्रकारं दर्शयति—**नानेत्यादिना** नानाप्रकाराणि यानि नामानि लक्षणवाक्येऽर्थप्रतिपादकाः सुबन्ताः शब्दास्तानाश्रित्योत्पन्नः उत्पाद आक्षेपप्रतिसमाधानयोर्यत्र । ननु नामपदेषु कथमाक्षेपप्रतिसमाधाने । आह—**निघण्टुना**ऽभिधानकोशेन रूढिषु । अन्येषु प्रकृतिप्रत्ययविभागनिगमनया । **अन्वित**मन्वयो यत्रोत्पादे । यानि च लक्षणवाक्ये तिङन्तानि पदानि तेषु प्रकारमाह—**धात्वर्थस्य** क्रियाया **हेतूनां च** क्रियानिमित्तानां कारकाणां संयोजनं विचारो यत्र स्थापने । इयता लक्षणवाक्ये पूर्वं शब्दपरीक्षा दर्शिता । अयं शब्दः कथमत्रार्थे वर्तत इत्याक्षेपः । इत्थमिति च प्रतिसमाधानम् । एतत् प्रदर्शितवस्तुप्रणीतमेव ।

अर्थपरीक्षामपि दर्शयति—**नाना**प्रकारैः सर्वतन्त्रप्रतितन्त्रादिभिः **सिद्धान्तैः** । प्रमाणमूलैरर्थैः **साधित**माक्षेपोत्तरयोः साधना यत्र स्थापने । एव परीक्षाऽनेन दर्शिता । तन्त्रादिन्यायास्तु तदङ्गम् । निरुक्तमपि । तच्चतुर्धा—नाम्ना वा—ऊर्ध्वं खमस्योलूखलः । धातुना वा रस्यत इति रसः । द्वाभ्यां वा—पिशितमश्नातीति पिशाचः । समयेन च—सोऽपि त्रिधा—लौकिको यथा—भू सत्तायाम् । वैदिको यथा—दीधीङ् दीप्तिदेवनयोः, वेवीङ् वेतिना तुल्ये । प्रतिशास्त्रपार्षद यथा—गान्धर्ववेदे गीतकविशेषे ओवेणकादिशब्दः । तदेतदुक्तं **नाने**त्यादिना । निरुक्तस्य तु प्रयोजनं संक्षेपेणार्थावधारणम् । तदुक्तं **सथापित** इति । (१२-१३)

अथोद्दिष्टानां विभागं सूत्रयति—**सङ्ग्रहो यो मयेति। तस्येति** सङ्ग्रहस्य । सङ्ग्रह एव विस्तारितो विभाग इत्यर्थः किं तदुक्तावेव सर्वं सम्पन्नम् । नेत्याह । **सनिरुक्तं** परीक्षापर्यन्तमित्यर्थः । अन्तवचनेऽव्ययीभावः । न चालक्षितस्य परीक्षेत्याह—**सकारिकं** कारिकासम्पदोपेतम् । सम्पत्तौ समासः ।

तत्र विभागं तावदाह—**शृङ्गारहास्येत्यादिना नाट्यसङ्ग्रह** (६-३१) इत्यन्तेन । तत्र नाट्यं नाम नटगताभिनयप्रभावसाक्षात्कारायमाणैकघनमानसनिश्चलाध्यवसेयः समस्तनाटकाद्यन्यतमकाव्यविशेषाच्च द्योतनीयोऽर्थः । स च यद्यप्यनन्तविभावाद्यात्मा तथापि सर्वेषां जडानां संविदि तस्याश्च भोक्तरि भोक्तृवर्गस्य च प्रधाने भोक्तरि पर्यवसानान्नायकाभिधानभोक्तविशेषस्थायिचित्तवृत्तिस्वभावः ।

---

१. K.S.S. M.G. निघण्टुं G.O.S. N.S. निघण्टु ।

स्थापितोऽर्थो भवेद्यत्र समासेनार्थसूचकः ।
धात्वर्थवचनेनेह निरुक्तं तत्प्रचक्षते[1] ॥ १३ ॥

सङ्ग्रहो यो मया प्रोक्तः समासेन द्विजोत्तमाः ।
विस्तरं तस्य वक्ष्यामि सनिरुक्तं सकारिकम् ॥ १४ ॥

शृङ्गारहास्यकरुणा रौद्रवीरभयानकाः ।
बीभत्साद्भुतसंज्ञौ चेत्यष्टौ नाट्ये रसाः स्मृताः ॥ १५ ॥

सा चैकचित्तवृत्तिः स्वपरकीयमिति (परमिति प्रतीय) मानानन्तचिवृत्त्यन्तरशतविशेषिता लौकिकगीतगेयपदादिलास्याङ्गदशकोपजीवनस्वीकृतलक्षणगुणा अलङ्कारगीतातोद्यादिसम्यक्सुन्दरीभूतकाव्यमहिमप्रयोगमालाऽभ्यासविशेषाश्रयत्वात् प्रच्याविता अत एव साधारणीभूततया सामाजिकानपि स्वात्मसद्भावेन समावेशयन्ती तादात्म्यादेव चानुमानागमयोगिप्रत्यक्षादिकरणकतटस्थप्रमातृप्रमेयपरकीयलौकिकचित्तवृत्तिविलक्षणतया निर्भासमाना परिमितस्वात्मान्याश्रयतानिर्भासनाविरहाच्च लौकिकप्रमदादिजनितनिजरतिशोकादिवत् षड्ज (तज्ज) हानादिचित्तवृत्त्यन्तरजननाक्षमा तत एव निर्विघ्नस्वसंवेदनात्मक (हर्ष) विश्रान्तिलक्षणेन रसनापरपर्यायेण व्यापारेण गृह्यमाणत्वाद्रसशब्देनाभिधीयते ।

तेन रस एव नाट्यम् । यस्य व्युत्पत्तिः फलमित्युच्यते । तथा च रसादृत (ना. शा. ६-३१) इत्यत्रैकवचनोपपत्तिः । ततश्च मुख्यभूतात् महारसात् स्फोटदृशीवासत्यानि वा अन्विताभिधानदृशीवोपायात्मकानि सत्यानि वा अभिहितान्वयदृशीव तत्समुदायरूपाणि वा रसान्तराणि भागा (वा) भिनिवेशदृष्टानि रूप्यन्ते । तद्वक्ष्यन्ते "काव्यार्थान् भावयन्ति" इति । तेन प्रथमं रसाः । ते च नव । शान्तापलापिनस्त्वष्टाविति तत्र पठन्ति ।

तत्र कामस्य सकलजातिसुलभतयाऽत्यन्तपरिचितत्वेन सर्वान्प्रतिहृत्येति (हृद्यतेति) पूर्वं शृङ्गारः । तदनुगामी च हास्यः निरपेक्षभावत्वात् । तद्विपरीतस्ततः करुणः । ततस्तन्निमित्त रौद्रः । स चामर्षप्रधानः । ततः कामार्थयोर्धर्ममूलत्वाद्वीरः । स हि धर्मप्रधानः । तस्य च भीताभयप्रदानसारत्वात् । तदनन्तरं भयानकः । तद्विभावसाधारण्यसंभावनात् । ततो बीभत्सः इति यद्वीरेणाक्षिप्तम् । वीरस्य पर्यन्तेऽद्भुतः फलमित्यनन्तरं तदुपादानम् । तथा च वक्ष्यते "पर्यन्ते कर्तव्यो नित्यं हि रसोऽद्भुतः ।" (ना. शा. १८-४३) इति ।

---

१. K.S.S. विदुर्बुधाः M.G. N.S. G.O.S. प्रचक्षते ।

एते ह्यष्टौ रसाः प्रोक्ता द्रुहिणेन महात्मना ।
पुनश्च भावान्वक्ष्यामि स्थायिसञ्चारिसत्त्वजान् ॥ १६ ॥

रतिर्हासश्च शोकश्च क्रोधोत्साहौ भयं तथा ।
जुगुप्सा विस्मयश्चेति स्थायिभावाः प्रकीर्तिताः ॥ १७ ॥

निर्वेदग्लानिशङ्काख्यास्तथासूया मदः श्रमः ।
आलस्यं चैव दैन्यं च चिन्ता मोहः स्मृतिर्धृतिः ॥ १८ ॥

व्रीडा चपलता हर्ष आवेगो जडता तथा ।
गर्वो विषाद औत्सुक्यं निद्रापस्मार एव च ॥ १९ ॥

सुप्तं विबोधो[1]ऽमर्षश्चाप्यवहित्थमथोग्रता ।
मतिर्व्याधिस्तथो[2]न्मादस्तथा मरणमेव च ॥ २० ॥

ततस्त्रिवर्गात्मकप्रवृत्त(त्ति)धर्मविपरीतनिवृत्त(त्ति)धर्मात्मको मोक्षफलः शान्तः । तत्र स्वात्मावेशेन रसचर्वणेत्युक्तम् ।

स च विभावादिबलादिति भावा वक्तव्याः । तत्र नाज्ञातलौकिकरत्यादि-चित्तवृत्तेः कवेर्नटस्य वा तद्विषयविशिष्टविभावाद्याहरणं शक्यमिति स्थायिन उद्दिष्टाः । तत्र शान्तस्य स्थायी 'विस्मयशमा" इति कैश्चित्पठितः । उत्साह एवास्य स्थायीत्यन्ये । जुगुप्सेति केचित् । सर्व इत्येके । तत्त्वज्ञानजो निर्वेदोऽस्य स्थायी । एतदर्थमेत्रोभयधर्मोपजीवित्वख्यापनायामङ्गलभूतोऽप्यसौ पूर्वं निर्दिष्टो व्यभिचारित्वा(षु । अ)भिनयत्वो(स्यो)पजीवका इति (तदनन्तरं) सात्त्विकाः । स्थायिषु च सङ्ख्या नोक्तेत्यपरे । अत एव स्थायिन एते तु व्यभिचारिणोऽपि भवन्ति । एतच्चग्रे वितनिष्यामः ।

व्यभिचारिण एत इत्युभयतो नियमार्थं सङ्ख्योपादानम् । सात्त्विका व्यभिचारिवृत्तमभिनयवृत्तं चोपजीवन्तीति पृथगभिनयादिभ्यो गणिताः ।

चत्वार इति । आहार्यस्यापि धनुःप्रतिशीर्षकमुकुटादेः प्रत्यक्षबुद्धावुपयोगे-ऽन्तरङ्गत्वं सूचयति । **नाट्यसंश्रया** इति । लोके तु कदाचिन्न भवत्यपि गृहीत-

---

१. K.S.S. M.G. प्रबोधः G.O.S. N.S. विबोधः ।
२. K.S.S. M.G. अथ G.O.S. N.S. तथा ।

त्रासश्चैव वितर्कश्च विज्ञेया व्यभिचारिण: ।
त्रयस्त्रिंशदमी भावा: समाख्यातास्तु नामत: ॥ २१ ॥

स्तम्भ: स्वेदोऽथ रोमाञ्च: स्वरभ[1]ङ्गोऽथ वेपथु: ।
वैवर्ण्यमश्रु प्रलय इत्यष्टौ सात्त्विका: स्मृता: ॥ २२ ॥

आङ्गिको वाचिकश्चैव ह्या[2]हार्य: सात्त्विकस्तथा ।
चत्वारोऽभिनया ह्येते विज्ञेया नाटयसंश्रया: ॥ २३ ॥

त्वात् । नाटचे तु त एव जीवितम् । अत एव रसभावानन्तरमभिनया उद्दिष्टा: । (१४-२३)

अभिनयाश्च लौकिकं धर्मं तन्मूलमेव तदुपजीविनं सामयिकं वानुवर्तन्त इत्यतस्तदनन्तरं धर्मी । न चाभिनयोऽभिनेतव्यमन्तरेणास्तीति दशरूपकयोगद्वारेण तदुपकारिण्यो वृत्तय: । द्वे तिस्र: पञ्चेति निराकरणाय **चतस्र** इत्युक्तम् । ता अपि देशवशाद्भूयसा भवन्तीति तदनन्तरं प्रवृत्तय: । सर्वमेतत्सिद्धिपर्यवसानमिति ततो द्विविधा सिद्धि: । स्वरा: पाठ्यं गानसंगृहीता अपि पृथगुपात्ता: । केवलानामपि प्रयोगोपरञ्जकत्वं यल्लक्ष्ये दृश्यते यत्रान्तरालाप इति प्रसिद्धिस्तदभ्युपगमार्थम् । **लक्षणान्वितमिति** । अन्यत्तु मल्लकपटफलकज्वालामुखपक्षवाद्यादि लौकिकं नैतत्सङ्गृहीतं वाध्यत्वादित्यर्थ: । एतच्चान्ते लक्ष्यते । यदपि चतुर्विधं न सर्वमिदं बहुलचर्मकारादिवाद्यमपि च वक्ष्यमाणलक्षणान्वितम् । आतूद्यतेऽभिहन्यत इत्यर्थ: । पुष्करशब्दश्रवणादागतं पुष्करवर्तकदेवताधिष्ठितं पद्मपत्राकारं चर्मपुटभावं चेति पौष्करम् । हन्यते कलासाम्यार्थमिति घन: । अत एव तालैकप्रमाणत्वात्स्वरवर्णसम्भवात्ताल इत्युक्त: कांस्यतालादि: । **एवकार:** काहलादिव्युदासाय ।

पात्रस्य **प्रवेशे** भावप्रकृत्यवस्थानादिसूचकं यद्गीयते तत्**प्रवेशगानम्** । प्रविष्टस्यान्तर्गतां चित्तवृत्तिं सामाजिकान्प्रति प्रसादयितुं प्रथयितुं **प्रसादगानम्** । रसान्तरोपक्षेपार्थ**माक्षेपगानम्** । **आन्तरमिति** गतिपरिक्रमणनिरूपणादिरवसर: । तत्र यद्गीयते **तदान्तरं** गानम् । पात्रस्य निष्क्रमणे तु **निष्क्रामगानम्** । प्रवेशा-

---

१. K.S.S. M.G. स्वरसाद: G.O.S. N.S. स्वरभङ्ग: ।
२. K.S.S. M.G. N.S. omit हि G.O.S. reads it.

लोकधर्मी नाट्यधर्मी धर्मीति[1] द्विविधः स्मृतः ।
भारती सात्वती चैव कैशिक्यारभटी तथा ॥ २४ ॥

चतस्रो वृत्तयो ह्येता यासु नाट्यं प्रतिष्ठितम् ।
आवन्ती दाक्षिणात्या च तथा चैवौढ्रमागधी ॥ २५ ॥
पाञ्चालमध्यमा चेति विज्ञेयास्तु प्रवृत्तयः[2] ।
दैविकी मानुषी चैव सिद्धिः स्याद्द्विविधैव तु ॥ २६ ॥
शारीराश्चैव वैणाश्च[3] सप्त षड्जादयः स्वराः ।
[निषादर्षभगान्धारमध्यपञ्चमधैवताः[4] ॥]
ततं चैवावनद्धं च घनं सुषिरमेव च ॥ २७ ॥

चतुर्विधं च विज्ञेयमातोद्यं लक्षणान्वितम् ।
ततं तन्त्रीगतं ज्ञेयमवनद्धं तु पौष्करम् ॥ २८ ॥

घनस्तु तालो विज्ञेयः सुषिरो वंश एव च ।
प्रवेशाक्षेपनिष्क्रामप्रासादिकं[1]मथान्तरम् ॥ २९ ॥

दय उपचाराद्गाने । प्रसादोऽस्य प्रयोजनं प्रासादिकम् । अन्ये तु समासान्मत्वर्थीयं ठनं कृत्वा प्रसादिकमिति । ध्रुवा गीत्याधारो नियतः पदसमूहः । तत्र योगेन युज्यमानतया समन्वितं तदर्थप्राधान्येन नियतरूपत्वादिति गानस्य गान्धर्वाद्भेदः सूचितः ।

कक्ष्याविभागेन गत्युपकारेण सर्वाभिनयानुभावोपकारी गानातोद्योपकारी च मण्डपः । यथोक्तम् "यश्चाप्यास्यगतो भाव" (ना. शा. २-२०) इति, तथा

---

१. K.S.S. M.G. तु G.O.S. N.S. इति ।

२. K.S.S. M.G. पाञ्चाली मध्यमा चैव ज्ञेया नाट्य प्रवृत्तयः G.O.S. N.S. पाञ्चालमध्यमा चेति विज्ञेयास्तु प्रवृत्तयः ।

३. K.S.S. M.G. शारीरा वैणवाश्चैव G.O.S. N.S. शारीराश्चैव वैणाश्च ।

४. K.S.S. N.S. M.G. do not read this varse G.O.S. reads it.

१. K.S.S. निष्कामप्रासारिकमथापरम् M.G. निष्कामप्रासादिकमथान्तरम् G.O.S. N.S. निष्क्रामप्रासादिकमथान्तरम् ।

गानं पञ्चविधं ज्ञेयं ध्रुवायोगसमन्वितम् ।
चतुरश्रो विकृष्टश्च रङ्गस्त्र्यश्रश्च कीर्तितः ॥ ३० ॥

एवमेषोऽल्पसूत्रार्थो निर्दिष्टो[1] नाटयसंग्रहः ।
अतः परं प्रवक्ष्यामि सूत्रग्रन्थविकल्पनम् ॥ ३१ ॥

"गम्भीरस्वरता येन कुतपस्य" इत्यादि (ना. शा. २-८२) । रङ्गेणैव च कक्ष्याविभागः सङ्गृहीत इति नानुद्(द्दि)ष्टं कक्ष्यायाः । (२४-३०)

एतदुपसंहरत्येवमित्यादिना । एवमुद्देशविभागभेदेन द्विधा सङ्ग्रहमभिधाय लक्षणपरीक्षे वक्तुं प्रतिजानीते—**अतःपरमिति** । **सूत्रग्रन्थविकल्पनमिति** । सूत्रं सूत्रकं लक्षणं वक्ष्यामि । तेनैव च कारिका सङ्गृहीता । ग्रन्थो भाष्यम् । तत्कृतं च विकल्पनमाक्षेपप्रतिसमाधानात्मकमिति परीक्षा निरुक्तशब्दवाच्या प्रतिज्ञाता । सूत्रविवरणस्वभावा तु कारिका सूत्रमपि प्रकाशयन्ती बहुतराक्षेपसमाधानव्याकुलशिष्यजन(नं) स्थित(र)पक्षनिरूपणेनोपकरोतीति भाष्यस्य पश्चादस्याः पाठः ।

एवं सूत्रं भाष्यं परीक्षां च प्रवक्ष्यामीति प्रतिज्ञाय रसविषयमेव सूत्रप्रभृति प्रथमं वक्तव्यमित्यत्र परिकरबन्धं घटयितुमाह—**तत्रेति** । तेषां रसादीनां मध्ये । एवकारोऽवधारणे । **तावदिति** क्रमे । अभितः आदितः मूलग्रन्थपरीक्षाक्रमेण विभज्याख्यास्यामः ।

उद्देशक्रमस्यैव पर्यनुयोज्यतामाशङ्क्यापरं क्रमहेतुमाह—**न ह्रीति** । **हि** यस्मात् रसं विना विभावादिरर्थो बुद्धौ व्याख्येयतया न प्रवर्तते यतश्च तं विनाऽर्थः प्रयोजनं प्रीतिपुरस्सरं व्युत्पत्तिमयं न प्रवर्तते यतश्च रसं प्रत्यादृते रसनात्मकप्रतीत्येकघनविश्रान्ते सामाजिकलोकेऽन्यो भावादिरर्थः प्रविभागेन बुद्धौ न वर्तते । सर्वस्य जडस्य चित्तवृत्त्यन्तरोपकृतप्रधानस्थायिनामधेयचित्तवृत्तिमग्नत्वेन विभावानुभावादिवर्गस्यावभासात् । अतो व्याख्यातृनटसामाजिकाभिप्रायेण तस्यैव प्राधान्यमिति रस एव तावत्पूर्वमुद्दिष्ट इति तस्यैव लक्षणादि कर्तव्यमिति तात्पर्यम् ।

पूर्वत्र बहुवचनमत्र चैकवचनं प्रयुञ्जानस्यायमाशयः—एक एव तावत्परमार्थतो रसः सूत्रस्थानीयत्वेन रूपके प्रतिभाति । तस्यैव पुनर्भागदृशा विभागः ।

---

१. K.S.S. M.G. व्यादिष्टः G.O.S. N.S. निर्दिष्टः ।

तत्र रसानेव तावदादावभिव्याख्यास्या[1]मः ।

न हि रसादृते कश्चिद[2]र्थः प्रवर्तते ।

तत्र[3] विभावानुभावव्यभिचारिसंयोगाद्रसनिष्पत्तिः ।

सोऽपि च न तदेकमुखप्रेक्षितामतिवर्तते । एतच्चोद्देश एवास्माभिरभिहितचरम् । अभिधास्यते चाग्रे ।

एवं क्रमहेतुमभिधाय रसविषयं लक्षणसूत्रमाह—**विभावानुभावव्यभिचारिसंयोगाद्रसनिष्पत्तिः** । अत्र **भट्टलोल्लट**प्रभृतयस्तावदेवं व्याचख्युः—विभावादिभिः संयोगोऽर्थात् स्थायिनस्ततो रसनिष्पत्तिः । तत्र विभावश्चित्तवृत्तेः स्थाय्यात्मिकाया उत्पत्तौ कारणम् अनुभावाश्च न रसजन्या अत्र विवक्षिताः । तेषां रसकारणत्वेन गणनानर्हत्वात् । अपि तु भावानामेव । (ते) येऽनुभावाः व्यभिचारिणश्च चित्तवृत्त्यात्मकत्वात् यद्यपि न सहभाविनः स्थायिना तथापि वासनात्मनेह तस्य विवक्षिताः । दृष्टान्तेऽपि व्यञ्जनादिमध्ये कस्यचिद्वासनात्मकता स्थायिवत् । अन्यस्योद्भूतता व्यभिचारिवत् । तेन स्थाय्येव विभावानुभावादिभिरुपचितो रसः । स्थायी भवत्वनुपचितः । स चोभयोरपि । [मुख्यया वृत्त्या रामादौ] अनुकार्येऽनुकर्तर्यपि चानुसन्धानबलात्—इति ।

चिरन्तनानां चायमेव पक्षः । तथा हि **दण्डिना** स्वालङ्कारलक्षणेऽभ्यधायि ।

"रतिः शृङ्गारतां गता । रूपबाहुल्ययोगेन" इति (काव्यादर्शे २-२८१)

"अधिरुह्य परां कोटिं कोपो रौद्रात्मतां गतः ।" (२-२८३) इत्यादि च ।

एतन्नेति **श्रीशङ्कुकः** । विभावाद्ययोगे स्थायिनो लिङ्गाभावेनावगत्यनुपपत्तेर्भावानां पूर्वमभिधेयताप्रसङ्गात् स्थितदशायां लक्षणान्तरवैयर्थ्यात् मन्दतरतममाध्यस्थ्याद्यानन्त्यापत्तेः, हास्यरसे षोढात्वाभावप्राप्तेः, कामावस्थासु दशस्वसङ्ख्यरसभावादिप्रसङ्गात्, शोकस्य प्रथमं तीव्रत्वं कालात्तनुमान्द्यदर्शनं क्रोधोत्साहरतीनाममर्षस्थैर्यसेवाविपर्यये ह्रासदर्शनमिति विपर्ययस्य दृश्यमानत्वाच्च ।

तस्माद्धेतुभिर्विभावाख्यैः कार्यैश्चानुभावात्मभिः सहचारिरूपैश्च व्यभिचारिभिः प्रयत्नार्जिततया कृत्रिमैरपि तथानाभिमन्यमानैरनुकर्तृस्थत्वेन लिङ्ग-

१. K.S.S. M.G. अभिधास्यामः G.O.S. N.S. व्याख्यास्यामः ।

२. K.S.S. M.G. कश्चिदपि G.O.S. N.S. कश्चित् ।

३. K.S.S. omits तत्र G.O.S. N.S. M.G. retain it.

बलतः प्रतीयमानः स्थायी भावो मुख्यरामादिगतस्थाय्यनुकरणरूपः। अनुकरणरूपत्वादेव च नामान्तरेण व्यपदिष्टो रसः।

विभावा हि काव्यबलानुसन्धेयाः। अनुभावाः शिक्षातः। व्यभिचारिणः कृत्रिमनिजानुभावार्जनबलात्। स्थायी तु काव्यबलादपि नानुसन्धेयः। 'रतिः शोक' इत्यादयो हि शब्दा रत्यादिकमभिधेयीकुर्वन्त्यभिधानत्वेन। न तु वाचिकाभिनयरूपतयाऽवगमयन्ति। न हि वागेव वाचिकम्। अपि तु तया निर्वृत्तम्। अङ्गैरिवाङ्गिकम्। तेन—

[“विवृद्धात्माऽप्यगाधोऽपि दुरन्तोऽपि महानपि।]
बाडवेनेव जलधिः शोकः क्रोधेन पीयते॥” इति।

तथा—

“शोकेन कृतः स्तम्भः तथा स्थितो योऽनवस्थिताक्रन्दैः।
[हृदयस्फुटनभयार्तैर्रुदितुमभ्यर्थ्यते सचिवैः।’

इत्येवमादौ न शोकोऽभिनेयः। अपि त्वभिधेयः।

“भाति पतितो लिखन्त्याः [तस्या बाष्पाम्बुशीकरकणौघः।
स्वेदोद्गम इव करतलसंस्पर्शादेष मे वपुषि॥’] (रत्ना २-११)

इत्यनेन तु वाक्येन स्वार्थमभिदधता उदयनगतः सुखात्मा रतिः स्थायीभावोऽभिनीयते न तूच्यते। अवगमनशक्तिर्ह्यभिनयनं वाचकत्वादन्या। अत एव स्थायिपदं सूत्रे भिन्नविभक्तिकमपि नोक्तम्। तेन रतिरनुक्रियमाणा शृङ्गार इति तदात्मकत्वं तत्प्रभवत्वं च युक्तम्। अर्थक्रियापि मिथ्याज्ञानदृष्टा (नाद्दृष्टा)—

[“मणिप्रदीपप्रभयोर्मणिबुद्ध्याभिधावतोः।
मिथ्याज्ञानाविशेषेऽपि विशेषोऽर्थक्रियां प्रति॥” इति।]

न चात्र नर्तक एव सुखीति प्रतिपत्तिः। नाप्ययमेव राम इति। न चाप्ययं न सुखीति। नापि रामः स्याद्वा न वायमिति। न चापि तत्सदृश इति। किन्तु [सम्यङ्मिथ्यासंशयसादृश्यप्रतीतिभ्यो विलक्षणा चित्रतुरगादिन्यायेन] यः सुखी रामः असावयमिति प्रतीतिरस्तीति। तदाह—

“प्रतिभाति न सन्देहो न तत्त्वं न विपर्ययः।
धीरसावयमित्यस्ति नासावेवायमित्यपि॥
विरुद्धबुद्धिसम्भेदादविवेचितसंप्लवः।
युक्त्या पर्यनुयुज्येत स्फुरन्ननुभवः कया॥” इति।

तदिदमप्यन्तस्तत्त्वशून्यं न विमर्दक्षममित्युपाध्यायाः । तथा हि—अनुकरण-रूपो रस इति यदुच्यते तत्किं सामाजिकप्रतीत्यभिप्रायेण उत नटाभिप्रायेण किं वा वस्तुवृत्तविवेचकव्याख्यातृबुद्धिसमवलम्बनेन 'यथाहुर्व्याख्यातारः खल्वेवं विवेचयन्ति' इति ।

अथ भरतमुनिवचनानुसारेणाद्यः पक्षोऽसङ्गतः । किञ्चिद्धि प्रमाणेनोपलब्धं तदनुकरणमिति शक्यं वक्तुम् । यथा, 'एवमसौ सुरां पिबति' इति सुरापानानु-करणत्वेन पयःपानं प्रत्यक्षावलोकितं प्रतिभाति । इह च नटगतं किं तदुपलब्धं सदनुकरणतया भातीति चिन्त्यम् । तच्छरीरं तन्निष्ठं प्रतिशीर्षकादि रोमा-ञ्चकगद्गदिकादिभुजाक्षेपवलनप्रभृति भ्रूक्षेपकटाक्षादिकं च न रतेश्चित्तवृत्तिरू-पतयानुकारत्वेन कस्यचित्प्रतिभाति । जडत्वेन[भिन्नेन्द्रियग्राह्यत्वेन] भिन्नाधि-करणत्वेन च ततोऽतिवैलक्षण्यात् । मुख्या[मुख्या]वलोकने च तदनुकरणप्रति-भासः । न च रामगतां रतिमुपलब्धपूर्विणः केचित् । एतेन रामानुकारी नट इत्यपि निरस्तः प्रवादः ।

अथ नटगता चित्तवृत्तिरेव प्रतिपन्ना सती रत्यनुकारः शृङ्गार इत्युच्यते, तत्रापि किमात्मकत्वेन सा प्रतीयत इति चिन्त्यम् । ननु प्रमदादिभिः कारणैः कटाक्षादिभिः कार्यैः धृत्यादिभिश्च सहचारिभिर्लिङ्गभूतैर्या लौकिकी कार्यरूपा कारणरूपा सहचारिरूपा च चित्तवृत्तिः प्रतीतियोग्या तदात्मकत्वेन सा नटचित्त-वृत्तिः प्रतिभाति हन्त तर्हि रत्याकारेणैव सा प्रतिपन्नेति दूरे रत्यनुकरणतावा-चोयुक्तिः ।

ननु ते विभावादयोऽनुकार्ये पारमार्थिकाः । कारणता त्वनुकर्तरि न तथेति विशेषः । अस्त्वेवम् । किन्तु ते हि विभावादयोऽतत्कारणातत्कार्यातत्सहचार-रूपा अपि काव्यशिक्षादिबलोपकल्पिता कृत्रिमाः सन्तः किं कृत्रिमत्वेन सामाजिकैः गृह्यन्ते न वा । यदि गृह्यन्ते तदा तैः कथं रतेरवगतिः ।

नन्वत एव तत्प्रतीयमानं रत्यनुकरणबुद्धेः कारणम् । कारणान्तरप्रभवेषु हि कार्येषु (सु)शिक्षितेन न तथा ज्ञाने वस्त्वन्तरस्यानुमानं तावद्युक्तम् । असु-शिक्षितेन तु तस्यैव प्रसिद्धस्य कारणस्य । यथा वृश्चिकविशेषाद्गोमयस्यैवानु-मानम् । वृश्चिकस्यैव तत्परं मिथ्याज्ञानम् । यत्रापि लिङ्गज्ञानं मिथ्या तत्रापि न तदाभासानुमानमयुक्तम् । न हि बाष्पाद्धूमत्वेन ज्ञातादनुकारप्रतिभासमाना-दपि लिङ्गात्तदनुकारानुमानं(नम)युक्तम् ।

धूमानुकारत्वेन हि ज्ञायमानान्नीहारान्नाटच(न्य)नकारजपापुष्प-

नन्वक्रुद्धोऽपि नटः क्रुद्ध इव भाति । सत्यम् । क्रुद्धेन सदृशः । सादृश्यं च भ्रुकुट्यादिभिः । गौरिव गवयेन मुखादिभिरिति । नैतावताऽनुकारः कश्चित् । न चापि सामाजिकानां सादृश्यमतिरस्ति । सामाजिकानां च न भावशून्या नर्तके प्रतिपत्तिरित्युच्यते । अथ च तदनुकारप्रतिभास इति रिक्ता वाचोयुक्तिः ।

यच्चोक्तं रामोऽयमित्यस्ति प्रतिपत्तिः तदपि यदि तदात्वेति(वि)निश्चितं तदुत्तरकालभाविबाधकवैधुर्याभावे कथं न तत्त्वज्ञानं स्यात् । बाधकसद्भावे वा कथं न मिथ्याज्ञानम् । वास्तवेन च वृत्ते बाधकानुदयेऽपि मिथ्याज्ञानमेव स्यात् । तेन विरुद्धबुद्धिसंभेदादित्यसत् । नर्तकान्तरेऽपि च रामोऽयमिति प्रतिपत्तिरस्ति । ततश्च रामत्वं सामान्यरूपमित्यायातम् ।

यच्चोच्यते विभावाः काव्यादनुसन्धीयन्ते(इति) तदपि न विद्मः । न हि 'ममेयं सीता काचित्' इति स्वात्मीयत्वेन प्रतिपत्तिर्नटस्य । अथ सामाजिकस्य तथा प्रतीतियोग्याः क्रियन्त इत्येतदेवानुसन्धानमुच्यते तर्हि स्थायिनि सुतरामनुसन्धानं स्यात् । तस्यैव हि मुख्यत्वेन 'अस्मिन्नयम्' इति सामाजिकानां प्रतिपत्तिः ।

यत्तु 'वाग्वाचिकम्' इत्यादिना भेदाभिधानसंरम्भगर्भमहीयानभिनयरूपताविवेकः कृतः स उत्तरत्र स्वावसरे(ना. शा. अ-१४)चर्चयिष्यते । तस्मात्सामाजिकप्रतीत्यनुसारेण स्थाय्यनुकरणं रस इत्यसत् ।

न चापि नटस्येत्थं प्रतिपत्तिः 'रामं तच्चित्तवृत्तिं वाऽनुकरोमि' इति । सदृशकरणं हि तावदनुकरणमनुपलब्धप्रकृतिना न शक्यं कर्तुम् । अथ पश्चात्करणमनुकरणं तल्लोकेऽप्यनुकरणात्मतातिप्रसक्ता । अथ न नियतस्य कस्यचिदनुकारः अपि तूत्तमप्रकृतेः शोकमनुकरोति तर्हि केनेति चिन्त्यम् । न तावच्छोकेन तस्य तदभावात् । न चाश्रुपातादिना शोकस्यानुकारः तद्वैलक्षण्यादित्युक्तम् । इयत्तु स्यात्-उत्तमप्रकृतेर्ये शोकानुभावाःताननुकरोमीति । तत्रापि कस्योत्तमप्रकृतेः । यस्य कस्यचिदिति चेत्सोऽपि विशिष्टतां विना कथं बुद्धावारोपयितुं शक्यः । य एवं रोदितीति चेत्स्वात्मापि मध्ये नटस्यानुप्रविष्ट इति गलितोऽनुकार्यानुकर्तृभावः ।

किञ्च नटः शिक्षावशात्स्वविभावस्मरणाच्चित्तवृत्तिसाधारणीभावेन हृदयसंवादात्केवलमनुभावान्प्रदर्शयन् काव्यमुपचितकाकुप्रभृत्युपस्कारेण पठंश्चेष्टत

इत्येतावन्मात्रेऽस्य प्रतीतिर्नत्वनुकारं वेदयते। कान्तवेषानुकारवद्धि न रामचेष्टितस्यानुकारः। एतच्च प्रथमाध्यायेऽपि दर्शितमस्माभिः। नापि वस्तुवृत्तानुसारेण तदनुकारत्वम्। अनुसंवेद्यमानस्य वस्तुवृत्तत्वानुपपत्तेः। यच्च वस्तुवृत्तं तद्दर्शयिष्यामः। न च मुनिवचमेवंविधमस्ति क्वचित्स्थाय्यनुकरणं रसा इति। नापि लिङ्गमत्रार्थे मुनेरुपलभ्यते। प्रत्युत ध्रुवागानतालवैचित्र्यलास्याङ्गोपजीवनं(न)निरूपणादि विपर्यये लिङ्गमिति सन्ध्यङ्गाध्यायान्ते वितनिष्यामः। 'सप्तद्वीपानुकरणम्' (ना. शा. १-११७) इत्यादि त्वन्यथापि शक्यगमनिकमिति। तदनुकारेऽपि च क्व नामान्तरं कान्तवेषगत्यनुकरणादौ।

यच्चोच्यते वर्णकैर्हरितालादिभिः संयुज्यमान एव गौरित्यादि। तत्र यद्यभिव्यज्यमान इत्यर्थोऽभिप्रेतः। तदसत्। न हि सिन्दूरादिभिः पारमार्थिको गौरभिव्यज्यते प्रदीपादिभिरिव। किन्तु तत्सदृशः समूहविशेषो निर्वर्त्यते। अत एव हि सिन्दूरादयो गवावयवसन्निवेशसदृशेन सन्निवेशविशेषेणावस्थिता गोसदृगिति प्रतिभासस्य विषयः। नैवं विभावादिसमूहो रतिसदृशताप्रतिपत्तिग्राह्यः। तस्माद्भावानुकरणं रसा इत्यसत्।

येन त्वभ्यधायि—सुखदुःखजननशक्तियुक्ता विषयसामग्री बाह्यैव। साङ्ख्यदृशा सुखदुःखस्वभावो रसः। तस्यां च सामग्र्यां द(त)लस्थानीया विभावाः। संस्कारकाः अनुभावव्यभिचारिणः। स्थायिनस्तु तत्सामग्रीजन्या आन्तराः सुखदुःखस्वभावा इति। तेन 'स्थायिभावान् रसत्वम्' इत्यादावुपचारमङ्गीकुर्वता ग्रन्थविरोधं स्वयमेव बुध्यमानेन दूषणाविष्करणमौर्ख्यात् प्रामाणिको जनः परिरक्ष(क्षि)त इति किमस्योच्यते। यत्त्वत्यन्तं नः प्रतीतिवैषम्यप्रसङ्गादि तत्किं यदत्रोच्यताम्।

भट्टनायकस्त्वाह—रसो न प्रतीयते। नोत्पद्यते। नाभिव्यज्यते। स्वगतत्वेन हि प्रतीतौ करुणे दुःखित्वं स्यात्। न च सा प्रतीतिर्युक्ता। सीतादेरविभावत्वात् स्वकान्तास्मृत्यसंवेदनात्। देवतादौ साधारणीकरणायोग्यत्वात्। समुद्रलङ्घनादेरसाधारण्यात्। न च तद्वतो रामस्य स्मृतिः। अनुपलब्धत्वात्। न च शब्दानुमानादिभ्यः तत्प्रतीतौ लोकस्य सरसता प्रयुक्ता(सताऽपि युक्ता) प्रत्यक्षादिव। नायकयुगलकावभासे हि प्रत्युत लज्जाजुगुप्सास्पृहादिस्वोचितचित्तवृत्त्यन्तरोदयव्यग्रतयाकाश (यानेक) रसत्वमथापि स्यात्। तन्न प्रतीतिरनुभवस्मृत्यादिरूपा रसस्य युक्ता। उत्पत्तावपि तुल्यमेतद्दूषणम्। शक्तिरूपत्वेन पूर्वं स्थितस्य पश्चादभिव्यक्तौ विषयार्जनतारतम्यापत्तिः। स्वगतत्वपरगतत्वादि च पूर्ववद्विकल्प्यम्।

तस्मात्काव्ये दोषाभावगुणालङ्कारमयत्वलक्षणेन नाट्ये चतुर्विधाभिनयरूपेण निबिडनिजमोहसङ्कटकारिणा विभावादिसाधारणीकरणात्मनाऽभिधातो द्वितीयेनांशेन भावकत्वव्यापारेण भाव्यमानो रसोऽनुभवस्मृत्यादिविलक्षणेन रजस्तमोऽनुवेधवैचित्र्यबलाद्द्रुतिविस्तारविकासलक्षणेन सत्त्वोद्रेकप्रकाशानन्दमयनिजसंविद्विश्रान्तिलक्षणेन परब्रह्मास्वादसविधेन भोगेन परं भुज्यत इति।

तत्र पूर्वपक्षोऽयं भट्टलोल्लटपक्षानभ्युपगमादेव नाभ्युपगत इति तद्दूषणमनुत्थानोपहतमेव। प्रतीत्यादिव्यतिरिक्तश्च संसारे को भोग इति न विद्मः। रसनेति चेत्। सापि प्रतिपत्तिरेव। केवलमुपायवैलक्षण्यान्नामान्तरं प्रतिपद्यतां दर्शनानुमितिश्रुत्युपमिति प्रतिभानादिनामान्तरवत्। निष्पादनाभिव्यक्तिद्वयानभ्युपगमे च नित्यो वा असद्वा रस इति न तृतीया गतिरस्याम्। न चाप्रतीतं वस्त्वस्ति व्यवहारे योग्यम्।

अथोच्यते—प्रतीतिरिति तस्य भोगीकरणम्। तच्च भू(र)त्यादिस्वरूपम्। तदस्तु। तथापि न तावन्मात्रम्। यावन्तो हि रसास्तावन्त एव रसनात्मानः प्रतीतयो भोगीकरणस्वभावाः। (सत्त्वादि)गुणानां चाङ्गाङ्गिवैचित्र्यमनन्तं कल्प्यमिति कर्तृ (का त्रि)त्वेनेयत्ता—

("अभिधा भावना चान्या तद्भोगीकृतमेव च।
अभिधाधामतां याते शब्दार्थालङ्कृती ततः॥)

भावनाभाव्य एषोऽपि शृङ्गारादिगणो भ(हि)यत्)यत्।
(तद्भोगीकृतरूपेण व्याप्यते सिद्धिमान्नरः॥") इति।

यत् "काव्येन भाव्यन्ते रसाः" इत्युच्यते तत्र विभावादिजनितचर्वणात्मकास्वादरूपप्रत्ययगोचरतापादनमेव यदि भावनं तदभ्युपगम्यत एव।

यत्तूक्तम्—

"संवेदनाख्य(ख्यया) व्यङ्ग्यपरसंवित्तिगोचरः।
आस्वादनात्माऽनुभवो रसः काव्यार्थ उच्यते॥" इति।

तत्र व्यज्यमानतया व्यङ्ग्यो लक्ष्यते। अनुभवेन च तद्विषयः इति मन्तव्यम्।

नन्वेवं कथं रसतत्त्वमास्ताम्।

किं कुर्मः ।

आम्नायसिद्धे किमपूर्वमेत-
त्संविद्विकासेऽधिगतागमित्वम् ।
इत्थं स्वयंग्राह्यमहार्हहेतु-
द्वन्द्वेन किं दूषयिता न लोकः ॥

ऊर्ध्वोर्ध्वमारुह्य यदर्थतत्त्वं
धीः पश्यति श्रान्तिमवेदयन्ती ।
फलं तदाद्यैः परिकल्पितानां
विवेकसोपानपरम्पराणाम् ॥

चित्रं निरालम्बनमेव मन्ये
प्रमेयसिद्धौ प्रथमावतारम् ।
सन्मार्गलाभे सति सेतुबन्ध-
पुरप्रतिष्ठादि न विस्मयाय ॥

तस्मात्सतामत्र न दूषितानि
मतानि तान्येव तु शोधितानि ।
पूर्वप्रतिष्ठापितयोजनासु
मूलप्रतिष्ठाफलमामनन्ति ॥

तदुच्यतां परिशुद्धतत्त्वम् ।

उक्तमेव मुनिना न त्वपूर्वं किञ्चित् । तथाह्याह—काव्यार्थान् भावयन्ति" इति (ना. शा. अ-७) तत्काव्यार्थो रसः ।

यथा हि 'रात्रिमासत । 'तामग्नौ प्रादात्' इत्यादावर्थितादिलक्षितस्याधिकारिणः प्रतिपत्तिमात्रादतितीव्रप्ररोचिततात्प्रथमप्रवृत्तादनन्तरमधिकैवोपात्तकालतिरस्कारेणैवास्ते (से)प्रददानीत्यादिरूपा संक्रमणादिस्वभावा यथादर्शनप्रतिभाभावनाविध्युद्योगादिभाषाभिर्व्यवहृता प्रतिपत्तिस्तथैव काव्यात्मकादपि शब्दादधिकारिणोऽधिकाऽस्ति प्रतिपत्तिः ।

अधिकारी चात्र विमलप्रतिभानशालिहृदयः । तस्य च "ग्रीवाभङ्गाभिरामम् ।" इति (शाकु-अ.१) "उमापि नीलालक" इति (कुमा-३-६२) 'हरस्तु किञ्चित्' (कुमा-३.६७) इत्यादिवाक्येभ्यो वाक्यार्थप्रतिपत्तेरनन्तरं मानसी साक्षात्कारात्मिकाऽपहसिततत्तद्वाक्योपात्तकालादिविभागा तावत्प्रतीतिरुपजायते । तस्यां च यो मृगपोतकादिर्भाति तस्य विशेषरूपत्वाभावाद्भीत इति त्रासकस्यापारमार्थिकत्वाद्भयमेव परं देशकालाद्यनालिङ्गितम् । तत एव 'भीतोऽहं भीतोऽयं शत्रुर्वयस्यो मध्यस्थो वा' इत्यादिप्रत्ययेभ्यो दुःखसुखादिकृतहानादिबुध्यन्तरोदयनियमवत् ? तय । विघ्नबहुलेभ्यो विलक्षणं निर्विघ्नप्रतीतिग्राह्यं साक्षादिव हृदये निविशमानं चक्षुषोरिव विपरिवर्तमानं भयानको रसः । तथाविधे हि भये नात्माऽत्यन्ततिरस्कृतो न विशेषत उल्लिखितः ।

एवं परोऽपि । तत एव न परिमितमेव साधारण्यम् । अपि तु विततम् । व्याप्तिग्रह इव धूमाग्न्योः । भयकम्पयोरेव वा तदत्र साक्षात्कारायमाणत्वे परिपोषिका नटादिसामग्री । यस्यां वस्तुसतां काव्यार्पितानां च देशकालप्रमात्रादीनां नियमहेतूनामन्योन्यप्रतिबन्धबलादत्यन्तमपसरणे स एव साधारणीभावः सुतरां पुष्यति । अत एव सर्वसामाजिकानामेकघनतयैव प्रतिपत्तेः (त्तिः) सुतरां रसपरिपोषाय । सर्वेषामनादिवासनाचित्रीकृतचेतसां वासनासंवादात् । सा चाविघ्ना संवित् । चमत्कारस्तज्जोऽपि कम्पपुलकोल्लुकसनादिर्विकारः । चमत्कारो यथा—

"अज्ज वि हरी चमक्कइ कहविण मंदरेण दळिआइ ।
चदकळादळसच्छीआइं ळच्छीएं अंगाइ ॥"

तथा हि—स चातृप्तिव्यतिरेकेणाविच्छिन्नो भोगावेश इत्युच्यते । भुञ्जानस्याद्भुतभोगस्पन्दाविष्टस्य च मनःकरणं चमत्कार इति । स च साक्षात्कारस्वभावो मानसोऽध्यवसायो वा सङ्कल्पो वा स्मृतिर्वा तथात्वेन स्फुरत्य(न्न)स्तु । । यदाह—

"रम्याणि वीक्ष्य मधुरांश्च निशम्य शब्दान्
पर्युत्सुको भवति यत्सुखितोऽपि जन्तुः ।
तच्चेतसा स्मरति नूनमबोधपूर्वं
भावस्थिराणि जननान्तरसौहृदानि ॥" (शाकु ५—) इत्यादि ।

अत्र हि स्मरतीति या स्मृतिरुपदर्शिता सा न तार्किकप्रसिद्धा । पूर्वमेतस्यार्थस्याननुभूतत्वात् । अपि तु प्रतिभानापरपर्यायसाक्षात्कारस्वभावेयमिति ।

सर्वथा तावदेषास्ति प्रतीतिरास्वादात्मा यस्यां रतिरेव भाति । तत एव विशेषान्तरानुपहितत्वात्सा रसनीया सती न लौकिकी न मिथ्या नानिर्वाच्या न लौकिकतुल्या न तदारोपादिरूपा । तथैव चोपचयावस्थासु देशाद्यनियन्त्रणादनुकारोऽप्यस्तु । भावानुगामितया करणात् विषयसामग्र्यपि भवतु विज्ञानवादावलम्बनात् । सर्वथा रसनात्मकवीतविघ्नप्रतीतिग्राह्यो भाव एव रसः ।

तत्र विघ्नापसारका विभावप्रभृतयः । तथा हि—लोके सकलविघ्नविनिर्मुक्ता संवित्तिरेव चमत्कारनिर्वेशरसनास्वादनभोगसमापत्तिलयविश्रान्त्यादिशब्दैरभिधीयते । विघ्नाश्चास्यां प्रतिपत्तावयोग्यता संभावनाविरहो नाम स्वगतत्वनियमेन देशकालविशेषावेशो निजसुखादिविवशीभावः प्रतीत्युपायवैकल्यं स्फुटत्वाभावो अप्रधानता संशययोगश्च ।

तथाहि—संवेद्यमसंभावयमानः संवेद्ये संविदं विनिवेशयितुमेव (यो) न शक्नोति का तत्र विश्रान्तिरिति प्रथमो विघ्नः । तदपसारणे हृदयसंवादो लोकसामान्यवस्तुविषयः । अलोकसामान्येषु तु चेष्टितेष्वखण्डितप्रसिद्धिजनितगाढारूढप्रत्ययप्रसरकारी प्रख्यातरामादिनामधेयपरिग्रहः । अत एव निस्सामान्योत्कर्षोपदेशव्युत्पत्तिप्रयोजने नाटकादौ प्रख्यातवस्तुविषयत्वादि नियमेन निरूपयिष्यते । न तु प्रहसनादाविव । तच्च स्वावसर एव वक्ष्याम इत्यास्तां तावत् ।

स्वैकगतानां च सुखदुःखसंविदामास्वादे यथासंभवं तदपगमभीरुतया वा तत्परिरक्षाव्यग्रतया वा तत्सदृशार्जिजीषया वा तज्जिहासया वा तत्प्रचिख्यापयिषया वा तद्गोपनेच्छया वा प्रकारान्तरेण वा संवेदनान्तरसमुद्गम एव परमो विघ्नः ।

परगतत्वनियमभाजामपि सुखदुःखानां संवेदने नियमेन स्वात्मनि सुखदुःखमोहमाध्यस्थ्यादिसंविदन्तरोद्गमनसंभावनादवश्यंभावी विघ्नः । तदपाकरणे 'कार्यो नातिप्रसङ्गोऽत्र' (ना. शा. ५-१५८) इत्यादिना (पूर्वरङ्गविधिं प्रतीति) पूर्वरङ्गानिगूहनं ("नटीविदूषको वापि' इति लक्षित) प्रस्तावनावलोकनेन च यो नटरूपताधिगमस्तत्पुरस्सरः प्रतिशीर्षकादिना तत्प्रच्छादनप्रकारोऽभ्युपायः अलौकिकभाषादिभेदलास्याङ्गरङ्गपीठमण्डपगतकक्ष्यादिपरिग्रहनाट्यधर्मिसहितः। तस्मिन् हि 'तस्यैवात्रैवैतस्यैव च सुखं वा' इति न भवति । प्रतीतिस्वरूपस्य निह्नवात् । रूपान्तरस्य चारोपितस्य प्रतिभासंविद्विश्रान्तिवैकल्येन स्वरूपे विश्रान्त्यभावात् । सत्ये तदीयरूपनिह्नवमात्र एव पर्यवसानात् ।

तथा हि—आसीनपाठ्यपुष्पगन्धिकादि लोके न दृष्टम् । न च नन्न किञ्चित् । कथञ्चित्संभाव्यत्वात् इति का एष सर्वो मुनिना साधारणीभाव-

सिद्धया रसचर्वणोपयोगित्वेन परिकरबन्धः समाश्रित इति तत्रैव स्फुटीभविष्यतीति तदिह तावन्नोद्यमनीयम् । ततः स एष स्वपरनियतताविघ्नापसरणप्रकारो व्याख्यातः ।

निजसुखादिविवशीभूतश्च कथं वस्त्वन्तरे संविदं विश्रामयेदिति तत्प्रत्यूहव्यपोहनाय प्रतिपादार्थनिष्ठैः साधारण्यमहिम्ना सकलभोग्यत्वसहिष्णुभिः शब्दादिविषयमयीभि (मयैः) रातोद्यगानविचित्रमण्डपपदविदग्धगणिकादिभिरुपरञ्जनं समाश्रितम् । येनाहृदयोऽपि हृदयवैमल्यप्राप्त्या सहृदयीक्रियते । उक्तं हि "दृश्यं श्रव्यं च" (ना. शा. १-११) इति ।

किञ्च प्रतीत्युपायानामभावे कथं प्रतीतिः । स्फु (अस्फु) टप्रतीतिकारिशब्दलिङ्गसम्भवेऽपि न प्रतीतिर्विश्राम्यति । स्फुटप्रतीतिरूपप्रत्यक्षोचितप्रत्ययसाकाङ्क्षत्वात् ।

यथाऽऽहुः 'सर्वा चेयं प्रमितिः प्रत्यक्षपरा' (न्यायसू. भा. १-३) इति । स्वसाक्षात्कृते आगमानुमानशतैरप्यनन्यथाभावस्य स्वसंवेदनात् । अलातचक्रादौ साक्षात्कारान्तरेणैव बलवता तदवधारणादिति लौकिकस्तावदयं क्रमः । तस्मात्तदुभयविघ्नविघातेऽभिनया लोकधर्मिवृत्तिप्रवृत्त्युपस्कृताः समभिषिच्यन्ते । अभिनयनं हि सशब्दलिङ्गव्यापारविसदृशमेव प्रत्यक्षव्यापारकल्पमिति निश्चेष्यामः ।

अप्रधाने च वस्तुनि कस्य संविद्विश्राम्यति । तस्यैव प्रत्ययस्य प्रधानान्तरं प्रत्यनुधावतः स्वात्मन्यविश्रान्तत्वात् । अतोऽप्रधानत्वं जडे विभावानुभाववर्गे व्यभिचारिनिचये च संविदात्मकेऽपि नियमेनान्यमुखसंप्रेक्षिणि संभवतीति तदतिरिक्तः स्थाय्येव तथा चर्वणापात्रम् ।

तत्र पुरुषार्थनिष्ठाः काश्चित्संविद इति (एव) प्रधानम् । तद्यथा—रतिः कामः तदनुषङ्गिधर्मार्थनिष्ठा । क्रोधस्तत्प्रधानेष्वर्थनिष्ठः । कामधर्मपर्यवसितोऽप्युत्साहः समस्तधर्मादिपर्यवसितः । तत्त्वज्ञानजनितनिर्वेदप्रायो विभावो मोक्षोपाय इति तावदेषां प्राधान्यम् । यद्यपि चैषामप्यन्योन्य गुणभावोऽस्ति तथापि तत्तत्प्रधाने रूपके तत्तत्प्रधानं भवतीति रूपकभेदपर्यायेण सर्वेषां प्राधान्यमेषां ल (व) क्ष्यते । अदूरभागाभिनिविष्टदृशस्त्वेकस्मिन्नपि रूपके पृथक्प्राधान्यम् ।

तत्र सर्वेऽमी सुखप्रधानाः । स्वसंविच्चर्वणरूपस्यैकघनस्य प्रकाशस्यानन्दसारत्वात् । तथा हि—एकघनशोकसंविच्चर्वणेऽपि लोके स्त्रीलोकस्य हृदयाविश्रान्तिरन्तरायशून्यविश्रान्तिशरीरत्वात् (सुखस्य) । अविश्रान्तिरूपतैव दुःखम् । तत एव कापिलैर्दुःखस्य चाञ्चल्यमेव प्राणत्वेनोक्तं रजोवृत्तितां वदद्भिरित्यानन्दरूपता सर्वरसानाम् ।

किन्तूपरञ्जकविषयवशात्तेषामपि कटुकिं नास्ति । स्पर्शो वीरस्य । स हि क्लेशसहिष्णुतादिप्राण एव । एवं रत्यादीनां प्राधान्यम् । हासादीनां तु सातिशयं सकललोकसुलभविभावतयोपरञ्जकत्वमिति (न) प्राधान्यम् । अत एवानुत्तमप्रकृतिषु बाहुल्येन हासादयो भवन्ति । पामरप्रायः सर्वोऽपि हसति शोचति बिभेति परनिन्दामाद्रियते । अल्पसुखभाषितत्वेन च सर्वत्र विस्मयते । रत्याद्यङ्गतया तु पुमर्थोपयोगित्वमपि स्यादेषाम् । एतद्गुणप्रधानभावकृत एव च दशरूपकादिभेद इति वक्ष्यामः ।

स्थायित्वं चैतावतामेव । जात एव हि जन्तुरियतीभिः संविद्भिः परीतो भवति । तथा हि—

"दुःखसंश्लेषविद्वेषी सुखास्वादनसादरः ।"

इति न्यायेन सर्वो रिरंसया व्याप्तः स्वात्मन्युत्कर्षमानितया परमुपहसन्नभीष्टवियोगसंतप्तस्तद्धेतुषु कोपपरवशोऽशक्तौ च ततो भीरुः किञ्चिदार्जिजीषुरप्यनुचितवस्तुविषयवैमुख्यात्मकतयाक्रान्तः किञ्चिदनभीष्टतयाऽभिमन्यमानस्तत्तत्स्वकर्तव्यदर्शनसमुदितविस्मयः किञ्चिच्च जिहासुरेव जायते । न ह्येतच्चित्तवृत्तिवासनाशून्यः प्राणी भवति । केवलं कस्यचित्काचिदधिका चित्तवृत्तिः काचिदूना । कस्यचिदुचितविषयनियन्त्रिता कस्यचिदन्यथा । तत्काचिदेव पुमर्थोपयोगिनीत्युपदेश्या । तद्विभाव(ग) कृतश्चोत्तमप्रकृत्यादिव्यवहारः ।

ये पुनरमी ग्लानिशङ्काप्रभृतयश्चित्तवृत्तिविशेषास्ते समुचितविभावाभावाज्जन्ममध्येऽपि न भवन्त्येव । तथा हि—रसायनमुपयुक्तवतो मुनेर्ग्लान्यालस्यश्रमप्रभृतयो नोत्तिष्ठन्ति । यस्यापि भवन्ति विभावबलात्तस्यापि हेतुप्रक्षये क्षीयमाणाः संस्कारशेषतां तावत् नावश्यमनुबध्नन्ति । उत्साहादयस्तु संपादितस्वकर्तव्यतया प्रलीनकल्पा अपि संस्कारशेषतां नातिवर्तन्ते । कर्तव्यान्तरविषयस्योत्साहादेरखण्डनात् ।

यथाह **पतञ्जलिः**—"न हि चैत्र एकस्यां स्त्रियां रक्त इत्यन्यासु विरक्तः ।" (पातञ्जल. व्यास. भा. २.४) इत्यादि ।

तस्मात्स्थायिरूपचित्तवृत्तिसूत्रस्यूता एवामी व्यभिचारिणः स्वात्मानमुदयास्तमयवैचित्र्यशतसहस्रधर्माणं प्रतिलभमाना रक्तनीलादिसूत्रस्यूतविरलभावो (गो) पलम्भनसम्भावितभङ्गीसहस्रगर्भस्फटिककाचभ्र (भ्रा) मकपद्मरागमरकतमहानीलादिमयगोलकवत्तस्मिन् सूत्रे स्वसंस्कारवैचित्र्यमनिवेशयन्तोऽपि तत्सूत्रकृतमुपकारसन्दर्भं बिभ्रतः स्वयं च विचित्रार्थस्थायिसूत्रं च विचित्रयन्तोऽन्तरान्तरा शुद्धमपि स्थायिसूत्रं प्रतिभासावकाशमुपनयन्तोऽपि पूर्वापरव्यभि-

चारिरतनच्छायाशबलिमानमवश्यमानयन्तः प्रतिभासन्त इति व्यभिचारिण उच्यन्ते।

तथा हि—ग्लानोऽयमित्युक्ते कुत इति हेतुप्रश्नेन स्थायी तस्य सूच्यते। न तु राम उत्साहशक्तिमानित्यत्र हेतुप्रश्नमाहुः। अत एव विभावास्तत्रोद्बोधकाः सन्तः स्वरूपोपरञ्जकत्वं विदधाना रत्युत्साहादेरुचितानुचितत्वमात्रमावहन्ति। न तु तदभावे सर्वथैव ते निरुपाख्याः। वासनात्मना सर्वजन्तूनां तन्मयत्वेनोक्तत्वात्। व्यभिचारिणां तु स्वविभावाभावे नामापि नास्तीति। वितनिष्यते चैतद्यथायोगं व्याख्यावसरे। एवमप्रधानत्वनिरासः स्थायिनिरूपणायां "स्थायिभावान् रसत्त्वम् (ना. शा. अ-६) इत्यनया सामान्यलक्षणशेषभूतया विशेषलक्षणनिष्ठया च कृतः।

तत्रानुभावानां विभावानां व्यभिचारिणां च पृथक्स्थायिनि नियमो नास्ति। बाष्पादेरानन्दाक्षिरोगादिजत्वदर्शनात्। व्याघ्रादेश्च क्रोधभयादिहेतुत्वात्। 'भ्र (श्र) मचिन्तादेरुत्साहभयाद्यनेकसहचरत्वावलोकन......... व्यभिचारिणि। तथा हि—बन्धुविनाशो यत्र विभावः परिदेविताश्रुपातादिस्त्वनुभावः चिन्तादैन्यादिर्व्यभिचारी सोऽवश्यं शोक एवे (व वे) त्येवं संशयोदये शङ्कात्मकविघ्नशमनाय संयोग उपात्तः।

तत्र लोकव्यवहारे कार्यकारणसहचारात्मकलिङ्गदर्शने स्थाय्यात्मपरचित्तवृत्त्यनुमानाभ्यासपाटवादधुना तैरेवोद्यानकटाक्षवीक्षादिभिर्लौकिकीं कारणत्वादिभुवमतिक्रान्तैर्विभावनानुभावनासमुपरञ्जकत्वमात्रप्राणैः, अत एवालौकिकविभावादिव्यपदेशभाग्भिः प्राच्यकारणादिरूपसंस्कारोपजीवनख्यापनाय विभावादिनामधेयव्यपदेश्यैर्भावाध्यायेऽपि वक्ष्यमाणस्वरूपभेदैर्गुणप्रधानतापर्यायेण सामाजिकधियि सम्यग्योगं सम्बन्धमैकाग्र्यं वाऽऽसादितवद्भिरलौकिकनिर्विघ्नसंवेदनात्मकचर्वणागोचरतां नीतोऽर्थश्चर्व्यमाणतैकसारो न तु सिद्धस्वभावः तात्कालिक एव न तु चर्वणातिरिक्तकालावलम्बी स्थायिविल (चिल) क्षण एव रसः। ननु (न तु) यथा शङ्कुकादिभिरभ्यधीयत, "स्थाय्येव विभावादिप्रत्याय्यो रस्यमानत्वाद्रस उच्यते।" इति। एवं हि लौकिकोऽपि किं न रसः। असतोऽपि हि यत्र रसनीयता स्यात्तत्र वस्तुमतः कथं न भविष्यति। तेन स्थायिप्रतीतिरनुमितितरूपा प्राच्या (प्या)। न रसः। अत एव सूत्रे स्थायिग्रहणं न कृतम्। तत्प्रत्युत शल्यभूतं स्यात्। केवलमौचित्यादेवमुच्यते स्थायी रसीभूत इति। औचित्यं तु तत्स्थायिगतत्वेन कारणादितया प्रसिद्धानामधुना चर्वणोपयोगितया विभावादित्वावलम्बनात्।

तथा (दा) हि लौकिकचित्तवृत्त्यनुमाने का रसता। तेनालौकिकचमत्कारात्मा रसास्वादः स्मृत्यनुमानलौकिकसंवेदनविलक्षण एव।

तथाहि—लौकिकेनानुमानेन संस्कृतः प्रमदादिना (दि न) ताटस्थ्येन प्रतिपद्यते । अपि तु हृदयसंवादात्मकसहृदयत्वबलात्पूर्णीभविष्यद्रसास्वादाङ्कुरीभावेनानुमानस्मृत्यादिसोपानमारुह्येव तन्मयीभावोचितचर्वणाप्राणतया । न च सा चर्वणा प्राङ्मानान्तरात् येनाधुना स्मृतिः स्यात् । न चात्र लौकिकप्रत्यक्षादिप्रमाणव्यापारः । किन्त्वलौकिकविभावादिसंयोगबलोपनतैवेयं चर्वणा । सा च प्रत्यक्षानुमानादिलौकिकप्रमाणजनितरत्याद्यवबोधतः तथा योगिप्रत्यक्षजगिततटस्थपरसंवित्तिज्ञानात्सकलवैषयिकोपरागशून्यशुद्धपरयोगिगतस्वात्मानन्दैकघनानुभवाच्च विशिष्यते । एतेषां यथायोगमर्जनादिविघ्नान्तरोदयात्ताटस्थ्येऽस्फुटत्वविषयावेशवैवश्यकृतसौन्दर्यविरहात् । अत्र तु स्वात्मैकगतत्वनियमासंभवात् (न विषयावेशवैवश्यम्) स्वानुप्रवेशात्परगतत्वनियमाभावात् (न ताटस्थ्यास्फुटत्वं) तद्विभावादिसाधारण्यवशसंप्रबुद्धोचितनिजरत्यादिवासनावेशवशाच्च न विघ्नान्तरादीनां सम्भव इत्यवोचाम बहुशः । अत एव विभावादयो न निष्पत्तिहेतवो रसस्य । तदबोधापगमेऽपि रससंभवप्रसङ्गात् । नापि ज्ञप्तिहेतवः येन प्रमाणमध्ये पतेयुः । सिद्धस्य कस्यचित्प्रमेयभूतस्य रसस्याभावात् । किं तर्ह्येतद्धि विभावादय इति । अलौकिक एवायं चर्वणोपयोगी विभावादिव्यवहारः । क्वान्यत्रेत्थं दृष्टमिति चेद्भूषणमेतदस्माकमलौकिकत्वसिद्धौ । पानकरसास्वादोऽपि किं गुडमरीचादिषु दृष्ट इति समानमेतत् ।

नन्वेवं रसोऽप्रमेयः स्यादेवम् । युक्तं भवितुमर्हति । रस्यतैकप्राणो ह्यसौ न प्रमेयादिस्वभावः । तर्हि सूत्रे निष्पत्तिरिति कथम् ? नेय रसस्य, अपि तु तद्विषयरसनायाः । तन्निष्पत्त्या तु यदि तदेकायत्तजीवितस्य रसस्य निष्पत्तिरुच्यते न कश्चिदत्र दोषः । सा च रसना न प्रमाणव्यापारो न कारकव्यापारः । स्वयं तु नाप्रामाणिकः, स्वसंवेदनसिद्धत्वात् । रसना च बोधरूपैव । किन्तु बोधान्तरेभ्यो लौकिकेभ्यो विलक्षणैव । उपायानां विभावादीनां लौकिकवैलक्षण्यात् । तेन विभावादिसंयोगाद्रसना यतो निष्पद्यतेऽतस्तथाविधरसनागोचरो लोकोत्तरोऽर्थो रस इति तात्पर्यं सूत्रस्य ।

अयमत्र संक्षेपः । मुकुटप्रतिशीर्षकादिना तावन्नटबुद्धिराच्छाद्यते । गाढप्राक्तनसंवित्संस्काराच्च काव्यबलानीयमानापि न तत्र रामधीर्विश्राम्यति । अत एवोभयदेशकालत्यागः । रोमाञ्चादयश्च भूयसा रतिप्रतीतिकारितया दृष्टास्तत्रापि लौकिका (त्रावलोकिता) देशकालानियमेन तत्र रतिं गमयन्ति । यस्यां स्वात्माऽपि तद्वासनावत्त्वादनुप्रविष्टः । अत एव न तटस्थतया रत्यवगमः । न च नियतकारणतया । येनार्जनाभिषङ्गादिसम्भावना । न च नियतपरात्मैकगततया । येन दुःखद्वेषाद्युदयः । तेन साधारणीभूता सन्तानवृत्तेरेकस्या एव वा संविदो गोचरभूता रतिः शृङ्गारः । साधारणी(भावना च)विभावादिभिरिति । तत्र विभावप्राधान्यस्य धामणिमया (प्राधान्येन साधारणीभावो यथा—)

"केलीकन्दलितस्य विभ्रममधो(:)धुर्यं वपुस्ते दृशो-
र्भङ्गी भङ्गुरकामकार्मुकमिदं भ्रूर्नर्मकर्मक्रमः ।
आपाते (घ्रातो)ऽपि विकारकारणमहो वक्त्राम्बुजन्माऽऽसवः
सत्यं सुन्दरि वेधसस्त्रिजगतीसारः त्वमेका कृतिः ॥"

अत्र च विभावकृतं तत्सौन्दर्यं प्राधान्येन भाति । तदनुगतत्वेन केलीविभ्रमभङ्गुरनर्मवचोमहिम्ना चानुभाववर्गो भङ्गीक्रमविकारादिशब्दवलाच्च व्यभिचारिवर्गः प्रतिभातीत्यत एव नास्फुटत्वाशङ्काऽत्र रत्यास्वादमये शृङ्गारे विधेया ।

अनुभावप्राधान्यं यथा शुद्धसारस्वतप्रवाहपवित्रसकलवाङ्मयमहार्णवपूर्णभावसंपादनात् द्विजराजस्येन्दुराजस्य—

"यद्विश्रम्य विलोकितेषु बहुशो निःस्थेमनी लोचने
यद्गात्राणि दरिद्रति प्रतिदिनं लूनाब्जिनीनालवत् ।
दूर्वाकाण्डविडम्बकश्च निबिडो यत्पाण्डिमा गण्डयोः
कृष्णे यूनि सयौवनासु वनितास्वेषैव वेषस्थितिः ॥" । इति ।

अत्र विश्रम्येति बहुश इति प्रतिदिनमिति च पदसमर्पितो व्यभिचारिगणः कृष्ण इत्यादिपदार्पितश्च विभावो गुणत्वेन प्रतिभासते । विश्रान्तिलक्षणस्तम्भविलोकनवैचित्र्यगात्रतानवतारतम्यपुलकवैवर्ण्यप्रभृतिस्त्वनुभावसञ्चयः प्रधानतया । व्यभिचारिणां तु प्राधान्यं तद्विभावानुभावप्राधान्यकृतम् । तत्राद्यम् । यथा महाकवेः **कालिदासस्य (कलशकस्य)** —

"आत्तमात्तमधिकान्तमी(मु)क्षितुं कातरा शफरशङ्किनी जहौ ।
अञ्जलौ जलमधीरलोचना लोचनप्रतिशरीरलाञ्छितम् ॥"

इत्यत्र सुकुमारप्रमदाजनभूषणभूतस्य व्यभिचारिवर्गस्य वितर्कत्रासशङ्कादेः प्राधान्यं तद्विभावानां प्राधान्यादि(त्)सौन्दर्यातिशयकृतम् । आत्तमित्याद्यर्पितानुभाववर्गस्तु तदनुयायी ।

एवं द्वयप्राधान्ये चोदाहार्यम् । किन्तु समप्राधान्य एव रसास्वादस्योत्कर्षः । तच्च प्रबन्ध एव भवति । वस्तुतस्तु दशरूपक एव । यदाह वामनः—"सन्दर्भेषु दशरूपकं श्रेयः । तद्धि चित्रं चित्रपटवद्विशेषसाकल्यात् ।" (काव्यालं.सू १.३.३०-३१) इति तद्रूपरसचर्वणया तु प्रबन्धे भाषावेषप्रवृत्त्यौचित्यादिकल्पनात् । तदुपजीवनेन मुक्तके । तथा च तत्र सहृदयाः पूर्वापरमुचितं परिकल्प्य ईदृगत्र वक्तास्मिन्नवसरे इत्यादि बहुतरं पीठबन्धरूपं विदधते । तेन ये काव्याभ्यास-

कोदृष्टान्तः । अत्राह—यथा हि नानाव्यञ्जनौषधिद्रव्यसंयोगाद्रसनिष्पत्तिः[1] तथा नानाभावोपगमाद्रसनिष्पत्तिः[2] । यथा हि—गुणादिभिर्द्रव्यैर्व्यञ्जनैरौषधिभिश्च षाड[3]वादयो रसा निर्वर्त्यन्ते[4] तथा[5] नानाभावोपगता[6] अपि

प्राक्तनपुण्यादिहेतुबलादिति (भिः) सहृदयास्तेषां परिमितविभावाद्युन्मीलनेऽपि परिस्फुट एव साक्षात्कारकल्पः काव्यार्थः स्फुरति । अत एव तेषां काव्यमेव प्रीतिव्युत्पत्तिकृदनपेक्षितनाट्यमपि । तेषामपि तु नाट्य "निपतिताः स्फुरिताः शशिरश्मयः" इति न्यायेन सुतरां निर्मलीकरणम् । अहृदयानां च तदेव नैर्मल्याधायि । यत्र पति(प्रती)ता गीतवाद्यगणिकादयो न व्यसनितायै पर्यवस्यन्ति नाट्योपलक्षणात् । तत्र च नटो ध्यायिनामिवेदंध्यानपदम् । न हि तत्रायमेव सिन्दूरादिमयो वासुदेवः स्मरणीय इति प्रतिपत्तिः । अपि तु तदुपायद्वारेणातिस्फुटीभूतसङ्कल्पगोचरो देवताविशेषो ध्यायिनां फलकृत् । तद्वन्नटप्रक्रिया द्वारोदितातिस्फुटाध्यवसायविषयीकृतो नियतदेशकालाद्यस्पृष्टो 'अत इदं फलम्' इति विधिस्थानीयोऽर्थो व्युत्पत्तिं वितरति । युते(यत्र)दृश्या(दृश्येऽ)न्यनियमादौ चित्तवृत्त्यादौ वा न बाधकोदयः सम्यग्ज्ञानभूतं ह्येवेदं पूर्णम् । तेन राम इत्येव प्रतीतिर्न त्वयं (यं न) रामोऽन्योऽयमिति । स्फुटीकरिष्यते चैतदग्रतः ।

तत्रालौकिकोऽयमर्थो न दृष्टान्तमन्तरेण हृदयङ्गमो भवेदित्याशयेनाह—**को दृष्टान्त** इति । बहूनां संयोगादपूर्वो रस उत्पद्यमानः क्व दृष्ट इत्यर्थः ।

अत्र प्रश्ने भाष्येण प्रतिवचनमाह—**यथे**त्यादिना **आप्नुवन्ती**त्यन्तेन । व्यञ्जनमुपसेचनद्रव्यम् । तच्च नानान्तप्रम(नानातिक्तम)धुरचुक्रादिभेदादधिकाञ्जिकादि । ओषधयश्चिञ्चागोधूमदलहरिद्रादयः । द्रव्यं गुडादि । एषां पाकक्रमेण सम्यग्योजनारूपात्कुशलसम्पाद्यात्संयोगात् । **षाडवादय** इति लोकप्रसिद्धेभ्यः परस्परविविक्तेभ्यो मधुरतिक्ताम्ललवणकटुकषायेभ्यो मिश्रेभ्यश्च

---

१. N.S. Reads भवति after रसनिष्पत्ति G.O.S. M.G. K.S.S. dc not read it.

२. N.S. does not read तथा नानाभावोपगमाद् रसनिष्पत्तिः । यथा हि G.O.S. K.S.S. M.G. read it.

३. K.S.S. M.G. षड् G.O.S. N.S. षाडवादयः ।

४. N.S. निवर्तन्ते G.O.S. M.G. K.S.S. निर्वर्त्यन्ते ।

५. K.S.S. M.G. एवं G.O.S. N.S. तथा ।

६. G.O.S. N.S. उपगता K.S.S. M.G. उपहिता ।

स्थायिनो भावा रसत्वमाप्नुवन्तीति । अत्राह[1]—रस इति कः पदार्थः । उच्यते—आस्वाद्यत्वात् । कथमास्वाद्यते[2] रसः । यथा हि नानाव्यञ्जनसंस्कृतमन्नं भुञ्जाना रसानास्वादयन्ति सुमनसः पुरुषा हर्षादींश्चाधिगच्छन्ति तथा नानाभावाभिनयव्यञ्जितान् वागङ्गसत्त्वोपेतान् स्थायिभावानास्वादयन्ति

विलक्षणः षाडवशब्दवाच्यः । तत्प्रधाना बहुतरा रसनयोग्याः क्रियन्ते । तथैव नानाभूतैर्विभावादिभिरुप समीपं प्रत्यक्षकल्पतां गता लोकापेक्षया ये स्थायिनो भावास्ते रस्यमानतैकजीविन रसत्वं तत्र प्रतिपद्यन्ते ।

एतदुक्तं भवति—पाकरूपया सम्यग्योजनया तावदलौकिको रसो जायते । तत्र च प्रधानत्वेन जलस्य रसाभिव्यञ्जकत्वमिति व्यञ्जनं विभावस्थानीयम् । चिञ्चाहरिद्राद्यनुभावप्रायम् । द्रव्याणि तु गुडा(दीनि)तदीयचुक्रादिरसविलक्षमधुरादियोगाद्व्यभिचारिकल्पम् । स्वात्मनि तदुपजीवनेन च परत्र च स्वरससङ्क्रमणया वैचित्र्याधायकत्वात् । अत्र तु स्थायिकल्पस्तन्मिश्रणासमयभावी रसविशेषो विभावकल्पव्यञ्जनजनितो मन्तव्यः । स हि लौकिकः । अयन्तु कुशलैकनिर्वर्त्यस्तद्विदां रसनीयो भवति । तेनाद(दनीय)स्येत्यध्याहारो न युक्तः । यथा हि दार्ष्टान्तिकसूत्रे स्थायिग्रहणं शल्यकल्पमिति त्रयमेवोपात्तं तथा दृष्टान्तेऽपि त्रयस्यैवोपादानं युक्तम् ।

एवं सूत्रं व्याख्याय लक्षणपदं परीक्षितुमाक्षिपति—**रस इति क** इत्यादिना । मधुरादौ पारदे विषये सारे जलसंस्कारेऽभिनिवेशे क्वाथे देहधातोर्नि (तौ नि) र्यासे वाऽयं प्रसिद्धो न त्वन्यत्र । तेन रस इति पदस्य शृङ्गारादिषु प्रवर्तितस्य कोऽर्थः । किं प्रवृत्तिनिमित्तं कथ्यते स्वाभिधेयनियमाय शब्देन यदि वा तत्प्रयोक्तृप्रतिपत्तृभिरिति । **अर्थः** प्रवृत्तिनिमित्तम् । **आस्वाद्यत्वात्** । प्रवृत्तिहेतोर्यतः प्रश्नस्तेनोत्तरं हेतुविभक्त्यैव दत्तम् । तेन क्रिया प्रवृत्तिनिमित्तमस्येत्युक्त भवति ।

यस्तु भङ्क्त्वा व्याचष्टे—रस इति योऽयं(**कोऽयं**)शब्दः । तत्रोत्तरम् । **पदार्थः । उच्यत इति** । तस्यानेनेत्यध्याहारं बिना प्रकृतपदार्थवाचकोऽयं शब्दः । इति [न]तात्पर्यकल्पनं विना नातीव सङ्गतमुत्तरम् । अन्नोत्तरम् । प्रश्नमन्तरेण **चास्वाद्यत्वादि**त्यल्पपदप्रायमित्यास्तामेतत् ।

---

१. K.S.S. ऋषय उचुः G.O.S. M.G. N.S. अत्राह ।

२. K.S.S. आस्वाद्यः G.O.S. M.G. N.S. आस्वाद्यते ।

३. K.S.S. M.G. चाप्यधिगच्छन्ति G.O.S. N.S. चाधिगच्छन्ति ।

सुमनसः प्रेक्षकाः हर्षादींश्चाधिगच्छन्ति[1] **। तस्मान्नाट्यरसा इत्यभिव्याख्याताः । अत्रानुवंश्यौ श्लोकौ भवतः—**

अथ प्रवृत्तिनिमित्तं व्याक्षिपति—**कथमास्वाद्यत** इति । आस्वादनं हि रसनेन्द्रियजज्ञानं प्रसिद्धमिति भावः । अत्रोपचरितक्रियाश्रयेणोत्तरमाह—**यथा नाने**त्यादिना । यथातथाशब्दाभ्यां सादृश्यमत्रोपचारे निमित्तमिति दर्शयति । तत्र भोग्यस्य भोक्तुः फलस्य च साम्यं दर्शयति । यथा हि व्यञ्जनसंस्कृतेऽन्ने आस्वाद्यता । एकाग्रमनसि च भोक्तर्यास्वादयितृता । अन्यचित्तस्य भुञ्जानस्याप्यास्वादाभिमानाभावात् । प्रहर्षाप्यायजीवनपुष्टिबलारोग्याणां चास्वादफलता । तथाभियव्यञ्जिते (तेऽपि) चिन्त्या । स्थायिशब्दव्यपदेश्ये रसे आस्वाद्यता । एकाग्रे च सामाजिके तन्मयीभूत आस्वादयितृता । हर्षप्रधानानां धर्मादिव्युत्पत्तिवैदग्ध्यादीनामास्वादफलत्वमिति कर्मकर्तृफलसादृश्याद्विभावादिजः प्रतीतिविशेषो रसनाक्रियेति व्यपदिष्ट इति तात्पर्यम् । येन सुमनसो भुञ्जाना हर्षादींश्च यान्ति तेन रसानास्वादयन्तीत्यनेन शब्देन । **अभितः** सर्वत्र । **विशेषेण** अन्यभोक्तृविलक्षणतया । **आ** समन्तात् । **ख्याताः** प्रसिद्धाः । यथा चैते तथा प्रेक्षका अपि । तेन तेऽपि स्थायिनः आस्वादयन्तीति आभिमुख्येन सादृश्ये व्याख्याता अस्माभिर्व्यवहृताः । अत्रोपसंहारः । तस्मान्नाट्यरसाः ।

अन्येत्वादिशब्देन शोकादीनामत्र सङ्ग्रहः । स च न युक्तः । सामाजिकानां हि हर्षैकफलं नाट्यं न शोकादिफलम् । तथात्वे निमित्ताभावात्तत्परिहारप्रसङ्गाच्चेति मन्यमाना **हर्षांश्चाधिग**च्छन्तीति पठन्ति ।

एवं ग्रन्थयोजनायां स्पष्टायां यत् **कैश्चि**दत्र चोदितं दृष्टान्ते आत्मा रसना मनश्चेति त्रयम् । प्रकृते तु रसनैवेति । परिहृतं चात्मन एवात्र स्थानान्तरसङ्क्रान्तस्य मनःस्थानीयता । मनसश्च रसनास्थानीयतेति । तत्सर्वं वृथा नाट्यमात्रम् । उपचारबीजस्य सादृश्यस्यात्र प्राधान्येन प्रतिपिपादयिषितत्वादित्यास्ताम् ।

एवं रसत्वं केन तेषामिति यत्प्रश्नितं तत्प्रतिसमाहितम् । **अत्रेति** भाष्ये अनुवंशे भवौ शिष्याचार्यपरम्परासु वर्तमानौ श्लोकाख्यौ वृत्तविशेषौ सूत्रार्थसंक्षेपप्रकटीकरणेन कारिकाशब्दवाच्यौ भवतः । तौ पठति—**यथे**त्यादि । मधुरादिभेदाद्बहूनि द्रव्याणि गुडादीनि । **बहुभिरिति** दधिकाञ्जिकादिभिः ।

---

१. K.S.S. does not read हर्षादींश्चाधिगच्छन्ति G.O.S. M.G. N.S. read it.

यथा बहुद्रव्ययुतैर्व्यञ्जनैर्बहुभिर्युतम् ।
आस्वादयन्ति भुञ्जाना भक्तं[1] भक्त[2]विदो जनाः ।। ३२ ।।
भावाभिनयसंबद्धान्स्थायिभावांस्तथा बुधाः[3] ।
आस्वादयन्ति मनसा तस्मान्नाटचरसाः स्मृताः ।। ३३ ।।

अनेन विभावभेदं रसभेदे हेतुत्वेन सूचयति । **भुञ्जाना आस्वादयन्तीति ।** रसनाव्यापाराद्भोजनाधिको यो मानसो व्यापारः स एवास्वादनमिति दर्शयति ।

एतदुक्तं भवति—न रसनाव्यापार आस्वादनम् । अपि तु मानस एव । स चात्राविकलोऽस्ति । केवलं लोके रसनाव्यापारानन्तरभावी स प्रसिद्ध इत्युपचार इह दर्शित इति । शुद्धतत्स्वरूपज्ञानस्वभावा अत्र **भावा** विभाव-व्यभिचारिणः । **अभिनया** अनुभावा एव । इयं(दं)पृथग्वचनं प्राधान्यात् । तैर्यैः सम्यग्**बद्धा** हृदयसंवादक्रमेण तन्मयीभावापन्नप्रमातृभूम्यभेदमुपसम्प्राप्ता अचिन्त्याः स्थायिनः **आ** समन्तात्साधारणीभावेन निर्विघ्नप्रतिपत्तिवशात् । **मनसा** इन्द्रियान्तरविघ्नसंभावनाशून्येन **स्वादयन्ति** स्वपरविवेकशून्यस्वादचमत्कारपरवशतया लौकिकात्प्रत्ययादुपार्जनादिविघ्नबहुलाद्योगिप्रत्ययाच्च विषयास्वादशून्यतापरुषाद्विलक्षणाकारसुखदुःखादिविचित्रवासनानुवेधोपनतहृद्यतातिशयसंविच्चर्वणात्मना भुञ्जते । **बुधा** इति पूर्वो(र्णो)पयोगो लौकिकानां प्रत्यक्षादीनामत्र दर्शितः ।

एतदुपसंहरति—**तस्मादिति** । नाटचात्समुदायरूपाद्रसाः । यदि वा नाटचमेव रसाः । रससमुदायो हि नाटचम् । (न)नाटच एव च रसाः । काव्येऽपि नाटचायमान एव रसः । काव्यार्थविषये हि प्रत्यक्षकल्पसंवेदनोदये रसोदय इत्यु**पाध्यायाः** ।

यदाहुः **काव्यकौतुके**—

"प्रयोगत्वमनापन्ने काव्ये नास्वादसम्भवः ।" इति ।
"वर्णनोत्कलिता भोगप्रौढोक्त्या सम्यगर्पिताः ।
उद्यानकान्ताचन्द्राद्या भावाः प्रत्यक्षवत्स्फुटाः ।।" इति ।।

---

१. K.S.S. मुक्तं, G.O.S. N.S. M.G. भक्तं ।
२. K.S.S. मुक्त G.O.S. N.S. M.G. भक्त ।
३. K.S.S. भावाभिनयसंयुक्ताः स्थायिभावास्ततो बुधाः । M.G. भावाभिनयसंयुक्ताः स्थायिभावांस्तथा बुधाः । G.O.S. N.S. भावाभिनयसंबद्धान्स्थायिभावांस्तथभा बुधाः ।

अन्ये तु काव्येऽपि गुणालङ्कारसौन्दर्यातिशयकृतं रसचर्वणमाहुः । वयं तु ब्रूमः—काव्यं तावन्मुख्यतो दशरूपकात्मकमेव । तत्र ह्युचितैर्भाषावृत्तिकाकुनैपथ्यप्रभृतिभिः पूर्यते रसवत्ता । सर्गबन्धादौ हि नायिकाया अपि संस्कृतैवोक्तिरित्यादि बहुतरमनुचितं केवलं शक्तिरहितत्वाद्व्यावर्ण्यते । तावतीव हृद्यमिति न्यायेनानौचित्यं न प्रतिहारि (न प्रतिजहाति) । तत एवोच्यते 'सन्दर्भेषु दशरूपकम्' (वामन. का.) इति । तेन तदंश (दङ्ग) सन्ध्यादिसङ्घटनमुद्धव्य सर्गबन्धादि यावन्मुक्तं (वतकम्) । यत्तु दशरूपकं तस्य योऽर्थस्तदेव नाटचम् । यद्वक्ष्यते 'नाटचस्यैषा तनूः' (ना. शा. १४.२) इति । तस्य हृदयसंवादतारतम्यापेक्षया श्रोतृप्रतिपत्तृस्फुरणं स्फुटत्वेनातिविचित्रम् । तत्र ये स्वभावतो निर्मलमुकुरहृदयास्त एव संसारोचितक्रोधमोहाभिलाषपरवशमनसो न भवन्ति । तेषां तथाविधदशरूपकाकर्णनसमये साधारणरसनात्मकचर्वणग्राह्यो रससञ्चयो नाटचलक्षणः स्फुट एव । ये त्वतथाभूतास्तेषां प्रत्यक्षोचिततथाविचर्वणालाभाय नटादिप्रक्रिया । स्वगतक्रोधशोकादिसङ्कटहृदयग्रन्थिभञ्जनाय गीतादिप्रक्रिया च मुनिना विरचिता । सर्वानुग्राहकं हि शास्त्रमिति न्यायात् । तेन नाटच एव रसा न लोक इत्यर्थः । काव्यञ्च नाटचमेव ।

अत एव च नटे न रसः कुत्र तर्हि । विस्मृतिशीलो न बौध्यते । उक्तं हि देशकालप्रमातृभेदानि (न्नि) यन्त्रितो रस इति । केयमाशङ्का । नटे तर्हि किम् । आस्वादनोपायः । अत एव च पात्रमित्युच्यते । न हि पात्रे मद्यास्वादः । अपि तु तदुपायकः । तेन प्रमुखमात्रे नटोपयोग इत्यलम् ।

चित्रपुस्ताद्यपि च नाटचस्यैवार्थभागाभिष्यन्दो यथा सर्गबन्धादिशब्दभागाभिष्यन्दः । एतच्च 'योऽर्थो हृदयसंवादी ।' (ना. शा. ७.१०) इत्यत्र वितत्य वक्ष्यामः ।

अन्ये त्वभिनयादिसामग्रीमयं बहिर्दृश्यमानं नाटचं नटधर्मः कर्म रूपमित्याशयेन नाटचाद्रसा इत्याहुः । स्मृता इति सम्प्रदायाविच्छेदं दर्शयति । ये तु रत्याद्यनुकरणरूपं रसमाहुः अथ चोदयन्ति शोकः कथं सुखहेतुरिति । परिहरन्ति च अस्ति कोऽपि नाठ्यगतानां विशेष इति । तत्र चोद्यं तावदसत् । शोको हि प्रतीयमानः किं स्वात्मनि प्रत्येतुर्दुःखं वितनोतीति नियमः । शत्रुदुखे प्रहर्षात् । अन्यत्र च मध्यस्थत्वात् । उत्तरं तु भावानां वस्तुस्वभावमात्रेणे (त्रते) ति न किञ्चिदत्र तत्त्वम् ।

अस्मन्मते संवेदनमेवानन्दघनमास्वाद्यते । तत्र का दुःखाशङ्का । केवलं तस्यैव चित्रताकरणे रतिशोकादिवासनाव्यापारः । तदुद्बोधने चाभिनयादिव्यापारः । (३३)

अत्राह—किं रसेभ्यो भावानामभिनिर्वृत्ति[1] रुताहो भावेभ्यो रसानामिति। केषाञ्चिन्मतं परस्परसम्बन्धादेशामभिनिर्वृत्तिरिति। तन्न। कस्मात्? दृश्यते हि भावेभ्यो रसानामभिनिर्वृत्तिर्न तु रसेभ्यो भावानामभिनिर्वृत्तिरिति। भवन्ति चात्र श्लोकाः—

यदेतदुक्तं रसतत्त्व तदेवोपशोधयितुमुपक्रमते—अत्राहेत्यादिना चोद्यमुखेन। नर्तकगतेभ्यो रसेभ्यो भावः सामाजिके। यथा करुणाच्छोकः। ततो विभाव सुपचितसामाजिके करुण इति रसाद्भावो भावाद्रस इति सन्देहः। अत एव परस्परमपि जन्म कालभेदेनेति तृतीयः पक्षः। यदि वा नट एव राम एव चापूर्वं भाव। तत उपचये रसः। ततोऽप्यपचये भाव इत्येवं पक्षत्रयोत्थानम्। इदं चासत्। एवम्भूतस्य रसस्वरूपस्य निराकृतत्वात्।

श्रीशङ्कुकस्त्वाह—अनुकर्तरि रसानास्वादय तोऽनुकार्ये भावप्रतीतिः प्रयोगे। लोके प्रकृतिं(तिः) रसं निष्पादयतीति। द्वितीयपक्षो नाट्याचार्याभिप्रेत-शिक्षानुसारेण। अत एव च तृतीयोऽपि संभवति। एतदप्यसत्। न हि सामाजिकोऽनुकार्यानुकर्तृ विभागमवैति। दूषितः स्वा(तश्चा)नुकरणवादः।

तस्मादित्थमेतत्—किं रसेभ्यो भावा उत विपर्ययः आहो अन्योन्यजनकतेति त्रयः प्रश्नाः। आहोशब्दो भिन्नक्रमः। विभावादिभ्यस्तावद्रसनिष्पत्ति-रुक्ता। स एव द्वितीयः पक्षोऽभ्युपगतपूर्वमे (गतः पूर्वम् ए)तच्च कथम्। न हि लोके विभावानुभावादयः केचन भवन्ति। हेतुकार्यावस्थामात्रत्वाल्लोके, तेषाम्। अथ त एव रसनोपयोगित्वे विभावादिरूपतां प्रतिपद्यन्ते। तर्हि रसप्रसादाद्भावा विभावादयः। अथोच्यते विभावादिप्रसादाद्रसो यथोक्तं प्राक्। रसप्रसादाच्च विभावादिरूपत्वम्। तर्हि परस्पराश्रयत्वम्। इतरेतराश्रयाणि च न प्रकल्पन्त इत्याक्षेपः।

अत्र सिद्धान्तमाह—दृश्यते हीति। प्रमदादयः प्रतीता सन्तो रसास्वादं विधदते यथोक्त प्राक्। अतो न रसेभ्यो भावाः। भावशब्दार्थपर्यालोचनया चैतदेवोपपन्नमिति श्लोकेनाह—नानाभिनयैः सम्यग्बद्धान् हृदयं गतान् भावयन्ति सम्पादयन्ति रसांस्तस्माद्भावाः। (३४)

नन्वेतद्भावशब्दप्रवृत्तिनिमित्तम्। न तत्प्रकृतं किञ्चिदुक्तमित्याशङ्क्य प्रकृते योजयितुमाह—नानाद्रव्यैरिति। व्यज्यत इति व्यञ्जनञ्चानुपानादि

---

१. G.O.S. M.G. अभिनिर्वृत्तिः K.S.S. अभिनिर्वृतिः N.S. अभिनिष्पतिः।

नानाभिनयसम्बद्धान्भावयन्ति रसानिमान् ।
यस्मात्तस्मादमी भावा विज्ञेया नाट्ययोक्तृभिः ॥ ३४ ॥

नानाद्रव्यैर्बहुविधैर्व्यञ्जनं भाव्यते यथा ।
एवं भावा भावयन्ति रसानभिनयैः सह ॥ ३५ ॥

न भावहीनोऽस्ति रसो न भावो रसवर्जितः ।
परस्परकृता सिद्धिस्तयोरभिनये भवेत् ॥ ३६ ॥

व्यञ्जनौषधिसंयोगो यथाऽन्नं स्वादुतां नयेत्[1] ।
एवं भावा रसाश्चैव भावयन्ति परस्परम् ॥ ३७ ॥

रसोऽत्राभिप्रेतः । **बहुविधैरिति** व्यञ्जनस्योपलक्षणम् । अभिनयैरित्यस्य वा विशेषणम् ।

एवं स्थितपक्षमुपसंहरति—**न भावहीनोऽस्ति रस** इति । अत्र चोद्यवादी स्वाशयमुन्मीलयति—**न भावो रसवर्जित** इति । लोके हि न कश्चिद्विभावादिव्यवहार इति भावाः । अथोत्तरमाह—**परस्परकृता सिद्धिस्तयोरभिनये भवेत् ।** अभिनये साक्षात्कारे संपन्ने तदुपयोगितया विभावादिव्यपदेश इत्यतो या परस्परकृता सिद्धिः सा भद्रं भवेदिति संभाव्यते । एवम्भूतमितरेतराश्रयजं न दूषणमित्यर्थः ।

अत्रैव दृष्टान्तमाह—**व्यञ्जनौषधिसंयोग** इति । व्यञ्जनौषधिसंयोगोऽन्नं च कर्तृ यथा परस्परमन्योन्यं कर्मभूतं स्वादुतां नयेत् तथा भावा रसाश्चान्योन्यं भावयन्ति । भावा रसान्भावयन्ति निष्पादयन्ति । रसास्तु भावान् भावयन्ति । भावान्कुर्वन्ति । भावादिव्यपदेश्यान्कुर्वन्तीत्यर्थः ।

एतदुक्तं भवति—एकत्रैकदा क्रियायामन्योन्याश्रयत्वं दोषो न तु क्रियाभेदे । यथा व्यञ्जनादिसंयोगेनान्नस्याह्लादि रसवत्ता क्रियते । अन्नेन चाश्रयरूपेण सता व्यञ्जनसुखयोग्यता क्रियते । एवं भावैः रस्यमानता । रसैश्च विभावादिव्यपदेश्यता कारणादीनाम् । यथा पटापेक्षया तन्तवः पटकारणमिति व्यपदेश्याः । तन्त्वपेक्षया पटः कार्यः । न चेत(रेत)राश्रयं(यत्वं) तथा प्रकृतेऽपीति । (३७)

---

१. K.S.S. व्यञ्जनौषधिसंयोगद्यथा न स्यादुता भवेत् M.G. N.S. G.O.S. (Same as above) ।

यथा बीजाद्भवेद्वृक्षो वृक्षात्पुष्पं फलं यथा ।
तथा मूलं रसाः सर्वे तेभ्यो[1] भावा व्यवस्थिताः ॥ ३८ ॥
तदेषां रसानामुत्पत्तिवर्णदैवतनिदर्शनान्यभिव्याख्यास्यामः ।

ननु यदि भावेभ्यो रसास्तर्हि कथमुक्तं 'न हि रसादृते काश्चिदप्यर्थः प्रवर्तते । तेन पूर्वं त एवोद्देश्याः' इत्याशंक्याह—**यथे**त्यादिना । बीजं यथा वृक्षमूलत्वेन स्थितं तथा रसाः । तन्मूलादि(हि)प्रीतिपूर्विका व्युत्पत्तिरिति ततरे(त एव) च व्याख्यानार्हाः । कविगतसाधारणीभूतसंविन्मूलश्च काव्यपुरस्सरो नटव्यापारः । सैव च संवित्परमार्थतो रसः । सामाजिकस्य च तत्प्रतीत्या वशीकृतस्य पश्चादपोद्धारबुद्धया विभावादिप्रतीतिरिति प्रयोजने (नं)नाट्ये काव्ये सामाजिकधियि च । तदेवं मूलं बीजस्थानीयात्क(यः क)विगतो रसः । कविर्हि सामाजिकतुल्य एव । तत एवोक्तं "शृङ्गारी चेत्कविः ।" (ध्वन्या० ३-४२) इत्याद्या**नन्दवर्धनाचार्येण** । ततो वृक्षस्थानीयं काव्यम् । तत्र पुष्पादिस्थानीयोऽभिनयादिनटव्यापारः । तत्र फलस्थानीयः सामाजिकरसास्वादः । तेन रसमयमेव विश्वम् ।

अत्र च विज्ञानवादो द्विधाभिधानं स्फोटतत्त्वं सत्कार्यवाद एकत्वदर्शनमित्यादि च द्रष्टव्यम् । वयं तु प्रकृतानुपयोगिश्रुतलवसन्दर्शनमिथ्याप्रयाससंश्रयमशिक्षितपूर्विण इत्यास्ताम् ।

अन्ये तु बीजादिव भावाद्रसवृक्षस्ततोऽप्यभिनयकुसुमसुन्दरात्फलमिव भावः प्रतीत्या भुज्यत इति व्याचक्षते । तैः प्रकृतविरुद्धं सर्वं व्याख्यातम् । एवं हि भावस्यैवोपक्रमपर्यवसानवर्तित्वमुक्तं स्यादित्यास्तां चैतत् । एवं त्रयोऽपि पक्षाः कथञ्चिदुपगता अभिप्रायवैचित्र्येणेति तात्पर्यम् ।

एवमुद्दिष्टानां विभक्तानां च रसानां सामान्यलक्षणं परीक्षापरिशुद्धमभिधाय तदनुवादपूर्वकं विशेषलक्षणं वक्तुं पीठबन्धं दर्शयति—**तदेषामि**त्यादिना । यतः सामान्यलक्षणमेतेषां कृतं तस्माद्विशेषलक्षणांशपूरकाण्युत्पत्त्यादीनि व्याख्यास्यामः । तत्रोत्पत्तिरुत्पादकानामुत्पाद्यानां च विशेषलक्षणम् । अन्योन्यतो व्यवच्छेदात् । उत्पादकानामप्येतदुत्पादकत्वमुत्पादकान्तराद्वैलक्षण्यमुत्पाद्यकृतम् । एवमुत्पाद्यानामुत्पादककृतमिति परस्परलक्षणत्वम् । वर्णः श्वेतादि तु(स्तु) सुस्पष्टं वि(शेष)लक्षणादि । एवं निदर्शनं तु शृङ्गारो नामेत्यादिना विभावादिविशेषसंयोगः । उत्पत्तिलक्षणा(णं) ह्यन्योन्याश्रयङ्का वर्णदेवतयोस्त्वा-

---

१. K.S.S. तेषु G.O.S. N.S. तेभ्यः M.G. ततः ।

तेषामुत्पत्तिहेतवश्चत्वारो रसाः । तद्यथा—शृङ्गारो रौद्रो वीरो बीभत्स इति । अत्र—

शृङ्गाराद्धि भवेद्धास्यो रौद्राच्च[1] करुणो रसः ।
वीराच्चैवाद्भुतोत्पत्तिर्बीभत्साच्च भयानकः ॥ ३९ ॥
शृङ्गारानुकृतिर्या तु स हास्यस्तु प्रकीर्तितः ।[2]
रौद्रस्यैव[3] च यत्कर्म स ज्ञेयः करुणो रसः ॥ ४० ॥

गमानुविद्धत्वमिति स्फुटं निश्चयदर्शनोपायत्वमुत्पत्त्यादीनां न संभवति । विभावादिविशेषसंयोगस्तु तद्वैलक्षण्यान्निदर्शनमित्युक्तम् । (३८)

तत्रोत्पत्तिं तावदाह—**तेषामि**त्यादिना । तेषां रसानामुत्पत्तौ हेतवः सूचकाश्चत्वारः । रसानामुत्पाद्योत्पादकप्रकारो यावान् सम्भवति स चतुर्भिरेव सूचित इति यावत् । तथा हि—तदाभासत्वेन तदनुकाररूपतया हेतुत्वं शृङ्गारेण सूचितम् । यतो विभावाभासादनुभावाभासाद्व्यभिचार्याभासाद्रत्याभासे प्रतीते चर्वणाभाससारः शृङ्गाराभासः कामना । अभिलाषमात्ररूपा हि रतिरत्र व्यभिचारिभावाः, न स्थायी । तस्य स तु स्थायिकल्पत्वेनाभाति । तद्वशाद्विभावाद्याभासता अतश्च स्थाय्याभासत्वं रतेः । यतो रावणस्य सीता द्विष्टा मय्युपेक्षिका वेति हृदयं नैव स्पृशतीति । तत्स्पर्शे ह्यभिमानोऽस्या (स्य) विलीयत एव । 'मयीयमनुरक्ता' इति तु निश्चयो ह्यनुपयोगी । कामजमोहसारत्वात् । शुक्तौ रूप्याभासवत् । यद्यपि—

"दूराकर्षणमोहमन्त्र इव मे तन्नाम्नि याते श्रुतिं
(चेतः कालकलामपि प्रसहते नावस्थितिं तां विना ।
एतैराकुलितस्य विक्षतरतेरङ्गैरनङ्गातुरैः
सम्पद्येत कथं तदाप्तिसुखमित्येतन्न वेद्मि स्फुटम् ॥")

इत्यादौ रावणवाक्ये तावति रत्याभासतैव । न तु हासः स्फुरति । तथापि सीताविभावल(विल)क्षणं रावणवयः (चः) । प्रकृति(त)विरुद्धञ्च(श्च) चिन्तादैन्यमोहादिकव्यभिचारिगणम(णोऽ)श्रुपातपरिदेवितादि चानुभावजानम-

---

१. K.S.S. M.G. तु G.O.S. N.S. च ।
२. K.S.S. M.G. इति संज्ञितः G.O.S. N.S. तु प्रकीर्तितः ।
३. K.S.S. M.G. अपि तु G.O.S. N.S. एव च ।

नौचित्यात्तदाभासरूपं सद्धास्यविभावरूपम् । तद्वक्ष्यते—विकृतपरवेषालङ्कारे-त्यादि । एवं तदाभासतया (तायाः) प्रकारः शृङ्गारेण सूचितः । तेन करुणाद्याभासेष्वपि हास्यत्वं सर्वेषु मन्तव्यम् । अनौचित्यप्रवृत्तिकृतमेव हि हास्यविभावत्वम् । तच्चा (त्रा) नौचित्यं सर्वरसानां विभावानुभावादौ सम्भाव्यते । तेन व्यभिचारिणामप्येषैव वार्ता । अत एव संवित्सतत्त्वनिपुणैश्चिरन्तनै रसभावतदाभासव्यवहारस्तत्र तत्र क्रियते । अमोक्षहेतावपि तदाभासतायां शान्ताभासो हास्य एव प्रहसनरूपस्य (रूपः ।) अनौ (स्वानौ) चित्यत्यागः सर्वपुरुषार्थेषु व्युत्पाद्यः । एतच्च लक्षणे वक्ष्यते । तत्र हास्याभासो यथाऽस्मत्पितृव्यस्य **वामनगुप्तस्य** ।

"लोकोत्तराणि चरितानि न लोक एष
सम्मन्यते यदि किमङ्ग वदाम नाम ।
यत्त्वत्र हासमुखत (र) त्वममुष्य तेन
पार्श्वोपपीडमिह को न विजाहसीति ।।"

एवं यो यस्य न बन्धुस्तच्छोके करुणोऽपि हास्य एवेति सर्वत्र योज्यम् । एतदेवोदाहरणम् । एवमन्यत्तेनानुमेयमिति मुनिना यथाग्रहणं कृतम् ।

यदीयफलानन्तरं द्वितीयरसोऽवश्यंभावी तस्योदाहरणं रौद्रः । रौद्रस्य हि फलं वधबन्धादि । तद्विभावकेनावश्यं करुणेन भाव्यम् । यथा **वेणीसंहारे**—

"अद्यैवावां रणमुपगतौ तातमम्बां च दृष्ट्वा
घ्रातस्ताभ्यां शिरसि विनतोऽहं च दुश्शासनश्च ।
तस्मिन्बाले प्रसभमरिणा प्रापिते तामवस्थां
पित्रोः पार्श्वं व्यपगतघृणः किं नु वक्ष्यामि गत्वा ।।"

एवं रौद्रानन्तरं नियमेन भयानकः । शृङ्गारानन्तरं नियमेन करुणं (णः) । व्याप्रियते त्वसौ तज्जन्मनि यथा **तापसवत्सराजे** वासवदत्तादाहाद्वत्सराजस्य । ननु तत्रा (त्र) रतेरवि (र्वि) च्छेदाद्बन्धुताकृतः शोकः । नैतत् । करुणोत्पत्तिकालेऽपि हि क्रोधस्य विच्छेद एव । यदाह—

'निर्वाणवैरदहनाः प्रशमादरीणां नन्दन्तु पाण्डुतनयाः' (वेणी. १-७) इति । न च बन्धुमा (तामा) त्रं हेतुः । एवं हि सति—

('उत्कम्पिनी भयपरिस्खलितांशुकान्ता)
ते लोचने प्रतिदिशं विधुरे क्षिपन्ती ।

(क्रूरेण दारणतया सहसैव दग्धा
धूमान्वितेन दहनेन न वीक्षितासि ॥')
(तापसवत्सराजे २-१६)

इत्यादौ ते इति प्राणभूतं (पदं) निरुपयोगतां गमितं स्यात् ।
रतिप्रलापेषु च शृङ्गार एव करुणस्य जीवितम्—
'हृदये वससीति (मत्प्रियं यदवोचस्तदवैमि कैतवम् ।
उपचारपदं न चेदिदं त्वमनङ्गः कथमक्षता रतिः ॥'(कुमार. ४-९)

इत्याद्युक्तिषु । एवं वीराद्भयानकोत्पत्तिः ।'यथा—

'कर्णस्यात्मजमग्रतः शमयतो भीतं जगत् फाल्गुनात्' (वेणी. ५-५)

यत्त्वत्र श्रीशङ्कुकेनोक्तम्—नात्रोत्साहस्य व्यापार इति । तदसत् । एवं हि निर्विषय एवोत्साहः स्यात् कर्तव्याननुसन्धानात् । युद्धवीरे च परपराजयजनितः प्रतापापरपर्यायः शत्रुहृदयदाहदायी तद्वनितादिषु भयानक एव । जीवितम् । यथा—

'स पातु वो यस्य हतावशेषास्तत्तुल्यवर्णाञ्जनरञ्जितेषु ।
लावण्ययुक्तेष्वपि वित्रसन्ति दैत्याः स्वकान्तानयनोत्पलेषु ॥'

नियमेन तु भवतीति वक्तव्यम् । नियमश्चकारेणोक्तो रौद्रादित्यानन्तर्यसूचकपञ्चम्यनन्तरं प्रयुक्तेन ।

यस्तु रसो रसान्तरं फलत्वेनाभिसन्धाय प्रवर्तते तस्योदाहरणं वीरः । महापुरुषोत्साहो हि जगद्विस्मयफलाभिसन्धानैव । यथा—

'दोर्दण्डाञ्चितचन्द्रशेखरधनुर्दण्डावभङ्गोद्यत' (महावीर २-५४) इत्यादि । रौद्रस्तु परविनाशनं फलत्वेनाभिसन्धाय प्रवर्तते न करुणमिति शेविशे)षः । विदूषकहासस्तु नायिकाहासं फलत्वेनाभिसन्धत्त इति मन्तव्यम् ।

यस्तु रसस्तुल्यविभावत्वान्नियमेन रसान्तरं हि परमाक्षिपति तस्योदहणं बीभत्सः । तस्य हि ये विभावा रुधिरप्रभृतयस्तेऽवश्यं भयहेतवः । तथा तद्व्यभिचारिणो मरणमोहापस्माराद्याः । तदनुभावास्तु मुखविकूणनादयः । यथा **वेणीसंहारे**—

'संस्तभ्यन्तां निहतदुश्शासनपीतशेषशोणितपी (तस्नपि) नबीभत्सवृकोदरदर्शनवैक्लब्यस्खलितप्रहरणानि रणाद्विवन्ति बलानि' इति (वेणी. ४.)

वीरस्यापि च यत्कर्म सोऽद्भुतः परिकीर्तितः
बीभत्सदर्शनं यच्च[1] ज्ञेयः स तु भयानकः ॥ ४१ ॥

एवं तदाभासतद्द्वा(सद्वा)रेण रसान्तराक्षेपकत्वे श्रृङ्गार उदाहरणम् । तेन श्रृङ्गारानुकृतिरित्यत्र तुशब्दो वीप्सायाम् । द्वितीयो हेतौ । तेनैवं योजना—या अनुकृतिः स हास्यो यतः प्रकीर्तितः एवंविभावको हास्य इति शेषः । तद्यथा शृङ्गार आद्यः (रः स्यात्) । शृङ्गारवत्य(वद)नुकृतिरित्यर्थः ।

यत्त्वत्र श्रृङ्गारादद्भुतोत्पत्तेराशङ्का 'दृशः प्रथुतरीकृता' (रत्ना २-१५) इत्यादौ (तत्) निर्मूलमेव । उदयने हि शृङ्गारः । ब्रह्मणि विस्मयसम्भावना । सा च न तात्कालिकत्वेन नोत्तरकालिकत्वेन । किन्तु पूर्वतरमेवेति न किञ्चिदेतत् ।

परस्पर(रम्परा) फलत्वेन रसान्तराक्षेपे रौद्र उदाहरणम् । रौद्रस्य यत्कर्म फलात्मकं वधादि चकारात्तस्य यत्कर्म फलरूपं स एव करुणः । एवकारेणात्यन्तव्यवहितां परम्परां पराकरोति । (४०)

समनन्तरफलत्वेन रसान्तराक्षेपे उदाहरणं त्वस्यायोगः वीरस्य (**वीरस्यापीति**—यो वीरस्य) सम्यङ्निकटं यत्फलं सोऽद्भुतः **परितः** समन्ताद्या **कीर्तिः** यशःप्रतापरूपा ततो हेतोः । **अपिशब्दाच्छृङ्गारोपि** वीरस्यानन्तरं फलं द्रौपदीस्वयंवरादौ । सहभावेन रसान्तराक्षेपे बीभत्स उदाहरणम् ।

यदेव **बीभत्सस्य दर्शनं** विभावादिरूपं स एव भयानकः । तद्विभावत्वादुपचारस्य । सहभावप्रतीतः(तिः) फलम् । तमेव **च**शब्दो द्योतयति । **तुः** पूर्वतो विशेषमाह । अयमेव चाक्षेपः प्रकाशत्वात्संभाव्यते न त्वधिक इति । सा त्वस्यापि सन्न नोक्तः । ये चात्रोत्पत्तिहेतव उक्तास्ते यथा स्वयं पुरुपार्थचतुष्कव्याप्ताः । तद्धि तत्सौन्दर्यातिशयजननरूपम् । रञ्जका भा(हा)सादयस्तदनुगामित्वेन रूपकेपु निबन्धनीयाः ।

एतावन्त एव च रसा इत्युक्तं पूर्वम् । तेनानन्त्येऽपि पार्षदप्रसिद्ध्यैतावतां प्रयोज्यत्वमिति **भट्टलोल्लटेन** निरूपितं तदवलेपेनापरामृश्येत्यलम् । (४१)

वर्णाभिधानं पूजादौ ध्यान उपयोगि । मुखरागेऽपीत्यन्ये । **स्वच्छपीतौ श्यामाद्भुताविति** शान्तिवादिनां पाठः । तत्तद्रससिद्धौ सा सा देवता पूज्येति देवतानिरूपणम् । **विष्णुः** कामदेवः **प्रमथा** भगवतो **गणाः** क्रीडापराः । **रुद्रस्तै-**

---

१. N.S. यत्र G.O.S. K.S.S. M.G. यच्च ।

अथ वर्णाः—

श्यामो भवति[1] शृङ्गारः सितो हास्यः प्रकीर्तितः ।
कपोतः करुणश्चैव रक्तो रौद्रः प्रकीर्तितः ॥ ४२ ॥
गौरो वीरस्तु विज्ञेयः कृष्णश्चैव भयानकः ।
नीलवर्णस्तु बीभत्सः पीतश्चैवाद्भुतः स्मृतः ॥ ४३ ॥

अथ [2]दैवतानि

शृङ्गारो विष्णुदेवत्यो हास्यः प्रमथदैवतः ।
रौद्रो रुद्राधिदैवत्यः करुणो यमदैवतः ॥ ४४ ॥
बीभत्सस्य महाकालः कालदेवो भयानकः ।
वीरो [*]महेन्द्रदेवः स्यादद्भुतो ब्रह्मदैवतः ॥ ४५ ॥

एवमेतेषां रसानामुत्पत्तिवर्णदैवतान्यभिव्याख्यातानि । इदानीमनुभावविभावव्यभिचारिसंयुक्तानां लक्षणनिदर्शनान्यभिव्याख्यास्यामः । स्थायिभावांश्च रसत्वमुपनेष्यामः ।[3]

लोक्यसंहारकर्ता । अत एव चोदयतीति निय(च यमयतीति य)मेन वधादिके सम्पादिते करुणः । महाकालोऽधिदैवतमिति शेषः स हि तद्विभावं कङ्कालं श्मशानादि सेवते । महेन्द्रस्त्रैलोक्यराजः । ब्रह्मा अचिन्त्याद्भुतस्रष्टा । (४५)

'बुद्धः शान्तेऽब्जजोऽद्भुते' इति शान्तवादिनः केचित्पठन्ति । बुद्धो जिनः परोपकारैकपरः प्रबुद्धो वा । तत्रोत्पत्तिलक्षणमन्योन्यश्रयत्वान्न निश्चयकारि । वर्णदैवतात्मकमप्यागमसिद्धत्वादित्येकप्रघट्टकेनोपसंहरत्येवमित्यादिना । एतेषामिति सर्वेषामित्यर्थः ।

अथ विशेषलक्षणानि वक्तुमासूत्रयतीदानीमित्यादिना । विशेषलक्षणं सजातीयाद्यवच्छेदकम् । न विजातीयाद्व्यवच्छेदं विना सजातीयत्वम् । न चासौ सामान्यलक्षणं विनेति तत्पृष्ठे विशेषलक्षणमिति दर्शयितुं सामान्यलक्षणमनुवदत्यनुभावेत्यादिना । लक्षणानि च तानि निदर्शनानि च विशेषात्मकानि ।

---

१. K.S.S. M.G. भवेतु G.O.S. N.S. भवति ।
२. N.S. अधिदैवतानि G.O.S. K.S.S. M.G. दैवतानि ।
३. N.S. रसानामनुक्रमिष्यामः G.O.S. M.G. K.S.S. रसत्वमुपनेष्यामः ।

तत्र शृङ्गारो नाम रतिस्थायिभावप्रभवः । उज्ज्वलवेषात्मकः । यत्किञ्चिल्लोके शुचि मेध्यमुज्ज्वलं दर्शनीयं व तच्छृङ्गारेणोपमीयते[1] ।

तेन प्रत्येकं लक्षणविशेषा उच्यन्त इत्यर्थः । विशेषलक्षणानि वा सामान्यलक्षणस्य निदर्शनानि । येषु सामान्यलक्षणं निर्दिश्यते योज्यते उदाह्रियते च । तद्विना तस्योदाहर्तुमशक्यत्वात् । चकारो लोकोत्तरतयाऽऽदरं सूचयति । ये स्थायिनो भावो लोके चित्तवृत्त्यात्मानो बहुप्रकारपरिश्रमप्र वनिबन्धनकर्तव्यताप्रबन्धायिनस्तानपि नाम रसत्वं विश्रान्त्येकायतनत्वेनोपदेशदिशा नेष्यामः । विभावान् यथायोगमुपहरद्भिः कविनटैर्हि ते रसतां नीयन्ते । यदाह—

"या व्यापारवती रसान्रसयितुं काचित्कवीनां नवा
(दृष्टिर्या परिनिष्ठितार्थविषयोन्मेषा च वैपश्चिती ।
ते द्वे अप्यवलम्ब्य विश्वमनिशं निर्वर्णयन्तो वयं
श्रान्ता नैव च लब्धमब्धिशयन त्वद्भक्तितुल्यं सुखम् ॥") इति ।
(ध्वन्या ३.४३)

नटानां तु तदुपजीवितत्वान्न नवा दृक्पश्यति न रसयत्यतो नवेति । तस्माद्रसनोपयोगिविभावाद्यौचित्यमस्माभिरुपदिशद्भिः स्थायिनो रसतां नीता भवन्तीत्यनेन लक्षणरूपस्य फलं दर्शयति ।

अथ शृङ्गाररसप्रकरणम्

तत्र कामस्य फलत्वादशेषहृदयसंवादित्वाच्च तत्प्रधानं शृङ्गारं लक्षयति— **तत्रेत्यादिनोज्ज्वलवेषात्मक** इत्यन्तेन सूत्रेण । **तत्रेति** क्रमनिर्धारणे । एवं सतीत्यर्थे वा । एतत्सूत्रभाष्येण व्यक्तम् । यल्लक्ष्यपदं **नामेति** । व्याचष्टे **यत्किञ्चिदित्यादिना** । हस्तपृष्ठतादि (हारादि) मण्डितः शृङ्गारवान् । तेन शुचिमेध्याद्युपमीयते । तेनोज्ज्वलवेषात्मके शृङ्गारशब्दः । न चातिप्रसङ्गः । आप्तोपदेशस्य नियामकत्वादिति **चिरन्तनाः** । तदनुपपन्नम् उपमानोमेययोर्विशेषविषयविभागानवभासात्तथा ।

तस्मादयमत्रार्थः । रतिरेवास्वाद्यमानो मुख्यः शृङ्गारः । रतिमास्वादयद्भिस्तद्बहुमानपरः शृङ्गारीत्युच्यते । यस्तु सज्जनादिप (दिः अप) र एव तद्व्यसनिता- (तु व्यसनी) । सा रसनास्वाददशा लोके भवन्त्यपि न चिरमवतिष्ठते । तदास्वादे चोपयोगि यथास्वंविभावादि तथा शास्त्र (स्त्रा) निषिद्धमजुगुप्सितं संस्फुटं (यत् स्फुटं) मनोहरं च तदुपचाराच्छृङ्गारशब्दवाच्यम् । तदाह— **उपमीयते** । तदुपयोगितया तथा मीयते लक्ष्यत इति यावत् ।

---

१. K.S.S. अनुमीयते G.O.S. M.G. N.S. उपमीयते ।

यस्तावदुज्ज्वलवेषः स शृङ्गारवानित्युच्यते । यथा च गोत्रकुलाचारोत्पन्नान्याप्तोपदेशसिद्धानि पुंसां नामानि भवन्ति तथैवैषां रसानां भावानां च नाट्याश्रितानां चार्थानामाचारोत्पन्नान्याप्तोपदेशसिद्धानि नामानि । एवमेष आचारसिद्धो[1] हृद्योज्ज्वलवेषात्मकत्वाच्छृङ्गारो रसः । स च स्त्रीपुरुषहेतुक उत्तमयुव[3]प्रकृतिः ।

क्व य(त)थेति दर्शयति-**यस्तावदिति** । तावद्ग्रहणेनावधारणवाचिना शृङ्गारवाच्यो मुख्योऽर्थस्तत्र नास्तीति दर्शयति—**स शृङ्गारवानिति** । तदनु-(दु)ज्ज्वलवेषे शृङ्गारशब्द उपचरित इत्याह । ननु मुख्यतया रत्यास्वादे शृङ्गारशब्दस्य प्रवृत्तौ किं निबन्धनमित्याशङ्क्याह-**यथा** चेत्यादि । **गोत्रं** पितृसन्तानादि । **कुलं** मातृसन्तानं सूचयति । **आचारो** व्यवहारः । तत **उत्पन्नानि** लोके प्ररूढानि । मूले तु न । आद्या**प्तोपदेशेन** नामकरणलक्षणेन समयेन **सिद्धानि । पुंसमिति** मनुष्यजातेर्नराणां नारीणां च । नराणां हि पितृसन्तानानुसारि नाम विष्णुशर्मेत्यादि । स्त्रीणां तु मातृवंशानुसारि कनकप्रभा चन्द्रप्रभेति । एवं रसादीनां तच्छास्त्रवेदिवृद्धव्यवहारतो निरूढानि प्राक्तनब्रह्माद्याप्तप्रणीतानि नामानि ।

तदेवोपसंहरति—**एवं** शृङ्गारो रसः । **स आचार**व्यवहाराल्लोकेऽपि **सिद्धः** । कुतो हेतोः । हृद्यादिवेषात्मकत्वात् । एतदुक्तं भवति—प्रतिशास्त्रसमयानुसारिणोऽपि शब्दास्तद्वृद्धव्यवहारपरम्परया लोके प्रसिद्धा उपचारतोऽन्यत्रापि व्यवह्रियन्ते । यथा—'साङ्ख्यपुरुषोऽयं न किञ्चित्करोति । पूर्वरङ्गोऽत्र तेन मे विरचितः । अत्र महत(त्ता)न्योन्यस्य' इति । तद्वदमी शृङ्गारादिशब्दा इहैव विषये मुख्याः । लोके तु साङ्ख्यपुरुषादिशब्दवत् ।

यस्तु शृङ्गारशब्दस्यान्मीयेन(स्य मत्वर्थीयेन)व्युत्पत्तिमाह तस्य रूपमपि विस्मृतम् । आरकन् हि प्रत्ययोऽत आरब्धः । ('शृङ्गबृन्दाभ्यामारकन्') (वार्तिक. ५-२-१२१) बृन्दारक इति यथा । अत एवोणादिषु निपातितोऽयं शब्दः । (शृङ्गारभृङ्गारौ । उ. सू) ।

यस्तु पृथग्भावेन गोत्रादिनामानि व्याचष्टे व्यावर्त्याभावात् तत्तदीक्षितानि ।

---

१. K.S.S. तदेवमेव गुर्वाचारसिद्धः G.O.S. N.S. M.G. एवमेव आचारसिद्ध ।

२. K.S.S. आत्कक: G.O.S. N.S. M.G. आत्मकत्वात् ।

३. K.S.S. मुवति G.O.S. N.S. M.G. युव ।

तस्य प्रकृते न किञ्चिदियमु (दप्यु) पयुज्यते । न च गोत्राचारोत्पन्ने नामनि नियामक आप्तोपदेशो लोके इत्यास्तामेतत् ।

अथ रतिः स्थायीति सूत्रभागं भाष्येण स्पष्टयति—**स चेत्यादिना** । स्त्रीपुरुषशब्देन परस्पराभिलाषसंभोगलक्षणया लौकिक्या 'अस्येयं स्त्री' इति या-(धिया) । तेनाभिलाषमात्रसारायाः कामावस्थानुवर्तिन्या व्यभिचारिरूपाणीतिया (पानीताया) विलक्षणैव इयं स्थायिरूरा प्रारम्भादिफलप्राप्तिपर्यन्ता व्यापिनी परिपूर्णसुखैकफला रतिश (रु) क्ता भवति हेतुरस्य ।

कविर्हि लौकिकरतिवासनानुविद्धस्तथा विभावादीनाहरति नाट्यं चा (नटश्चा) नुभावान् यथा रत्यास्वादः शृङ्गारो भवतीति । आस्वादयितुरपि प्राक्कक्ष्यायां रत्यवगम उपयोगीत्युक्तः प्राक् ।

एतदुक्तं भवति—रतिक्रीडासाधं च (रतिःक्रीडा । सा च) परमार्थतः कामिनोरेव । तत्रैव सुखस्य धाराविश्रान्तेः । अपरस्य तु माल्यादिविषयसौन्दर्यस्य कविना कृतस्य संकल्पत्वात्संवेदनद्वितयान्योन्यनिमज्जनात्मकमीलनाख्यो हि परमो भोगः । संविद एव प्रधानत्वात् । अन्यत्र तु जडस्य भोग्यत्वात् ।

अत एवाह—'श्वासायासविडम्बनैव वपुषि प्राणाः पुनर्जानकी' इति ।

अत एव यत्कैश्चिदचोद्यत—रतेराधारभेदेन भेदात्कथमेको रस इति । तदनभिज्ञतया । एकैव ह्यसौ तावती रतिः । यत्रान्योन्यसंविदा एकत्रियोगो न भवति । अत एवोत्तमयुवप्रकृतिः । उत्तमश्चोत्तमा चोत्तमौ । एवं युवानौ । तत्रोत्तमयुवशब्देन तत्संविदुच्यते । न तु कायः । चैतन्यस्यैव हि परमार्थत उत्तमयुवत्वं विशेषः । स (सा) चावस्थावान् तत्र तत्र (स्था यत्र तत्र) व्यवहारस्य भूतत्वात् तत्प्रकृतिः । सा संविदास्वादयोग्यत्वात् शृङ्गाररसीभवतीति । अनुत्तमत्वे तु (न) दार्ढ्यमयुतत्वे चेति न सा रतिसंवित् । वियोगस्य संभावनात् । अवियुक्तसंवित्प्राणस्तु शृङ्गारः । यथा—

"वारिसिणि०चरिहिअदि हिल०गणाहुकंहविएक्व ।
हुहिमुळजळमरणिमअळहुतीतिहविप०सि ।। " इति ।

व्याख्याता (तः) परस्परं जीवितसर्वस्वाभिमानरूपा (पः) । वेषयति व्यापयति चित्तवृत्तिमन्यत्र ज्ञापनया संक्रमयतीति वेषो विभावानुभावात्मा । वेषयति

तस्य द्वे अधिष्ठाने सम्भोगो विप्रलम्भश्च । तत्र सम्भोगस्तावत् ऋतु-माल्यानुलेपनालङ्कारेष्टजनविषयवरभवनोपभोगोपवनगमनानुभवनश्रवणदर्शन - क्रीडालीलादिभिर्विभावैरुत्पद्यते ।

(न्ति) व्याप्नुवन्ति स्थायित्वमिति व्यभिचारिणः । ते चोज्ज्वला उत्कृष्टा यस्मिस्तथाभूत आत्मा यस्येति ।

सूत्रे संक्षिप्य यद्विभावादि निरूपितं तद्विभागेन व्याख्येयमित्याशयेन शृङ्गारस्यावस्थाभेदमाह—**तस्य द्वे** इत्यादिना । **अधिष्ठाने** अवस्थे इत्यर्थः । अधिष्ठीयतेऽवस्थात्र(त्रा) शृङ्गाररूपेण । तेन शृङ्गारस्येमौ भेदौ । गोत्वस्येव शावलेयत्वबाहुलेयत्वे । अपि तु तद्दशाद्वयेऽप्यनुयायिनी या रतिरास्वादनात्मिका तस्याश्चास्वाद्यमानं रूपं शृङ्गारः । यदाहुः—

"(एतस्मान्मां कुशलिनमभिज्ञानदानाद्विदित्वा
मा कौलीनादसितनयने मय्यविश्वासिनी भूः ।)
स्नेहानाहुः किमपि विरहह्रासिनस्तेऽप्यभोगा-
दिष्टे वस्तुन्युपचितरसाः प्रेमराशीभवन्ति ।। इति ।।
(मेघ० उ० ४५)

अत एव सम्भोगे विप्रलम्भसम्भावनाभीरुत्वं विप्रलम्भेऽपि सम्भोगमनो राज्या (रथा)नुवेध इति इयच्छृङ्गारस्य वपुः । अभिलाषेर्ष्याप्रवासादिदशास्त्वत्रै-वान्तर्भूताः । सत्यामास्थाबन्धात्मिकायां रतौ तेन(?)सम्भोगशृङ्गार इत्यादि-व्यपदेशोऽभोगेऽप्युपचारात् । अत एतद्दशाद्वयमेलन एव सत्यतः सातिशयचम-त्कार । यथा—

"एकस्मिन् शयने पराङ्मुखतया वीतोत्तरं ताम्यतो-
रन्योन्यं हृदयस्थितेऽप्यनुनये संरक्षतोर्गौरवम् ।
दम्पत्योः शनकैरपाङ्गवलनान्मिश्रीभवच्चक्षुषो-
र्भग्नो मानकलिः सहासरभसव्यासक्तकण्ठग्रहम् ।।" (अ०श०-२३.)

तत्र ह्रीर्ष्याविप्रलम्भसम्भोगमेलनात्मिकैवैकप्राणीभूतोभयगतविभावानुभावव्य-भिचारिकृता सातिशया रसानुभूतिः । तेन यच्चोदितं **श्रीशङ्कुकेन** पुरूरवस उन्मादे वत्सराजस्य तापसत्वे चानुज्ज्वलवेषत्वं विप्रलम्भशृङ्गारेऽपि (इति) तदनवकाशमेव । भोगस्य रसत्वाभावात् स्नानाद्यवस्थानमिव । यत्त्वत्रोत्तरं

तावद्दत्तं स्थैर्यादुज्ज्वलवेषाभावेऽपि रतिमुत्तमा न विजहतीति तद्यक्षभाषितम्। प्रकृतचोद्यापरिहारात्।

न हि (नु) चोदितमनुज्ज्वलवेषे कथं शृङ्गार इति। तदेवास्तु चोद्यमिति चेत्—न वचनस्यातिभारोऽस्ति। न तु मुनिनैवमुक्तं सत्युज्ज्वलवेषे शृङ्गार इति। अपि तु विपर्यय इत्यास्तामेतत्।

तत्रेति। द्वयोरवस्थयोर्मध्ये सम्भोगावस्था तावदुच्यते। तत्रेह वस्तुतः स्त्रीपुंसौ परस्परं **विभावौ**। तयोरुत्तमत्वे चोपयोगीनि ऋत्वादीनि। उत्तमस्यानवसरे रत्यभावात्। **ऋतुर्वसन्तादिः**। **माल्यं** कुसुमादिः। **अनुलेपनं** समालम्भनं यद्यत्कामस्योद्दीपकम्। **अलङ्कारः** कटकादिः। **इष्टजनः** विदूषकादिः। एतदुभयमुत्तमत्वसूचकम्। यदाह—

'असमाप्तजिगोषस्य स्त्रीचिन्ता का मनस्विनः।
अनाक्रम्य जगत्कृत्स्नं किं सन्ध्यां भजते रविः॥' इति॥
(राज. तर.४.४४२.)

विषया गीतादयः। तदन्तर्भूतमपि माल्यादि प्राधान्यात्पृथगुक्तम्। **वरभवनं** हर्म्यादि। एतद्देशविशेषोपलक्षणम्। एषामुपभोगः। उपवनस्योद्यानस्यानुभवनं श्रवणं वा प(व)रभवनस्थस्यापि। एतत्सङ्कल्पादेरप्युपलक्षणम्। **क्रीडा** जलावगाहनादिका। **लीला** जनस्यानुकृतिः। अनु(आदि)ग्रहणादन्यदपि हृद्यं हंसयुगलकचित्रपुस्तकदर्शनादि। एतच्च समस्तमेव शृङ्गारविभावत्वेन मन्तव्यम्। यावान्कश्चिदयं विषयसम्भारो हृद्यतमस्तत्पूर्णतायां सत्यामुत्तमस्य रत्युदयः। अत एव **रत्नावल्यां** हर्म्यवर्णनमुद्यानगमनं कामदेवपूजा वसन्तइत्यादि सर्वमेवात्र संगृहीतं 'राज्यं निर्जितशत्रु योग्यसचिवे न्यस्तम्' इत्यादिना। एवञ्च सर्व एव समुदितो विभाव इति काल्पनिकमालम्बनविभाव इति। अत एव मुनिना नायं क्वचिद्विभाग उक्तः सूचितो वा। युक्तञ्चैतत्। यथैकत्रैव रूपके उद्यानर्तुमाल्यादीनां सर्वेषां दर्शनादेको रसः स्यात्। विभावाभेदात्।

ननु प्रथम (प्रमदामात्र) दर्शने नोद्यानभवनादिसम्भवः। क एवमाह। ऐश्वर्यपूर्णस्य हि तावदात्मीयसमृद्धिसम्भारसंस्कारानव(राव)गमात् पूर्णतैव विभाववर्गस्य। तत्प्रधानं हि रूपकं तत्र तत्रोदाहरणम् तेन पृथक्पृथगुदाहरणदानमनुपपन्नम्।

या तु मुक्तकादौ पृथक्तया भावेऽपि रससंवित् तत्रोत्तमे च तापस(तावत) स्तत्रानुसन्धानाच्चमत्कार इति। इयांस्त्वनुत्तमादिविषयेऽपरिपूर्णोद्दीपनत्वे न चमत्कारो दृश्यते—

तस्य नयनचातुर्य[1]**भ्रूक्षेपकटाक्षसञ्चारललितमधुराङ्गहारवाक्यादिभिरनुभावैरभिनयःप्रयोक्तव्यः ।**

यथा हि 'वर्धते लुनाहि पणीलुर्दिसिगमिहा अमहंह भुवं हचदुघरीदुल्लए लंघा ।' इति तथा 'कमसूपे रङ्ग' इत्यादि (?) । तत्रैकाङ्गस्य सौभाग्यस्य प्राधान्याच्चमत्कारोदय इति तात्पर्यम् । न तु तदभावकृता चमत्कृतिः ।

एतैः कविनोपनिबद्धैर्नटेन च साक्षात्कारकल्पतामानीतैः सम्यगित्यविघ्नभोगात्मकसम्भोगो रस उत्पद्यते झटित्येव । न हि गमनक्रियावत् पर्यन्ते रसनाक्रिया निष्पद्यते । अपि तु प्रथम एवावसरे । स च विभावसाक्षात्कारात्मक एव । तस्य तु प्रथमकक्ष्यायामेव रसनागोचरत्वाभिमतस्य नयनचातुर्यादिभी रसै(सो) रसनाद्याभिमुख्यं नीयते । अत एव तेऽभिनया अनुभावाश्च । आभिमुख्यनयनमनुभावनं च । तद्रसास्वादे समर्थाचरणमुद्दीपनम् । अत एव तदभावे विभावादिवर्णनप्रधानेऽपि काव्ये न चमत्कारः । रसनायास्तत्राभावात् । यथा विन्दो(कवीन्दो)**र्भट्टेन्दुराजस्य**—

"उपपरिसरं गोदावर्याः परित्यजताध्वगाः
सरणिमपरो मार्गस्तावद्भवद्भिरवेक्ष्यताम् ।
इह हि विहितो रक्ताशोकः कयापि हताशया
चरणनलिनन्यासोदञ्चन्नवाङ्कुरकञ्चुकः ।।" इति ।

एवमन्यत्राप्युपपद्यत इति तस्याभिनयादिर(दि यो)जनीयम् ।

ननु विभावानां साधारण्यं कथम् । नियमेनैवं हि न नाट्ये । इयांश्चात्र कविप्रयत्नसमर्प्यमाणः । तेन तद्भावात्प्रयोजकधर्मोद्रेकप्रकाशविशिष्टसमबलात्प्रमुख एव विशेषविश्रान्ततां याति । तथा 'हा प्रिये जनकराजपुत्रीति' इत्ययं श्रुत एव न रतिव्यतिरेकेण भावान्तरविभावता शङ्क्या । 'एतेन कुणपं(पे) कामिनी' इत्यादिसम्भावनं प्रत्युक्तम् ।

तत्र **नयनचातुर्या**दिना कान्ता दृष्टिर्वक्ष्यते । यत्तु भ्रुवोर्मूलसमुत्क्षेपश्चतुरमिति (ना. शा. ८-४७) वक्ष्यते । सभ्रूक्षेपेण चोक्तम्—'विवर्तनं कटाक्ष' (ना. शा. ८-१००) इति ताराकर्म । एवं च योजना—नयनानां चातुर्येण सभ्रूक्षेपेण कटाक्षेण च यद्यत्सञ्चारणं ललितं मन्थरं मधुरं नयनाभिरामं कृत्वा

---

१. K.S.S. M.G. G.O.S. चातुर्ये N.S. चातुरी ।

व्यभिचारिणश्चा[1]स्यालस्यालस्यौग्र्यजुगुप्सावर्ज्याः । **विप्रलम्भकृतस्तु निर्वेदग्लानिशङ्कासूयाश्रमचिन्तौत्सुक्यनिद्रास्व[2]प्नविबोधव्याध्युन्मादापस्मारजाड्य[3]मरणादिभिरनुभावैरभिनेतव्यः ।**

यान्यङ्गानां हरणानि स्वकर्तव्यकाले ललितानि सुकुमाराभिधेयानि मधुराणि च श्रवणसुखकराणि यानि । वाक्यानीत्युपाङ्गाभिनय आङ्गिको वाचिकश्च लक्षितः ।

अत एव सामान्याभिनयाध्याय (ना. शा. अ-२२) वक्ष्यमाणाशेषचेष्टालङ्कारलाभ इति ललितमधुरशब्दौ तदर्थावित्यसत् । **आदि**ग्रहणात्सात्त्विको मुखरागपुलकादिर्गृह्यते । अनुभावकत्वेन ताटस्थ्यपरिहारः । आभिमुख्यनयनेन स्वात्मैकविश्रान्तिशङ्कानिरासः । एवमुत्तरत्रापि ।

एवं विभावसमय एव रसनीयस्यानुभावावसरेऽवस्थावेशवैरस्यास्पदस्य पश्चाद्व्यभिचारिणः स्वामेव रसनीयतां चित्रयन्तः सातिशयं पुष्यन्तीति पश्चात्ते निरूप्यन्ते—**व्यभिचारिणश्चास्येति** । आलस्यौग्र्यजुगुप्सा वर्ज्यमाना येभ्यस्ते सर्वे व्यभिचारिणः । **अस्येति** दशाद्वयमयस्येत्यर्थः । जुगुप्सा स्थायिन्यपीह निषिद्धा स्थायिनामपि व्यभिचारित्वमनुज्ञापयति । आलस्यादि च स्वविभावप्रमा (म) दादिविषयमेव निषिद्धम् । तेन 'वपुरलसलसद्बाहु लक्ष्म्याः' (वेणी० १-२) इति । तथा 'कतिचिदहानि वपुरभूत् केवलमलसेक्षणं तस्याः' (विक्र० ५-८) । इत्यादिनापि रूपकं मन्तव्यम् । एवं प्रयोगे काव्ये च विभावादीनां क्रम एव समाश्रयणीयः । उत्पूर्वस्य (उद्भूतस्य) लब्धप्रतिष्ठता । तथाभूतस्य परिवारसघटनमिति हि प्रतीतिक्रमः ।

ननु निर्वेदादयः सम्भोगे न व्यभिचारिण इत्याशङ्क्याह—**विप्रलम्भकृतस्त्विति** । तुशब्दो विशेषं द्योतयति ।

वाक्यैकवाक्यतया दुःखप्रायनिर्वेदादि मुक्त्वा आलस्यादिव्यतिरिक्ताश्च सुखमया एव धृत्यादयोऽत्र व्यभिचारित्वेन सम्भोग उपन्यस्ता इति प्रकटयति ।

---

१. N.S. M.G. K.S.S. त्रास G.O.S. अस्य ।

२. K.S.S. N.S. सुप्तस्वप्नविब्बोक M.G. सुप्तस्वप्नविबोध G.O.S. स्वप्नविबोध ।

३. M.G. Reads मोह after जाड्य G.O.S. N.S. K.S.S. do not read it.

परस्परांशोपजीवनं चात्र जीवितमिति दर्शयितुमस्येत्यनुद्भिन्नमेवोक्तम् । तत एव च भगवदनुग्रहपवित्रवाचा **कालिदासेन रघुवंशे** सम्भोगविप्रलम्भात्मकव्यामिश्ररसनासम्पत्तये प्रत्यनीकोद्देशेन रामभद्रस्य स्वकर्म पूर्वावस्थावर्णनेनादृतम् ।

स्वप्ना(सुप्ता)न्तर्भूतोऽपि **स्वप्नाः** प्राधान्यादुपात्तः । 'क्व नीलकण्ठ व्रजसि' इति (कु०स०५-५४) । 'सिविणवए विहुदोसुजपउसुमराविउतरुढसंखुआसिपुअगळगाळविउति ।' तथा 'आहूतोऽपि सहायैः' इत्यादौ हि स एव प्राणः । सम्भोगदशायां तु विभावसान्निध्ये निद्राद्यभावाद्विबोधोऽपि व्यभिचारी । सम्भोगेऽपि रतिश्रमकृतनिद्रादि यद्यप्यस्ति तथाऽपि न रतौ तच्चित्रतामाधत्ते । विप्रलम्भे तु तद्रतिभावनापरस्परोऽत(नापरम् । अत)एव निद्रादिबाहुल्यापेक्षं चेत्थमभिधानम् ।

उन्मादापस्मारव्याधीनां या नात्यन्तं कुत्सिता दशा सा काव्ये प्रयोगे च दर्शनीया । कुत्सिता तु सम्भवेऽपि नेति **वृद्धाः । वयं** तु ब्रूमः । तादृश्यां दशायां स्वजीवितनिन्दात्मिकायां तद्देहोपभोगसाररत्यात्मकावस्थाबन्धोऽपि विच्छिद्यत एवेति सम्भव एव । **मरणम**चिरकालप्रत्यापत्तिमयमत्र मन्तव्यम् । येन शोकोऽवस्थानमेव न लभते । यथा—

तीर्थे तोयव्यतिकरभवे जह्नुकन्यासरय्वो-
देहत्यागादमरगणनालेख्यमासाद्य सद्यः ।
पूर्वावस्थाधिकचतुरया सङ्गतः कान्तयाऽसौ
लीलागारेष्वरमत पुनर्नन्दनाभ्यन्तरेषु ॥ (रघु.८-९४)

अत एव सुकविना वाक्यभेदेनापि मरणमाख्यातम् । प्रतीतिविश्रान्तिस्थानत्वपरिहाराय तृतीयपादेन विभावानुसन्धानकं दर्शनम् । पुनर्ग्रहणेन स एवार्थः सुतरां द्योतितः ।

अन्ये त्वाहुः मरणमिति न जीवितवियोग उच्यते । अपि तु चैतन्यावस्थैव प्राणत्यागकर्तृतात्मिका । या सम्बन्धाद्यवसरगता मन्तव्या व्यभिचारिभावेनेति सुलभोदाहरणमेतदिति । **आदिशब्देन** दैन्यमोहादयः । एते व्यभिचारिणोऽपि स्वानुभावैरनुभाविता विप्रलम्भमनुभावयन्ति । तस्मादनुभावैरित्युक्तम् ।

अन्ये त्वादिशब्दं करुणवाचिनमाश्रित्य तदीयानुभावान्प्राधान्येन दर्शयन्ति । एकशेषेण द्वयमप्यन्ये । विप्रलम्भो विडम्बनं सिद्धम् । इह तूपचारात्तदीयं फल विरहात्मकं गृह्यते । न हि परस्परं रतिमतोर्विडम्बनमस्ति । तेन विरहेण कृतः सुष्ठुतमां प्रो(पो)षित इति दर्शयन्मुनिरनेन विना शृङ्गारो न प्रयोगे न काव्ये हृद्यतामवलम्बत इति दर्शयति ।

अत्राह—यद्ययं[1] रतिप्रभवः शृङ्गारः कथमस्य करुणाश्रयिणो भावा भवन्ति । अत्रोच्यते—पूर्वमेवाभिहितं सम्भोगविप्रलम्भकृतः शृङ्गार इति । वैशिकशा[2]स्त्रकारैश्च दशावस्थोऽभिहितः । ताश्च सामान्याभिनये वक्ष्यामः ।

करुणस्तु शापक्लेशविनिपतितेष्ट[3]जनविभवनाशवधबन्धसमुत्थो निरपेक्षभावः । औत्सुक्यचिन्तासमुत्थः सापेक्षभावो विप्रलम्भकृतः ।

तथा हि—सम्भोगेऽप्येकघनशर्करास्वादस्थानीयतापरिहाराय वैषम्यं गोत्रस्खलितस्पर्धामन्यद्वा कलहविप्रलम्भहेतुभूतं कवयो निबध्नन्ति । 'वामो हि कामः' (काम. शा. २-७-१) इति वात्स्यायनादिभिरहितम् । मुनिनापि वक्ष्यते 'यद्वामाभिनिवेशित्वम्' इति (ना. शा. २२-२०७) । एते च व्यभिचारिणो विद्युदुन्मेषनिमेषयुक्त्यैव स्थायिसूत्रमध्ये प्रकटयन्तस्तिरोदधतश्च तद्वैचित्र्यमावहन्ति । न त स्थिराः । यद्यपि स्थाय्यपि न स्थिरः तथाऽपि संस्काररूपतया धारावाहिसजातीयप्रवाहरूपतया च स्थिर एव । व्यभिचारिणस्तु नैवं क्षणमपि भवन्ति । संस्कारमपि स्वकं स्थायिसंस्कार एव प्रौढयन्ति । तथैव स्मरणाच्च ।

तेन व्यभिचारिषु पृथक्पृथग्यैः कै (थग्यत्कै)श्चिदुदाहृतं तन्न तन्त्रन्यायानुपाति तथा हि—धृतौ यदुदाहृतं 'असम्भाव्यं देवात्' इत्यादि । तत्रापि हर्षविस्मयगर्वमतिप्रभृतीनां च 'तेति माम्' इति (?) वलितेत्यादिसूचितानां सम्भार एव । 'किमपरं त्रैलोक्यम्' इत्यादौ चावान्तरवाक्यारम्भे स्मृतिप्रभृतिभिः सर्वत्र भाव्यम् । अन्यथा हि धृत्येकवचनत्वे सर्वत्र श्लोकार्थे दृष्टिरेकैव चित्रन्यस्तेव भवेत् । 'अस्यास्सर्गविधौ' (विक्रमो० १-१०) इत्यत्राप्यवान्तरवाक्यसमाप्तौ धृतिहर्षविस्मयादयो भवन्त्येव । अत एव विच्छिद्य विच्छिद्य वितर्कान्तरं समुदेति । न तु व्यभिचारी क्षणमप्यवतिष्ठते । चलं हि गुणवृत्तमिति हि तत्रभवन्तः । अत एव प्रयोगवैचित्र्यम् । अन्यथाऽवैचित्र्यात्स एव प्रयोगः स्यात् । मध्येऽन्ते चाश्रयाः स्फुताः । ते च विस्मयधृतिप्रभृती त्यास्तामेतत् ।

वाक्यैकवाक्यत्वेनावस्थाद्वयस्यूतस्य शृङ्गारस्य यत्स्वरूपमुक्तमेतदेव परिशोधयितुं पूर्वपक्षयति—अत्राहेति । करुणविषये आश्रयणं विघ्नं येषां भूम्ना । अत एव कर्मधारयमत्वर्थीयाभ्यामितीह नाश्रितम् । भूम्ना वहति ह्यत्र (वहतीत्यत्र) पूर्वपक्षस्य प्राणितम् ।

---

१. K.S.S. एवं G.O.S N.S. M.G. अयम् ।

२. K.S.S. M.G. वैशिकशास्त्रैश्च G.O.S. N.S. वैशिकशास्त्रकारैश्च ।

३. N.S. विनिपतितेष्टजनविप्रयोग K.S.S. विनिपातनेष्टजनविप्रयोग M.G. विनिपतनेष्टजनविप्रयोग G.O.S. विनिपतितेष्टजनं ।

एवमन्यः करुणोऽन्यश्च विप्रलम्भ इति । एवमेष सर्वभावसंयुक्तः शृङ्गारो भवति ।

सुखप्रायेषु सम्पन्न[1] ऋतुमाल्यादिसेवकः ।
पुरुषः प्रमदायुक्तः शृङ्गार इति संज्ञितः ॥ ४६ ॥

ननु त्वयोक्तमसदेवास्त्वित्याशङ्क्याह—**वैशिश्ये(के)त्यादि** । वेशो वेश्यावर्गः । करणं च सम्भोगात्मकम् । तत्प्रयोजनं शास्त्रं कामसूत्रं ये कृतवन्तस्तैः । शृङ्गारो दशभिरभिलषितादिभिर्मरणान्ताभिरवस्थाभिर्युक्तो दर्शितः । अवस्थाग्रहणेन च तावन्तो बहवो विप्रलम्भा इत्याशङ्कां निराकरोति । तेन चिन्तादयोऽपि व्यभिचारित्वेन रतेस्तेरनुज्ञाता इति तात्पर्यम् । चकारेणेदमाह—परस्परास्थाबन्धात्मकत्वे रतिरूपे स्थिते सति तदङ्गभूता दशावस्था विप्रलम्भाङ्गम् । यथोदयनस्य चित्रफलकावलोकनतः प्रभृति ।

ननु तत्रापि [न] रतिः क्व । अस्य विषयस्यानवगमात् । न हि चित्रमात्रम् । नलिनीसंस्तरादेः साक्षिणो विद्यमानत्वात् । आकृत्या च काम्यमानतौचित्यस्य लाभात् । यदि परं नाम तज्ज्ञास्त (न ज्ञातं त) त्कुत्रोपयोगीति । यदा तु विप्रलम्भाङ्गता न भवति तदा स्वातन्त्र्यं—यथा रावणस्यापि । तदुक्तमस्मदुपाध्यायभट्टतोतेन—

'स्वातन्त्र्येण प्रवृत्तौ तु सर्वप्राणिषु सम्भवः ।' इति ।

नन्वेवं व्यभिचार्यभेदात्करुणः कथं विप्रलम्भाद्भिद्यत इत्याशङ्क्याह—**करुणस्त्विति** । अधमप्रकृतेस्तावन्न विप्रलम्भः । स्थाय्यभावात् । तदभावो विभावसामग्रीवैकल्यादिति । तत्र तावत्करुणः पृथक् लब्धप्रतिष्ठः । एवमुत्तमप्रकृतावपि रतिविपरीतः शोकः करुणे स्थायी । अत एवाह निरपेक्षः । बन्धुजनादिविषये याऽपेक्षा रताविवालम्बनम् ।

यथोक्तम्--"आशाबन्धः कुसुमसदृशप्राणम्" इति (मेघ०पू०१०) । ततो निष्क्रान्तो भावः शोकाख्यो यस्मिन् । **शापक्लेशे विनिपतितस्येष्टजनस्य** यो **विभवनाशो वधबन्धो** वा ततः **समुत्थानं** यस्य । शापग्रहणेनाप्रतिकार्यत्वे सत्युत्तमप्रकृतेः शोकोदयस्थानमेतदिति दर्शयति । अन्यथोत्साहक्रोधादिविभावत्वं स्यात् । शोकत्वमेव च पराकर्तुं कविकुलचक्रवर्तिना पुरूरवस ऊर्वशीशापप्राप्तिरनु रूप (रनुप) लक्षितत्वेन निबद्धा । एवं विभावस्थायिविभेदो दर्शितः । येऽपि

---

१. N.S. K.S.S. M.G. सुखप्रायेष्टसम्पन्नः G.O.S. सुखप्रायेषु सम्पन्नः ।

अपि चात्र सूत्रा[1]र्थानुविद्धे आर्ये भवतः ।

ऋतुमाल्याङ्कारैः प्रियजनगान्धर्वकाव्यसेवाभिः ।
उपवनगमनविहारैः शृङ्गाररसः समुद्भवति ॥ ४७ ॥

नयनवदनप्रसादैः स्मितमधुरवचोधृतिप्रमोदैश्च ।
मधुरैश्चाङ्गविहा[2]रैस्तस्याभिनयः प्रयोक्तव्यः ॥ ४८ ॥

चैते निर्वेदाद्यास्तेऽपि वस्तुतो रत्यननुगृहीता निरपेक्षाच्छोकाद्भवन्त्यऽन्योन्य (न्तोऽन्य)एव । ततोऽप्याह निरपेक्षभाव इति ।

एवं प्रसङ्गात्करुणस्य स्वरूपमभिधाय प्रकृते योजयति—**औत्सुक्यचिन्तेति** । चिन्ताशब्दोऽशेषनिर्वेदाद्युपलक्षणम् । औत्सुक्यप्रधाना ये चिन्तादयस्तेभ्यः सम्यगुत्थानं विजृम्भो यस्य । अत एव सापेक्षो यत्र रत्याख्यो भावः । ते च सापेक्षाद्रत्याख्याद्भवन्ति । न हि विप्रलम्भे विभावः स्थायी च सम्भोगाद्भिद्यते । एक एवासाविति हि बहुश उक्तम् ।

एतदुक्तं भवति । औत्सुक्यं विषयौन्मुख्यम् । तच्च नष्टे विषये न सम्भवति । एवं परीक्ष्य परीक्षाफलमुपसंहरति—**एवमेष** इति । शृङ्गार इत्येकवचनेनैक एव शृङ्गार इत्युपसंहृतम् ।

एवं सूत्रार्थे परीक्ष्य स्थापिते तदर्थस्य सुखग्रहणार्थं सूत्रार्थविवरणरूपत्वात्सूत्रसमीपेऽप्युपचितपाठात्कारिकामधुना पठति—**अपि चेति** । न केवलं सूत्रं परीक्षाऽपि यावदियं कारिकेति ससुच्चयार्थः । एवं सर्वत्र मन्तव्यम् ।

तामेव कारिकां पठति **सुखेति** । **पुरुष** इति भोक्ता संवेदनात्मकोऽभिप्रेतः । भोक्तैव च स्थायिसंविद्रूपः । व्यभिचारिणस्तु भोगस्वभावाः । तेन रतिरेव पुरुषः । तथा चोक्तम्—'श्रद्धामयोऽयं पुरुष' इति । एवं प्रमदाऽपि । तत्र भोक्तत्वे पुरुषस्य प्राधान्यम् । प्रमदायास्तु भोग्यत्वम् । प्राधान्यादेव च तस्य भोग्येनापरतन्त्रीकरणमिति नायिकान्तरयोगेऽपि न शृङ्गारहानिः । भोग्यस्य तु पारतन्त्र्यादेवान्यसम्मीलने शृङ्गारभङ्ग इति दर्शितम् । अत एव न स्थायिभेदः शङ्कनीयः । **सुखप्रायेषु सम्पन्न** इत्यादिपुरुषविशेषणत्वेन समुदितस्य विभावत्वं दर्शयति । विभावादयो (न) रसोदयं विनाऽऽस्वादैश्च भोक्तरीति निमग्नत्वे भोक्तृप्रधानत्वं च दर्शयन्ति । विषयसम्भारपूर्णताभिमानजैव रतिरुचिता ।

---

१. K.S.S. N.S. M.G. सूत्रानुविद्धे G.O.S. सूत्रार्थानुविद्धे ।

२. N.S. M.G. K.S.S. विकारैः G.O.S. विहारैः ।

अथ हास्यो नाम हासस्थायिभावात्मकः । स च विकृतपरवेषालङ्कार-धाष्टर्यलौल्यकुहकासत्प्रलापव्यङ्गदर्शनदोषोदाहरणादिभिर्विभावैरुत्पद्यते

एतदर्थमेव 'जंस अहं तादेण दिण्णेति' 'ईरिसव्स कण्णपूरदंसणव्से' ति (?) न । एतत्सर्वसम्पन्नत्वमेव नायिकायाः प्रदर्शितम् । अन्यथा नोत्तमत्वं स्यात् । निजजातिकुलानुरूपसम्पदभावे तु रतिः पुरुषार्थरूपत्वा(भावाद)नुपदेश्या । अत एव तत्र सर्वस्य प्रतीतिवैर(स्य)स्यानन्तरसंभावनमिति श्लोकस्य तात्पर्यार्थः ।

विषयसामग्रीसम्पूर्णो रस इति ये मन्यन्ते तेषामभ्रान्तिकारणमयं श्लोकः । स चेत्थं व्याख्यातो न भ्रान्तिजनकः । **संश्रीयत (संज्ञित)** इत्यनेनान्वर्थतां पराकरोति । तथा हि—उणादिषु शृङ्गारशब्दो निपातित इति ।

न केवलं श्लोकवृत्तमिदं **सूत्रार्थानुविद्धं यावदार्ये अपी**त्यपि चेत्यस्य भिन्नक्रमस्यार्थः । **प्रियो जनो** विदूषकादिः । **गान्धर्व**शब्दो गीतादिहृद्यविषयोपलक्षणम् । **काव्यसेवा**शब्देन विषयसङ्कल्पं विभावत्वेन लक्षयति ।

यस्त्वाह काव्यार्थीभूताद्रसात्काव्यार्थविदो भावान्तरं प्रादुर्भवति । अतः सुखजनकत्वात्काव्यार्थो रस इति । स प्रत्युक्तः । न हि विषयसामग्री रस इति पूर्वं दर्शितम् । **धृतिप्रमोद**शब्देन व्यभिचारिणो लक्षयति । एक एव च परमार्थतः शृङ्गार इत्यभिप्रायेणादाववस्थोपलक्षणद्वारेण सर्व एवोपसंहृतो मन्तव्यः ॥

इति शृङ्गाररसप्रकरणम् ॥

अथ हास्यरसप्रकरणम्

अथ हास्यं लक्षयितुमाह—**अथेति । आत्म**शब्देनेदमाह—रतिरास्वादनाख्यां प्रतीतिं विदधाना न तां रतिरूपामेव विधत्ते । प्रमुखे विभावादौ साधारण्यात् । हासे तु य आस्वादः सोऽपि विकृतवेषादीनां सामाजिकान्प्रति लोकवृत्तेन हासहेतुतेति विभावसाधारण्यद्वारेण तदेकस्वभाव एवेति हासात्मकरसनाख्यचर्वणीयत्वाच्चास्य । रतिशोकावेव परमतज्जातीयसंविदास्वादौ धारारूढसुखदुःखरूपत्वेन निस्साधारणात्मीयत्वनियमग्रहगृहीतहेतुबलादेवोत्पद्येते यतः अतोऽनयोर्मुनिना प्रभवग्रहणं कृतम् । अन्येषु तु विभावे साधारण्यसम्भावनात्तदात्मकग्रहणम् । नयविनयादेरन्यायकारिणः समानं कालादेरपूर्ववस्तुनश्च सर्वान्प्रत्युत्साहक्रोधभयजुगुप्साविस्मयहेतुत्वेन साधारण्यविभावत्वादित्यलं बहुना ।

तस्योष्ठ[1]नासाकपोलस्पन्दनदृष्टि व्याकोशाकुञ्चनस्वेदास्यरागपार्श्वग्रहणादिभिरनुभावैरभिनयः प्रयोक्तव्यः। व्यभिचारिणश्चास्यावहित्थालस्यतन्द्रानिद्रास्वप्नप्रबोधासूयादयः। द्विविधश्चायमात्मस्थः परस्थश्च। यदा स्वयं हसति तदाऽऽत्मस्थः। यदा तु[2] परं हासयति तदा परस्थः।

तत्र **वेशः** केशादिरचना। **अलङ्कारः** कटकादिः। स चोभयोऽपि विकृतो देशकालप्रकृतिवयोऽवस्थाविपरीतो हास्यस्य विभावः। एतेन सर्वे रसा हास्येऽन्तर्भूता इति दर्शितम्। अथ विदूषकोऽपि तद्वेषं विदधद्धास्याभासं प्रागेवोक्तम्। परस्य सम्बन्धी परः। एवंभूतो देवदत्तस्य वेषोऽयमलङ्कारो वा इत्युद्धट्टक (ना. शा. ४-१८७) भाण्डनृत्तादौ दर्श्यमानौ। हासं करोति। वेषालङ्कारौ गतागतिकादेरप्युपलक्षणम्। **धाष्ट्यं** निर्लज्जता। **लौल्यं** विषयेष्वनियतता। **कुहकं** कक्षग्रीवादिस्पर्शनं विस्मापनविधिप्रसिद्धं बालानाम्। अङ्गविगमो विखुनादि **व्यङ्गम्**। एषां **दर्शनमिति** समासः। **दोषा** अतत्प्रकृतेरपि भयादयः अकार्यकरणादयश्च विकृतवेषादय एव वा। तेषा**मुदाहरणं** वर्णनम्। **आदि**ग्रहणात्सङ्कल्पस्मृत्यादि।

ओष्ठादेः स्पन्दनशब्देन संबन्धः। **व्याकोशनं** विकासो निमीलनं च। **आकुञ्चनं** त्वीषत्। एतद्दृष्ट्या योज्यम्। **आस्यरागो** मुखरागः। **पार्श्वयोर्ग्रहणं** पीडनम्। **तन्द्राशब्देन** मोहः। एते च विभावा अनुभावा व्यभिचारिश्च प्रकृतित्रयभेदेन ये स्मितादिभेदा वक्ष्यन्ते तेषु यथायोगं योजनीयाः।

द्विविधश्चायमिति। आत्मस्थैर्विभावैर्विकृतवेषादिभिर्विदूषकः स्वयं हसति स तस्यात्मस्थः। देवीं च हासयतीति तस्याः परस्थः—तदिदमसत्। एवं हि विभावानामात्मस्थत्वविभागः स्यात्। न हासस्य। किञ्च स्वामिनः शोकोऽनुजीविषु शोकं करोतीति परस्थता सर्वत्र स्यात्। स्वयंभूर्हि परत्र देव्यादौ व्यक्तः परस्थ इति चेद्गम्भीरस्यप्र भोरनुजीविगतोऽनुभावव्यक्तक्रोधोऽपि परस्थो भवेत्। नद्विभाव आत्मस्थोऽतो(न्य)विभावकस्त्वन्य इत्यप्यसत्। परहासोपि तद्धासे विभावः स्यात्। एतच्च रत्यादिषु सर्वेष्वप्यस्ति। तस्मादयमत्रार्थः—परं हसन्तं दृष्ट्वा स्वयं विभावानपश्यन्नपि हसन् लोके दृष्टः। तथा विभावादिदर्शनेऽपि। परकीयहासावलोकेन तत्क्षणं हासविशेषः सम्पद्यत एवेति स्वभावः। यथाऽम्लदाडिमादिरसास्वादः सङ्क्रमणस्वभावोऽन्यत्रापि दन्तोदकविकारानु

---

१. K.S.S. M.G. ओष्ठदंशन G.O.S. N.S. ओष्ठ।
२. M.G. K.S.S. यदापरं G.O.S. N.S. यदा तु परं।

अत्रानुवंश्ये आर्ये भवतः ।

विपरीतालङ्कारैर्विकृताचाराभिधानवेषैश्च ।
विकृतैरर्थवि[1]शेषैर्हसतीति रसः स्मृतो हास्यः ॥ ४९ ॥

विकृता[2]चारैर्वाक्यैरङ्गविकारैश्च विकृतवेषैश्च ।
हासयति जनं यस्मात्तस्माज्ज्ञेयो रसो हास्यः ॥ ५० ॥

स्त्रीनीचप्रकृतावेष भूयिष्ठं दृश्यते रसः ।
षड्भेदाश्चास्य विज्ञेयास्तांश्च वक्ष्याम्यहं पुनः ॥ ५१ ॥

स्मितमथ हसितं विहसितमुपहसितं चापहसितमतिहसितम् ।
द्वौ द्वौ भेदौ स्यातामुत्तममध्याधमप्रकृतौ ॥ ५२ ॥

तत्र

स्मितहसिते ज्येष्ठानां मध्यानां विहसितोपहसिते च ।
अधमानामपहसितं ह्य[3]तिहसितं चापि विज्ञेयम् ॥ ५३ ॥

रूपसङ्क्रमदर्शनादेव सङ्क्रामति एवं हासः स्वभावतः सङ्क्रमशील इति **काष्ठा** (काऽस्य) भूयिष्ठता । नानाभेदा इत्याह—**षड्भेदाश्चेति** । **द्वौ द्वाविति** । यथाक्रमं विभावतारतम्यमित्यादीति केचित् । तत्त्वसत् । भेदान्तराणामपि प्रसङ्गात् ।' तस्मात्सङ्क्रमणाभिप्रायेणैतत् । स्मितं हि यदुत्तमप्रकृतो तत्सङ्क्रान्तं हसितं सम्पद्यते । अत एव त्र्यवस्थो हास इति वक्ष्यते । षडवस्थो ह्यन्यथा स्यात् ।

स्मितस्ये(च्चे)षत्तायाम् । हसितं ततो विशेषेण । ततोऽपि परस्य गतं समीपगतमन्यत् । अपहसितमतिशयेन चेत्युपसर्गभेदादर्थभेदः । (५३)

सौष्ठावमनुल्बणता । **द्विजा** दन्ताः । **धीरमिति** मन्थरं कृत्वा ईषत्त्वनिर्वाहः । **विकसितैरिति** । **अथेति** । स्मितानन्तरं संक्रमणकाल इत्यर्थः । **तदिति** । स्मितमेव संक्रान्तं सदेवंरूपतामेतीत्यर्थः ।

---

१. M.G. N.S. अङ्गविकारैः G.O.S. K.S.S. अर्थविशेषैः ।
२. N.S. G.O.S. आचारैः K.S.S. M.G. आकारैः ।
३. K.S.S. तथा G.O.S. N.S. M.G. हि ।

अत्र श्लोका:—

ईषद्विकसि[1]तैर्गण्डैः कटाक्षैः सौष्ठवान्वितैः ।
अलक्षितद्विजं धीरमुत्तमानां स्मितं भवेत् ॥ ५४ ॥

उत्फुल्लाननेत्रं[2] तु गण्डैर्विकसितै[3]रथ ।
किञ्चिल्लक्षितदन्तं च हसितं तद्विधीयते ॥ ५५ ॥

अथ मध्यमानाम् :—

आकुञ्चिताक्षिगण्डं[4] यत्सस्वनं मधुरं तथा ।
कालागतं सास्यरागं तद्वै विहसितं भवेत् ॥ ५६ ॥

उत्फुल्लनासिकं यत्तु[5] जिह्मदृष्टिनिरीक्षितम्[6] ।
निकुञ्चिताङ्गकशि[7]रस्तच्चोपहसितं भवेत् ॥ ५७ ॥

जिह्माख्याया भाविन्या दृष्टया: निरीक्षणं यत्र काल उचितं तेन संस्थानादौ । (५७)

अस्थान इत्यकालेशोकाद्यवसरे । **विकृष्टं** श्रवणकटु । **नाटक** इति । नाटकशब्दो रूपकमात्रवृत्तिः । **स्वसमुत्थ** इत्यसंक्रान्तस्मितविहसितापहसितलक्षणः । **परसमुत्थः** संक्रान्तो हसितोपहसितातिहसितरूपः । हसितादिरूपसंक्रमणयो(मेवो)त्कृष्टप्रकृतौ स्मितादिरूपम् । रतिक्रोधशोकादेस्तु न संक्रमणं भवतीत्युक्तमेव । तत्र हि युगपदेव वा स एव विभावस्तच्चित्तवृत्तिमान्वा पुरुषो विभावतामेति । न तु त एव विभावास्तस्य चित्तवृतिं प्रस्तूय संक्रमयाद्यस्य(मयन्त्यन्यस्य)प्रस्तुवतः । हासमिव(स एव) सर्वेषामात्मस्थपरस्थभेदोपलक्षणमेतदित्यन्ये । एतच्चासत् । अनुभवसिद्धमेव हीदं हासः संक्रामतीति ।

---

१. K.S.S. विहसितैः G.O.S. N.S. M.G. विकसितैः ।
२. K.S.S. M.G. नेत्रैस्तु N.S. G.O.S. नेत्रं तु ।
३. K.S.S. विहसितैः G.O.S. N.S. M.G. विकसितै ।
४. K.S.S. M.G. सस्वरं G.O.S. N.S. सस्वनं ।
५. M.G. K.S.S. यच्च G.O.S. N.S. यत्तु ।
६. K.S.S. निरीक्षणम् G.O.S. N.S. M.G. निरीक्षितम् ।
७. K.S.S. N.S. निकुञ्चितांमकशिरः M.G. निहञ्चितांमकशिरः G.O.S. निकुञ्चिताङ्गकशिरः ।

अथाधमानाम् :—

अस्थानहसितं यत्तु[1] साश्रुनेत्रं तथैव च ।
उत्कम्पितांसकशिरस्तच्चापहसितं भवेत् ॥ ५८ ॥

संरब्धसाश्रुनेत्रं च विकृष्टस्वर[2] मुद्धतम् ।
करोपगूढपार्श्वं च तच्चातिहसितं भवेत् ॥ ५९ ॥

हास्यस्थानानि यानि स्युः कार्योत्पन्नानि नाटके ।
उत्तमाधममध्यानामेवं तानि प्रयोजयेत् ॥ ६० ॥

इत्येष स्वसमुत्थस्तथा परसमुत्थश्च विज्ञेयः ।
द्विविधस्त्रिप्रकृतिगतस्त्र्यवस्थभावो रसो हास्यः[3] ॥ ६१ ॥

अथ करुणो नाम शोकस्थायिभावप्रभवः । स च शापक्लेशविनिप[4]तितेष्ट-जनविप्रयोगविभवनाशवधबन्धविद्रवोपघातव्यसनसंयोगादिभिर्विभावैः समुप-

---

अन्यस्त्वाह—तिसृषु प्रकृतिषु त्र्यवस्थो विभावतारतम्यात् द्विरूपः । पुनरात्मपरस्थत्वेन द्विधेति द्वादशभेदोऽयमिति कारिकातात्पर्यमिति । अत्र च पृथग्विभावनमपि भवति । । तत्त्वतिप्रसङ्गावहं तन्मतमिति नोदाहृतम् । (६१)

इति हास्यरसप्रकरणम् ॥

अथ करुणरसप्रकरणम्

इदानीमवसरायातं करुणं लक्षयति—**अथ करुणो** नामेति । अथेति क्रमे । तत्र चायं क्रमः—सम्भोगेन हास्योऽङ्गत्वेनापेक्षितः । विप्रलम्भेन च समानव्य-भिचारिकत्वात्करुण इति **टीकाकारः** ।

---

१. M.G. K.S.S. यत्र G.O.S. N.S. यत्तु ।

२. M.G. N.S. K.S.S. विक्रुष्ट G.O.S. विकृष्ट ।

३. M.G. K.S.S एवमात्मसमुत्थं च तथा परसमुत्थितम् । द्विविधस्त्रिप्रकृतिकः षड्भेदोऽथरसःस्मृतः G.O.S. N.S. (Same as above) except N.S. reads समुत्थितः in plaee of समुत्थः ।

४. K.S.S. M.G. विनिपाते G.O.S. N.S. विनिपतित ।

जायते । तस्याश्रुपातपरिदेवनमुखशोषणवैवर्ण्यस्रस्तगात्रतानिश्श्वासस्मृतिलोपादिभिरनुभावैरभिनयः प्रयोक्तव्यः । व्यभिचारिणश्चास्य निर्वेदग्लानिचिन्तौत्सुक्यावेगभ्रममोहश्रमभयविषाददैन्यव्याधिजडतोन्मादापस्मारत्रासालस्यमरणस्तम्भवेपथुवैवर्ण्याश्रुस्वरभेदादयः ।

एतच्च पूर्वापरविरुद्धम् । अस्माभिस्तूद्देशविभाग एव क्रमो दर्शितः । तस्याभिनयः प्रयोज्यो यस्यास्वाद्यमानस्य करुण इति व्यपदेशः । सदयहृदयता हि करुणा लोके प्रसिद्धा । सा च लिङ्गैरनुकर्तरि शोकं प्रतियतां सामाजिकानामिति करुणव्यपदेश इति **श्रीशङ्कुकः ।**

एतच्च पूर्वापरविस्मरणविजृम्भितमस्य । यतः शोकं प्रतिकृतिस्तस्य (शोकप्रकृतिकस्य) करुणा । दया च नाम परित्राणेच्छा । सा कथं शोकानुकरणम् । किं प्रति च तेषां दयेति न विद्मः ।

तस्मात् **करुण** इति शोकः । सर्वसाधारणत्वेन प्राग्युवत्या आस्वाद्यमानस्य संज्ञा । तदर्थमेव **नाम**शब्दः । तत्प्रभवत्वं शृङ्गारवद्याख्येयम् अशक्यप्रतीकारहेतूपलक्षणं शापग्रहणम् । **शापक्लेशे** पतितस्येष्टजनस्य ये **विप्रयोगा**दयः । तत्र विप्रयोगोऽयं सङ्गमः (योगोऽसङ्गमः) । **विभवनाश**नादि प्रसिद्धम् । **विद्रवो** देशादुच्चाटनम् । तच्च विप्रयोगेऽपीति विशेषः । उपघातोऽग्न्यादिमरणम् । अग्न्यादिकृतो विद्रवः चोरादिकृत उपघात इति त्वसत् । विभवनाशेन गतत्वात् । **व्यसनेन** मृगयाक्षादिनाऽनर्थजनकेन **संयोगः** । विभवनाशादयोऽपि स्वात्मगता नोत्तमप्रकृतेः शोकं कुर्युः । मध्यमाधमप्रकृतीनां तु कुर्युरेवेत्यादिग्रहणम् । **परिदेवन**मात्मनो दैवस्यान्यस्य चोपालम्भः । **निश्वास**शब्देन तदनन्तरभावी उच्छ्वासोऽप्यूर्ध्वसनरूपो लक्ष्यते । **स्मृतिलोपेन** स्तम्भप्रलयौ लक्ष्येते । **वैवर्ण्याश्रुस्वरभेदा** अत्र बहिरुद्भिन्नस्वभावाश्चित्तवृत्त्यात्मानो गृह्यन्ते । तथा हि वक्तारो भवन्ति 'अश्रुणा पूर्णोऽस्य कण्ठो न च नयनजलं दृष्टम्' इति । एते ह्यश्रुप्रभृतयो व्यभिचारित्वाभिनेयत्वोपजीवनायैव मध्ये निर्दिष्टा इत्यवोचाम वक्ष्यामश्च । तेन न पौनरुक्त्यम् । एवमन्यत्रापि । **व्याधेरुन्मादापस्मारो** भेदेन वक्ष्यामः ।

वधशब्दो बन्धादेरप्युपलक्षणम् । **विप्रिय**मिष्टजनवधादि येन वाक्येनोच्यते तस्य श्रवणात् । तेन चेष्टजनस्य विभवनाशादि दृश्यमानं श्रूयमाणं वा कविभिः

अत्रार्ये भवतः—

इष्टवधदर्शनाद्वा विप्रियवचनस्य संश्रवा[1]द्वापि ।
एभिर्भावविशेषैः करुणरसो नाम संभवति ॥ ६२ ॥

सस्व[2]नरुदितैर्मोहागमैश्च[3] परिदेवितैर्विलपितैश्च ।
अभिनेयः करुणरसो देहायासाभिघातैश्च ॥ ६३ ॥

अथ रौद्रो नाम क्रोधस्थायिभावात्मको रक्षोदानवोद्धतमनुष्यप्रकृ[4]तिः संग्रामहेतुकः । स च क्रोधाधर्षणाधिक्षेपा[5]नृतवचनोपघात[6]वाक्पारुष्याभिद्रोह-

---

करुणविभावत्वेनोपनिबन्धनीयमिति तात्पर्यम् । **एभिरित्येवंप्रकारैः । भावशब्दो-**ऽत्रार्थानां विभाववाची । अनुभावांस्तद्द्वारेण च व्यभिचारिणोऽप्युपलक्षयितुमार्यान्तरं **सस्वनेत्यादि** । बहुवचनं प्रकृतिदेशकालदशाहेत्वादिभेदेनानेकप्रकारत्वज्ञापनार्थम् । **मोहो** जडता । तेनान्ये व्यभिचारिण उपलक्ष्यन्ते । **देहस्यायासनं** पातनवेष्टनादि । **अभिघात** उरस्ताडनादिः । एते चानुभावाः प्रकृतिभेदेन यथायोगं विभजनीयाः । करुणो रौद्रादित्युक्तम् । स की(ही) दृग्रौद्र इति क्रमं केचिदाहुः ॥ (६३)

इति करुणरसप्रकरणम् ॥

अथ रौद्ररसप्रकरणम्

अधुना रौद्ररसं लक्षयति—**अथ रौद्रो नामेति** । आत्मग्रहणस्यायमाशयः । अन्यायकारिता प्राधान्येन क्रोधस्य विषयः । तादृशि च जने सर्वो(र्वे)ऽपि मनोरथैरपि रुधिरपानमपि नामाद्रियन्ते । तथा चाह लोकः—तादृशो यदि लभ्यते तत्तदीय रुधिरमपि पीत्वा न तृप्यते । महाकविना **भासेनापि** स्वप्रबन्ध उक्तः—

---

१. K.S.S. संश्रयात् G.O.S. N.S. M.G. संश्रवात् ।
२. K.S.S. श्वसन G.O.S. N.S. M.G. सस्वन ।
३. K.S.S. उद्गमैः G.O.S. N.S. M.G. आगमैः ।
४ K.S.S. M.G. प्रभवः G.O.S. N.S. प्रकृतिः ।
५. M.G. N.S. K.S.S. धर्षण G.O.S. आधर्षण ।
६. K.S.S. M.G. N.S. read अवभान after अधिक्षेप G.O.S. om..

मात्सर्यादिभिर्विभावैरुत्पद्यते । तस्य च ताडनपाटनपीडनच्छेदनभेदनप्रहरणाहरणशस्त्रसम्पातसम्प्रहाररुधिराकर्षणाद्यानि कर्माणि । पुनश्च रक्तनयनभ्रु[१]कुटीकरणदन्तोष्ठपीडनगण्डस्फुरणहस्ताग्रनिष्पेषादिभिरनुभावैरभिनयः[२] प्रयोक्तव्यः ।

'त्रेतायुगं तद्धि न मैथिली सा
रामस्य रागपदवी मृदु चास्य चेतः ।
लब्धा जनस्तु यदि रावणमस्य कायं
प्रोत्कृत्य तन्न, तिलशो न वितृप्तिगामी ॥' इति ॥

तेन हास्यवत्साधारणविभावत्वाच्चर्वणापि क्रोधमय्येवेति तद्रसनाचरणौ(शरणो) रौद्रः क्रोधात्मक एव । उद्रिक्तं हन्तृत्वं येषां त **उद्धताः** । तद्वेषधारिणो ये नटास्ते । प्रकृतिश्चर्वणोदयहेतुरस्य । अत्र व्याचक्षते—युद्धहेतुक उद्धतमनुष्येषु भीमसेनादिषु रुधिरपानादिलक्षणः । रक्षोदानवास्तु स्वभावरौद्रा इति । तदसत् । भीमस्य रुधिरपानं न युद्धहेतुकम् अपि तु विषर्ययेण । उद्धतस्वभावत्वादेव ह्यसौ क्रोधपरवशः सन्ननुचितमपि प्रतिज्ञातवान् । तन्निर्वाह्ययैव च राक्षसाधिष्ठानमस्य कविना **वेणीसंहारे** वर्णितम् । तस्मात्सर्व एवैते स्वभावात् क्रोधनाः । तदनुसारिणि नटे रौद्र आस्वाद्यत इति **मनुष्यप्रकृतिः** । **सङ्ग्रमहेतुक** इति चायमर्थः—युद्धस्य कविनटप्रदर्श्यमान(स्य) हेतुकः कुत्सितंहेतुधी(ति)रोहितः । तस्योचितो हेतुर्न क्रोधः । तथा च प्राधान्येन युद्धेन वीर एव व्यपदेक्ष्यते ।

नन्वेते स्वभावक्रोधना अपि किमुद्दीपनमपेक्षन्ते । ओमित्याह—**सचेति** । **क्रोधादि** परकर्तृकम् । **आधर्षणं** दारादिखलीकरणम् । **अधिक्षेपो** देशजात्यभिजनविद्याकर्मनिन्दा । **अनृतस्य** कस्याप्यपसत्यस्य **वचनम्** । **उपघातो** गृहभृत्याद्युपमर्दनम् । **वाक्पारुष्यं** वधाद्युपन्यासेन तर्जनम् । **अभिद्रोहो** जिघांसा । **मात्सर्यं** गुणेष्वसूया । **आदि**ग्रहणाद्राज्यापहरणादि । एतैरुत्पद्यते कविना विभावत्वेन वर्ण्यमानैः ।

---

१. G.O.S. N.S. Read उपघात after अनृतवचन K.S.S. M.G. omit.

२. N.S. K.S.S. Reads स्वेद after नयन and N.S. read अबष्टमा after भ्रुकुटीकरण K.S.S. omits it N.S. G.O.S. omits bvth स्वेद and भ्रुकुटीकरण ।

भावाश्चास्या[1] सम्मोहोत्साहावेगामर्षचपलतौग्र्यगर्व[2]स्वेदवेपथुरोमाञ्च-गद्गदादयः ।

अत्राह—यदभिहितं रक्षोदानवादीनां रौद्रो रसः । किमन्येषां नास्ति । उच्यते—अस्त्यन्येषामपि रौद्रो रसः । किन्त्वधिकारोऽत्र गृह्यते । ते हि स्वभावत एव रौद्राः । कस्मात् ? बहुबाहवो बहुमुखाः प्रोद्धूतविकीर्णपिङ्गल-

---

अस्य ताडनादीनि कर्माणि रक्तनयनादयोऽनुभावा इति पृथङ्निरूपणं तुल्येऽप्यनुधावत्वे विशेषख्यापनार्थम् । विशेषस्तु पूर्वेषां वचनमात्रेण व्यावर्ण्यनम् । रङ्गे प्रत्यक्षतोऽप्रदर्शनीयत्वात् । यद्वक्ष्यते—

'युद्धं राज्यभ्रंशो मरणं नगरोपरोधनं चैव ।
अप्रत्यक्षकृतानि प्रवेशकैः संविधेयानि ॥' इति ॥ (ना.शा.१८-३८)

रक्तनयनादि रङ्गे प्रत्यक्षेण कृतम् ।

प्रहरणाहरणं तु पूर्वत्र प्रमादपठितमिति केचित् । इदं तु पृथगभिधाने तुच्छं प्रयोजनम् । अयं चात्राशयः—रक्षोदानवोद्धतमनुष्या उद्दीपनहेतुभिर्विनाऽपि चेष्टितमात्रं यदपि कुर्वते नर्मगोष्ट्याद्यपि च तत्र ताडनादि प्रधानम् । तद्वक्ष्यति—'यच्च किञ्चिदारभन्ते' इति । उद्दीपनसम्भवे ताडनादिग्रस्त एव रक्तनयनाद्यधिकीभवति । अत एव **पुनश्शब्दः** । तत्र **ताडनं** तलाद्यभिघातः । **पाटनं** द्विधाकरणम् । **पीडनं** मर्दनम् । (**छेदनं**) कर्तनम् । **भेदनं** परस्परमित्या (रमैत्र्या) दिवियोजनम् । भात्रे ण्यदन्तौ । **प्रहरणानामासमन्ताद्धरणम्** । शस्त्रस्य सम्पातनमविदारयतोऽपि । सम्प्रहरणं विदारयतः पातनम् । तेन रुधिरस्याकर्षणम् । रक्षःप्रभृतयो हि नर्मणाऽपि प्रहरन्ति । किन्तु रुधिरागमनमात्रफलं न त्वधिकम् । रक्ते च ते नयने । भ्रुवोर्मूलसमुत्क्षेपो भ्रुकुटी । दन्तोष्टस्य यथायोगं पीडनम् । हस्ताग्रयोरन्योन्यनिष्पेषः सङ्घर्षणम् ।

भावा इति व्यभिचारिणः । असंमोहः सम्मोहविपरीतः । विरोधे न । तत्रावृत्तिरुङ्गृहीतः सम्यग्बोधः । उत्साहोऽत्र व्यभिचारी । क्रोधस्य प्राधान्येन रसनीयत्वात् । स्वेदादयो बाह्याः । आभ्यन्तराः सात्त्विका (क) भावेऽपि विषस्पर्शज्वरादिना भवन्ति । ततोऽनैकान्तिकाः । आन्तरा अनुद्रिक्ता व्यजनग्रहणा-

---

१. K.S.S. G.O. संम्मोह G.O.S. N.S. असम्मोह ।

२. N.S. reads विकृतेक्षण after गर्व K.S.S. M.G. omiit गर्व and read विकृतेक्षण G.O.S. (Same as above)

शिरोजा: रक्तोद्वृत्तविलोचना भीमासितरूपिणश्चैव। यच्च किञ्चित्समारभन्ते स्वभावचेष्टितं वागङ्गादिकं तत्सर्वं रौद्रमेवैषाम्[1]। (शृङ्गारश्च तै: प्रायश: प्रसभं सेव्यते[2]।) तेषां चानुकारिणो ये पुरुषास्तेषामपि सङ्ग्रा[3]मसम्प्रहारकृतो रौद्रो रसोऽनुमन्तव्य:।

अत्रानुवंश्ये आर्ये भवत:—

दिभिरुद्रिक्त:। बाह्यै: स्वेदादिभिर्व्यक्ता व्यभिचारिरूपा: पठिता:।

एष्वेव रौद्ररस इत्यभिप्रायं गृहीत्वा चोदक आह—**यदभिहितमिति**। सिद्धान्ती त्वेषु रौद्रो भवत्येवेत्यभिप्रायेणाह—**अस्त्यन्येषामिति**। अन्येषां कविनटाभ्यां प्रयुज्यमानानां सम्बन्धिजन्यत्वेन। अधिकारोऽनुवृत्ति:। अत्रेति-राक्षसादिषु। एतदेव व्यनक्ति—**ते हीति**। स्वभावशब्दानन्तरमेवकारेण भवन्त्येवेत्ययोगव्यवच्छेद एव सूचित:। स्वयं तेषां भवनं तत इत्यर्थ:। तेनाङ्ग-रौद्रोपन्यासोऽप्यविरुद्ध:। अन्यथा स्वभावरौद्र एव रक्ताक्षादिभिरभिधेय: स्यात्। न बहुबाहुमुखादि। तत्र राक्षसादयोऽपि न परिजने सदा क्रुद्धा इति प्रतीयन्त इत्याशयेनाह—**कस्मादिति**।

अत्रोत्तरं **बहुबाहव** इति। लोकप्रसिद्धाकारविपरीतो हि तेषामाकार:। तत्र च परविनाशनाभिसन्धिर्जनितं तपश्चर्यादिकं दृष्टं वा कर्म तेषां व्याप्रियते। अतस्तादृशेष्वदृ(षु दृ)ष्टेषु स एव क्रोधात्मकोऽभिसन्धिर्गम्यत इति सामाजिकानां नान्तदृ(कानान्तुदृ)श्यते रौद्रास्वाद:। तेन च रागादिव यत्क्रोधकाले दृष्टं तत्सदैव तेषामुद्वृत्त तारकयो: रक्तविलोचनम्। अत एव भीममसितं कृष्णं सदैव रूपं येषाम् नित्ययोग इनि:। अत एव बहुवचनबहुव्रीहिरत्र कृत:।

न केवलं कायस्तदीय इत्थं यावच्चेष्टितमपि तदीयं दृश्यमानं रौद्रास्वादजनकमेवेति दर्शयति—**यच्चेति**। **स्वभावेनेति**(वेति)। चित्तस्याविकारेऽपि यच्चेष्टितं वाचिकं कायिकं वा तदेषां ताडनादिप्रधानमिति दृश्यमानं काव्ये प्रयोगे च रौद्रास्वादहेतु। वागङ्गे आदिकारणे यस्य। मानसं तु चेष्टितमप्रत्यक्षत्वान्नोक्तम्।

---

१. K.S.S. M.G. इति N.S. G.O.S. एषाम्।

२. K.S.S. Does not read शृङ्गारश्च...सेव्यते G.O.S. N.S. M.G. Read it.

३. K.S.S. सम्प्रहारकृत: G.O.S. N.S. M.G. सङ्ग्रामसम्प्रहारकृत:।

युद्ध[1]प्रहारघातनविकृतच्छेदनविदारणैश्चैव ।
सङ्ग्रामसम्भ्रमाद्यै[2]रेभिः सञ्जायते रौद्रः ॥ ६४ ॥

नानाप्रहरणमोक्षैः[3] शिरःकबन्धभुजकर्तनैश्चैव ।
एभिश्चार्थविशेषैरस्याभिनयः प्रयोक्तव्यः ॥ ६५ ॥

इति रौद्ररसो दृष्टो रौद्रवागङ्गचेष्टितः ।
शस्त्रप्रहारभूयिष्ठ उग्रकर्मक्रियात्मकः ॥ ६६ ॥

सर्वमिति यदुक्तं तत्स्फुटयति—**शृङ्गारश्चेति**। शृङ्गारशब्देनात्र तद्विभावः प्रमदोद्यानादिः । सोऽपि तैः प्रसभमिति क्रूराकारतया सेव्यते । यत्रौग्र्यस्य वर्जनमुक्तं किं पुनरन्यदिति चशब्दस्यार्थः । तथा 'आः सीते पतिगर्वविभ्रमह(भ) रभ्राम्यद्भ्रु' इत्याद्युदाहरणम् । तथा नानादेवावि 'गाढाम्रेडं मलयमरुतः शृङ्खलादाम दत्त' (बाल. रामा. ५-५१) इति रोद्ररसत्वेन कदाचिदनुनयेनापीति दर्शयति—**प्रायश** इति ।

ननूद्धतमनुष्येषु तर्हि कथं रौद्रादिविकारः । न हि ते बहुबाहुत्वादियुक्ता इत्याशङ्क्याह—**तेषां चेति** । राक्षसादीनाम् । **अनुकारिण** इति । तामसप्रकृतितया तत्सदृशा अनुगामित्वेन मन्तव्या इत्यर्थः । कथमित्याह—सङ्ग्रामसम्प्रहारग्रहणेन पूर्वोक्तं ताडनपाटनादि गृह्यते । तेन बहुबाहुत्वाद्यभावेऽप्युद्धतमनुष्या वागङ्गचेष्टितेन क्रोधोचितेन रौद्रप्रकृतय इति लक्ष्यन्ते । एवं रक्षोदानवेत्यादावयोगव्यवच्छेदो निश्चितः । अन्येऽपि तु वीरप्रधाना अश्वत्थामजामदग्न्यादयः । तेषु कारणमहिम्ना भवत्येव क्रोधो रौद्रास्वादयोग्यः । राक्षसादीनामपि च हासशोकादिः स्वकारणोदितोऽभिभूतक्रोधः । हास्यकरुणादेश्चेह योगो भवत्येव । तेनैषां न रौद्र एव रसः । ननु सामाजिकानां तथाभूतराक्षसादिदर्शने कथं क्रोधात्मक आस्वादः । उच्यते—हृदयसंवादः आस्वादः । क्रोधे च हृदयसंवादस्तामसप्रकृतीनामेव सामाजिकानामिति दानवादिसदृशास्तन्मयीभूता एवान्यायकारिविषयं क्रोधमास्वादयन्तीति न किञ्चिदवद्यम् ।

विकृतं यच्छेदनं व्यङ्गादिकरणं युद्धादीति परेण क्रियमाणौचित्यम् । तेन युद्धाद्यनुमितस्य परक्रोधादेर्विभावत्वमुक्तम् । सङ्ग्रामाय सम्भ्रमः शस्त्राहरणे त्वरा ।

---

१. K.S.S. सत्त्व G.O.S. N.S. M.G. युद्ध ।
२. K.S.S. उत्थै. G.O.S. N.S. M.G. आद्यैः ।
३. K.S.S. संकुल M.G. N.S. G.O.S. मोक्षैः ।

अथ वीरो नामोत्तमप्रकृतिरुत्साहात्मकः । स चासंमोहाध्यवसायनयविनयब[1]लपराक्रमशक्तिप्रतापप्रभावादिभिर्विभावैरुत्पद्यते । तस्य स्थैर्यधैर्यशौर्यत्यागवैशारद्यादिभिरनुभावैरभिनयः प्रयोक्तव्यः । भावाश्चास्य धृतिमतिगर्वावेगौग्र्यामर्षस्मृतिरोमाञ्चादयः[2] ।

अत्रार्ये रसविचारमु[3]खे—

अनुभावानाह—**नाना**ेति । मारणप्राधान्यं नानाप्रहरणेन दर्शयति । शिरःकर्तनादिहृतशरीरस्यापि क्रोधातिशयं सूचयन्वीराद्भेदमाह । युद्धवीरेपि हि तन्नास्ति । इह तु वक्ष्यते—**उग्रकर्मेति** । उग्राण्यौग्र्यप्रधानानि यानि शिरःकर्तनादीनि तेषां या क्रिया अभिनीतिः सा आत्मा प्रधानं यस्येति । **भरतमुनि**स्त्वेकेन श्लोकेनोपसंहरति—**इति रौद्ररस** इति ॥ (६६)

इति रौद्ररसप्रकरणं समाप्तम् ।

अथ वीररसप्रकरणम्

क्रमप्राप्तं वीरं लक्षयति—(**अथ वीरेति**) युद्धवीरे हि संग्रामसम्प्रहारयोगो रौद्रेऽपीति **वीरे** जिघांसेति । आनन्तर्यम**थ**शब्देनाह । उत्तमानां प्रकृतिः स्वभावो यत उत्साहोऽतो वीररसोऽपि तथा । यदि वा काव्ये नाट्ये च प्रयुज्यमान उत्तमप्रकृतिर्हेतुर्यस्य । उत्तमवर्णानां हि सर्वत्रोत्साह आस्वाद्यो भवति । अत एव चतुर्ष्वपि नायकेषु वी(धी)रत्वमनुयायित्वेन वक्ष्यते धीरोदात्त इत्यादि । तत्र सर्वो जन उत्साहवानेव । किन्त्वविषय इत्यनुपदेश्यचरितता । यदीयं तु चरितमुपदेशार्हं तेषामुचित एवावसरे उत्साहाभिव्यक्तिः । उचितत्वं चावसरस्यासमोहादिसम्पत्तिरिति सैव विभावत्वेनोपदिष्टा । असंमोहेनाध्यवसायो हि वस्तुतत्त्वनिश्चय इति मन्त्रशक्तिर्दर्शिता । असद्वस्त्वभिनिवेशोऽसंमोहो रावणादिगत उत्साहकारीत्यसत् । अशब्दार्थत्वात् । तत्रापि च पराक्रमनयादिरेव विभावः । सन्ध्यादिगुणानां सम्यक्प्रयोगो **नयः** । इन्द्रियजयो **विनयः** । **बलं**

---

१. K.S.S. बहुल N.S. M.G. G.O.S. बल ।

२. N.S. Reads रोमाञ्चप्रतिबोधादयः G.O.S. M.G. K.S.S. रोमाञ्चादयः ।

३. G.O.S. अत्रार्ये रसविचारमुखे N.S. K.S.S. अत्रानुवंश्ये आर्ये भवतः M.G. अत्रार्ये भवतः ।

उत्साहा (होऽ) ध्यवसायादविषादित्वादविस्मयामो[1]हात् ।
विविधादर्थविशेषाद्वीररसो नाम सम्भवति ॥ ६७ ॥
स्थितिधैर्यवीर्यग[2]र्वैरुत्साहपराक्रमप्रभावैश्च ।
वाक्यैश्चाक्षेपकृतैर्वीररसः सम्यगभिनेयः ॥ ६८ ॥

हस्त्यश्वरथपादातम् । **पराक्रमः** परकीयमण्डलाद्याक्रमेणावस्कन्दः । युद्धादिके सामर्थ्यं **शक्तिः** । **प्रतापः** शत्रुविषये सन्तापकारिणी प्रसिद्धिः । **प्रभावो**ऽभिजन-धनमन्त्रिसम्पत् । **आदि**ग्रहणेन यशःप्रभृति । एते च सम्पूर्णस्वभावा एव विभावा भवन्ति । उत्तमस्य कदाचित्कश्चिदधिक इति पृथक्पृथगुदाहरणम् वस्तुतो ह्यत्रोदाहरणं सर्वमेव रामादिचरितम् । सचिवायत्तसिद्धौ च **वत्सराजप्राये** नायके यथायोगं सचिवगता अप्येते मन्तव्याः । प्रतिनायकगता अपि च ते उत्साहव्यञ्जका इति यथायोगं व्यस्तसमस्तभेदकल्पनं कविना कार्यम् ।

स्थैर्यमचलनम् गाम्भीर्यकृतं संवरणं **धैर्यम्** । **शौर्यं** युद्धादिक्रिया । **त्यागो** दानम् । **वैशारद्य** सामाद्युपायचतुष्कस्यैकाद्वित्रिचतुरादिभेदैर्यथाविषयं नियोजनम् ।

विविधधर्मादिलक्षणमर्थनीयं विशेषमभिसन्धाय · अविषादित्वादविस्मयाद-मोहाच्च योऽध्यवसायो निश्चयः स चोत्साहयतीत्युत्साहः ।

एतदुक्तं भवति—आपद्यङ्क (त्सङ्गति) निमग्नतां स्वल्पे सन्तोषं मिथ्याज्ञानं चापास्य यस्तत्त्वनिश्चयः स एवोत्साहहेतुः प्रधानतया । रौद्रे तु तमःप्राधान्या-दशास्त्रीयानुचितबन्धाद्यपीति मोहविस्मयप्राधान्यम् ।

स्थितिः स्थैर्यम् । **वीर्यं** शोर्यम् । **गर्व**पदेन तदनुभावो लक्ष्यते । उत्साहन-**मुत्साहो**ऽबलस्य विषण्णप्रायस्योत्तेजनं यथा **सेतुबन्धकाव्ये पराक्रमः** पराक्रमणं । इत्थमत्र भवद्भिरासितव्यं योद्धव्यमिति बलस्य व्यापारणादितिकर्तव्यानां भृत्यानां प्रभावना प्रभावसम्पादनम् । **आक्षेपो** वस्त्वन्तरस्य सूचनं तेन कृतानि तत्प्रधानानि यानि वाक्यानीति गम्भीरदुरवगाहार्थत्वं वाक्यानामित्युक्तम् । (६८)

इति वीररसप्रकरणं समाप्तम् ।

---

१. N.S. K.S.S. अविस्मयान्मोहात् M.G. G.O.S. (Same as above).
२. K.S.S. शौर्य G.O.S. N.S. M.G. गर्व

अथ भयानको नाम भयस्थायिभावात्मकः। स च विकृतरवसत्त्वदर्शनशिवोलूकत्रासोद्वेगशून्यागारारण्यगमनस्वजनवधबन्धदर्शनश्रुतिकथादिभिर्विभावैरुत्पद्यते। तस्य प्रवेपितकरचरणनयनचपलपुलकमुखवैवर्ण्यस्वरभेदादिभिरनुभावैरभिनयः प्रयोक्तव्यः।

भावाश्चास्य स्तम्भस्वेदगद्गदरोमाञ्चवेपथुस्वरभेदवैवर्ण्यशङ्कामोहदैन्यावेगचापलजडतात्रासापस्मारमरणादयः।

अत्रार्या:—

विकृतरवसत्त्वदर्शनसंग्रामारण्यशून्यगृहगमनात्।
गुरुनृपयोरपराधात्कृतकश्च भयानको ज्ञेयः॥ ६९॥

अथ भयानकरसप्रकरणम्

वीरस्य भीतावयव (भीताभय) प्रधानत्वाद्भयानकं लक्षयति—**अथेति**। विकृतो रवोऽट्टहासादिः। सत्त्वानां पिशाचानां दर्शनम्। त्रासोद्वेगौ परगतौ। शून्यागारस्यारण्यस्य च गमनं प्राप्तिः। स्वजनस्य यौ वधबन्धौ तयोर्दर्शनं प्रत्यक्षेण। श्रवणमागमेन। कथादि अतिक्रान्तयोरपि पुनरनुसन्धानेन स्मरणम्।

वेपितुं प्रवृत्तं यत्करचरणं आ (तदा) दिकमेंव भयव्यञ्जकं व्याध्यादिवैलक्षण्यसूचनात्। पुलको रोमकूपोन्नतिः। स्वरस्य भेदः स्वभावविपर्ययः।

गुरुनृपयोरिति। अयमाशयः—भयं तावत्स्त्रीनीचबालादिषु वक्ष्यते। नोत्तममध्यमप्रकृतिषु। तेऽपि तु गुरुभ्यो राज्ञश्च भयं दर्शयेयुः। तदभा (द्भा)वेऽप्येवं सुतरामुत्तमत्वं भवति। अप्रभुत्वं चामात्यानाम्। यथाह—'स्वेच्छाचारी भीत एवास्मि' इति। (रत्ना. १.७)। अनुभावाश्च तथा श्लिष्टास्तत्र क्रियन्ते लोके येन सत्यत एव भीतोऽयमिति गुर्वादीनां प्रतीतिर्भवति। अस्वाभाविकत्वाच्च कृतकत्वं बहुतरकालानुवर्तनेनास्वाद्यत्वाच्च रसत्वम्। न च व्यभिचारित्वम्। तद्धि तदा स्याद्यदि स्वभावत एव [न]। (६९)

---

१. K.S.S. प्रवेशमरण M.G. प्रवेशस्मरण G.O.S. N.S. (Same as above)

२. K.S.S. M.G. चलन G.O.S. N.S. चपल।

गात्रमुखदृष्टिभेदैरूरुस्तम्भाभिवीक्षणोद्वेगैः ।
सन्नमुखशोषहृदयस्पन्दनरोमोद्गमैश्च भयम् ॥ ७० ॥
एतत्स्वभावजं स्यात्सत्त्वसमुत्थं तथैव कर्तव्यम् ।
पुनरेभिरेव भावैः कृतकं मृदुचेष्टितैः कार्यम् ॥ ७१ ॥
करचरणवेपथुस्तम्भगात्र[1]हृदयप्रकम्पेन ।
शुष्कोष्ठतालुकण्ठैर्भयानको नित्यमभिनेयः ॥ ७२ ॥

गात्रादीनां भेदो वर्णकर्मसंस्थानादिविपर्ययः । वीक्ष्यमति(भि)क्र(क्रा)म्यति वीक्षणं कान्दिशीकत्वेन निर्लक्षचक्षुःकृतम् । 'उद्वेगः चलनम् । सादो गात्राणां स्रस्तता । मुखस्य तालुनि शोषः । हृदयस्पन्दनमतिवेगेन । इह **भय**मित्यभिनेयमिति वीररस इत्यार्यातः सम्बध्यते ।

ता एता ह्यार्या एकप्रघट्टकतया पूर्वाचार्यैर्लक्षणत्वेन पठिताः । मुनिना तु सुखसङ्ग्रहाय यथास्थानं निवेशिताः ।

सत्त्वसमुत्थमिति । सत्त्वं मनस्समाधानं तज्जन्मकमिति नटस्येयं शिक्षा । सा च सर्वविषयेति **टीकाकारः** । तदिदमसत् कविनटशिक्षार्थमेव सर्वमिदं प्रकरणम् । लोके विभावानुभावाभिनयादिव्यवहाराभावात् । तस्मादयमत्रार्थः—एतत्तावद्भयं स्वभावजं रजस्तमःप्रकृतीनां नीचानामित्यर्थः । येऽपि च सत्त्वप्रधानास्तेषां सत्त्वसमुत्थं प्रयत्नकृतमेभिरेवानुभावैः कार्यम् । किन्तु मृदुचेष्टितैः यतस्तत्कृतकम् । पुनःशब्दो विशेषद्योतकः । ननु च राजादि किमिति गुर्वादिभ्यो भयं कृतं(तकं) दर्शयित्वा किमिति मृदून् गात्रकम्पनादीन्प्रदर्शयति । किमिति च भयानक एव कृतकत्वमुक्तम् । सर्वस्य हि कृतकत्वमुक्तं भवति । यथा वेश्या धनार्थिनीति कृतकां रतिमादर्शयति—इत्याशङ्क्य साधारणमुत्तरमाह—**तथैव कार्य**मिति । भये हि प्रदर्शिते गुरुर्विनीतं जानाति । मृदुचेष्टिततया चाधमप्रकृतिमेनं गणयति । कृतकशृङ्गारा(रात्) वेश्योपदिष्टानां न काचित्पुरुषार्थसिद्धिः । तेनैव ह्युक्तेन प्रकारेण कार्यपुरुषार्थविशेषो लभ्यते । यत्र तु राजा न कृतकं परानुग्रहाय क्रोधविस्मयादीन्दर्शयति तत्र व्यभिचारितैव तेषां न स्थायितेत्येतदर्थसूचिकामेव गुरुवंशान्तरप्रसिद्धामार्यां पठति—**करचरणेति** । **नित्यमिति** । कृतकत्वेऽकृतकत्वे च । (७२)

इति भयानकरसप्रकरणम् ॥

---

१. M.G. N.S. गात्रसंकोचहृदय G.O.S. K.S.S. गात्रहृदय ।

अथ बीभत्सो नाम जुगुप्सास्थायिभावात्मकः। सचाहृद्याप्रि[1]याचोष्यानिष्टश्रवणदर्शनकीर्तनादिभिर्विभावैरुत्पद्यते । तस्य सर्वाङ्गसंहारमुखविकूण[2]नोल्लेखननिष्ठीवनोद्वेजनादिभिरनुभावैभिनयः प्रयोक्तव्यः । भावाश्चास्यापस्मारोद्वेगावेगमोहव्याधिमरणादयः । अत्रानुवंश्ये आर्ये भवतः—

अनभिमतदर्शनेन च गन्धरसस्पर्शशब्ददोषैश्च ।
उद्वेजनैश्च बहुभिर्बीभत्सरसः समुद्भवति ॥ ७३ ॥

मुखनेत्रविकूणन[3]या नासाप्रच्छादनावनमितास्यैः ।
अव्यक्तपादपतनैर्बीभत्सः[4] सम्यगभिनेयः ॥ ७४ ॥

अथ बीभत्सरसप्रकरणम्

अवसरप्राप्तं बीभत्सरसं लक्षयति—**अथेति**। हृदयस्थापि किञ्चित्कस्यचिन्निसर्गतोऽप्रयतं(तोऽप्रियं)लशुनमिव द्विजानाम्। **अप्रियं** जात्यादिदोषात् । यथा श्लेष्मोपहतस्य क्षीरम् । अचोक्षं स्वरूपेणादुष्टमपि तु मलाद्युपहतम्। **अनिष्टं** यत्रानिशं भुक्तत्वेनेच्छा निवृत्ता। **संहारः** पिण्डीकरणम्। मुखस्येति तदङ्गानां सङ्कोचनम्। उल्लेखनमुल्लाघः। निष्ठीपनं कफनिरासनम्। उद्वेजनं गात्रोद्धूननम्। नासाप्रच्छादनं दुर्गन्धप्राये दृष्टम्। प्रतिघातादव्यक्तानि पादयोः पतनानि । यदि वाऽस्थिकङ्कालाद्याकुले पितृवने सञ्चरतोऽस्फुटितानि पादपतनानि क्वचिद्दीर्घाणि अन्यत्र ह्रस्वानि इति । (७४)

इति बीभत्सरसप्रकरणम् ॥

---

१. N.S. अप्रशस्ताप्रियावेक्षानिष्टश्रवणदर्शनोद्वेजनया...M.G. अप्रियाचोक्षानिष्ट...K.S.S. अवेक्षानिष्टश्रवण...G.O.S. (Same as above).

२. K.S.S. सर्वाङ्गहारमुखनेत्रविघूर्णनं G.O.S. N.S. M.G. (Same as above) except M.G. reads नेत्र before विकूणन।

३. K.S.S. मुखनेत्रविघूर्णननयन G.O.S. N.S. M.G.(Same as above).

४. K.S.S. सभ्यगमि नमः प्रयोक्तव्यः G.O.S. N.S. M.G. (Same as above).

अथाद्भुतो नाम विस्मयस्थायिभावात्मकः। स च दिव्यजनदर्शनेप्सित-मनोरथवाप्त्युपवन[1]देवकुलादिगमनसभा[2]विमानमायेन्द्रजालसम्भावनादिभिर्वि-भावैरुत्पद्यते। तस्य नयनविस्तारानिमेषप्रेक्षणरोमाञ्चाश्रुस्वेदहर्षसाधुवाददान-प्रबन्धहाहाकारबाहुवदनचेलाङ्गुलिभ्रमणादिभिरनुभावैरभिनयः प्रयोक्तव्यः। भावाश्चास्य स्तम्भाश्रुस्वेदगद्गदरोमाञ्चावेगसम्भ्रमजडताप्रलयादयः। अत्रानु-वंश्ये आर्ये भवतः—

यत्त्वतिशयार्थयुक्तं वाक्यं शिल्पं च कर्मरूपं वा।
तत्सर्वमद्भुतरसे विभावरूपं हि विज्ञेयम्[3] ॥ ७५ ॥

अथाद्भुतरसप्रकरणम्

सर्वत्रान्तेऽद्भुत इत्युक्तं लक्षयितुमाह— **अथेति**। **दिव्या** गन्धर्वादयः। **ईप्सितः** शक्यप्राप्तिरर्थः। अन्यो **मनोरथः**। तयोः **प्राप्तिरुपचयनम्**। देवकुले च गमनम्। तस्याद्भुतविभावो येन तत्रत्यं सरसनिवेशादि न क्वचित् दृष्टम्। सभा गृहविशेषः। **विमानादीनि** दिव्यरथः। **माया** रूपपरिवर्तनादिका। **इन्द्रजालं** मन्त्रद्रव्यवस्तुयुक्त्यादिना असम्भवद्वस्तुप्रदर्शनम्। **तस्ये**त्यद्भुतस्य। **हर्ष**शब्देनात्र तदनुभावाः। साध्विति वदनं **साधुवादः**। **दानं** धनादेः **प्रबन्धं** सततं कृत्वा। हाहाशब्दस्य करणम्। **चेलस्याङ्गुलेश्च भ्रमणम्**।

अतिशेत इत्य**तिशयः**। अन्यापेक्षया योऽर्थ उत्कृष्टः। तेन वाच्यभूतेन युक्तं **यद्वाक्यं** यच्च **शिल्पं कर्मरूपं** कर्मात्मकं 'प्रशंसायां रूपप्'। **सर्वमि**त्येवं-प्रकारमिति यावत्। **स्पर्शग्रह**शब्देन तद्विभावादयः। अभिनयो ल(व)क्ष्यमाणो लक्ष्यते।

'किञ्चिदाकुञ्चिते नेत्रे कृत्वा भ्रूक्षेपमेव च।
तथांसगण्डयोः स्पर्शात्स्पर्शमेवं विनिक्षिपेत् ॥'
(ना. शा. २२.७७) इति।

---

१. M.G. उत्तमभवन K.S.S. उत्तमभवन N.S. G.O.S. उपवन।
२. K.S.S. असंभाव्यमानमाहेन्द्रजालसाधनादिभिः G.O.S. N.S. M.G. (Same as above).
३. K.S.S. M.G. एभिस्त्वर्थविशेषै रसोऽद्भुतो नाम विज्ञेयः G.O.S. N.S. (Same as above).

स्पर्शग्रहोल्लुकसनैर्हाहाकारैश्च साधुवादैश्च ।
वेपथुगद्गद्वचनैः स्वेदाद्यै रभिनयस्तस्य ॥ ७६ ॥
शृङ्गारं त्रिविधं विद्याद्वाङ्नैपथ्यक्रियात्मकम् ।
अङ्गनैपथ्यवाक्यैश्च हास्यरौद्रौ त्रिधा स्मृतौ ॥ ७७ ॥
धर्मोपघातजश्चैव तथार्थापचयोद्भवः ।
तथा शोककृतश्चैव करुणस्त्रिविधः स्मृतः ॥ ७८ ॥

गात्रस्योर्ध्वं साह्लादं धूननमुल्लुकसनम् । बहुवचनं प्रकृतिभेदेन प्रकारवैचित्र्यं सूचयति ॥ (७६)

इत्यद्भुतरसप्रकरणं समाप्तम् ।

अथ प्रधानभूतविभावप्रतिपादनं भेदप्रदर्शनव्याजेन करोति—**शृङ्गार-**मित्यादिना । **वाक्यरौद्रो** हि तत्र स्वभावरौद्र इति व्यवहरिष्यते । स्वभावानुसारित्वाद्वाक्यस्य । **धर्मोपघातज** उत्तमानामपि शोभ(च)नहेतुत्वात् । **शोक-**शब्देन स्वजनादिनासौ चैते (शश्च । एते)त्रयो विभावाः । **धर्म**शब्देनाग्निष्टोमादिक्रिया । अत एतद्यजनादीनि नि(जनादि नि)यमानुभावात्मकम् । प्रतिनायकगतं तु विभावरूपमपि । **व्याजादिति** । कृतक इत्यर्थः । अनेनानुभावमार्दवं दर्शितम् । अपराध्यन्तीत्यपराद्धा(धा)श्चोरादयः । यत्तु स्वभावत्रस्तहृदयानां स्त्रीबालादीनां तृणेऽपि कम्पमाने भयं तद्वि**त्रासितकम्** । विशेषेण त्रास्यत इति वित्रासितो बालादिः । तत्प्रकृतित्वाद्भयानकं तथोक्तम् । ततः संज्ञायां कन् ।

गुर्वाद्यपराधात्परमार्थतोऽप्युत्तमानां भयावेग इति त्वसत् । भयं हि विनाशशङ्कात्मकं नोत्तमेषु संभवति । यथा च भयं नाम स्त्रीनीचप्रकृतिकमिति सामान्येन न(मान्ये व)क्ष्यते ।

रुधिरान्त्रादिदर्शनाद्यो वीभत्सः क्षोभणत्वाच्छुद्धः । यस्तु विष्टादिभ्यः स उद्वेगी हृदयं चलयति सोऽशुद्धः । अशुद्धविभावकत्वात् । **उपाध्यायस्त्वाह**—वीभत्सस्तावद्विभावविशेषात् । यत्र तु संसारनाट्यनायकराग प्रतिपक्षतया **मोक्ष**साधनत्वाच्छुद्धः । यदाहुः—'शौचात्स्वाङ्गजुगुप्सा' इति । तथा 'वितर्क-

दानवीरं धर्मवीरं युद्धवीरं तथैव च ।
रसवीरमपि प्राह[1] ब्रह्मा त्रिविधमेव हि ॥ ७९ ॥
व्याजाच्चैवापराधाच्च वित्रासितकमेव च ।
पुनर्भयानकञ्चैव विद्यात् त्रिविधमेव हि ॥ ८० ॥
बीभत्सः क्षोभजः[2] शुद्ध उद्वेगी स्यात् द्वितीयकः[3] ।
विष्ठाकृमिभिरुद्वेगी क्षोभजो रुधिरादिजः ॥ ८१ ॥
दिव्यश्चानन्दजश्चैव द्विधा ख्यातोऽद्भुतो रसः ।
दिव्यदर्शनजो[4] दिव्यो हर्षादानन्दजः स्मृतः ॥ ८२ ॥

बाधने प्रतिपक्षभावनम् ।' (योगसू. २.४०.३३)इति । तेन सोऽपि परमार्थतस्त्रिविध एव । **द्वितीयक** इत्यनेन तस्य दुर्लभत्वेनाप्राचुर्यं सूचयति ।

दिव्य इति । यत्र सभाविमानादयोऽनुभावाः । आनन्दयतीत्या**नन्दो** मनोरथावाप्त्यादिः । स एव हर्षयतीति **हर्षः** ।

एषु **च** 'शृङ्गारम्' इत्यादिषु श्लोकेषु चकारा विभानुभावान्तरनिरासशङ्कां परार्कर्तुम् । एवकाराः इयन्त एव तेषां मुख्यत्वेन सङ्गता इति दर्शनार्थाः । तथाशब्दा अनुक्तविभावाद्यूहनार्था इति यथायोगं योज्यम् । (८२)

इत्यद्भुतरसप्रकरणं समाप्तम् ।

अथ शान्तरसविचारः ।

ये पुनर्नव रसा इति पठन्ति तन्मते शान्तस्वरूपमभिधीयते । तत्र केचिदाहुः—शान्तः शमस्थायिभावात्मकस्तपस्या योगिसम्पर्कादिभिः विभावै-

---

१. K.S.S. M.G. तथा त्वयचयोद्भवः G.O.S. N.S.(Same as above).
२. M.G. प्राहुस्तज्ज्ञास्मिविधमेव हि K.S.S. प्राहुस्तज्ज्ञास्त्रिविधसामनम् G.O.S. N.S. (Same as above).
३. N.S. क्षोमणः G.O.S. M.G. K.S.S. क्षोमजः ।
४. K.S.S. M.G. तृतीयकः G.O.S. N.S. द्वितीयकः ।

अथ[1] शान्तो नाम शमस्थायिभावात्मको मोक्षप्रवर्तकः। स तु तत्त्वज्ञानवैराग्याशयशुद्ध्यादिभिर्विभावैः समुत्पद्यते। तस्य यमनियमाध्यात्मध्यानधारणोपासनसर्वभूतदयालिङ्गग्रहणादिभिरनुभावैरभिनयः प्रयोक्तव्यः। व्यभिचारिणश्चास्य निर्वेदस्मृतिधृतिसर्वाश्रमशौचस्तम्भरोमाञ्चादयः। अत्रार्याः श्लोकाश्च भवन्ति—

मोक्षाध्यात्मसमुत्थस्तत्त्वज्ञानार्थहेतुसंयुक्तः।
नैःश्रेयसोपदिष्टः शान्तरसो नाम सम्भवति॥

रुत्पद्यते। तस्य कामक्रोधाद्यभावरूपैरनुभावैरभिनयः। व्यभिचारी धृतिमतिप्रभृतिः (इति)।

एतदपरे न सहन्ते। शमशान्तयोः पर्यायत्वात्। एकान्नपञ्चाशद्भावा इति सङ्ख्यात्यागात्। किञ्च विभावा ऋतुमाल्यादयस्तत्समनन्तरभाविनि शृङ्गारादावनुसन्धीयन्ते इति युक्तम्। तपोऽध्ययनादयस्तु न शान्तस्य शमनस्य (शमस्य) [ये]हेतवः। तत्त्वज्ञानस्यानन्तरहेतव इति चेत्पूर्वंकरोदित(र्वोदित) तत्त्वज्ञानेऽपि तर्हि प्रयोज्यतेति तपोऽध्ययनादीनां विभावता त्यक्ता स्यात्। कामाद्यभावोऽपि नानुभावः। शा(अशा)न्ताद्विपक्षादव्यावृत्तेः। अगमकत्वात्प्रयोगासमवायित्वाच्च। न हि चेष्टाव्युपरमः प्रयोगयोग्यः। सुप्तमोहादयोऽपि हि निःश्वासोच्छ्वासपतनभूषणादिभिश्चेष्टाभिरेवानुभाव्यन्ते। धृतिप्रभृतिरपि प्राप्तविषयोपभोगः कथं शान्ते स्यात्। त चाकिञ्चित्करत्वमात्रेण तत्त्वज्ञानोपाये व्युत्पाद्यन्ते। विनेये चैते परदुःखदुःखितमनसो दृश्यन्ते सम्यग्दर्शनसमावस्थां प्राप्ताः। अपि तु संसारे। तन्न शान्तो रस इति।

अत्रोच्यते—इह तावद्धर्मादित्रितयमेव(मिव) मोक्षोऽपि पुरुषार्थः। शास्त्रेषु स्मृतीतिहासादिषु च प्राधान्येनोपायतो व्युत्पाद्यत इति सुप्रसिद्धम्। यथा च कामादिषु समुचिताश्चित्तवृत्तयो रत्यादिशब्दवाच्याः कविनटव्यापारेणास्वादयोग्यताप्रापणद्वारेण तथाविधहृदयसंवादवतः सामाजिकान्प्रति रसत्वं शृङ्गारादिनया नीयन्ते तथा मोक्षाभिधानपरमपुरुषार्थोचिता चित्तवृत्तिः किमिति रसत्वं नानीयत इति वक्तव्यम्। या चासौ तथाभूता चित्तवृत्तिः सैवात्र

---

१. K.S.S. M.G. donot read the text on Santa Rasa G.O.S. N.S. Read it.

२. N.S. शमः G.O.S. शान्तः।

बुद्धीन्द्रियकर्मेन्द्रियसंरोधाध्यात्मसंस्थितोपेत: ।
सर्वप्राणिसुखहित: शान्तरसो नाम विज्ञेय: ।।
न यत्र दुखं न सुखं न द्वेषो नापि मत्सर: ।
सम: सर्वेषु भूतेषु स शान्त: प्रथितो रस: ।।
भावा: विकारा रत्याद्या: शान्तस्तु प्रकृतिर्मत: ।

स्थायिभाव: । एतत्तु चिन्त्यम् किं नामासौ—तत्त्वज्ञानोत्थितो निर्वेद इति केचित् । तथा हि—दारिद्र्यादिप्रभवो यो निर्वेद: स ततोऽन्य एव । हेतोस्तत्त्वज्ञानस्य वैलक्षण्यात् । स्थायिसञ्चारिमध्ये चैतदर्थमेवायं पठित: । अन्यथा माङ्गलिको मुनिस्तथा न पठेत् । जुगुप्सां च व्यभिचारित्वेन शृङ्गारे निषेधन्मुनिर्भावानां सर्वेषामेव स्थायित्वसञ्चारित्वचिन्तनात्तावत्वानुभावस्थत्वान्नि (भावत्वानि) योग्यतोपनिपातितानिश्श(तानि श)ब्दार्थबलाकृष्टन्यनुजानाति ।

तत्त्वज्ञानजश्च निर्वेद: स्थाय्यन्तरोपमर्दक: । भाववैचित्र्यसहिष्णुभ्यो रत्यादिभ्यो य: परम: स्थायिशील: स एव हि स्थाय्यन्तराणामुपमर्दक: । इदमपि पर्यनुयुञ्जते—तत्त्वज्ञानजो निर्वेदो[व्यव](दोऽस्य च) स्थायीति वदतातत्त्वज्ञानमेवात्र विभावत्वेनोक्तं स्यात् । वैराग्यबीजादिषु कथं विभावत्वम् । तदुपायता(त्वा)दिति चेत्कारणकारणो(णे)ऽयं विभावताव्यवहार: । स चातिप्रसङ्गावह: ।

किञ्च निर्वेदो नाम सर्वत्रानुपादेयताप्रत्यय: । वैराग्यलक्षणस्य च(ण: । स च) तत्त्वज्ञानस्थ प्रयुक्तो(तो)पयोगि । विरक्तो हि तथा प्रयतते यथा अस्य तत्त्वज्ञानमुत्पद्यते । तत्त्वज्ञानाद्धि मोक्ष: । न तु तत्त्वं ज्ञात्वा निर्विद्यते निर्वेदाच्च मोक्ष इति । 'वैराग्यात्प्रकृतिलय: ।' इति हि तत्रभवन्त: (सांख्यकारिका ४५.) ।

ननु तत्त्वज्ञानिन: सर्वत्र दृढतरं वैराग्यं दृष्टम् । तत्रभवद्भिरप्युक्तं—'तत्परं पुरुषख्यातेर्गुणवैतृष्ण्यम्' इति (योगसूत्र-१-१६) । भवत्येवम् । तादृशं तु 'वैराग्यं ज्ञानस्यैव पराकाष्ठा ।' इति (व्यासभाष्य-१-१६) भुजङ्गविभुनैव भगवताऽभ्यधायि । ततश्च तत्त्वज्ञानमेवेदं तत्त्वज्ञानमालया परिपोष्यमाणमिति न निर्वेद: स्थायी । किन्तु तत्त्वज्ञानमेव स्थायीति भवेत् । यत्तु व्यभिचारिव्याख्यानावसरे वक्ष्यते तच्चिरकालविभ्रमविप्रलब्धस्योपादेयत्वनिवृत्तये । यत्सम्यग्ज्ञानम्—

विकारः प्रकृतेर्जातः पुनस्तत्रैव लीयते ॥

स्वं स्वं निमित्तमासाद्य शान्ताद्भावः प्रवर्तते ।
पुर्निनिमित्तापाये च शान्त एवोपलीयते ॥

एवं नवरसा दृष्टा नाट्यज्ञैर्लक्षणान्विताः ।

यथा—

'वृथा दुग्धोऽनड्वांस्स्तनभरनता गौरिति परं
परिष्वक्तः षण्डो युवतिरिति लावण्यरहितः ।
कृता वैदूर्याशा विकचकिरणे काचशकले
मया मूढेन त्वां कृपणमगुणज्ञं प्रणमता ॥' इति

तन्निर्वेदस्य खेदरूपस्य भावत्वेन । एतच्च तत्रैव वक्ष्यामः ।

ननु मिथ्याज्ञानमूलो विषयगन्धस्तत्त्वज्ञानात्प्रशाम्यतीति **दुःखजन्मसूत्रेणाक्षपादपादैर्वदद्भिर्**मिथ्याज्ञानापचयकारणं तत्त्वज्ञानं वैराग्यस्य दोषापायलक्षणस्य कारणमुक्तम् । ननु ततः किम् । वैराग्यं निर्वेदः । क एवमाह । निर्वेदो हि शोकप्रवाहप्रसररूपश्चित्तवृत्तिविशेषः । वैराग्यं तु रागादीनां प्रध्वंसः ।

भवतु वा वैराग्यमेव निर्वेदः । तथापि तस्य स्वकारणवशान्मध्यभाविनोऽपि न मोक्षे साध्ये सूत्रस्थानीयतात्यपादाचारीव (प्रत्यपादि) । किञ्च तत्त्वज्ञानोत्थितो निर्वेद इति शमस्यैवेदं निर्वेदनाम कृतं स्यात् । शमशान्तयोः पर्यायत्वं तु हासहास्याभ्यां व्याख्यातम् । सिद्धसाध्यते यद(तथा लौकिका) लौकिकत्वेन साधारणासाधारणतया च वैलक्षण्यं शमशान्तयोरपि सुलभमेव । तस्मान्न निर्वेदः स्थायीति ।

अन्ये मन्यन्ते रत्यादय एवाष्टौ चित्तवृत्तिविशेषा उक्ताः । त एव कथितविभावविविक्तया(तया)श्रुता (त्या) ह्यलौकिकविभावविशेषसंश्रया विचित्रा एव तावत् । ततश्च तन्मध्यादेवान्यतमोऽत्र स्थायी । तत्राना(व्या)हृताननमय-(तानन्दमय)स्वात्मविषया रतिरेव मोक्षसाधनमिति सैव शास्त्रे(न्ते)स्थायिनीति । यथोक्तम्—

'यश्चात्मरति रेव स्यादात्मतृप्तश्च मानवः ।
आत्मन्येव च सन्तुष्टस्तस्य कार्यं न विद्यते ॥' इति ॥ (गीता ३-१७) ।

एवं समस्तत्रिषयं वैकृतं पश्यतो विश्वं च शोच्यं विलोकयतः सांसारिकं च

वृत्तान्तमपकारित्वेन पश्यतः सातिशयमसम्मोहप्रधानं विनय (वीर्यं) माश्रितवतः सर्वस्माद्विषयसार्थाद्वाह्यतः (द्विभ्यतः) सर्वलोकस्पृहणीयादपि प्रमदादेर्जुगुप्समानस्य (स्या) पूर्वस्वात्मातिशयलाभाद्विस्मयमानस्य मोक्षसिद्धिरिति ।

हासा (रतिहासा) दीनां विस्मयान्तानामन्यतमस्य स्थायित्वं निरूपणीयम् । न चैतन्मुनेर्न सम्मतम् । यावदेत्र हि विशिष्टान्विभावान्परिगणयति आदिशब्देन च तत्प्रकारानेवान्यान्संगृह्णीते तावदेव तद्व्यतिरिक्तालौकिकहेतूपनतानां रत्यादीनामनुजानात्येवापवर्गविषयत्वम् । एवंवादिना तु परस्परमेव विचारयतामेकस्य स्थायित्वं विशीर्यत एव । तदुपायभेदात्तस्य तस्य स्थायित्वमित्यप्युच्यमानं प्रगुणमेव (प्रत्युक्तमेव) । स्थायिभेदेन प्रतिपुरुषं रसस्याप्यानन्त्यापत्तौ मोक्षैकफलत्वादेको रस इति चेत् क्षमै (क्षयै) कफलत्वे वीररौद्रयोरप्येकत्वं स्यात् । अन्ये तु पानकरसवदविभागं प्राप्ताः सर्व एव रत्यादयोऽत्र स्थायिन इत्याहुः । चित्तवृत्तीनामयुगपद्भावादन्योन्यं च विरोधादेतदपि न मनोज्ञम् ।

कस्तर्ह्यत्र स्थायी । उच्यते—इह तत्त्वज्ञानमेव तावन्मोक्षसाधनमिति तस्यैव मोक्षे स्थायिता युक्ता । तत्त्वज्ञानं च नामात्मज्ञानमेव । आत्मनश्च (श्चा) व्यतिरिक्तमिद्रिय (क्तं स्याद) स्यैव ज्ञानम् । परो ह्येबमात्माऽनात्मैव स्यात् । विपञ्चितं चैतदस्मद्गुरुभिः । अस्माभिश्चान्यत्र वितन्यत इतीह नातिनिबन्धः कृतः ।

तेनात्मैव ज्ञानानन्दादिविशुद्धधर्मयोगी परिकल्पितविषयोपरागरहितोऽत्र स्थायी । न चास्य (स्या) स्थायितया स्थायित्वं वचनीयम् । रत्यादयो हि तत्तत्कारणान्तरोदयप्रलयोत्पद्यमानवि (नि) रुध्यमानवृत्तयः कञ्चित्कालमापेक्षिकतया स्थायिरूपात्मभित्तिसंश्रयाः षट् (सन्तः) स्थायिन इत्युच्यन्ते । तत्त्वज्ञानं तु सकलभावान्तरभित्तिस्थानीयं सर्वस्थायिभ्यः स्थायितमं सर्वाः रत्यादिकास्स्थायिचित्तवृत्तीर्व्यभिचारीभावयत् निसर्गत एव सिद्धस्थायिभावमिति तन्त्रवचनेन (तन्न वचनीयम्) । अत एव पृथगस्य गणना न युक्ता । न हि खण्डमुण्डयोर्मध्ये तृतीयं गोत्वमिति गण्यते । तेनैकान्नपञ्चाशद्भावा इत्यव्याहतमेव ।

अस्यापि कथं (न) पृथग्गणनेति चेत्- पृथगास्वाद (दा) योगादिति ब्रूमहे । न हि रत्यादय इवेतरासम्पृक्तेन वपुषा तथाविधमात्मरूपं लौकिकप्रतीतिगोचरः (रम् ।) स्वगतमप्यविकल (ल्प) रूपं व्युत्थानावसरेऽनुसन्धीयमानं चित्तवृत्त्यन्तरकलुषमेवावभाति ।

भासतां वा लोके तथा । तथापि न सम्भवन्मात्र (सम्भावनामात्र) स्थायिनां गणनम् । रसेषूक्तेष्वनुपयोगात् । अपि तु व्यभिचारित्वाल्लक्षणीयत्वं विज्ञायते

नेति (नेतरथा)। तथाह्येकान्नपञ्चाशता भावैरित्येतत्प्रघट्टकोपपत्तिः । न चास्यात्मस्वभावस्य व्यभिचारित्व(म) सम्भवादवैचित्र्यावहत्वादनौचित्याच्च । स(श) मा(म आ)त्मस्वभावस्य(वः । स) द(श)म शब्देन मुनिव्यं (मुनिव्य) पदिष्टः । यदि तु स एव शमशब्देन व्यपदिश्यते निर्वेदशब्देन वा तन्न कश्चिद्भावः- (द्बाधः) । केवलं शमश्चित्तवृत्त्यन्तरम् । निर्वेदोऽपि दारिद्र्यादिविभावान्तरोत्थितनिर्वेदतुल्यजातीयो न भवति तज्जातीय एव । हेतुभेदेऽपि तद्व्यपदेश्यो रतिभयादिभिरिव ।

तदिदमात्मस्वरूपमेव तत्त्वज्ञानं शमता च(मः । तथा च) यत्कालुष्योपरागविशेषा एवात्मनो रत्यादयः । तदनुगमेऽपि रूपव्यवधानसमाधिबलादधिशय्य व्युत्थानेऽपि प्रशान्तिता(न्तता) भवति । यथोक्तं—'(तस्य) प्रशान्तवाहिता संस्कारात्' (योगसू. ३-१०) इति । तत्त्वज्ञानलक्षणस्य च स्थायिनः समस्तोऽयं लौकिकालौकिकचित्तवृत्तिकलापो व्यभिचारितामभ्येति । तदनुभावा एव च यमनियमाद्युपकृता अनुभावा उपाङ्गाभिनस्य (आङ्गिका)ध्यायत्रये च ये स्वभावाभिनया वक्ष्यन्ते । अत एते तद्विषया एव । अयमेव हि स्वभावः । विभावा अपि कथम् । ईश्वरानुग्रहप्रभृतयः । प्रक्षयाश्च रत्यादयोऽत्रास्वाद्याः केवलम् । यथा विप्रलम्भे औत्सुक्यं संभोगेऽपि वा 'प्रेमसमाप्तोत्सवम्' (तापसवत्सराज. १-१७) इति । यथा च रौद्रे औग्रयं यथा च करुणवीरभयानकाद्भुतेषु निर्वेदधृतित्रासहर्षा व्यभिचारिणोऽपि प्राधान्येनावभासन्ते तथा न जुगुप्सायाम् । सर्वथैव रागप्रतिपक्षत्वात् ।

तथा हि महाव्रते नरकपालादिधारणमसु(स्व)भार्यादिसम्पदादिविस्तारसंक्षेपादिकर्मीकृतिर्हि धर्मे जुगुप्साहेतुत्वेनैव । निजाभ्यण(घृताञ्जनेन)च देवरात्पुत्रजन्माद्युपदिष्टम् ।

स्वात्मनि च कृतकृत्यस्य परार्थघटनायामेवोद्यम इत्युत्साहोऽस्य परोपकारविषयेच्छाप्रयत्नरूपो दयापरपर्यायोऽयधिकोऽन्तरङ्गः । अत एव तत्केचिद्दयावीरत्वेन व्यपदिशन्ति । अन्ये धर्मवीरत्वेन ।

ननूत्साहोऽहङ्कारप्राणः । शान्तस्त्वहङ्कारशैथिल्यात् द्वैविध्या(त्तद्विरुद्धा)-त्मकः । व्यभिचारित्वं हि विरुद्धस्यापि न नोचितं रताविव निर्वेदादेः ।

'शय्या शाद्वलम्' (आसनं शुचि शिला सद्म द्रुमाणामधः
शीतं निर्झरवारि पानमशनं कन्दाः सहाया मृगाः ।
इत्यप्रार्थितसर्वलभ्यविभवे दोषोऽयमेको वने
दुष्प्रापार्थिनि यत्परार्थघटनावन्ध्यैर्वृथा स्थीयते ॥)

(नागानन्द. ४-२)

इत्यादौ हि परोपकारकरणे ह्युत्साहस्यैव प्रकर्षो लक्ष्यते । न तूत्साहशून्या काचिदप्यवस्था । इच्छाप्रयत्नव्यतिरेकेण पाषाणतापत्तेः । यत एव परिदृष्टपरापरत्वेन स्वात्मोद्देशेन कर्तव्यान्तरं नावशिष्यते अत एव शान्तहृदयानां परोपकाराय शरीरसर्वस्वादिदानं न शान्तविरोधि । 'आत्मानं गोपायेत्' (गौतमधर्मसूत्र-९.३५) इत्यादिना ह्यकृतकृत्यविषयं शरीररक्षणमुपदिश्यते । सन्न्यासिनां तद्रक्षादितात्पर्याभावात् । तथा हि—

'धर्मार्थकाममोक्षाणां प्राणाः संस्थितिहेतवः ।

तान्निघ्नता किन्न हतं रक्षता किं न रक्षितम् ।।' (हितोपदेश-१.८३)

इति । सुप्रसिद्धचतुर्वर्गसाधकत्वमेव देहरक्षायाः निदानं दर्शितम् । कृतकृत्यस्य 'जलेऽग्नौ श्वभ्रे वा पतेत्' इति सन्न्यासित्वे श्रवणात् । तद्यथाकथञ्चित्त्याज्यं शरीरं यदि परार्थं न त्यज्यते तत्किमिव[न]सम्पादितं भवति । जीमूतवाहनादीनां न यतित्वमिति चेत् किं तेन नः । तत्त्वज्ञानित्वं तावदवश्यमस्ति । अन्यथा देहात्ममानिनां देह एव सर्वस्वभूते (तः) । धर्माद्यनुद्देशेन परार्थे त्यागस्यासम्भवात् । युद्धेऽपि हि न शरीरस्य त्यागायोद्यमः । परापजयोद्देशेनैव प्रवृत्तेः । भृगुपतनादावपि शुभतरदेहान्तरसम्पिपादयिषैवाधिकं विजृम्भते । तत्स्वार्थानुद्देशेन परार्थसम्पत्त्यै यद्यच्चेष्टितं देहत्यागपर्यन्तमुपदेशदानादि तत्तदलब्धात्मतत्त्वज्ञानानामसम्भाव्यमेवेति तेऽपि तत्त्वज्ञानिनः । 'ज्ञानिनां सर्वेष्वाश्रमेषु मुक्तिः' इति स्मार्तेषु श्रुतौ च । यथोक्तम्—

'देवार्चनरतस्तत्त्वज्ञाननिष्ठोऽतिथिप्रियः ।

श्राद्धं कृत्वा ददद्द्रव्यं गृहस्थोऽपि हि मुच्यते ।।' इति

केवलं परार्थाभिसन्धिजाद्धर्मात्परोपकारात्मकफलत्वेनैवाभिसंहितात् पुनरपि देहस्य तदुचितस्यैव प्रादुर्भावो बोधिसत्त्वादीनाम् । तत्त्वज्ञानिनामपि विश्रान्तिलाभस्वभावौचित्यात् । यथा रामस्य वीरोऽङ्गं पितुराज्ञां पालयितुः । एवं शृङ्गाराद्यङ्गेष्वपि मन्तव्यम् । अत एव शान्तस्य स्थायित्वेऽप्यप्राधान्यम् ।

जीमूतवाहने त्रिवर्गसम्पत्तेरेव परोपकृतिप्रधानायाः फलत्वात् । अनेनैवाशयेन नाटकलक्षणे वक्ष्यते 'ऋद्धिविलासादिभिर्गुणैः' (ना. शा. १८-११) इति । अनेन हि ऋद्धिविलासप्रधानमर्थकामोत्तरं सर्वं चरितं सकललोकहृदयसंवादसुन्दरप्रयोजनं नाटके निवेशयितव्यमित्युक्तम् । एतच्च तत्रैव वर्णयिष्यामः ।

अनेनैव चाशयेन न शान्ते कश्चन (क्वचन) मुनिना जात्यङ्को विनियोक्ष्यते । तेन जात्यङ्कविनियोगाभावात्तदसत्त्वमिति प्रत्युक्तम् ।

अन्ये तु जीमूतवाहनः 'कस्ते पुत्र त्राता भविष्यति' (नागानन्द. ४-९) इति शरणार्थिनीं वृद्धामेव त्रातवान् । शक्तिश्चास्य न काचित् । परहिंसा च न

काचिदित्येवमाहुः । तच्चानुमतमेव । न हि बोधिसत्त्वानां पुनरप्युत्थानात्मक-जीवितमभिसन्धानानुप्रविष्टं शक्तिश्चेदिति (श्चेति) । न च काकतालीयवृत्त्या शास्त्रमुपदिशति । तत्सिद्धं दयालक्षणो ह्युत्साहोऽत्र प्रधानम् ।

अन्ये तु व्यभिचारिणो यथायोगं भवन्ति । यथोक्तं 'तच्छिद्रेषु प्रत्ययान्तराणि संस्कारेभ्यः ।' (योगसूत्र ४-२७) इति । अत एव निश्चेष्टत्वादनुभावाभाव इति प्रत्युक्तम् । यदा तु पर्यन्तभूमिकालाभ (हेतुभाव) स्तदास्याप्रयोज्यत्वम् । रतिशोकादावपि पर्यन्तदशायामप्रयोगस्यैव युक्तत्वात् । हृदयसंवादोऽपि तथा-विधतत्त्वज्ञानबीजसंस्कारभावितानां भवत्येव । यद्वक्ष्यति 'मोक्षे चापि विरागिणः' (ना. शा. २७-५८) इति । 'सर्वस्य तु' (ना. शा. १-१०७) इत्यत्र हृदय-संवादे भयानके वीरप्रकृतेरभावात् ।

ननु तादृशि प्रयोगे वीरस्य क आस्वादः । उच्यते—यत्रेयं (त्रायं) निबध्यते तत्रावश्यं पुरुषार्थोपयोगि शृङ्गारवीराद्यन्यतममस्त्येव । तन्निष्टस्तेषामास्वादः । यत्रापि प्रहसनादौ हास्यादेः प्रधानता तत्राप्यनुनिष्पादिरसान्तरनिष्ठ एवा-स्वादभिन्नादिकार्यम्...धिकादोऽप्युद्देशे दैवरूपक (एवास्वादो भिन्नभिन्ना-धिकारिणः । एतदुद्देश एव रूपक) भेदचिन्तननिमित्तमिति केचित् ।

तस्मादस्ति शान्तो रसः । तथा च चिरन्तनपुस्तकेषु 'स्थायिभावान् रसत्व-मुपनेष्यामः' (ना. शा. पु. २९९) इत्यनन्तरं 'शान्तो नाम शमस्थायिभावात्मकः' (ना.शा. पु. ३३२) इत्यादिशान्तलक्षणं पठ्यते । तत्र सर्वरसानां शान्तप्राय एवास्वादो न विषयेभ्यो विपरिवृत्त्या । तन्मुख्यतालाभात्केवलं वासनान्तरो-पहित इत्येस्य सर्वप्रकृतित्वाभिधानाय पूर्वमभिधानम् । लोके च पृथक्पृथक्-सापान्यस्य न गणनमिति स्थाय्यस्य पृथग्युक्त (ङ्नोक्तः) । सामान्यमपि तु विवेचकेन पृथगेव गणनीयमिति विवेचकाभिमतसामाजिकास्वादलक्षणप्रतीति-विषयतया स पृथग्भूत एव । इतिहासपुराणाभिधानकोशादौ च नवरसाः श्रूयन्ते श्रीमत्सिद्धान्तशास्त्रेष्वपि । तथा चोक्तम्—

'अष्टानामिह देवानां शृङ्गारादीन् प्रदर्शयेत् ।
मध्ये च देवदेवस्य शान्तं रूपं प्रकल्पयेत् ॥' (इति) ।

तस्य च वैराग्यसंसारभीरुतादयो विभावाः । स हि तैरुपनिबद्धैर्विज्ञायते । मोक्षशास्त्रचिन्तादयोऽनुभावाः । निर्वेदमतिस्मृतिधृत्यादयो व्यभिचारिणः । अत एवेश्वरप्रणिधानविषये भक्तिश्रद्धे स्मृतिमतिधृत्युत्साहाद्यनुप्रविष्टेभ्योऽन्यथैवा (न्ये एवा) ङ्गमिति न तयोः पृथक्सत्वेन गणनम् । अत्र सङ्ग्रहकारिका—

मोक्षाध्यात्मनिमित्तस्तत्त्वज्ञानार्थहेतुसंयुक्तः ।
निःश्रेयसधर्मयुतः शान्तरसो नाम विज्ञेयः ॥

विभावस्थाय्यनुभावयोगः क्रमाद्विशेषणत्रयेण दर्शितः ।

स्वं स्वं निमित्तमासाद्य शान्ताद्भावः प्रवर्तते ।
पुनर्निमित्तापाये तु शान्त एव प्रलीयते ॥

इत्यादिना रसान्तरप्रकृतित्वमुपसंहृतम् ।

यत्तु डिमे हास्यशृङ्गारपरिहारेण षड्सत्वं च वक्ष्यते तत्रायं भावः । 'दीप्तरसकाव्ययोनिः' (ना. शा. १८-८५) इति भाविना लक्षणेन रौद्रप्रधाने तावड्डिमे तद्विरुद्धस्य शान्तस्य सम्भावनैव न । किं निषेधेन । शान्तासम्भवे तु दीप्तरसकाव्ययोनिरित्येतेन किं व्यवच्छेद्यम् । शृङ्गारहास्यवर्जं षड्सयुक्तः' (ना. शा. १८-८४) इति ह्युक्ते कस्तत्र प्रसङ्गः ।

ननु करुणबीभत्सभयानकप्राधान्यमनेन पादेन व्यवच्छेद्यते । नैतत् । 'सात्त्वत्यारभटीवृत्तिसम्पन्नः' (१८-८८)इत्यनेनैव तन्निरासात् । शान्ते तु सात्त्वत्येव वृत्तिरिति तद्यवच्छेदकमेवैतत् । तेन डिमलक्षणं प्रत्युत शान्तरसस्य सद्भावे लिङ्गम् । शृङ्गारस्तु प्रसभं सेव्यमानः सम्भाव्य एव । तदङ्गं च हास्य इति तयोरेव प्रतिषेधः कृतः प्राप्तत्वात्सर्वसाम्याच्च । विशेषतो वर्ण-देवताभिधानमनुचितमप्यस्य तत्कल्पितमिति ज्ञेयम् । उत्पत्तिस्तु शान्तस्यापि दर्शितैव । सत्त्वाभावो हि हास्यः । सहविभावत्वेन चास्य वीरबीभत्सौ । अत एवास्य रसस्य यमनियमेश्वरप्रणिधानाद्युपदेशः अनुपयो(भो)गितया महाफलत्वं सर्वप्राधान्यमितिवृत्तव्यापकत्वं चोपपन्नमित्यलमतिप्रसङ्गेन ।

तत्त्वास्वादोऽस्य कीदृशः । उच्यते—उपरागदायिभिरुत्साहरत्यादिभिरु-परक्तं यदात्मस्वरूपं तदेव विरलोम्भितरत्नान्तरालनिर्भासमानसितंतरसूत्र-वदाभातस्वरूपं सकलेषु रत्यादिषूपरञ्जकेषु तथाभावेनापि सकृद्विभातो-ऽयमात्मेति न्यायेन भासमानं परोन्मुखतात्मसकलदुःखजालहीनं परमानन्दलाभ-संविदेकत्वेन काव्यप्रयोगप्रबन्धाभ्यां साधारणतया निर्भासमानमन्तर्मुखावस्था-भेदेन लोकोत्तरानन्दानय(न्दाय)नं तथाविधहृदयं विधत्त इति ।

एवं ते नवैव रसाः । पुमर्थोपयोगित्वेन रञ्जनाधिक्येन वा इयतामेवोपदेश्य-त्वात् । तेन रसान्तरसंभवेऽपिचार्षप्रसिद्ध्या सङ्ख्यानियम इति यदन्यैरुक्तं तत्प्रयुक्तम् । भावाध्यायेऽपि चैतद्वक्ष्यते । आर्द्रतास्थायिकः स्नेहो रस इति त्वसत् । स्नेहो ह्यभिसङ्गः । स च सर्वो रत्युत्साहादावेव पर्यवस्यति । तथा हि—बालस्य मातापित्रादौ स्नेहो भये विश्रान्तः । यूनोर्मित्रजने रतौ । लक्ष्मणादौ

एवमेते रसा ज्ञेयास्त्वष्टौ लक्षणलक्षिताः ।

अत ऊर्ध्वं प्रवक्ष्यामि भावानामपि लक्षणम् ॥ ८३ ॥

इति भारतीये नाटचशास्त्रे रसाध्यायः षष्ठः ॥

भ्रातरि स्नेहो धर्ममय एव। एवं वृद्धस्य पुत्रादाविति द्रष्टव्यम्। एषैव गन्धस्थायिकस्य लौल्यरसस्य प्रत्याख्याने सरणिर्मन्तव्या। हासे वा रतौ वान्यत्र पर्यवसानात्। एवं भक्तावपि वाच्यमिति।

अध्यायार्थमुपसंहरन् भाविनोऽवकाशं ददत्सङ्गतिं प्रकटीकर्तुमाह—**एवमेते रसा ज्ञेया नवेति** (स्त्वष्टाविति)। रसवद्गीतमित्यादिव्यपदेशात् स्तूयते। स-(शास्तु ये ते रस)मूला एवोपचारा इति दर्शयति—**लक्षणलक्षिता इति।** भावानामपि लक्षणं रसलक्षणमेव पूरयति। विभावव्यभिचार्यनुभावलक्षणेन रसलक्षणमेव पूर्यते। रतिस्थायिभावप्रभवः ऋतुमाल्यादिविभावको नयन-चातुर्याद्यनुभावक इत्युक्तमपि साकाङ्क्षमेव। कीदृशी हि रतिः कश्च विभावः कश्चानुभावः। तेन यद्यप्यापाततो भावानां लक्षणमिदं प्रतिभाति महाचार्या-(साहचर्यात्) तथापि वाक्यैकवाक्यतया रसलक्षणमेवेदमित्यपिशब्दस्यार्थ इति शिवम्।

इ(र)त्यादिशक्त्यष्टकमध्यवृत्तिर्यस्य स्वहृन्मण्डलसम्प्रयोज्या(ज्यः)।

स्थायी शिवश्चेतसि तेन वृत्तिः कृता रसाध्याय इह क्रमेण ॥

इति श्रीमहामाहेश्वराभिनवगुप्तविरचितायां नाटचवेदविवृतावभिनवभारत्यां रसाध्यायः षष्ठः समाप्तः

सप्तमोऽध्यायः ।

भावानिदानीं व्याख्या[1]स्यामः । अत्राह—भावा इति कस्मात् । [2]किं भवन्तीति भावाः किं वा भावयन्तीति भावाः । उच्यते—वागङ्गसत्त्वोपेतान्काव्यार्थान्भावयन्तीति भावा इति ।

स्थायी प्रबुद्धहृदये व्यभिचारिभूतः
कामाकुलासु जनतासु महानुभावः ।
अन्तर्विभावविषयो रसमात्रमूर्तिः
श्रीमान्प्रसन्नहृदयोऽस्तु मम त्रिणेत्रः ॥

भावानिदानीमिति । नन्वध्यायान्त एवैतदासूत्रितमिति किमनेन पुनरुक्तेन । 'भावाश्चापि कथं प्रोक्ताः' (ना. शा. ६-३) इत्यत्रैव प्रश्ने कृते पुनरिहाध्याये 'किं भवन्ति' इत्यादि च किमर्थमुच्यते ।

अत्र केचिदाहु—'भावाश्चापि' इत्यध्यायादौ 'भावानामपि लक्षणम्' इत्यध्यायान्ते च विभावादीनां सर्वे(षां) साधारण्येन प्रश्नप्रतिज्ञादि । अधुना तु विभावादिषु वक्तव्येषु प्रथमं तावत्प्राधान्याच्चित्तवृत्तिरूपाः स्थायिव्यभिचारिणो लक्षणीया इति तद्विषयैवेयं प्रतिज्ञा प्रश्नश्च ।

वयं तु ब्रूमः—भावशब्देन तावच्चित्तवृत्तिविशेषा एव विवक्षिताः । तथा च 'एकोनपञ्चाशता भावैः' इत्यादौ तानेवोपसंहरिष्यति । तेषां तु योग्यतावशाद्यथायोगं स्थायिसंचारिविभावानुभावरूपता संभवति । ये त्वेते ऋतुमाल्यादयो विभावा बाह्याश्च बाष्पप्रभृतयोऽनुभावा एकान्तजडस्वभावाः ते न भावशब्दव्यपदेश्याः ।

ननु रससंवित्स्वभावे निमज्जनादत एवोन्मज्जनाच्च तेऽपि संविदात्मकाः । एवं तर्हि विश्वमेव भावमयं स्यादुपचारात् विज्ञानवादाश्रयाद्वेत्यभिनयधर्म्या-

---

१. K.S.S. M.G. वक्ष्यामः G.O.S. N.S. व्याख्यास्यामः ।

२. K.S.S. M.G. donot read किं भवन्तीति भावाः G.O.S. N.S. read it.

दीनां पृथक्तानुपपत्तिः। तस्मात्स्थायिव्यभिचारिसात्त्विका एवं भावाः। विभावानुभावानां च प्रासङ्गिकं लक्षणम् एतच्च वक्ष्यामः।

यच्च पौनरुक्त्यं चोदितं तदसत्। तथा हि—रसाध्यायप्रारम्भे चोदितमङ्गमध्ये भावा अनुद्दिष्टा एव कथं तत्र तत्रोदीरिता इति। तन्निराकरणार्थमाह—**भावानिति**। यतोऽतीताध्यायान्ते भावानां रसलक्षणमेव अत इदानीमपि गतचोद्यांशकेऽवसरे भावान्वक्ष्यामो रसानामङ्गमध्ये पठितत्वादिति।

ननु चित्तवृत्त्यात्मान एव चेद्भावास्तर्हि तेषु व्युत्पत्तिद्वयमपि संभाव्यते। तथा हि 'भवति' रतिभूतप्रादुर्भावे प्रकर्षगतिश्च। पुनरभिधानात्तेन येन तरतमपूर्वतयैव प्रादुर्भवति न तु क्षणं व्यवतिष्ठते। तेभ्यो भावाश्चित्तवृत्त्यात्मा (नो)नुभावज्ञानस्य परिमितकालभावित्वात्। यदि वा भावयन्ति आस्वादनं कुर्वन्ति हृदयं व्याप्नुवन्तीति। ततश्च व्युत्पत्तिद्वयसंभावनात्कथं 'भवन्ति' इति पक्षमनाशङ्क्यैव 'किं वा ते भावयन्ति' इति प्रश्नोऽयुक्त इत्यभिप्रायेणानुद्भिन्नमर्थं प्रश्नस्योद्भेदयन् प्रश्नार्थमेवानुभाषते—**किं भवन्तीत्यादि**। भवन्ति भावयन्ति वा। भावयन्तीति च किमेतत्कुर्वन्ति व्याप्नुवन्ति वा। तत्र च द्वयेऽपि किं कर्म।

एवं प्रश्नार्थमनुभाष्योत्तरमाह—**वागङ्गसत्त्वोपेतानित्यादि**। कोः कवतेर्वा कवनीयं काव्यम्। तत्र च पदार्थवाक्यार्थौ रसेष्वेव पर्यवस्यत इत्यसाधारण्यात्प्राधान्याच्च काव्यस्यार्थाः रसाः। अर्थ्यन्ते प्राधान्येनेत्यर्थाः। न त्वर्थशब्दोऽभिधेयवाची। स्वशब्दानभिधेयत्वं हि रसादीनां ध्वनिकारादिभिर्दर्शितम्। तच्च मदीयादेव तद्विवरणात्**सहृदयालोकलोचनाद**वधारणीयम्। इह तु यथावसरं वक्ष्यत एव।

एवं काव्यार्थान् रसान् भावयन्ति कुर्वते। स्थायिव्यभिचारिकलापेनैव ह्यास्वाद्योऽलौकिकार्थो निर्वर्तते। पूर्वं हि स्थाय्यादिकमवगच्छन्ति ततः सर्वसाधारणतयाऽऽस्वादयन्ति। तेन पूर्वाविगमगोचरीभूतः सन्नुत्तरभूमिकाभागिन आस्वाद्यस्य भावको निष्पादक उच्यते। तेन भावयन्तीति करणे दर्शयति—**वागङ्गेति**। वागादयस्तत्कर्मसु वर्तन्ते। तेन वर्णनात्मना वाचिकेन संनिवेशवलनादीनाङ्गिकेनान्तर्बहिरात्मना सात्त्विकेन करणभूतेनोपेतान् सम्बद्धान्।

करणं हि कर्मणि कर्तरि च यद्यपि संबध्यते तथापि(पी)हास्य प्राधान्यात्संबन्धदृशि करणत्वमेव दर्शयितुं तृतीयादि(यया) निर्दिश्यते—**वागङ्गमुखरागेणेति**। अत (त्र) आहार्यं तु यद्यपि नृत्यकलाध्रुवापातयोरन्तरङ्गं तथापि तदनन्तरचित्तवृत्त्यवगतौ वाचिकादीनामेवान्तरङ्गता। तथा हि काव्यादपि रसास्वादो भवतीत्युक्तम्। तत्र च न पूर्णताऽऽहार्यस्य। तेनाहार्यस्य नोपादानम्।

भू इति करणे धातुस्तथा च भावितं कृतमित्यनर्थान्तरम्[1] **। लोकेऽपि च प्रसिद्धम्**[2] **। अहो ह्यनेन**[3] **गन्धेन रसेन वा सर्वमेव भावितमिति ।**

एतदुक्तं भवति—चित्तवृत्तय एवालौकिकाः वाचिकाद्यभिनयप्रक्रिया-रूढतया स्वात्मानं लौकिकदशायामनास्वाद्यं कुर्वन्तीत्यतस्ता एव भावाः । भवतिर्हि ण्यन्तः प्रकृतं करोत्यर्थमाहेति दर्शयति—**भू इतीति** । त (च) कार उच्चारणार्थः । णिचा संबन्धेनेति (सनाद्यन्तेति) इकारप्रत्यये सति भूधातुः करोत्यर्थे वर्तते । एतदेवोपसंहरति—**भावमिति** .(**भावितमिति**) **अनर्थान्तर-मिति** । एकोऽर्थ इति यावत् ।

नन्वास्वाद्यान्तरान्तर्भाव्ये वाचिकादौ करणमितिकर्तव्यतांशे वक्तव्यमित्या-शङ्क्य तन्त्रेण व्युत्पत्त्यन्तरं दर्शयन् तमाह—**लोकेऽपि चेति** । न केवलं भावितं कृतमिति लोके प्रसिद्धं यावद्व्याप्तमित्यपि । एतदपि चेत्यनेनोक्तम् । सर्वमित्ये-तद्गन्धरसमपि ।

ननु तत्रापि कृतमित्येवार्थोऽस्त्वित्याशङ्क्याह—**तच्च** व्याप्त्यर्थमिति । न हि कस्तूरिकागन्धेन वस्त्रं तद्गन्धं क्रियते । गुणस्यासंक्रान्तेः । न च तत्स-दृशगुणान्तरोत्पत्तिः । यावद्द्रव्यभावित्वाद्गन्धादीनाम् । वस्त्रादौ च विनाश-प्रतिपत्तेः । केवलं कस्तूरिकाद्रव्यमेव तावद्रूपदेशचैतन्याक्रमणस्वभावं वस्त्रादिके-ऽपि तथा प्रतिपत्तिमाधत्ते । तद्वत्प्रकृतेऽपि । त एव हि वाचिकाद्या अभिनयाः प्रमुखदशायां देशकालविशेषगतत्वेन यद्यपि भान्ति तथापि नटस्य निर्गुणादिह न त (णत्वादिहत) त्वात् रामादेः पर (देरपर) मार्थसत्त्वात् भ्रान्तिज्ञानाभावाच्च नियततां विजहतः साधारणीभावमनुप्राप्ताः सामाजिकजनमपि मृगमदामोददि-शा व्याप्नुवन्ति स्वचित्तव्यापनाद्वारेण । तेन भावयन्ति सामाजिकात्मानमिति भावाः ।

अथ व्युत्पत्त्यन्तरमपि दर्शयितुं प्राक्तनीं च व्युत्पत्तिं संग्रहीतुमाह—**श्लोका श्चात्रेति** । विभावो विषयः । तेन यः आहृतो निष्पादितः । तेन विभावापेक्षया भाव्यते क्रियत इति भावः । अनुभावानेभ्यो निरूपयति—**वागङ्गेति** ।

---

१. K.S.S. M.G. भाव इतिकरणसाधनं—यथा भावितः वासितः कृत इत्यनर्थान्तरम् । G.O.S. N.S. (Same as above).

२. M.G. K.S.S. N.S. सिद्धं G.O.S. प्रसिद्धम् ।

३. K.S.S. M.G. ह्यन्योऽन्यगन्धेन G.O.S. N.S. ह्यनेन गन्धेन ।

तच्च[1] व्याप्त्यर्थम् । श्लोकाश्चात्र—

विभावेनाहृतो योऽर्थो ह्यनु[2]भावैस्तु गम्यते ।
वागङ्गसत्त्वाभिनयैः स भाव इति संज्ञितः ॥ १ ॥

वागङ्गमुखरागेण[3] सत्त्वेनाभिनयेन च ।
कवेरन्तर्गतं भावं भावयन्भाव उच्यते ॥ २ ॥

नानाभिनयसंबद्धान्भावयन्ति रसानिमान् ।
यस्मात्तस्मादमी भावा विज्ञेया नाट्ययोक्तृभिः ॥ ३ ॥

अन्ये तु वागङ्गसत्त्वाद्यभिनया येषामिति तद्‌गुणसंविज्ञानेन बहुव्रीहिणा स्वाभिनयसहिता व्यभिचारिणो गृहीताः । तैरिति व्यभिचारिभिश्च भाव्यते मिश्रीक्रियत इति व्यभिचारिणामपि च व्यभिचारिणो भवन्ति । यथा निर्वेदस्य चिन्ता श्रमस्य निर्वेद इत्यादि निरूपयन्ति । तच्चासत् । स्थायिनो हि व्यभिचारिता भवति । न तु व्यभिचारिणां स्थायिता । एवं हि सति तदास्वादे रसान्तरमपि स्यात् । यत्रापि व्यभिचारिणि व्यभिचार्यन्तरं संभाव्यते तद्यथा— पुरूरवस उन्मादेऽपि तर्कचिन्तादि तत्रापि रतिस्थायिभावस्यैव व्यभिचार्यन्तरयोगः । स केवलममात्यस्थानीयेनोन्मादेन कृतोपरागः । एतच्च 'यथा नरेन्द्र' (ना. शा. ७-१०) इत्यत्र वक्ष्यामः ।

एवं लोकानुसारेण कविनटशिक्षोपयोगिना व्युत्पत्त्यन्तरमभिधाय सामाजिकाभिप्रायेण यो व्युत्पत्तिद्वयनिरूपितोऽर्थः तत्संग्रहाय श्लोकद्वयमाह—**वागङ्गमुखरागेणे**ति । वागङ्गमुखरागात्मनाऽभिनयेन सत्त्वलक्षणेन चाभिनयेन करणेन कवेः साधारणं तद्वापि (रणस्यापि) वर्णनानिपुणस्य यः अन्तर्गतोऽनादिप्राक्तनसंस्कारप्रतिभानमयो न तु लौकिकविषयजो रागान्त (गरस) एव देशकालादिभेदाभावात्सर्वसाधारणीभावेनास्वादयोग्यस्तं **भावयन्** आस्वादयोग्यीकुर्वन् **भाव**श्चित्तवृत्तिलक्षण एवोच्यते । सत्त्वं चित्तैकाग्र्यं तज्जनितं च कृतकं बाष्पादिप्राप्त्यवस्थात्मकं (व्यभिचारिपरातिशयप्राप्त्यतिशयात्मकं) चेति यथायोगं मन्तव्यम् । तदन्तर्भूतोऽपि वैवर्ण्यात्मा मुखरागः प्राधान्यात्पुनरुक्तः । यद्वक्ष्यति—

---

१. K.S.S. M.G. अपिच G.O.S N.S. तच्च ।
२. K.S.S. M.G. त्वनुभावेन गम्यते G.O.S. N.S. ह्यनुभावैस्तु गम्यते ।
३. K.S.S. M.G. रागैश्च G.O.S. N.S. रागेण ।

अथ विभाव इति कस्मात् । उच्यते—विभावो विज्ञानार्थः । विभावः कारणं निमित्तं हेतुरिति पर्यायाः । विभाव्यन्तेऽनेन वागङ्गसत्त्वाभिनया इत्यतो विभावः । यथा विभावितं विज्ञातमित्यनर्थान्तरम् ।

अत्र श्लोकः—

बहवोऽर्था विभाव्यन्ते वागङ्गाभिनयाश्रयाः[1] ।
अनेन यस्मात्तेनायं विभाव इति संज्ञितः ॥ ४ ॥

अथानुभाव इति कस्मात् । उच्यते—

अनुभाव्यतेऽनेन वागङ्गसत्त्वकृतोऽभिनय[2] इति ।

अत्र श्लोकः—

वागङ्गाभिनयेनेह यतस्त्वर्थोऽनुभाव्यते ।
शा[3]खाङ्गोपाङ्गसंयुक्तस्त्वनुभावस्ततः स्मृतः ॥ ५ ॥

'शाखाङ्गोपाङ्गसंयुक्तः कृतोऽप्यभिनयः शुभः ।
मुखरागविहीनस्तु नैव शोभान्वितो भवेत् ॥' (ना. शा. ८-१६५) इति ।

अथेतिकर्तव्यतां निरूपयितुं सङ्ग्रहश्लोकमाह—**नानाभिनयेति** । रसनयोग्यान् चित्तवृत्तिविशेषान् भावयन्ति गमयन्ति बोधयन्ति बुद्धिविषयान् प्रापयन्ति । इमान् सामाजिकान् । भावयति बुद्धयर्थकत्वाद् द्विकर्मकः । अभिनयसहितानित्यभिनया अपि बुद्धिगोचरं नीयन्ते । इयमेव चासौ अधिवासनात्मा भावना तथा तथा रसान् रसनयोग्यान्निजेन योग्येन रूपेण भावयति यथा निर्वेदोपरक्ता रतिरौत्सुक्योपरक्तेति तथा रसानलौकिकास्वादविषयान् स्थायिनोऽधिवासयन्ति (ति) । लौकिकरतिवासनानुविद्धो हि शृङ्गाररस इत्यादि ।

विभावेनाहृत इत्युक्तम्—तत्र यद्यपि प्रकरणाच्चित्तवृत्त्युद्भवहेतुर्विषयो विभावशब्दस्यार्थ इति ज्ञातम् । तथापि तत्र प्रवृत्तिनिमित्तं जिज्ञासमानः तदेव

---

१. K.S.S. M.G. आश्रिताः G.O.S. N.S. आश्रयाः ।
२. K.S.S. यदयमनुभावयति नानार्थाभिनिष्पन्नो वागङ्गसत्त्वैः कृतोऽभिनय इति M.G. वागङ्गसत्त्वैः कृतोऽभिनय इति । N.S. G.O.S. वागङ्गसत्त्वकृतोऽभिनय इति ।
३. G.O.S. N.S. शाखा K.S.S. M.G. वाग्

एवं ते विभावानुभावसंयुक्ता भावा इति व्याख्याताः । अतो ह्येषां भावानां सिद्धिर्भवति[1] । तस्मादेषां भावानां[2] विभावानुभावसंयुक्तानां लक्षणनिदर्शनान्यभिव्याख्यास्यामः । तत्र विभावानुभावौ लोकप्रसिद्धौ । लोकस्वभावानुगतत्वा[3]च्च तयो[4]र्लक्षणं नोच्यतेऽतिप्रसङ्गनिवृत्त्यर्थम् ।

भवति चात्र श्लोकः—

लोकस्वभावसंसिद्धा लोकयात्रानुगामिनः[5] ।
अनुभावा विभावाश्च ज्ञेयास्त्वभिनये[6] बुधैः ॥ ६ ॥

तत्राष्टौ भावाः स्थायिनः । त्रयस्त्रिंशद्व्यभिचारिणः ।
अष्टौ सात्विका इति भेदाः[7] । एवमेते काव्यरसाभिव्यक्तिहेतव एकोनपञ्चाशद्भावाः प्रत्यवगन्तव्याः । एभ्यश्च सामान्यगुणयोगेन रसा निष्पद्यन्ते ।

प्रश्नयति— **विभाव इतीति** । **कस्मात्** । ऋतुमाल्यादयोऽत्र विभावशब्देन किमिति व्यपदिष्टा इति भावः ।

अत्रोत्तरं **विभाव्यन्त** इत्यादि । वागादयोऽभिनया येषां स्थायिव्यभिचारिणां ते वागाद्यभिनयसहिता विभाव्यन्ते विशिष्टतया ज्ञायन्ते यैस्ते विभावाः । अभिनयानामनेकहेतुजत्वम् । तद्यथा—हर्षादिभ्यो हासः । घर्मधूमरोगादिभ्यो बाष्पः । तद्बाष्पार्तिक प्रतीयताम् । विभावात्तु झडित्येव निश्चयः । अत एव—

१. K.S.S. M.G. Donot read एवं ते...सिद्धिर्भवति N.S. G.O.S. Read it.

२. K.S.S. M.G. एतेषां विभावानुभावसंयुक्तानां G.O.S. N.S. तस्मादेषां भावानां ।

३. K.S.S. M.G. उपगतत्वात् G.O.S. N.S. अनुगतत्वात् ।

४. K.S.S. M.G. एषां G.O.S. N.S. तयोः ।

५. G.O.S. N.S. अनुगामिनः K.S.S. M.G. अनुयायिनः ।

६. G.O.S. N.S. अभिनये K.S.S. M.G. अभिनयैः ।

७. N.S. त्रिभेदाः G.O.S. K.S.S. M.G. भेदाः ।

अत्र श्लोकः—

योऽर्थो हृदयसंवादी तस्य भावो रसोद्भवः ।
शरीरं व्याप्यते तेन शुष्कं काष्ठमिवाग्निना ॥ ७ ॥

अत्राह—यदि[1] काव्या[2]र्थसंश्रितैर्विभावानुभावव्यञ्जितैरेकोनपञ्चाशद्भावैः सामान्यगुणयोगेनाभिनिष्पद्यन्ते रसास्त[3]त्कथं स्थायिन एव भावा रसत्वमाप्नुवन्ति । उच्यते—यथा हि समानलक्षणास्तुल्यपाणिपादोदरशरीरा[4]: समाना-ङ्ग[5]प्रत्यङ्गा अपि पुरुषाः कुलशीलविद्याकर्मशिल्पविचक्षणत्वाद्राजत्वमाप्नुवन्ति तत्रैव चान्येऽल्पबुद्धयस्तेषामेवानुचरा भवन्ति तथा विभावानुभावव्यभिचारिणः स्थायिभावानुपाश्रि[6]ता भवन्ति । बह्वा[7]श्रयत्वात्स्वामिभूताः स्थायिनो भावाः । तद्वत्स्थानी[8]यपुरुषगुणभूता अन्ये भावास्तान्गुणतया[9] श्रयन्ते । स्थायिभावा रसत्वमाप्नुवन्ति[10] । परिजनभूता व्यभिचारिणो भावाः । अत्राह—को दृष्टान्त इति । यथा नरेन्द्रो बहुजनपरिवारोऽपि स[11] एव नाम लभते नान्यः सुमहानपि

---

१. K.S.S. यदा M.G. यद् G.O.S. N.S. यदि ।

२. K.S.S. M.G. अन्योन्यार्थ G.O.S. N.S. काव्यार्थ ।

३. K.S.S. कथमिदानीमेते स्थायिनोऽष्टौ भावाः M.G. G.O.S. N.S तत्कथं स्थायिन एव भावाः ।

४. K.S.S. समानाः G.O.S. N.S. M.G. शरीराः ।

५. K.S.S. M.G. समानप्रत्ययाः N.S. G.O.S. समानाङ्गप्रत्यङ्गाः ।

६. K.S.S. उपासृताः G.O.S. N.S. M.G. उपाश्रिताः ।

७. G.O.S. N.S. बह्वाश्रयत्वात् K.S.S. M.G. आश्रयत्वात् ।

८. K.S.S. M.G. स्थायिनि वपुषि गुणीभूता G.O.S. N.S. स्थानीय-पुरुषगुणभूता ।

९. K.S.S. M.G. गुणवत्तयाऽऽश्रयन्ते G.O.S. N.S. गुणतया आश्रयन्ते ।

१०. K.S.S. N.S. M.G. Omit स्थायिभावा रसत्वमाप्नुवन्ति G.O.S. Reatins it.

११. G.O.S. स K.S.S. N.S. M.G. सन् ।

पुरुषः[१] तथा विभावानुभावव्यभिचारिपरिवृतः स्थायी भावो रसनाम लभते[२]।

भवति चात्र श्लोकः—

यथा नराणां नृपतिः शिष्याणां च यथा गुरुः।
एवं हि सर्वभावानां भावः स्थायी महानिह ॥ ८ ॥

लक्षणं खलु पूर्वमभिहितमेषां रससंज्ञकानाम्[३]। इदानीं भावसामान्य-लक्षणमभिधास्यामः[४]। तत्र स्थायिभावान्वक्ष्यामः—

रतिर्नाम प्रमोदात्मिका[५] ऋतुमाल्यानुलेपनाभरणभो[६]जनवर-भवनानुभवनाप्रातिकूल्यादिभिर्विभावैः समुत्पद्यते। तामभिनयेत्स्मितवदन[७]-मधुरकथनभ्रूक्षेपकटाक्षादिभिरनुभावैः।

अत्र श्लोकः—

इष्टार्थविषयप्राप्त्या रतिरित्युपजायते।
सौम्यत्वादभिनेया सा वाङ्माधुर्याङ्गचेष्टितैः ॥ ९ ॥

हासो नाम—परचेष्टानुकरणकुहकासम्बद्धप्रलापपौरोभाग्य[८]मौर्ख्यादि-भिर्विभावैः समुत्पद्यते। तमभिनयेत्पूर्वोक्तैर्हसितादिभिरनुभावैः।

---

१. K.S.S. Reads in addition after पुरुषः। बहुषु गच्छत्सु कश्चित् क्वचित् पृच्छति कोऽयमिति स च तमाह राजेत्येव।

२. K.S.S. Reads in addition नरेन्द्रवत्।

३. N.S. reads in addition, निदर्शनं तु after रससंज्ञकानाम् G.O.S. K.S.S. M.G. omit it.

४. K.S.S. N.S. G.O.S. अभिधास्यामः M.G. व्याख्यास्यामः।

५. K.S.S. M.G. आमोदात्मको भावः G.O.S. N.S. प्रमोदात्मिका।

६. K.S.S. M.G. प्रियजनपर G.O.S. N.S. भोजनवर।

७. K.S.S. M·G. वचन G.O.S. N.S. वदन।

८. K.S.S. सौख्य G.O.S. M.G. N.S. मौर्ख्यं।

भवति चात्र श्लोकः—

परचेष्टानुकरणाद्धासः समुपजायते ।
स्मितहासातिहसितैरभिनेयः स पण्डितैः ॥ १० ॥

शोको नाम—इष्टजनवियोगविभवनाशवधबन्धदुःखानुभवनादिभिर्विभावैः समुत्पद्यते । तस्यास्रपातपरिदेवितविलपितवैवर्ण्यस्वरभेदस्रस्तगात्रताभूमिपतनसस्वनरुदिताक्रन्दितदीर्घनिःश्वसितजडतोन्मादमोहमरणादिभिरनुभावैरभिनयः प्रयोक्तव्यः ।

रुदितमत्र त्रिविधम्—आनन्दजमार्तिजमीर्ष्यासमुद्भवं चेति । भवन्ति चात्रार्याः—

[आनन्देर्ष्यार्तिकृतं त्रिविधं रुदितं सदा बुधैर्ज्ञेयम् ।
तस्य त्वभिनययोगान्विभावगतितः प्रवक्ष्यामि ॥]

हर्षोत्फुल्लकपोलं सानुस्मरणापाङ्गनिसृतास्रम् ।
रोमाञ्चगात्रमनिभृतमानन्दसमुद्भवं भवति[1] ॥ ११ ॥

पर्याप्तविमुक्तास्रं सस्वनमस्वस्थगात्रगतिचेष्टम् ।
भूमिनिपातनिवर्तितविलपितमित्यार्तिजं भवति ॥ १२ ॥

प्रस्फुरितौष्ठकपोलं सशिरःकम्पं तथा सनिःश्वासम् ।
भ्रुकुटीकटाक्षकुटिलं स्त्रीणामीर्ष्याकृतं भवति[2] ॥ १३ ॥

स्त्रीनीचप्रकृतिष्वेष[3] शोको व्यसनसम्भवः ।
धैर्येणोत्तममध्यानां नीचानां रुदितेन च ॥ १४ ॥

---

१. K.S.S. रोमाञ्चितगण्डं रोदनमानन्दजं भवति M.G. Same except गात्रं in place of गण्डं G.O.S. N.S. (Same as above).

२. K.S.S. reads कारणमपेक्षमाणः प्रायेणायासलिङ्गसंयुक्तः । वीररसान्तरचारी कार्यः कृतको भवेच्छोकः this verse in addition after verse No. 13. G.O.S. N.S. M.G. omit it.

३. N.S. एव G.O.S. K.S.S. M.G. एष ।

क्रोधो नाम—अधर्षणाक्रुष्टकलहविवादप्रतिकूलादिभिर्विभावैः समुत्पद्यते। अस्य विकृ[1]ष्टनासापुटोद्वृत्त[2]नयनसन्दष्टोष्ठपुटगण्डस्फुरणादिभिरनुभावैरभिनयः प्रयोक्तव्यः।

रिपुजो गुरुजश्चैव प्रणयिप्रभवस्तथा।
भृत्यजः कृतकश्चेति क्रोधः पञ्चविधः स्मृतः॥ १५॥

अत्रार्या भवन्ति—

भ्रुकुटीकुटिलोत्कटमुखः सन्दष्टोष्ठः स्पृशन्करेण करम्।
क्रुद्धः स्वभुजप्रेक्षी शत्रौ निर्यन्त्रणं रुष्येत्॥[3] १६॥

किञ्चिदवाङ्मुखदृष्टिः सास्र[4]स्वेदापमार्जनपरश्च।
अव्यक्तोल्बणचेष्टो गुरौ विनययन्त्रितो रुष्येत्॥[5] १७॥

अल्पतरप्रविचारो विकिरन्नश्रूण्यपाङ्गविक्षेपैः।
सभ्रुकुटीस्फुरितोष्ठः प्रणयोपगतां प्रियां रुष्येत्॥ १८॥

अथ परिजने तु रोषस्तर्जननिर्भर्त्सनाक्षिविस्तारैः।
विप्रेक्षणैश्च विविधैर[6]भिनेयः क्रूरतारहितः॥ १९॥

कारणमवेक्ष[7]माणः प्रायेणायासलिङ्गसंयुक्तः।
वीर[8]रसान्तरचारी कार्यः कृतको भवति कोपः॥ २०॥

---

१. K.S.S. M.G. उत्फुल्ल G.O.S. N.S. विकृष्ट।
२. K.S.S. उद्धत G.O.S. N.S. M.G. उद्वृत्त।
३. K.S.S. स्पृष्टभुजशिरोवक्षाः शत्रोर्विनियन्त्रणं कुप्येत् M.G. Same except धृष्ट in place of स्पृष्ट G.O.S. N.S. (Same as above).
४. K.S.S. M.G. किञ्चित् G.O.S. N.S. सास्र।
५. K.S.S. M.G. गुरोर्विनियन्त्रणं रुष्येत् G.O.S. N.S. गुरौ विनययन्त्रितो रुष्येत्।
६. K.S.S. M.G. तस्याभिनयः प्रयोक्तव्यः G.O.S. N.S. अभिनेयः क्रूरतारहितः।
७. K.S.S. M.G. N.S. अपेक्षमाणः G.O.S. अवेक्षमाणः।
८. K.S.S. M.G. उभय G.O.S. N.S. वीर।

उत्साहो नाम—उत्तमप्रकृतिः । स चाविषादशक्तिधैर्यशौर्यादिभिर्विभावैरुत्पद्यते । तस्य धैर्यत्यागवैशारद्यादिभिरनुभावैरभिनयः प्रयोक्तव्यः ।

अत्र श्लोकः—

असम्मोहादिभिर्व्यक्तो व्यवसायनयात्मकः ।
उत्साहजस्त्वभिनेयः स्या[1]दप्रमादोत्थितादिभिः ॥ २१ ॥

भयं नाम—स्त्रीनीचप्रकृतिकम् । गुरुराजापराधश्वापदशून्यागाराटवीपर्वतगहनगजाहिदर्शननिर्भर्त्सनकान्तारदुर्दिननिशान्धकारोलूकनक्तञ्चरारावश्रवणादिभिर्विभावैः समुत्पद्यते । तस्य प्रकम्पितकचरणहृदयकम्पनस्तम्भमुखशोषजिह्वापरिलेहनस्वेदवेपथुत्रासपरित्राणान्वेषणधावनोत्क्रुष्टादिभिरनुभावैरभिनयः प्रयोक्तव्यः ।

अत्र श्लोकाः—

गुरुराजापराधेन रौद्राणां चापि दर्शनात् ।
श्रवणादपि घोराणां भयं मोहेन जायते ॥ २२ ॥
गात्रकम्पनवित्रासैर्वक्त्रशोषणसम्भ्रमैः ।
विस्फारितेक्षणैः कार्यमभिनेयक्रियागुणैः[2] ॥ २३ ॥
सत्त्[3]ववित्रासनोद्भूतं भयमुत्पद्यते नृणाम् ।
स्रस्ताङ्गाक्षिनिमेषैस्तदभिनेयं तु नर्तकैः ॥ २४ ॥

आत्रार्या भवति—

करचरणहृदयकम्पैर्मुखशोषणवदनलेहनस्तम्भैः ।
सम्भ्रान्तवदनवेपथुसन्त्रासकृतैरभिनयोऽस्य[4] ॥ २५ ॥

---

१. K.S.S. M.G. असावप्रमादक्रियादिभिः G.G.S. N.S. स्यादप्रमादोत्थितादिभिः ।

२. K.S.S. M.G. अभिनेयः क्रियागुणैः M.G. अभिनेयं G.O.S. N.S. अभिनेयक्रियागुणैः ।

३. K.S.S तत्र G.O.S. N.S. M.G. सत्त्व

४. K.S.S. M.G. N.S. करचरणहृदयकम्पैः स्तम्भनजिह्वोपलेहमुखशोषैः । स्रस्तसुविषण्णगात्रैस्तस्याभिनयः प्रयोक्तव्यः । G.O.S. (Same as above).

जुगुप्सा नाम—स्त्रीनीचप्रकृतिका। सा चाहृद्यदर्शनश्रवणादिभिर्विभावैः समुत्पद्यते। तस्याः सर्वाङ्गसङ्कोचनिष्ठीवनमुखविकूणनहृल्लेखादिभिरनुभावैरभिनयः प्रयोक्तव्यः।

भवति चात्र श्लोकः—

नासाप्रच्छादनेनेह[1] गात्रसङ्कोचनेन च।
उद्वेजनैः सहृल्लेखैर्जुगुप्सामभिनिर्दिशेत्॥ २६॥

विस्मयो नाम—मायेन्द्रजालमानुषकर्मातिशयचित्रपुस्तशिल्पविद्यातिशयादिभिर्विभावैः समुत्पद्यते। तस्य नयनविस्तारानिमेषप्रेक्षितभ्रूक्षेपरोमहर्षणशिरःकम्पसाधुवादादिभिरनुभावैरभिनयः प्रयोक्तव्यः।

भवति चात्र श्लोकः—

कर्मातिशयनिर्वृत्तो विस्मयो हर्षसम्भवः।
सिद्धिस्थाने त्वसौ साध्यः प्रहर्षपुलकादिभिः[3]॥ २७।

एवमेते स्थायिनो भावा रससंज्ञाः प्रत्यवगन्तव्याः।

व्यभिचारिण इदानीं व्याख्यास्यामः। अत्राह—व्यभिचारिण इति उच्यते—वि अभि इत्येतावुपसर्गौ। चर इति गत्यर्थो धातुः। विविधमाभिमुख्येन रसेषु चरन्तीति व्यभिचारिणः। वागङ्गसत्त्वोपेताः[4] प्रयोगे रसान्नयन्तीति व्यभिचारिणः। अत्राह—कथं नयन्तीति। उच्यते—लोकसिद्धान्त एषः—यथा सूर्य इदं दिनं नक्षत्रं वा नयतीति। न च तेन बाहुभ्यां स्कन्धेन वा नीयते। किं तु लोकप्रसिद्धमेतत्। यथेदं सूर्यो नक्षत्रं दिनं वा नयतीति। एवमेते व्यभिचारिण इत्यवगन्तव्याः। तानिह सङ्ग्रहाभिहितांस्त्रयस्त्रिंशद्व्यभिचारिणो भावान् वर्णयिष्यामः।

---

१. K.S.S. अपि G.O.S. N.S. K.S.S. इह।
२. K.S.S. स्वेद G.O.S. N.S. शिरः कम्प M.G. omits.
३. K.S.S. हर्षाश्रुप्रलयादिभिः G.O.S. N.S. M.G. प्रहर्षपुलकादिभिः।
४. K.S.S. N.S. वागङ्गसत्त्वोपेतान् G.O.S. वागङ्गसत्त्वोपेताः M.G. omits it.

तत्र निर्वेदो नाम—दारिद्र्यव्याध्यवमानाधिक्षेपाक्रुष्टक्रोधताडनेष्टजन-वियोगतत्त्वज्ञानादिभिर्विभावैः समुत्पद्यते स्त्रीनीचकुसत्त्वानाम् । रुदितनिःश्वसितोच्छ्वसितसम्प्रधारणादिभिरनुभावैस्तमभिनयेत् ।

अत्र श्लोकः—

दारिद्र्येष्टवियोगाद्यैः निर्वेदो नाम जायते ।
सम्प्रधारणनिःश्वासैस्तस्य त्वभिनयो भवेत् ॥ २८ ॥

अत्रानुवंश्ये आर्ये भवतः—

इष्टजनविप्रयोगाद्दारिद्र्याद्व्याधितस्तथा दुःखात् ।
ऋद्धिं परस्य दृष्ट्वा निर्वेदो नाम सम्भवति ॥ २९ ॥

बाष्पपरिप्लुतनयनः पुनश्च निःश्वासदीनमुखनेत्रः ।
योगीव ध्यानपरो भवति हि निर्वेदवान्पुरुषः ॥ ३० ॥

ग्लानिर्नाम — वान्तविरिक्तव्याधितपोनियमोपवासमनस्तापातिशयमदन-मद्यसेवनातिव्यायामाध्वगमनक्षुत्पिपासानिद्राच्छेदादिभिर्विभावैः समुत्पद्यते । तस्याः क्षामवाक्यनयनकपोलोदरमन्दपदोत्क्षेपणवेपनानुत्साहतनुगात्रवैवर्ण्यस्वर-भेदादिभिरनुभावैरभिनयः प्रयोक्तव्यः ।

अत्रार्ये भवतः—

वान्तविरिक्तव्याधिषु तपसा जरसा च जायते ग्लानिः ।
कार्श्येन साभिनेया मन्दभ्रमणेन कम्पेन ॥ ३१ ॥

गदितैः क्षामक्षामैर्नेत्रविकारैश्च दीनसञ्चारैः ।
श्लथभावेनाङ्गानां मुहुर्मुहुर्निर्दिशेद्ग्लानिम् ॥ ३२ ॥

---

१. K.S.S. M.G. दारिद्र्योपगमाधिक्षेपाक्रुष्टक्रोधताडनेष्टजनवियोगतत्त्व-ज्ञानादिभिः G.O.S. N.S. (Same as abobe).
२. K.S.S. M.G. परवृद्धिं वा G.O.S. N.S. ऋद्धिं परस्य ।
३. K.S.S. दीर्घ G.O.S. N.S. M.G. दीन ।
४. K.S.S. M.G. मन्दक्रमणानुकम्पेन G.O.S. N.S. मन्दभ्रमणेन कम्पेन ।

शङ्का नाम—सन्देहात्मिका स्त्रीनीचप्रभवा। चौर्याभिग्रहणनृपापराधपापकर्मकरणादिभिर्विभावैः समुत्पद्यते। तस्या मुहुर्मुहुरवलोकनावकुण्ठनमुखशोषणजिह्वापरिलेहनमुखवैवर्ण्यस्वरभेदवेपथुशुष्कोष्ठकण्ठायाससाधर्म्यादिभिरनुभावैरभिनयः प्रयोक्तव्यः।

चौर्यादिजनिता शङ्का प्रायः कार्या भयानके।
प्रियव्यलीकजनिता तथा शृङ्गारिणी मता॥ ३३॥

अत्राकारसंवरणमपि केचिदिच्छन्ति। तच्च कुशलैरुपाधिभिरिङ्गितैश्चोपलक्ष्यम्।

अत्रार्ये भवतः—

द्विविधा शङ्का कार्या ह्यात्मसमुत्था च परसमुत्था च।
या तत्रात्मसमुत्था सा ज्ञेया दृष्टिचेष्टाभिः॥ ३४॥
किञ्चित्प्रवेपिताङ्गस्त्वधोमुखो[1] वीक्षते च पार्श्वानि।
गुरुसज्जमानजिह्वः श्यामास्यः शङ्कितः पुरुषः॥ ३५॥

असूया नाम—नानापराधद्वेषपरैश्वर्यसौभाग्यमेधाविद्यालीलादिभिर्विभावैः समुत्पद्यते। तस्याश्च परिषदि दोषप्रख्यापनगुणोपघातेर्ष्याचक्षुःप्रदानाधोमुखभ्रुकुटीक्रियावज्ञानकुत्सनादिभिरनुभावैरभिनयः प्रयोक्तव्यः।

अत्रार्ये भवतः—

परसौभाग्येश्वरतामेधालीलासमुच्छ्रयान्दृष्ट्वा।
उत्पद्यते ह्यसूया कृतापराधो भवेद्यश्च॥ ३६॥
भ्रुकुटिकुटिलोत्कटमुखैः सेर्ष्याक्रोधपरिवृत्तनेत्रैश्च।
गुणनाशनविद्वेषैस्तत्राभिनयः प्रयोक्तव्यः॥ ३७॥

मदो नाम—मद्योपयोगादुत्पद्यते। स च त्रिविधः पञ्चविधभावश्च।

अत्रार्या भवन्ति—

ज्ञेयस्तु मदस्त्रिविधस्तरुणो मध्यस्तथावकृष्टश्च।
करणं पञ्चविधं स्यात्तस्याभिनयः प्रयोक्तव्यः॥ ३८॥

---

१. K.S.S. मुहुर्मुहुः G.O.S. N.S. अधोमुखः M.G. तथोन्मुखः।

कश्चिन्मत्तो गायति रोदिति कश्चित्तथा हसति कश्चित् ।
परुषवचनाभिधायी कश्चित्कश्चित्तथा स्वपिति ॥ ३९ ॥

उत्तमसत्त्वः शेते हसति च गायति च मध्यमप्रकृतिः ।
परुषवचनाभिधायी रोदित्यपि चाधमप्रकृतिः ॥ ४० ॥

स्मितवचनमधुररागो हृ[१]ष्टतनुः किञ्चिदाकुलितवाक्यः ।
सुकुमाराविद्धगतिस्तरुणमदस्तूत्तमप्रकृतिः ॥ ४१ ॥

स्खलिताघूर्णितनयनः स्रस्तव्याकुलितबाहुविक्षेपः ।
कुटिलव्याविद्धगतिर्मध्यमदो मध्यमप्रकृतिः ॥ ४२ ॥

नष्टस्मृतिर्हतगतिश्छर्दितहिक्काकफैः सुबीभत्सः ।
गुरुसज्जमानजिह्वो निष्ठीवति चाधमप्रकृतिः ॥ ४३ ॥

रङ्गे पिबतः कार्या मदवृद्धिर्नाट्ययोगमासाद्य ।
कार्यो मदक्षयो वै यः खलु पीत्वा प्रविष्टः स्यात् ॥ ४४ ॥

सन्त्रासाच्छोकाद्वा भयात्प्रहर्षाच्च कारणोपगतात् ।
उत्क्रम[२]य्यापि हि कार्यो मदप्रणाशः क्रमात्तज्ज्ञैः ॥ ४५ ॥

एभिर्भावविशेषैर्मदो द्रुतं सम्प्रणाशमुपयाति ।
अभ्युदयसुखैर्वाक्यैर्यथैवं शोकः क्षयं याति ॥ ४६ ॥

श्रमो नाम—अध्वव्यायामसेवनादिभिर्विभावैः समुत्पद्यते । तस्य गात्रपरिमर्दनसंवाहननिःश्वसितविजृम्भितमन्दपदोत्प्रेक्षणनयनवदनविकूणनसीत्करादिभिरनुभावैरभिनयः प्रयोक्तव्यः ।

अत्रार्या—

नृ[३]त्ताध्वव्यायामान्नरस्य सञ्जायते श्रमो नाम ।
निःश्वासखेदगमनैस्तस्याभिनयः प्रयोक्तव्यः ॥ ४७ ॥

---

१. K.S.S. धृष्ट G.O.S. N.S. M.G. हृष्ट ।
२. K.S.S. उत्क्रम्यापि G.O.S. N.S. M.G. उत्क्रम्यापि ।
३. K.S.S. M.G. अध्वगति G.O.S. N.S. नृत्ताध्व ।

आलस्यं नाम—खेदव्याधिगर्भस्वभावश्रमसौहित्यादिभिर्विभावैः समुत्पद्यते स्त्रीनीचानाम् । तदभिनयेत्सर्वकर्मानभिलाप[1]शयनासननिद्रातन्द्रीसेवनादिभिरनुभावैः ।

अत्रार्या—

आलस्यं त्वभिनेयं खेदोपगतं[2] स्वभावजं चापि ।
आहारवर्जितानामारम्भाणामनारम्भात् ॥ ४८ ॥

दैन्यं नाम—दौर्गत्यमनस्तापादिभिर्विभावैः समुत्पद्यते । तस्याधृतिशिरोरोगगात्रगौर[3]वान्यमनस्कतामृजापरिवर्जनादिभिरनुभावैरभिनयः प्रयोक्तव्यः ।

अत्रार्या—

चिन्तौत्सुक्यसमुत्था दुःखाद्या[4] भवति दीनता पुंसाम् ।
सर्वमृजापरि[5]हारैर्विविधोऽभिनयो भवेत्तस्य ॥ ४९ ॥

चिन्ता नाम—ऐश्वर्यभ्रंशेष्टद्रव्यापहारदारिद्र्यादिभावैरुत्पद्यते । तामभिनयेन्निःश्वसितोच्छ्वसितसन्तापध्यानाधोमुखचिन्तनतनुकार्श्यादिभिरनुभावैः ।

अत्रार्ये भवतः—

ऐश्वर्यभ्रंशेष्टद्रव्यक्षयजा बहुप्रकारा तु ।
हृदयवितर्कोपगता नृणां चिन्ता समुद्भवति ॥ ५० ॥

सोच्छ्वासैर्निःश्वसितैः सन्तापैश्चैव हृदयशून्यतया ।
अभिनेतव्या चिन्ता मृजाविहीनैरधृत्या च ॥ ५१ ॥

मोहो नाम—दैवोपघातव्यसनाभिघातव्याधिभयावेगपूर्ववैरानुस्मरणादिभिर्विभावैः समुत्पद्यते । तस्य निश्चैतन्यभ्रमणपतनाघूर्णनादर्शनादिभिरनुभावैरभिनयः प्रयोक्तव्यः ।

---

१. N.S. अनभिलाष K.S.S.M.G. प्रद्वेष G.O.S. अनभिलाप ।

२. G.O.S. N.S. खेदोपगतं K.S.S. M.G. खेदकाधिगतं ।

३. G.O.S. N.S. गौरवान्यमनस्कता K.S.S. स्तम्भमनःस्तम्भ M.G. स्तम्भ ।

४. G.O.S. N.S. दुःखाद्या K.S.S. M.G. दुःखाद्वा ।

५. N.S. परिमार्जनैः G.O.S. K.S.S. M.G. परिहारैः ।

अत्र श्लोकस्तावदार्या च—

अस्थाने तस्करान्दृष्ट्वा त्रासनैर्विवि[1]धैरपि ।
तत्प्रतीकारशून्यस्य मोहः समुपजायते ॥ ५२ ॥

व्यसनाभिघातभयपूर्ववैरसंस्मरणरो[2]गजो मोहः ।
सर्वेन्द्रियसम्मोहात्तस्याभिनयः प्रयोक्तव्यः ॥ ५३ ॥

स्मृतिर्नाम—सुखदुःखकृतानां भावानामनुस्मरणम् । सा चा स्वास्थ्यजघन्यरात्रिनिद्राच्छेदसमानदर्शनोदाहरणचिन्ताभ्यासादिभिर्विभावैः समुत्पद्यते । तामभिनयेच्छिरःकम्पनावलोकनभ्रूसमुन्नमनादिभिरनुभावैः । अत्रार्ये भवतः—

सुखदुःखमतिक्रान्तं तथा मतिविभावितं यथावृत्तम् ।
चिरविस्मृतं स्मरति यः स्मृतिमानिति वेदितव्योऽसौ[3] ॥ ५४ ॥

स्वास्थ्याभ्याससमुत्था श्रुतिदर्शनसम्भवा स्मृतिर्निपुणैः ।
शिरउद्वाहनकम्पैर्भ्रूक्षेपैश्चाभिनेतव्या ॥ ५५ ॥

धृतिर्नाम—शौर्यविज्ञानश्रुतिविभवशौचाचारगुरुभक्त्यधिकमनोरथार्थलाभक्रीडादिभिर्विभावैः समुत्पद्यते । तामभिनयेत्प्राप्तानां विषयाणामुपभोगादप्राप्तातीतोपहृतविनष्टानामननुशोचनादिभिरनुभावैः ।

अत्रार्ये भवतः—

विज्ञानशौचविभवश्रुतिशक्तिसमुद्भवा धृतिः सद्भिः ।
भयशोकविषादाद्यैः रहिता तु सदा प्रयोक्तव्या ॥ ५६ ॥

प्राप्तानामुपभोगः शब्दरसस्पर्शरूपगन्धानाम् ।
अप्राप्तैश्च न शोको यस्यां हि भवेद्धृतिः सा तु ॥ ५७ ॥

व्रीडा नाम—अकार्यकरणात्मिका । सा च गुरुव्यतिक्रमणावज्ञानप्रतिज्ञातानिर्वहणपश्चात्तापादिभिर्विभावैः समुत्पद्यते । तां निगूढवदनाधोमुखवि-

---

१. N.S. K.S.S. पृथगविधैः M.G. पृथग्विधः G.O.S. विविधैरपि ।
२. K.S.S. M.G. संस्मरणजः G.O.S. N.S. सस्भरणरोगजः ।
३. K.S.S. M.G. विस्मृतं च यथावृत्तं स्मरेद् यः स्मृतिमानसौ G.O.S. N.S. (Same as above).

चिन्तनोर्वीलिखनवस्त्राङ्गुलीयकस्पर्शननखनिकृन्तनादिभिरनुभावैरभिनयेत् ।

अत्रार्ये भवतः—

किञ्चिदकार्यं कुर्वन्नेवं[2] यो दृश्यते शुचिभिरन्यैः ।
पश्चात्तापेन युतो व्रीडित इति वेदितव्योऽसौ ॥ ५८ ॥

लज्जानिगूढवदनो भूमिं विलिखन्नखांश्च विनिकृन्तन् ।
वस्त्राङ्गुलीयकानां संस्पर्शं व्रीडितः कुर्यात् ॥ ५९ ॥

चपलता नाम—रागद्वेषमात्सर्यामर्षेर्ष्याप्रतिकूलादिभिर्विभावैः समुत्पद्यते । तस्याश्च वाक्पारुष्यनिर्भर्त्सनवधबन्धसम्प्रहारताडनादिभिरनुभावैरभिनयः प्रयोक्तव्यः ।

अत्रार्या भवति—

अविमृश्य तु यः कार्यं पुरुषो वधता[3]डनं समारभते ।
अविनिश्चितकारित्वात्स तु खलु चपलो बुधैर्ज्ञेयः ॥ ६० ॥

हर्षो नाम—मनोरथलाभेष्टजनसमागमनमनःपरितोषदेवगुरुराजभर्तृप्रसादभोजनाच्छादनलाभोपभोगादिविभावैः समुत्पद्यते । तमभिनयेन्नयनवदनप्रसादप्रियभाषणालिङ्गनकण्टकितपुलकितास्रस्वेदादिभिरनुभावैः ।

अत्रार्ये भवतः—

अप्राप्ये प्राप्ये[4] वा लब्धेऽर्थे प्रियसमागमे वाऽपि ।
हृदयमनोरथलाभे हर्षः सञ्जायते पुंसाम् ॥ ६१ ॥

नयनवदनप्रसादप्रियभाषालिङ्गनैश्च रोमाञ्चैः ।
ललितैश्चाङ्गविहारैः स्वेदाद्यैरभिनयस्तस्य ॥ ६२ ॥

---

१. N.S. निस्तोदन G.O.S. K.S.S. M.G. निकृन्तन ।
२. M.G. K.S.S. कुर्वत् यो हि नरः G.O.S. N.S. कुर्वन्नेवं यो दृश्यते ।
३. K.S.S. बन्धनादिकं G.O.S. N.S. M.G. ताडनं ।
४. K.S.S. प्राप्ते वा प्राप्ये M.G. प्राप्ये वा प्राप्ये वा N.S. G.O.S. अप्राप्ये प्राप्ये वा ।

आवेगो नाम—उत्पातवातवर्षाग्निकुञ्जरोद्भ्रमणप्रियाप्रियश्रवणव्यसनाभिघातादिभिर्विभावैः समुत्पद्यते । तत्रोत्पातकृतो नाम विद्युदुल्कानिर्घातप्रपतनचन्द्रसूर्योपरागकेतुदर्शनकृतः । तमभिनयेत्सर्वाङ्गस्त्रस्तताभवैमनस्यमुखवैवर्ण्यविषादविस्मयादिभिः । वातकृतं पुनरवकुण्ठनाक्षिपरिमार्जनवस्त्रसङ्गूहन[1]त्वरितगमनादिभिः । वर्षकृतं पुनः सर्वाङ्गसम्पिण्डनप्रधावनच्छन्नाश्रयमार्गणादिभिः । अग्निकृतं तु धूमाकुलनेत्रताऽङ्गसङ्कोचनविधूननातिक्रान्तापक्रान्तादिभिः । कुञ्जरोद्भ्रमणकृतं नाम त्वरितापसर्पणचञ्चलगमनभयस्तम्भवेपथुपश्चादवलोकनविस्मयादिभिः । प्रियश्रवणकृतं नामाभ्युत्थानालिङ्गनवस्त्राभरणप्रदानाश्रुपुलकितादिभिः । अप्रियश्रवणकृतं नाम भूमिपतनविषमविवर्तनपरिधावनविलापनाक्रन्दनादिभिः । व्यसनाभिघातजं तु सहसापसर्पणशस्त्रचर्मवर्मधारणगजतुरगरथारोहणसम्प्रधारणादिभिः ।

एवमष्ट[2]विकल्पोऽयमावेगः सम्भ्रमात्मकः ।
स्थैर्येणोत्तममध्यानां नीचानां चापसर्पणैः ॥ ६३ ॥

अत्रार्ये भवतः—

अप्रियनिवेदनाद्वा सहसा ह्यवधारि[3]तारिवचनस्य ।
शस्त्राक्षेपात् त्रासादावेगो नाम सम्भवति ॥ ६४ ॥

अप्रियनिवेदनाद्यो विषादभावाश्रयोऽनुभावोऽस्य ।
सहसारिदर्शनाच्चेत्प्रहरणपरिघट्टनैः कार्यः ॥ ६५ ॥

जडता नाम—सर्वकार्याप्रतिपत्तिः । इष्टानिष्टश्रवणदर्शनव्याध्यादिभिर्विभावैः समुत्पद्यते । तामभिनयेदकथनाविभा[4]षणतूष्णीम्भावाप्रतिभाऽनिमेषनिरीक्षणपरवशत्वादिभिरनुभावैः ।

---

१. M.G. संग्रहन K.S.S. G.O.S. N.S. सङ्गूहन ।

२. K.S.S. M.G. इत्येषोऽष्टविधः G.O.S. N.S. एवमष्टविकल्पः ।

३. N.S. अभिधारितारिवचनेन M.G. अवधीरितवचनस्य G.O.S. अवधारितारिवचनस्य K.S.S. अवधारितवचनस्य ।

४. N.S. अभिभाषण M.G. K.S.S. आभाषण G.O.S. अविभाषण ।

अत्रार्या भवति—

इष्टं वाऽनिष्टं वा सुखदुःखे वा न वेत्ति यो मोहात् ।
तूष्णीकः परवशगो भवति स जडसंज्ञितः पुरुषः ॥ ६६ ॥

गर्वो नाम—ऐश्वर्यकुलरूपयौवनविद्याबलधनलाभादिभिर्विभावैः समुत्पद्यते । तस्यासूयावज्ञाधर्षणानुत्तरदानासम्भाषणाङ्गावलोकनविभ्रमापहसनवाक्पारुष्य-गुरुव्यतिक्रमणाधिक्षेपवचनविच्छेदादिभिरनुभावैरभिनयः प्रयोक्तव्यः ।

अत्रार्या भवति—

विद्यावाप्ते रूपादैश्वर्यादथ धनागमाद्वापि ।
गर्वः खलु नीचानां दृष्ट्यङ्गविचारणैः[1] कार्यः ॥ ६७ ॥

विषादो नाम—कार्यानिस्तरणदैवव्यापत्तिसमुत्थः । तमभिनयेत्सहायान्वेषणोपायचिन्तनोत्साहविघातवैमनस्यनिःश्वसितादिभिरनुभावैरुत्तममध्यमानाम् । अधमानां तु विपरिधावनालोकनमुखशोषणसृक्वपरिलेहनानिद्रानिःश्वसितध्यानादिभिरनुभावैः ।

आत्रार्याश्लोकौ—

कार्यानिस्तरणाद्वा चौर्याभिग्रहणराजदोषाद्वा[2] ।
दैवादर्थविपत्तेर्भवति विषादः सदा पुंसाम्[3] ॥ ६८ ॥

वैचित्र्योपायचिन्ताभ्यां कार्य उत्तममध्ययोः ।
निद्रानिःश्वसितध्यानैरधमानां तु योजयेत् ॥ ६९ ॥

औत्सुक्यं नाम—इष्टजनवियोगानुस्मरणोद्यानदर्शनादिभिर्विभावैः समुत्पद्यते । तस्य दीर्घनिःश्वसिताधोमुखविचिन्तननिद्रातन्द्रीशयनाभिलाषादिभिरनुभावैरभिनयः प्रयोक्तव्यः ।

१. N.S. विचालनैः M.G. G.O.S. K.S.S. विचारणैः ।
२. M.G. K.S.S. दोषाद्यैः G.O.S N.S. दोषाद्वा ।
३. N.S. M.G. K.S.S. दैवादिष्टो योऽर्थस्तदसंप्राप्तौ विषादः स्यात् G.O.S. (Same as above).

अत्रार्या भवति—

इष्टजनस्य[1] वियोगादौत्सुक्यं जायते ह्यनुस्मृत्या ।
चिन्तानिन्द्रातन्द्रीगात्रगुरुत्वैरनभियोऽस्य ॥ ७० ॥

निद्रा नाम— दौर्बल्यश्रमक्लममदालस्यचिन्ताऽत्याहारस्वभावादिभिर्विभावैः समुत्पद्यते । तामभिनयेद्वदनगौरवशरीराव[2]लोकननेत्रघूर्णनगात्रविजृम्भणमान्द्योच्छ्वसितसन्नगात्रताऽक्षिनिमीलनादिभिरनुभावैः ।

अत्रार्ये भवतः—

आलस्याद्दौर्बल्यात्क्लमाच्छ्रमाच्चिन्तनात्स्वभावाच्च ।
रात्रौ जागरणादपि निद्रा पुरुषस्य सम्भवति ॥ ७१ ॥

तां मुखगौरवगात्रप्रतिलोलननयनमीलनजडत्वैः ।
जृम्भणगात्रविमर्दैरनुभावैरभिनयेत्प्राज्ञः ॥ ७२ ॥

अपस्मारो नाम—देवयक्षनागब्रह्मराक्षसभूतप्रेतपिशाचग्रहणानुस्मरणोच्छिष्टशून्यागारसेवनाशुचिकालान्तरापरिपतनव्या[3]ध्यादिभिर्विभावैः समुत्पद्यते । तस्य स्फुरितनिःश्वसितोत्कम्पितधावनपतनस्वेदस्तम्भनवदनफेनजिह्वापरिलेहनादिभिरनुभावैरभिनयः प्रयोक्तव्यः ।

अत्रार्ये भवतः—

भूतपिशाचग्रहणानुस्मरणोच्छिष्टशून्यगृहगमनात् ।
कालान्तरातिपातादशुचेश्च भवत्यपस्मारः ॥ ७३ ॥

सहसा भूमौ पतनं प्रवेपनं वदनफेनमोक्षश्च ।
निःसंज्ञस्योत्थानं रूपाण्येतान्यपस्मारे ॥ ७४ ॥

सुप्तं नाम— निद्रा[4]भिभवविषयोपगमनमोहनक्षितितलशयनप्रसारणानुकर्ष-

---

१. M.G. K.S.S. जनादि G.O.S. N.S. जनस्य ।
२. M.G. K.S.S. गात्रपरिलोडन G.O.S. N.S. शरीरावलोकन ।
३. M.G. K.S.S. धातुवैषम्यादिभिः G.O.S. N.S. व्याध्यादिभिः ।
४. N.S. इन्द्रियविषय M.G. निद्राभिभवेन्द्रियविषय K.S.S. omits from निद्रा ...to समुत्थम् G.O.S. निद्राभिभवविषय ।

णादिभिर्विभावैः समुत्पद्यते निद्रासमुत्थम् । तदुच्छ्वसितसन्नगात्राक्षिनिमीलनसर्वेन्द्रियसम्मोहनोत्स्वप्नायितादिभिरनुभावैरभिनयेत् ।

अत्रार्ये भवतः—

निद्राभिभवेन्द्रियोपरमणमोहनैर्भवेत्सुप्तम् ।
अक्षिनिमीलोच्छ्वसनैः स्वप्नायितजल्पितैः कार्यः[1] ॥ ७५ ॥

सोच्छ्वासैर्निःश्वासैर्मन्दाक्षिनिमीलनेन निश्चेष्टः ।
सर्वेन्द्रियसम्मोहात्सुप्तं स्वप्नैश्च युञ्जीत ॥ ७६ ॥

विबोधो नाम—आहारपरिणामनिद्राच्छेदस्वप्नान्ततीव्रशब्दस्पर्शश्रवणादिभिर्विभावैः समुत्पद्यते । तमभिनयेज्जृम्भणाक्षिपरिमर्दनशयनमोक्षणादिभिरनुभावैः ।

अत्रार्या भवति—

आहारविपरिणामाच्छब्दस्पर्शादिभिश्च सम्भूतः ।
प्रतिबोधस्त्वभिनेयो जृम्भणवदनाक्षिपरिमर्दैः ॥ ७७ ॥

अमर्षो नाम—विद्यैश्वर्यशौ[2]र्यबलाधिकैरधिक्षिप्तस्यावमानितस्य वा समुत्पद्यते । तमभिनयेच्छिरःकम्पनप्रस्वेदनाधोमुखचिन्तनध्यानाध्यवसायोपायसहायान्वेषणादिभिरनुभावैः ।

अत्र श्लोकौ—

आक्षिप्तानां सभामध्ये विद्याशौ[3]र्यबलाधिकैः ।
नृणामुत्साहसंयो[4]गादमर्षो नाम जायते ॥ ७८ ॥

उत्साहाध्यवसायाभ्यामधोमुखविचिन्तनैः ।
शिरःप्रकम्पस्वेदाद्यैस्तं प्रयुञ्जीत पण्डितः[5] ॥ ७९ ॥

---

१. K.S.S. omits this verse G.O.S. N.S M.G. reatin it.
२. K.S.S. M.G. धन G.O.S. N.S. शौर्य ।
३. K.S.S M G. N.S. विद्वैश्वर्य G.O.S. विद्याशौर्य ।
४. N.S. M.G. सम्पन्नः G.O.S. N.S. संयोगात् ।
५. K.S.S. M.G. नाट्यवित् G.O.S. N.S. पण्डितः ।

अवहित्थं नाम—आकारप्रच्छादनात्मकम् । तच्च लज्जाभयापजयगौरव-जैह्म्यादिभिर्विभावैः समुत्पद्यते । तस्यान्यथाकथनावलोकितकथाभङ्गकृतक-धैर्यादिभिरनुभावैरभिनयः प्रयोक्तव्यः ।

अत्र श्लोको भवति –

धाष्टर्यजैह्म्यादिसम्भूतमवहित्थं भयात्मकम् ।
तच्चागणनया कार्यं नाती[1]वोत्तरभाषणात् ।। ८० ।।

उग्रता नाम—चौर्याभिग्रहणनृपापराधासत्प्रलापादिभिर्विभावैः समुत्पद्यते । तां च वधबन्धनताडननिर्भर्त्सनादिभिरनुभावैरभिनयेत् ।

अत्रार्या भवति—

चौ[2]र्याभिग्रहणवशान्नृपापराधादथोग्रता भवति ।
वधबन्धताडनादिभिरनुभावैरभिनयस्तस्याः ।। ८१ ।।

मतिर्नाम—नानाशास्त्रविचिन्तनोहापोहादिभिर्विभावैः समुत्पद्यते । तामभिनयेच्छिष्योपदेशार्थविकल्पनसंशयच्छेदादिभिरनुभावैः ।

भवति चात्र श्लोकः—

नानाशास्त्रार्थबो[3]धेन मतिः संजायते नृणाम् ।
शिष्योपदेशार्थकृतस्तस्यास्त्वभिनयो भवेत् ।। ८२ ।।

व्याधिर्नाम—वातपित्तकफसन्निपातप्रभवः । तस्याः ज्वरादयो विशेषाः । ज्वरस्तु द्विविधः सशीतः सदाहश्च । तत्र सशीतो नाम—प्रवेपितसर्वाङ्गोत्कम्पननिकुञ्चनाग्न्यभिलाषरोमाञ्चहनुवलननासाविकूणनमुखशोषणपरिदेविता-दिभिरनुभावैरभिनेयः । सदाहो नाम—विक्षिप्ताङ्गकरचरणभूम्यभिलाषानुलेपन-शीताभिलाषपरिदेवनमुखशोषोत्क्रुष्टादिभिरनुभावैः । ये चान्ये व्याधयस्तेऽपि

---

१. K.S.S. तानि च M.G. N.S. नाति च G.O.S. नातीव ।

२. K.S.S. चौर्यग्रहणनिरोधात् M.G. N.S. चौर्याभिग्रहयोगात् G.O.S. चौर्याभिग्रहणवशान् ।

३. K.S.S. M.G. विनिष्पन्ना N.S. G.O.S. अर्थबोधेन ।

खलु मुखविकूणनगात्रस्तम्भस्रस्ताक्षिनिःश्वसनस्तनितोत्क्रुष्टवपनादिभिरनुभावैरभिनेयाः ।

अत्र श्लोको भवति—

समासतस्तु[1] व्याधीनां कर्तव्योऽभिनयो बुधैः ।
स्रस्ताङ्गगात्रविक्षेपैस्तथा[2] मुखविकूणनैः[3] ॥ ८३ ॥

उन्मादो नाम—इष्टजनवियोगावभवनाशाभि[4]घातवातपित्तश्लेष्मप्रकोपादिभिर्विभावैरुत्पद्यते । तमनिमित्तहसितरुदितोत्क्रुष्टासम्बद्धप्रलापशयितोपविष्टोत्थितप्रधावितनृत्तगीतपठितभस्मपांस्ववधूलनतृणनिर्माल्यकुचेलचीरघटकपालशरावाभरणधारणोपभोगैरनेकैश्चानवस्थितैश्चेष्टानुकरणादिभिरनुभावैरभिनयेत् ।

अत्रार्ये भवतः—

इष्टजनविभवनाशादभिघाताद्वातपित्तकफकोपात् ।
विविधाच्चित्त[5]विकारादुन्मादो नाम सम्भवति ॥ ८४ ॥
अनिमित्तरुदितहसितोपविष्टगीत[6]प्रधावितोत्क्रुष्टैः ।
अन्यैश्च विकारकृतैरुन्मादं सम्प्रयुञ्जीत ॥ ८५ ॥

मरणं नाम—व्याधिजमभिघातजञ्च । तत्र यदान्त्रयकृच्छूलदोषवैषम्यगण्डपिटकज्वरविषूचिकादिभिरुत्पद्यते तद्व्याधिप्रभवम् । अभिघातजन्तु शस्त्राहिदंशविषपानश्वापदगजतुरगरथपशुयानपातविनाशप्रभवम् । एतयोरभिनयविशेषान्वक्ष्यामः—तत्र व्याधिजं विषण्णगात्राव्यायताङ्गविचेष्टितनिमीलितनयनहिक्काश्वासोपेतानवेक्षितपरिजनाव्यक्ताक्षरकथनादिभिरनुभावैरभिनयेत् ।

---

१. G.O.S. समासतः N.S. M.G. K.S.S. सामान्यतः
२. K.S.S. M.G. रुजा N.S. G.O.S. तथा ।
३. K.S.S. M.G. विघूर्णनैः G.O.S. N.S. विकूणनैः ।
४. G.O.S. N.S. अभिघात K.S.S. M.G. व्यसनाभिधात ।
५. K.S.S. पित्त N.S. M.G. G.O.S. चित्त ।
६. M.G. गति K.S.S. G.O.S. N.S. गीत ।

अत्र श्लोको भवति—

व्याधीनामेकभावो हि मरणाभिनयः स्मृतः ।
विषण्णगात्रैर्निश्चेष्टैरिन्द्रियैश्च विवर्जितः ॥ ८६ ॥

अभिघातजे तु नानाप्रकारा अभिनयविशेषाः [1]शस्त्रक्षताहिदष्टविषपीतगजादिपतितश्वापदहताः । यथा तत्र शस्त्रक्षते तावत्सहसा भूमिपतनवेपनस्फुरणादिभिरभिनयः प्रयोक्तव्यः । अहिदष्टविषपीतयोर्विषवेगो यथा—कार्श्यवेपथुविदाहहिक्काफेनस्कन्धभङ्गजडतामरणानीत्यष्टौ विषवेगाः ।

अत्र श्लोकौ भवतः—

कार्श्यं तु प्रथमे वेगे द्वितीये वेपथुर्भवेत् ।
दाहं तृतीये हिक्कां च चतुर्थे सम्प्रयोजयेत् ॥ ८७ ॥

फेनञ्च पञ्चमे कुर्यात्षष्ठे स्कन्धस्य भञ्जनम् ।
जडतां सप्तमे कुर्यादष्टमे मरणं भवेत् ॥ ८८ ॥

अत्रार्या भवति—

श्वापदगजतुरगरथोद्भवं तु पशुयानपतनजं वाऽपि ।
शस्त्रक्षतवत्कुर्यादनवेक्षितगात्रसञ्चारम् । ॥ ८९ ॥

इत्येवं मरणं ज्ञेयं नानावस्थान्तरात्मकम् ।
प्रयोक्तव्यं बुधैः सम्यग्यथा भावाङ्गचेष्टितैः ॥ ९० ॥

त्रासो नाम—विद्युदुल्काशनिपातनिर्घाताम्बुधरम[2]हासत्त्वपशुरवादिभिर्विभावैरुत्पद्यते । तमभिनयेत्संक्षिप्ताङ्गोत्कम्पनवेपथुस्तम्भरोमाञ्चगद्गदप्रलापादिभिरनुभावैः ।

---

१. G.O.S. Reads in addition शस्त्रक्षताहिदष्टविषपीतगजादिपतितश्वापदहता । N.S. K.S.S. M.G. Omit it.

२. K.S.S. अम्बुदरवसत्त्वदर्शन M.G. G.O.S. N.S. अम्बुधरमहासत्त्व ।

अत्र श्लोको भवति–

महाभैरवनादाद्यैस्त्रासः समुपजायते ।
त्रस्ताङ्गाक्षि[1]निमेषैश्च तस्य त्वभिनयो भवेत् ॥ ६१ ॥

वितर्को नाम—सन्देहविमर्शविप्रतिपत्त्यादिभिर्विभावैरुत्पद्यते । तमभिनये-द्विविधविचारितप्रश्नसम्प्रधारणमन्त्रसंगूहनादिभिरनुभावैः ।

अत्र श्लोको भवति—

विचारणादिसम्भूतः सन्देहातिशयात्मक[2]: ।
वितर्कः सोऽभिनेयस्तु शिरोभ्रूक्षेप[3]कम्पनैः ॥ ६२ ॥

एवमेते त्रयस्त्रिंशद्व्यभिचारिणो भावा देशकालावस्थानुरूप्येणात्मगतपरगत-मध्यस्था उत्तममध्यमाधमैः स्त्रीपुंसैः स्वप्रयोगवशादुपपाद्या इति ।

त्रयस्त्रिंशदिमे भावा विज्ञेया व्यभिचारिणः ।
सात्त्विकांस्तु पुनर्भावान्प्रवक्ष्याम्यनुपूर्वशः ॥ ६३ ॥

अत्राह—किमन्ये भावाः सत्त्वेन विनाऽभिनीयन्ते यस्मादुच्यन्ते एते सात्त्विका इति ।

अत्रोच्यते—

इह हि सत्त्वं नाम मनःप्रभवम् । तच्च समाहितमनस्त्वादुच्यते । मनसः समाधौ सत्त्वनिष्पत्तिर्भवति[4] । तस्य च योऽसौ स्वभावो रोमा[5]ञ्चाश्रुवैवर्ण्यादि-लक्षणो यथाभावोपगतः स न शक्योऽन्यमनसा कर्तुमिति[6] । लोकस्वभावानु-

---

१. K.S.S. M.G. अर्धनिमेषाद्यैः G.O.S. N.S. अक्षिनिमेषः ।

२. K.S.S. M.G. जननात्मकः G.O.S. N.S. अतिशयात्मकः ।

३. K.S.S. M.G. पक्ष्म G.O.S. N.S. क्षेप ।

४. K.S.S. मनः समाधानाच्च सत्त्वनिवृत्तिर्भवति N.S. मनः समाधानाच्च सद्यो निर्वृतिरिति M.G. मनः समाधानाच्च सत्त्वनिष्पत्तिर्भवति G.O.S. मनसः समाधौ सत्त्वनिष्पत्तिर्भवति ।

५. K.S.S. reads in addition स्तम्भस्वेद M.G. N.S. G.O.S. Omit स्तम्भस्वेद ।

६. K.S.S. न दृश्यते मनसा कर्तुम् M.G. न शक्यतेऽन्यमनसा कर्तुम् N.S. G.O.S. न शक्योऽन्यमनसा कर्तुम् ।

करणत्वाच्च नाट्यस्य सत्त्वमीप्सितम् । को दृष्टान्तः—इह[1] हि नाट्यधर्मिप्रवृत्ताः सुखदुःखकृता भावास्तथा सत्त्वविशुद्धाः कार्याः यथा सरूपा भवन्ति । तत्र दुःखं नाम रोदनात्मकं तत्कथमदुःखितेन सुखं च प्रहर्षात्मकमसुखितेन वाभिनेयम् । एतदेवास्य सत्त्वं यत् दुःखितेन सुखितेन वाऽश्रुरोमाञ्चौ दर्शयितव्यौ इति कृत्वा सात्त्विका भावा इत्यभिव्याख्याताः ।

त इमे—

स्तम्भः स्वेदोऽथ रोमाञ्चः स्वरभेदोऽथ वेपथुः ।
वैवर्ण्यमश्रु प्रलय इत्यष्टौ सात्त्विका मताः ॥ ९४ ॥

अत्रार्याः । तत्र—

क्रोधभयहर्षलज्जादुःखश्रमरोगतापघातेभ्यः ।
व्यायामक्लमघर्मैः स्वेदः सम्पीडनाच्चैव ॥ ९५ ॥

हर्षभयशोकविस्मयविषादरोषादिसम्भवः स्तम्भः ।
शीताभयहर्षरोषस्पर्शजरारोगजः कम्पः ॥ ९६ ॥

आनन्दामर्षाभ्यां धूमाञ्जनजृम्भणाद्भयाच्छोकात्[2] ।
अनिमेषप्रेक्षणतः शीताद्रोगाद्भवेदश्रु[3] ॥ ९७ ॥

शीतक्रोधभयश्रमरोगक्लमतापजं च वैवर्ण्यम् ।
स्पर्शभयशीतहर्षात् क्रोधाद्रोगाच्च रोमाञ्चः ॥ ९८ ॥

स्वरभेदो भयहर्षक्रोधज[4]रारौक्ष्यरोगमदजनितः ।
श्रममूर्छामदनिद्राभिघातमोहादिभिः प्रलयः ॥ ९९ ॥

---

१. K.S.S. इह हि नाट्यधर्मः प्रवृत्तः सुखदुःखकृतो भावः तथा सत्वाविशुद्धाधिष्ठितः कार्यो यथास्वरूपो भवति । G.O.S. N.S. M.G. (Same as above).

२. K.S.S. M.G. Omit शोकात् G.O.S. N.S. Retain it.

३. K.S.S. M.G. read शोकानिमिषप्रेक्षणशीताद्रोगात् भवेदस्रम् । G.O.S. N.S. (Same as above).

४. K.S.S. M.G. ज्वररोगमदजनितः G.O.S. N.S. जरारौक्ष्यरोगमदजनितः ।

एवमेते बर्बुर्ज्ञेया भावा ह्यष्टौ तु सात्त्विकाः ।
कर्म चैषां प्रवक्ष्यामि रसभ[१]ावानुभावकम् ॥ १०० ॥

निः[२]संज्ञो निष्प्रकम्पश्च स्थितः[३] शून्यजडाकृतिः ।
स्कन्नगात्रतया[४] चैव स्तम्भं त्वभिनयेद्बुधः[५] ॥ १०१ ॥

व्यजनग्रहणाच्चापि स्वेदापनयनेन च ।
स्वेदस्याभिनयो योज्यस्तथा वाताभिलाषतः ॥ १०२ ॥

मुहुः कण्टकितत्वेन तथोल्लुकसनेन च ।
पुलकेन च रोमाञ्चं गात्रस्पर्शेन दर्शयेत्[६] ॥ १०३ ॥

स्वरभेदोऽभिनेतव्यो भिन्नगद्गदनिस्वनैः ।
वेपनात्स्फुरणात्कम्पाद्वेपथुं सम्प्रदर्शयेत् ॥ १०४ ॥

मुखवर्णपरावृत्त्या नाडीपीडनयोगतः ।
वैवर्ण्यमभिनेतव्यं प्रयत्नात्तद्धि दुष्करम् ॥ १०५ ॥

बाष्पाम्बुप्लुतनेत्रत्वान्नेत्रसम्मार्जनेन च ।
मुहुरश्रुकणापातैरास्त्रं त्वभिनयेबुधः[७] १०६ ॥

निश्चेष्टो निष्प्रकम्पत्वादव्यक्तश्वसितादपि ।
महीनिपातनाच्चापि प्रलयाभिनयो भवेत् ॥ १०७ ॥

---

१. G.O.S. N.S. रसभावानुभावकम् K.S.S. M.G. ह्यनुभावानुभावकम् ।

२. K.S.S. M.G. निश्चेष्टः G.O.S. N.S. निसंज्ञः ।

३. G.O.S. N.S. M.G. स्थितः शून्यजडाकृतिः K.S.S. स्मितशून्यजड़ाकृतिः

४. K.S.S. M.G. निःसंज्ञः स्तब्धगात्रश्च G.O.S. N.S. स्कन्नगात्रतया चैव ।

५. N.S. K.S.S. Read in addition after vesse No 101
वेपनात् स्फुरणात् कम्पाद्वेपथुं संप्रदर्शयेत् ।
स्वरभेदं तथा चैव भिन्नगद्गदनिःस्वनैः ॥ G.O.S. M.G. Omit it.

६. K.S.S. M.G. N.S. रोमाञ्चस्त्वभिनेयोऽसौ गात्रस्पर्शने नच G.O.S. (Same as above).

७. N.S.. K.S.S. M.G. नेत्रसंम्गार्जनैर्बाष्पैरश्रु चाभिनयेद्बुधः G.O.S. (Same as above).

एकोनपञ्चाशदिमे यथाव-

द्भावास्त्र्यवस्था गदिता मयेह ।

भूयश्च[1] ये यत्र रसे नियोज्या-

स्तान् श्रोतुमर्हन्ति च विप्रमुख्याः ॥ १०८ ॥

[अत्र[2] श्लोकाः—

शङ्काव्याधिस्तथाग्लानिश्चिन्तासूया भयं तथा ।
विस्मयश्च वितर्कश्च स्तम्भश्चपलता तथा ॥

रोमाञ्चहर्षौ निद्रा च तथोन्मादमदावपि ।
स्वेदश्चैवावहित्थं च प्रलयो वेपथुस्तथा ॥

विषादश्रमनिर्वेदा गर्वावेगौ धृतिः स्मृतिः ।
मतिर्मोहो विबोधश्च सुप्तमौत्सुक्यवर्जिते ॥

क्रोधामर्षौ च हासश्च शोकोऽपस्मार एव च ।
दैन्यं च मरणं चैव रतिरुत्साहसंयुता ॥

त्रासवैवर्ण्यरुदितैः स्वरभेदः शमोऽपि च ।
जडता च तथा षट् च चत्वारिंशत्प्रकीर्तिताः ॥]

आलस्यौग्र्यजुगुप्साख्यैरेवं भावैस्तु वर्जिताः ।
उद्भावयन्ति शृङ्गारं सर्वे भावाः स्वसंज्ञया[3] ॥ १०९ ॥

[यथाऽवसरमेते हि स्थायिसञ्चारिसत्त्वजाः ।
उद्दीपयन्ति शृङ्गारं रसमासाद्य संज्ञितम् ॥]

ग्लानिः शङ्का ह्यसूया च श्रमश्चपलता तथा ।
सुप्तं निद्रावहित्थं च हास्ये भावाः प्रकीर्तिताः ॥ ११० ॥

---

१. K.S.S. M.G. येषां G.O.S. N.S. भूयश्च ।

२. K.S.S. N.S. M.G. donot read verses in the bracket. G.O.S. reads them.

३. K.S.S. N.S. M.G. read before verse No 109
ग्लानिः शङ्का ह्यसूया च श्रमश्चपलता तथा ।
सुप्तं निद्रावहित्थं च शृङ्गारे वेपथुस्तथा ॥ G.O.S. Omits.

निर्वेदश्चैव चिन्ता च दैन्यं ग्लान्यास्रमेव च ।
जडता मरणं चैव व्याधिश्च करुणे स्मृता: ॥ १११ ॥

गर्वोऽसूया मदोत्साहावावेगोऽमर्ष एव च ।
क्रोधश्चपलतौग्र्यं च विज्ञेया रौद्रसम्भवा:[१] ॥ ११२ ॥

असम्मोहस्तथोत्साह आवेगो हर्ष एव च ।
मतिश्चैव तथोग्रत्वममर्षो मद एव च[२] ॥ ११३ ॥

रोमाञ्च: स्वरभेदश्च क्रोधोऽसूया धृतिस्तथा ।
गर्वश्चैव वितर्कश्च वीरे भावा भवन्ति हि ॥ ११४ ॥

स्वेदश्च वेपथुश्चैव रोमाञ्चो गद्गदस्तथा ।
त्रासश्च मरणञ्चैव वैवर्ण्यं च भयानके ॥ ११५ ॥

अपस्मारस्तथोन्मादो विषादो मद एव च ।
मृत्युर्व्याधिर्भयं चैव भावा बीभत्ससंश्रया: ॥ ११६ ॥

स्तम्भ: स्वेदश्च मोहश्च रोमाञ्चो विस्मयस्तथा ।
आवेगो जडता हर्षो मूर्च्छा चैवाद्भुताश्रया: ॥ ११७ ॥

ये त्वेते सात्त्विका भावा नानाभिनयसंश्रिता: ।
रसेष्वेतेषु सर्वे[३] ते ज्ञेया नाटचप्रयोक्तृभि: ॥ ११८ ॥

न ह्येकरसजं काव्यं किञ्चिदस्ति प्रयोगत: ।
भावो वापि रसो वापि प्रवृत्तिर्वृत्तिरेव च ॥ ११९ ॥

[बहूनां समवेतानां रूपं यस्य भवेद्बहु ।
स मन्तव्यो रस: स्थायी शेषा: संचारिणो मता: ॥

दीपयन्त: प्रवर्तन्ते ये पुन: स्थायिनं रसम् ।
ते तु संचारिणो ज्ञेयास्ते हि स्थायित्वमागता:[४] ॥

१. M.G. N.S. K.S.S. गर्वोऽसूया तथोत्साह आवेगो मद एव च ।
क्रोधश्चपलता हर्षो रौद्रे चोग्रत्वमेव च ॥ G.O.S. (Same as above)
२. K.S.S. M.G. हर्ष उन्माद एव च G.O.S. N.S. (Same as above)
३. K.S.S. N.S. M.G. सर्वेषु G.O.S. सर्वे ते ।
४. K.S.S. M.G. omit this verse N.S. G.O.S. read it.

विभावानुभावयुतो ह्यङ्गवस्तुसमाश्रयः ।
संचारिभिस्तु संयुक्तः स्थाय्येव तु रसो भवेत् ॥
स्थायी सत्त्वातिरेकेण प्रयोक्तव्यः प्रयोक्तृभिः ।
सञ्चार्याकारमात्रेण स्थायी यस्मादवस्थितः ॥
ये त्वेते सात्त्विका भावा नानाभिनययोजिताः ।
रसेष्वेतेषु सर्वेषु ते ज्ञेया नाट्यकोविदैः ॥
न ह्येकरसजं काव्यं नैकभावैकवृत्तिकम् ।[1]
विमर्दे रागमायाति प्रयुक्तं हि प्रयत्नतः ॥
भावा वाऽपि रसा वाऽपि प्रवृत्तिर्वृत्तिरेव वा ।
बीभत्साद्भुतशान्तानां त्रैविध्यं नात्र कथ्यते[2] ॥
षण्णां रसानां त्रैविध्यं नानाभावरसान्वितम् ।
सत्त्वप्रयोजितो ह्यर्थः प्रयोगोऽत्र विराजते ॥
विदित्वा हि विराजन्ते लोके चित्रं हि दुर्लभम्[3] ।]
नानाभावार्थसंपन्नाः स्थायिसत्त्वाभिचारिणः[4] ।
पुष्पावकीर्णाः कर्तव्याः काव्येषु हि रसा बुधैः ॥ १२० ॥
एवं रसाश्च भावाश्च व्यवस्था[5] नाटके स्मृताः ।
य एवमेताञ्जानाति स गच्छेत्सिद्धिमुत्तमाम् ॥ १२१ ॥

इति श्रीभारतीये नाट्यशास्त्रे भावव्यञ्जको नाम
सप्तमोऽध्यायः ॥

---

१. K.S.S. M.G. चित्राणि न विरज्यन्ते लोके चित्रं हि दुर्लभम् । G.O.S. N.S. न ह्येकरसजं काव्यं नैकभावैकवृत्तिकम् ।
२. K.S.S. M.G. omit this verse G.O.S. N.S. retain it.
३. K.S.S. M.G. omit verses in bracket G.O.S. N.S. retain it.
४. M.G. K.S.S. विचारिणः G.O.S. N.S. अभिचारिणः
५. K:S.S. M.G. व्यवस्था G.O.S. N.S. व्यवस्था ।

INDEX OF HALF VERSES OF THE NATYAŚASTRA